PREFACE

S0-ADD-810

Archaeometry 88 (the 26th International Archaeometry Symposium) was held at the University of Toronto from May 16 to May 20, 1988.

Entertainment and edification were provided for and by 190 participants from 18 different countries. Over the week, the participants viewed and discussed 63 poster presentations, and listened to, and sometimes berated, 62 oral presenters. Common interests were discussed, old friendships were rekindled, and new ones begun. Battles were fought, and some controversies will continue.

This Symposium would not have been possible without the financial assistance of:
NSERC (Natural Sciences and Engineering Research Council of Canada), which provided travel monies for speakers in the theme session " Archaeometry has the answers - but what are the questions?", and in the W.N. Irving Memorial Session;
the Province of Ontario which helped fund the Symposium banquet;

and the City of Toronto, which suffered through our presence at a non-verbose, and hence enjoyable, civic reception (even if they served the wrong beer).

The Dean of Arts and Science and the Provost of the University of Toronto, the Royal Ontario Museum, and Canberra-Packard Canada extended financial support. Also, the organizational and financial support of the Departments of Anthropology, Physics, and Metallurgy and Materials Science is gratefully acknowledged. Special thanks go to Ms. Shirley DesLauriers for invaluable help and advice over the long haul, and to all volunteers. D.L. Anderson of the Toronto Transit Commission (TTC) provided much helpful local information.

Forty-six of the 125 papers presented at the Symposium were accepted for publication. For the first time, peer reviews were carried out during the Symposium, thanks to the organizational skills of M. Wayman and M. Laver. Invaluable editorial assistance was provided by P.J. Julig and A.C. D'Andrea. R.P. Beukens generated the final Index with computer time provided by IsoTrace (A.E. Litherland).

Manuscript submitters are to be congratulated for their camera-ready papers and for the preparation of their subject indices. Although by brilliant, fiscal management the proceedings were eventually type-set, the original tables and figures were preserved and the styles of the individual authors were maintained. Thanks to L. Grace and G. Wickham of Network Litho for their typing and type-setting skills, and their unfailing good humour throughout the stressful period of document production.

Thanks go to all those reviewers who gave of their time during the Symposium, and who thereby made the compiling of this volume much easier and faster than it would otherwise have been.

The Local Organizing Committee claims all the credit for the dryness of the weather inside the buildings on campus during the Symposium, but transfers responsibility for the rainy periods outside to the local weather office, which had the effrontery to correctly predict rain during the week.

Finally, all opinions expressed, and conclusions drawn, in the papers published in this proceedings are solely the responsibility of their authors, and do not necessarily reflect the views of the editors.

R.M. Farquhar, R.G.V. Hancock, and L.A. Pavlish

LOCAL ORGANIZING COMMITTEE

INTERNATIONAL STANDING COMMITTEE

PROCEEDINGS OF THE 26th INTERNATIONAL ARCHAEOMETRY SYMPOSIUM

Held at

UNIVERSITY OF TORONTO, TORONTO, CANADA
May 16th to May 20th, 1988

Edited by
R. M. FARQUHAR, R. G. V. HANCOCK and L. A. PAVLISH

Symposium included: Ancient Technology, Dating,
Organic Materials and Bone, Mathematics and Statistics, Prospection,
Provenance of Ceramics, Provenance of Lithics, and Techniques

Archaeometry Laboratory
Department of Physics
University of Toronto
Toronto, Canada

TABLE OF CONTENTS

ORGANIC MATERIALS AND BONE

MATHEMATICS AND STATISTICS

METALS

PROSPECTION

ARCHAEOMETRY 88

LIST OF PARTICIPANTS

Participants are listed by given name, family name, current (1988) employment address and telephone number (ignoring country codes), and BITNET code. If there are any errors or omissions †, please contact Dr. Ernst Pernicka before May, 1989.

(* indicates author of paper published in this Proceedings)

Martin Aitken, Research Laboratory for Archaeology & the History of Art, 6 Keble, Rd.,Oxford, OX1 3QJ, U.K., 0865 515211

Ralph Allen, Department of Chemistry, University of Virginia, Charlottesville, VA 22901, U.S.A., (804) 924-3577

Meredith Aronson, MIT, Room 13-4069, 77 Mass. Ave, Cambridge, MA 02139, U.S.A., (617) 253-6894

Michael Baillie, Belfast, Palaeoecology Centre, Queen's University, Northern Ireland, BT7 1NN, 0232 245133 x 3488

June Barrette, Anthropology Department, University of Toronto, Toronto, Ontario, Canada, M5S 1A1 (416) 978-8647

Yannis Bassiakos, Archaeometry Laboratory,NRC Demokritos, 153 10 Aghia Paraskevi, Attikis, Greece 15310, 1-6513111/247

Leo Biek, City University, Northampton Square, London, England, EC1V 0HB, 01-794-8271(for messages and answer phone)

Richard E. Bisbing, McCrone Associates, 850 Pasquinelli Drive, Westmont IL, U.S.A., (312) 887-7100

*M. James Blackman, CAL/MSC, Smithsonian Institution, Washington, DC 20560, U.S.A., (301) 975-6278

William Blanchard, 766 Harvard St., St. Louis, MO 63130, U.S.A., (314) 726-5737

Rob Bonnichsen, Center for the Study of Early Man, 495 College Ave., Orono, Maine, 04473, U.S.A., (207) 581-2197

Victor J. Bortolot, Daybreak Nuclear & Medical Systems, 50 Denison Drive, Guilford, CT 06437, U.S.A., (203) 453-3299

*Nathan Bower, Department of Chemistry, Colorado College, Colorado Springs, CO 80903, U.S.A., (719) 473-2233

Ian Brindle, Chemistry Department, Brock University, St. Catherines, Ontario, Canada, L2S 3A1 (416) 688-5550

Gordon Brown, RR#3, Caledon East, Ontario, Canada, L0N 1E0 (416) 584-2457

Ileana Bucur, Laboratoire de Géomagnétisme du Parc Saint-Maur, 4, Ave. de Neptune, 94107 St. Maur-des-Fosses Cedex-, France, 1-48-86-32-72

*Paul Budd, Department of Archaeological Sciences, University of Bradford, Bradford BD7 1DP, West Yorkshire, U.K., 0274 733466X451

*Joao M. P. Cabral, Departamento de Quimica, ICEN, LNETI, 2685 Sacavém, Portugal, (19) 255-0021

Janice Carlson, Winterthur Museum, Winterthur, DE 19735, U.S.A., (302) 656-8591

Giles F. Carter, Chemistry Department, Eastern Michigan University, Ypsilanti, Mich. 48197, U.S.A., (313) 487-2039

W. Tom Chase, Sackler Gallery/Freer Gallery, Smithsonian Institution, Washington, DC 20560, U.S.A., (202) 357-2017

Stephen Cheesman, University of Toronto, 60 St. George St., Toronto, Ontario, Canada, (416) 978-5177

Hazel Croome, Metropolitan Museum of Art, Objects Conservation Laboratory, 5th Ave. at 82nd St., New York, NY 10028, U.S.A., (212) 570-3858

K. Cuik, West Asian Department, Royal Ontario Museum, Toronto, Ontario, Canada, M5S 2C6, (416) 586-5697

Michel Dabas, CRNS, Centre de Recherches Géophysiques, Garchy 58150 Pouilly Sur Loire, France, 86-26-30-23

Rinita Dalan, Geo-Recon, 312 S. Fillmore - Apt. A, Edwardsville, Il. 62025, U.S.A., (618) 656-5151

Margaret Darmanin, Anthropology Department, University of Toronto, Toronto, Ontario, Canada

*Paul De Paepe, Labo voor Aardkunde, RUG, Krijgslaan 281, B9000 Gent, Belgium, 091-22-57-15 x2677

*Guy Demortier, LARN - University of Namur, 22 rue Muzet, B-5000 Namur, Belgium, 81-22-90-61

*M. John M. Duke, Department of Geology, University of Alberta, Edmonton, Alberta, Canada, T6E 2N8 (403) 432-4749, USERMJMD@UALTAMTS

Allison Eason, Royal Ontario Museum, Toronto, Ontario, Canada, M5S 2C6 (416) 586-5678

*Mokhtar El-Homossani, Department of Metallurgy and Materials Science, University of Toronto, Toronto, Ontario, Canada, M5S 1A4

*James M. Elam, University of Missouri, 222 Research Reactor, Columbia, MO 65211, U.S.A., (314) 882-5268, C0365G@UMVMA

*M. E. (Ted) Evans, Department of Physics, University of Alberta, Edmonton, Alberta, Canada, T6J 2J1

Barry Fankhauser, Chaminade University, Honolulu, Hawaii, 96816-1577, U.S.A., (808) 735-4739

Ronald M. Farquhar, Department of Physics, 60 St. George St., Toronto, Ontario, Canada, M5S 1A7 (416) 978-2267

Bernice Field, Anthropology Department, University of Toronto, Toronto, Ontario, Canada, M5S 1A1, (416) 978-2442

C.O. Fischer, Hahn-Meitner-Institut, Glienicker Str. 100, D-1000, Berlin, West Germany, (030) 80092742

Stuart Fleming, MASCA, University Museum, 33rd. & Spruce Streets,
Philadelphia, PA 19104, U.S.A., (215) 898-4058

Giraud V. Foster, Johns Hopkins University, B2-202 Park, 600 N. Wolfe St., Baltimore, MD 21205, U.S.A., (301) 955-3399

Maria Foster, Johns Hopkins University, Baltimore, MD, U.S.A., (301) 467-5956

William A. Fox, Archaeology Branch, Ministry of Culture and Communications, 77 Bloor St., Toronto, Ontario, Canada, M7A 2R9 (416) 965-4490

Fabio Frachtenberg, Archaeology Department, Hebrew University, Jerusalem, Israel, 02 882 405

*Ursula M. Franklin, Department of Metallurgy and Materials Science, University of Toronto, 200 College St., Toronto, Ontario, Canada, M5S 1A4, (416) 978-4639

Noel H. Gale, University of Oxford, Department of Earth Sciences, Parks Rd, Oxford, U.K. OX1 3PR, 0865-272042

J. C. Gardin, CNRS, 23, rue du Maroc, 75019 Paris, France, 206 86 01, UIAC000@FRORS32.EARN

Frank Garrod, Environment Canada - Parks, 1570 Liverpool Court, Ottawa, Ontario, Canada, K1A 0H3, (613) 993-2125

*Rupert S. Gebhard, Physik-Department, E15 TUM, D-8046 Garching, Federal Republic of Germany,

*Michail Georgiev, Institute of Thracology, Bulgarian Academy of Sciences, 13 Moscovsca, Sofia, Bulgaria

*Thomas E. Gill, Crocker Nuclear Laboratory, University of California, Davis, CA 95616, U.S.A., (916) 752-4673

Gordon Gilmore, Universities Research Reactor, Risley, Warrington, U.K. WA3 6AT

William Glanzman, MASCA, University Museum, 33rd and Spruce Sts., Philadelphia, PA 19104, U.S.A., (215) 898-1164

*Michael D. Glascock, University of Missouri, 223 Research Reactor, Columbia, MO 65211, U.S.A., (314) 882-5270, C0365G@UMVMA

Andre Gob, University of Liege-C.I.P.L., Place du 20-aout, 32, Liege, Belgium, B-4000, 32-41-42-00-80

Martha Goodway, CAL-MSC, Smithsonian Institution, Washington, DC 20560, U.S.A., (202) 287-3733

*Robert B. Gordon, Yale University, P.O.Box 6666, New Haven, CT 06517, U.S.A., (203) 432-3125

Elizabeth Graham, Royal Ontario Museum, Toronto, Ontario, Canada, (416) 586-5730

Richard M. Gramly, Buffalo Museum of Science, Buffalo, NY 14211, U.S.A., (716) 896-5200 x 716

H. S. Grewal, 326 Fleetwood Crescent, Bramalea, Ontario, Canada, L6T 2E7

A. P. Grimanis, Nuclear Research Center Demokritos, 153 10 Aghia Paraskevi, Attikis, Greece, 651 3111

*Maria F. Guerra, Centro de Fisica Nuclear, Av. Prof. Gama Pinto, 2, 1699 Lisboa Codex, Portugal, 773338

*Debbie Gurfinkel, 32 Millwood Rd., Toronto, Canada, M4S 1J1

James Hager, SCIEX, 55 Glencameron Rd., Thornhill, Ontario, Canada, (416) 881-4646

Edward T. Hall, Research Laboratory for Archaeology, Oxford, 6 Keble Road, Oxford University, Oxford, OX1 3QJ, U.K., 0865-515211

Mark E. Hall, PO Box 40072, Berkeley, California, 94704, U.S.A., (415) 653-5681

*Ronald G.V. Hancock, SLOWPOKE Reactor Facility, University of Toronto, Toronto, Canada, M5S 1A4 (416) 978-7129

Garman Harbottle, Chemistry Department, Brookhaven National Laboratory, Upton, NY 11973, U.S.A., (516) 282-4387

Helen Hatcher, Research Laboratory for Archaeology, 6 Keble Road, Oxford OX1 3QJ U.K., 0865-515211

John W. Hayes, Greek and Roman Department, Royal Ontario Museum, Toronto, Ontario, Canada, M5S 2C6

K. Healey, West Asian Department, Royal Ontario Museum, Toronto, Ontario, Canada, M5S 2C6

*Fred T. Hedgcock, Physics Department, McGill University, Montreal, P.Q., Canada, H3A 2T8 (513) 398-6530

Robert B. Heimann, Alberta Research Council, 250 Karl Clark Road, Edmonton, Alberta, Canada, T6H 5X2, (403) 450-5403, HEIMANN@ARC.CDN

Elizabeth F. Henrickson, West Asian Dept., ROM, 100 Queen's Park, Toronto, Ontario, Canada, M5S 2C6, (416) 586-5694,

*Robert C. Henrickson, Royal Ontario Museum, 100 Queen's Park , Toronto, Ontario, Canada, M5S 2C6, (416) 586-5692

Albert Hesse, CRNS, Centre de Recherches Géophysiques, Garchy, Pouilly sur Loire, France 58150, 86 26 3023

Philip Hopke, University of Illinois, 1005 W. Western Ave., Urbana, Il 61801, U.S.A., (217) 333-6230

Patricia Houlihan, Museum of Modern Art, 11 West 55, New York, N.Y., 10019, U.S.A., (212) 708-9570

John S. Isaacson, ATAM-106 MRL, University of Illinois, 104 S. Goodwin St., Urbana, Il 61801, U.S.A., (217) 333-3524

*Emile C. Joel, Smithsonian Institution, CAL-MSC, Washington, DC 20560, U.S.A., (202) 287-3700

N. Johnson, Anthropology Department, University of Toronto, Toronto, Ontario, Canada, M5S 1A1, (416) 982-7778

*Patrick J. Julig, Department of Anthropology, University of Toronto, Toronto, Ontario, Canada, M5S 1A1, (416) 978-4005

Mima Kapches, New World Archaeology, Royal Ontario Museum, Toronto, Ontario, Canada, M5S 2C6 (416) 586-5727

*Edward J. Keall, West Asian Department, Royal Ontario Museum, Toronto, Ontario, Canada, M5S 2C6 (416) 586-5695

*W.E. Kieser, IsoTrace, University of Toronto, Toronto, Ontario, Canada, M5S 1A7, (416) 978-2241

Vassilis Kilikoglou, NRC Demokritos, 153 10 Aghia Paraskevi, Attikis, Greece, 15310

*David J. Killick, Anthropology Department, Yale University, 51 Hillhouse Ave., New Haven, CT 06511, U.S.A., (203) 624-8114, KILDAVB@YALEVM

Maxine R. Kleindienst, Department of Anthropology, University of Toronto, 100 St. George St., Toronto, Ontario, Canada, M5S 1A1 (416) 978-3028

*Mary Kovacheva, Geophysical Institute, Bulgarian Academy of Science, Block 3, Acad. G. Bonchev Str., Sofia 1113, Bulgaria, 70 0226

Renee Kra, Yale University - Radiocarbon - Kline Geological Laboratory, P.O. Box 6666, New Haven, CT 06511, U.S.A., (203) 432 3130 or (203) 389-5589 (IRDB)

Colleen Kriger, 11 Walmer Road, #305, Toronto, Ontario, Canada

*Bruce Kusko, Crocker Nuclear Laboratory, University of California, Davis, CA 95616, U.S.A., (916) 752-4673

*Joseph B. Lambert, Department of Chemistry, Northwestern University, Evanston, Il. 60201, U.S.A., (312) 491-5437

Ian Lancashire, Centre for Computing in the Humanities, Robarts Library, University of Toronto, Toronto, Canada, M5S 1A7, IAN@UTOREPAS

Marilyn E. Laver, Canadian Conservation Institute, Communications Canada, Ottawa, Ontario, Canada, K1A 0C8, (613) 998-3721

Paul Le Compte, Environment Canada-Parks, 1570 Liverpool Court, Ottawa, Ontario, Canada, K1A 0H3, (613) 993-2126

Donald R. Lewis, University of Texas at San Antonio, Center for Archaeological Research, San Antonio, Texas 78285, U.S.A., (512) 691-4455

Helen Lewis, Anthropology Department, University of Toronto, Toronto, Ontario, Canada, M5S 1A1

*A.E. (Ted) Litherland, IsoTrace Facility, Department of Physics, University of Toronto, Toronto, 60 St. George St., Toronto, Ontario, Canada, M5S 1A7, (416) 978-4628

Barbara E. Luedtke, Department of Anthropology, University of Mass., Boston, Mass. 02125, U.S.A., (617) 929-8150

Glen MacDonald, Geology Department, McMaster University, Hamilton, Ontario, Canada, L8S 4L8

Rinaldo Maldera, IRTEC-C.N.R. via Granarolo, No. 64, Faenza, Italy, 48018, 0546-46147

Yannis Maniatis, Laboratory for Archaeometry, Institute of Materials Science, NRCNS Demokritos, 153 10 Aghia Paraskevi, Attikis, Greece, 1-6513111

*Michael L. Marchbanks, Texas Archaeological Research Laboratory, Austin, Texas, 78758, U.S.A., (512) 471-5960

*Marianne Mareschal, IREM, Ecole Polytechnique, B.P. 6079, Succ. "A", Montreal, P.Q., Canada, H3C 3A7, (514) 340-4563

*Heather Marshall, Bureau of Radiation and Medical Devices, 775 Brookfield Rd., Ottawa, Ontario, Canada, K1A 1C1, (613) 954-6675

Chris Marti, Faunal Archaeo-Osteology Laboratory, University of Toronto, Toronto, Ontario, Canada, (416) 978-5260

*Robert B. Mason, Royal Ontario Museum, 100 Queen's Park , Toronto, Ontario, Canada, M5S 2C6, (416) 586-5696

Heikki Matiskainen, Finnish Glass Museum, Tehtaank 23, Riihimaki, SF-11910, Finland, (9) 14-641-490

*Heather I. McKillop, Trent University, Department of Anthropology, Peterborough, Ontario, Canada, K9J 7B8, (416) 342-3250

Duncan McNeill, Geonics Limited, 1745 Meyerside Dr., Mississauga, Ontario, Canada, (416) 676-9580

Alan McPherron, Anthropology Department, University of Pittsburgh, Pittsburgh, PA 15260, U.S.A., (412) 648-7513, 240451@PITTVMS

James McVay, University of Pittsburgh, Forbes Ave., Pittsburgh, PA, U.S.A., (412) 788-4772

*Nigel D. Meeks, The British Museum Research Laboratory, Great Russell Street, London WC1B 3DG, U.K., 01-636-1555 x 268

Pieter Meyers, LACMA-Conservation Centre, 5905 Wilshire Blvd., Los Angeles, CA 90036, U.S.A., (213) 857-6161

Christodoulos Michael, NRCNS Demokritos, 153 10 Aghia Paraskevi, Attikis, Greece

Rita Michael, 981 Main St. West, 907, Hamilton, Ontario, Canada

*Hans Mommsen, Institut für Stralen- und Kernphysik, Universität Bonn, Nussallee 14-16, D-5300 Bonn, West Germany, XRAYS@DBNISKP5

Catherine Mortimer, Research Laboratory for Archaeology, 6 Keble Rd, Oxford OX1 3QJ, U.K., 0865-515211

*June D. Morton, Department of Geology, McMaster University, Hamilton, Ontario, Canada, L8S 4L8

C.C. Mullick, Bharat Kala Bhavan, Banaras Hindu University, Varanasi - 221005, India

Erle Nelson, Anthropology Department, Simon Fraser University, Burnaby, B.C., Canada, V5A 1S6 (604) 291-3673

Richard Newman, Museum of Fine Arts, 465 Huntington Ave, Boston, MA 02115, U.S.A., (617) 267-9300 x 466

G. William A. Newton, Department of Chemistry, University of Manchester, Manchester M13 9PL, U.K., 061-275-4675

O.P. (Nick) Nicholson, Lesbury House, South Scarle, nr Newark, U.K.

H. Nicolet Pierre, Cabinet des Medailles, Bibliotheque Nationale, 58 rue Richelieu, 75084 Paris Cedex 02, France,

Alison M. Northover, Bodleian Library, Broad Street, Oxford, U.K. OX1 3BG,

J. Peter Northover, Department of Metallurgy & Science of Materials, University of Oxford, Parks Rd., Oxford, OX1 3PH, U.K., 865-273728

Michael Notis, Lehigh University, 452 Whitaker Lab, Bethlehem, PA 18015, U.S.A., (215) 758-4225

*Jacqueline Olin, Conservation Analytical Laboratory, Smithsonian Institution, Washington, DC 20560, U.S.A.

Anne O'Sullivan, Anthropology Department, University of Toronto, Toronto, Ontario, Canada, M5S 1A1,(416) 688-5550

Barbara Ottaway, Department of Archaeological Sciences, University of Bradford, Bradford, West Yorkshire BD7 1DP, U.K., 1274-733-466

William G. Parkins, Chemistry Department, Brock University, St. Catharines, Ontario, Canada, L2S 3A1

*Miclos Pattantyús-Á., Eötvös Loránd Geophysical Institute of Hungary, P.O.B. 35, Budapest, H-1440, Hungary

*Larry A. Pavlish, Room #244, McLennan Physical Laboratories, Department of Physics, University of Toronto, 60 St. George St., Toronto, Canada, M5S 1A7, (416) 978-5209

Ernst Pernicka, Max Plank Institut für Kernphysik, Postbox 103980, D-6900 Heidelberg, Federal Republic of Germany, (06221) 516-484, PERNI@DHDMPI5V

*Augustin Petkov, Institute de Thracologie, 13 Moskovska, Sofia, Bulgaria, 1000

Vincent C. Pigott, MASCA, The University Museum, 33rd & Spruce Streets, Philadelphia, PA 19104, U.S.A., (215) 898-4062

*A. Mark Pollard, Department of Chemistry, University College, Cardiff, Wales CF4 1XL

Ralph Powell, Eastern Michigan University, Ypsilanti, Michigan, 48197, U.S.A., (313) 487-0106

Christine Prior, Radiocarbon Laboratory, University of California at Irvine, Irvine, CA 92717, U.S.A., (714) 856-5783

Judith Pullar, British Institute of Persian Studies, 53 Danville Dr., Willowdale, Ontario, Canada

George Rapp (Jr), University of Minnesota, Duluth, MN 55812, U.S.A., (218) 726-7201, GRAPP@UMNDUL

Chandra Reedy, Conservation Center-LACMA, 5905 Wilshire Blvd., Los Angeles, CA 90036, U.S.A., (213) 857-6161

E.J. (Ned) Rehder, Department of Metallurgy and Materials Science, University of Toronto, Toronto, Ontario, Canada, M5S 1A5

Fauzia Rehman, Chemistry Department, University of Manchester, Manchester, U.K. M13 9PL, 061-275-4657

*Peter Roos, Institute for Nuclear Science, Proeftuinstraat 86 Ghent, Belgium 9000, 32-91-22-87-21

Irwin Rovner, North Carolina State University, Raleigh, NC 27695-8107, U.S.A., (919) 737-2491, ROVNER@NCSUMTE

Edward V. Sayre, CAL/MSC, Smithsonian Inst., Washington, DC 20560, U.S.A., (202) 238-3714

*Michael B. Schiffer, Department of Anthropology, University of Arizona, Tucson, AZ 85721, U.S.A., (602) 621-6296

*Gerwulf Schneider, Arbeitsgruppe Archaömetrie, Freie Universität Berlin, Institut für Anorganische und Analytische Chemie, Fabeckstrasse 34/36, D-1000 Berlin 33, West Germany, 030/8382417

Janet Schrenk, University of Delaware, 303 Old College, Newark, Delaware 19716, U.S.A., (302) 451-8238

*Henry Schwarcz, Geology Department, McMaster University, Hamilton, Ontario, Canada, L8S 4M1 (416) 525-9149 x 4186

David A. Scott, Getty Conservation Institute, 4503 Glencoe Ave., Marina Del Rey, California 90292-6537, U.S.A., (213) 459-7611

Lucy R. Sibley, Ohio State University, 1787 Neil Ave., Columbus, Ohio 43210-1295, U.S.A., (614) 292-8063

Ravindra N. Singh, Department of AIHC and Archaeology, Banaras Hindu University, Varanasi, U.P., India 221 005, 0542-52265

Paramjit Singh Suri, Geology Department, Panjab University, Chandigarh 160014, India

Krysia Spirydowicz, Art Conservation Programme, Queen's University, Kingston, Ontario, Canada, L7L 3N6 (613) 545-2156

Tamara Stech, LRSM, University of Pennsylvania, Philadelphia, PA 19104, U.S.A., (215) 898-6579

John Stewart, Environment Canada-Parks, 1570 Liverpool Court, Ottawa, Ontario, Canada, K1A 0H3, (613) 933-2125

Carole A. Stimmell, Department of Anthropology, University of Toronto, Toronto, Ontario, Canada, M5S 1A1

Susan Stock, Royal Ontario Museum, Toronto, Ontario, Canada, M5S 2C6

Mary Frances Striegel, Washington University, Box 1134, St. Louis, MO 63130, U.S.A., (314) 889-6590

Eugene Sucov, Westinghouse Research and Development Center, 1310 Beulah Road, Pittsburgh, PA 15235-5098, U.S.A., (412) 256-2314

Rachel Swan, Victoria and Albert Museum, South Kensington, London, SW7, U.K., 01-938-8597

Charles P. Swann, Bartol Research Institute, University of Delaware, Newark, DE 19716, U.S.A., (302) 451-1279

Alain Tabbagh, CRNS, Centre de Recherches Géophysiques, Garchy 58150, Pouilly sur Loire, France, 86-26-30-23

*Robert E. Taylor, Radiocarbon Laboratory, University of California, Riverside, CA 92521, U.S.A., (714) 796-3585, RETAYLOR @UCRVMS

*Michael S. Tite, British Museum, Research Laboratory, London, WC1B 3DG, U.K., 01-636-1555

*Bruce Trigger, Department of Anthropology, McGill University, Montreal, Canada, H3A 2T5

Beril Tugrul, Istanbul Technical University, Institute for Nuclear Energy, Ayazaga Kampüsü, Istanbul, Turkey 80626, 76-39-49

Pamela Vandiver, Smithsonian Institution, CAL-MSC, 4210 Silver Hill Rd., Suitland, Maryland 20746, U.S.A., (202) 287-3733

William Vernon, Dickinson College, Carlisle, PA 17013, U.S.A., (717) 245-1406

*Kenneth L. Verosub, Geology Department, University of California, Davis, CA 95616, U.S.A., (916) 752-0350, KLVEROSUB@UCDAVIS

Lucio Versino, Instituto per le Tecnologie Applicate ai Beni Culturali-CNR, CP 10, 00016 Monterotondo Stazione, Roma, Italy, 06-900-20363

*Vanda Vitali, Department of Metallurgy and Materials Science, University of Toronto, Toronto, Ontario, Canada, M5S, 1A4, (416) 978-8786

*Ursel Wagner, Physik-Department, E15 TUM, D-8046 Garching, Federal Republic of Germany

Ian N.M. Wainwright, Canadian Conservation Institute, 1030 Innes Road, Ottawa, Ontario, Canada, K1A 0C8, (613) 998-3721

Sir ‡‡ Stanley E. Warren, Physics Department, Bradford University, Bradford, W. Yorkshire, BD7 1DP, U.K., 274-733466 x 241

*Michael L. Wayman, Department of Mining, Metallurgy and Petroleum Engineering, University of Alberta, Edmonton, Alberta. Canada, T6G 2G6 (403) 434-3376, USERWAYM@UALTAMTS

Andrew Weiss, MASCA, University Museum, 33rd and Spruce Sts., Philadelphia, PA 19104, U.S.A., (215) 898-4058

*Charles A. Wert, University of Illinois, 1304 W. Green, Urbana, IL, U.S.A., (217) 244-0998

*Sir ‡‡ John Weymouth, University of Nebraska, Physics Department, Lincoln, NE 68588 0111, U.S.A.

John D. Wilcock, North Staffordshire Polytechnic, Blackheath Lane, Stafford, U.K., ST18 0AD, 785-53511 ext 66

Wendell Williams, Case Western Reserve University, Cleveland, Ohio, 44106, U.S.A., (216) 368-6485

Kris Wilson-Yang, Department of Chemistry, University of Toronto, 85 St. George St., Toronto, Ontario, Canada, M5S 1A1

Paul T. Wilthew, Research Laboratories, National Museums of Scotland, Government Training Complex, West Granton Road, Edinburgh, Scotland, EH5 1JA, U.K., 031-551-1202

Marcia F. Wiseman, Department of Anthropology, University of Toronto, Toronto, Ontario, Canada, M5S 1A1, (416) 978-2442

Sarah Wisseman, University of Illinois, 106 Materials Research Laboratory, 104 S. Goodwin, Urbana, IL 61801, U.S.A.,

Daniel Wolfman, Arkansas Archaeological Survey, ATU Box 1356, Russelville, AR 72801, U.S.A., (501) 968-0381

Joseph Yellin, Hebrew University, Mt. Scopus, Jerusalem, Israel, 2-882405

† Apologies to all participants whose accents of various types in their names and addresses were omitted. Our word-processing competence has not progressed far enough to handle them yet.

Eds.

* Indicates author of paper published here.

‡‡ Knight Commander of the Ancient Order of....(temporary)

1. Archaeology's Relations with the Physical and Biological Sciences: A Historical Review

B. G. TRIGGER
Department of Anthropology, McGill University, Montreal, P.Q. Canada, H3A 2T5

I have been asked to review the relations between prehistoric archaeology and the physical and biological sciences from a historical perspective. I will begin by making a point that at first may seem purely semantic, but which I believe is essential for understanding these relations. I did not say that I will discuss the ties between "archaeology" and "science." Yet those are the terms that physical scientists habitually use to refer to our respective disciplines. Major works on interdisciplinary research also speak of "Science in archaeology" (Brothwell and Higgs 1963; Berger 1970) in their titles, with the obvious implication that, whatever archaeology is, it is something other than science. My point is the contrary one, frequently maintained by my colleagues, that archaeology has as much right as physics, chemistry or biology to be called a science.

In my opinion the most fundamental distinction in academic disciplines is between humanities, which morally and aesthetically evaluate human actions and creations, and sciences, which seek an objective understanding of various kinds of phenomena, including human behaviour. Prehistoric archaeology, at least for the past 200 years, has not been a moralizing or aesthetic discipline and in that respect has been different from philosophy and literary criticism, which remain the core of the humanities. Instead, along with anthropology, psychology, sociology, political science, economics, linguistics, and (most of the time) history, archaeology seeks to understand rather than to evaluate human behaviour. It is on these grounds that archaeology can be designated as a scientific discipline. This status has long been recognized by sectional membership in National Associations for the Advancement of Science and the regular inclusion of reports about archaeology in journals such as Science, Nature, and The American Scientist.

The claim that archaeology is a science does not mean that it is a science like any other. Positivist assertions to the contrary, individual sciences differ from each other in terms of methodology as well as subject matter. Archaeology is not primarily an experimental science, like chemistry and physics. Yet this is also true of astronomy, geology, palaeontology, and ecology. Unlike the natural sciences, archaeology and the other human sciences study human behaviour, which is largely governed by culturally transmitted and situationally modified patterns of knowledge, beliefs, and values. Alien cultures can be exceedingly difficult to understand and the subjective motivations underlying even familiar human behaviour create special methodological problems for scientists who are seeking to explain the actions of their own species (Gellner 1985; Sperber 1985).

Archaeology also faces unique difficulties in trying to be a social science. Because archaeologists study the past, they are unable to observe human behaviour directly. Unlike historians, they also lack access to verbally encoded records of the past. Instead they must attempt to infer human behaviour and beliefs from the surviving remains of what people made and used before they can begin, like other social scientists, to explain phenomena. This makes archaeology very different from other human sciences, in terms of both problems and methodology (Clarke 1973; Schiffer 1976; Binford 1977, 1981).

HISTORICAL REVIEW

In this section I will sketch the changing long term relationship between archaeology and the physical and biological sciences. It will become clear that archaeologists have asked different questions at different periods. Some of these questions have encouraged close relations with the biological and physical sciences, while other equally important ones have discouraged them.

Archaeological relations with the physical and biological sciences can be traced as far back as the seventeenth century, almost two hundred years prior to the emergence of prehistoric archaeology as a scientific discipline. A major institution encouraging this development was the Royal Society of London, which promoted the Baconian goal of seeking knowledge through observation rather than by relying on the writings of classical authorities (Piggott [1950] 1985; Hunter 1971). Archaeological research played a significant role in the activities of the members of this society from its founding in 1660. Much of this research was directed towards describing artifacts more accurately and determining how they had been made and used. In 1720 the astronomer Edmund Halley examined the weathering on worked surfaces of sarsens from Stonehenge and expressed the opinion that this monument must be two to three thousand years old. Later the antiquarian William Stukeley, who was also a member of the Royal Society, concluded that the megalithic circles at Avebury must be even older than Stonehenge because their stones were more weathered (Lynch and Lynch 1968: 52). Although Stonehenge is somewhat older than Halley believed, both conclusions have withstood the test of time. Stukeley also deduced from stratigraphic observations that some Bronze Age barrows in Britain were older than the Roman roads which cut across them (Piggott 1985: 67). He, and still earlier William Camden, recognized that crop marks, which rural folklore had maintained were of supernatural origin, outlined the walls of buried structures (Daniel 1967: 37; Piggott 1950: 52).

Yet prehistoric archaeology as a scientific discipline did not grow out of this early and often fruitful cooperation between antiquarians and natural scientists. Instead it began in 1819, when the Danish businessman Christian Thomsen managed to assign the prehistoric artifacts in the Danish national collection to successive ages, not merely of stone, bronze, and iron, but of stone, stone and copper, bronze, early iron, and later iron. He did this, not by any arbitrary sorting of these finds according to evolutionary assumptions, but by carefully observing the material, functional types, shapes, decoration, and context of

1

discovery of sets of artifacts from single graves and other find spots that guaranteed the contemporaneity of their deposition. Then, by noting what characteristics occurred and did not occur together in the same depositional units, he was able to work out the first chronological seriation of archaeological material covering the whole of northern European prehistory (Heizer 1962: 21-26). Thomsen's seriation did not depend upon stratigraphy, written records, or any of the devices for inferring chronology that were used in other sciences. He appears to have become intuitively familiar with the concept of gradual technological and stylistic change as a result of studying a large numismatic collection. This experience led him to realize that cultural chronologies could be inferred by defining trends in the formal characteristics of artifacts instead of relying on inscriptions and historical data. Seriation depends upon the co-clustering of many features found on each artifact, not simply arranging individual ones into likely sequences.

By working out the first comprehensive relative chronology based on archaeological evidence alone, Thomsen laid the basis for the development of prehistoric archaeology as a scientific discipline. The methods he used were based entirely upon the study of products of human behaviour, such as style, burial customs, and technological change. This meant that prehistoric archaeology did not begin as the result of borrowing a dating device from some other discipline. Instead it started with the development of a new technique for relative dating that was appropriate to archaeological material. In pioneering the use of seriation as a chronological device, Thomsen made a contribution to scientific analysis that has been inadequately appreciated even by fellow archaeologists. This was largely because of his preference for teaching by example rather than expounding his ideas in written form (Gräslund 1974).

Between 1820 and 1860 the development of seriation was followed in Canada, Scotland, and Switzerland by the elaboration of an approach to post-Palaeolithic archaeology (by coincidence, earlier periods are not substantially represented in the archaeological records of those countries) that sought to document evolutionary change, but at the same time was keenly interested in determining how human beings had lived in prehistoric times. Thomsen's young assistant Jens Worsaae became an active field archaeologist and soon provided stratigraphic corroboration of Thomsen's seriation, while in Sweden Sven Nilsson systematically used world-wide ethnographic analogies to try to determine the uses that had been made of prehistoric artifacts. Interdisciplinary field research was pioneered in studies that were carried out on Danish shell mounds in the 1840's and 1850's by a team headed by the eminent geologist J.G. Forchhammer, the biologist Japetus Steenstrup, and the archaeologist Worsaae (Klindt-Jensen 1975: 71-3). While initiated in an effort to use archaeologically dated shell middens to trace changes in the Danish coastline, this research produced important evidence about how the inhabitants of Denmark had lived in Mesolithic times. The investigation of animal bones in refuse deposits indicated that people had inhabited the coast from autumn until spring. Palaeobotanical evidence was used to reconstruct the colder natural environment of the region at that time. Experimental archaeology began when Steenstrup suggested that bird carcasses be fed to dogs in order to determine if the scarcity of particular parts of bird bones in the middens resulted from the actions of people or canines (Morlot 1861: 300). Worsaae studied the internal stratigraphy of shell mounds to learn how they had accumulated and what individual seasonal occupations were like.

In his own work, Nilsson (1868: 4) proposed that archaeologists should seek to determine how different abrasion marks were produced on stone and bone tools in order to test inferences about their function based on ethnographic analogies. In Switzerland and Scandinavia there was increasing use of biological expertise to identify the sorts of wild and domesticated animals and plants that were being found in archaeological sites and to set prehistoric cultures into palaeoenvironmental contexts. The latter operation came to involve determining changing distributions of land, seas and lakes. All of this encouraged cooperation between archaeologists and physical and biological scientists (Bibby 1956: 183-97). This collaboration began on a basis of equality, with geologists looking to archaeology as an established discipline that could date post-glacial changes in coastlines. In the decades that followed, Scandinavian archaeologists continued to regard specialists in other disciplines, not as exemplars of scientific method, but as co-workers who could help to answer questions that their own research had already identified as important (Gräslund 1974).

Palaeolithic archaeology developed in England and France beginning in the late 1850's. Unlike Scandinavian-style archaeology, it was modelled on the analytical techniques of palaeontology and historical geology and shared with these disciplines a burning interest in tracing the antiquity and origins of humanity (Grayson 1983). Palaeolithic archaeologists also sought to demonstrate the evolution of ever more complex Stone Age cultures by tracing Thomsen's evolutionary sequence from stone to bronze to iron back through the Stone Age to the earliest and most primitive manifestations of cultural behaviour. In France, England, and much of central Europe, this unilinear evolutionary approach became the model for all prehistoric archaeology, not merely the study of the Palaeolithic period. Like palaeontologists, palaeolithic archaeologists relied almost exclusively upon stratigraphy as a primary dating technique, perhaps because stylistic trends were less obvious with stone than with metal artifacts. They also studied artifacts more as fossils that were diagnostic of particular stages in the evolution of stone tool technologies than as products of human behaviour.

Unlike the Scandinavian archaeologists, who sought to infer how people had lived in the past by determining how different kinds of artifacts had been made and used, Palaeolithic archaeologists looked for modern cultures with technologies that seemed to be at the same level of development as prehistoric ones. They assumed that the subsistence patterns, social organization, and beliefs of the former would apply equally to the latter. Thus the Tasmanians were sometimes claimed to be modern representatives of the stage of development that had been reached in Europe by Neanderthal Man, while parallels were drawn between the Upper Palaeolithic Solutrean culture and the modern Inuit (Lubbock 1865; Sollas 1911). This procedure was justified by the widely held unilinear evolutionary belief that cultures at the same stage of development would share their essential features in common regardless of when or in what part of the world they existed. The idea that all cultures must evolve according to a single plan dictated by a universally shared pattern of reasoning applied to the "conquest of nature" was expressed most vigorously and explicitly in archaeology by Gabriel de Mortillet (Daniel 1975: 119-20). While Palaeolithic archaeology developed in close contact with the biological and physical sciences and borrowed many of its concepts from these older and more prestigious disciplines, it ended up relying on ethnology to interpret its data. Thus, ironically, while it uncovered the earliest phases of human development, in the long run it made less effective use of the physical and biological sciences to interpret its data than did Scandinavian archaeology.

The next stage was that of culture-historical archaeology. Previous approaches had been concerned mainly with tracing temporal changes in the archaeological record and accounting for these in evolutionary terms. Their primary goal had been to demonstrate that cultural development had been the most important trend in human history. The culture-historical approach reflected growing awareness of geographical as well as temporal variations in archaeological data. Such awareness was already evident in the syntheses of European prehistory produced by the Swedish archaeologist Oscar Montelius in the 1880s, but the first examples of a fully developed culture-historical approach are found in the works of Gustaf Kossinna (1911) in Germany and Gordon Childe (1925) in Britain. Geographical variation was interpreted mainly as evidence of different ethnic groups that had lived adjacent to each other in prehistoric times, each with its own distinctive culture. Cultural changes were attributed increasingly to migrations and the diffusion of trait from one culture to another rather than to multiple inventions of the same items. The principal objective was no longer to trace cultural evolution in the archaeological record but to interpret the past as a history of numerous ethnic groups, some of which could be identified as the ancestors of modern nations.

The criteria used to define archaeological cultures were mainly stylistic ones. Archaeologists such as Childe (1929: vii, 248) compared homemade pottery, burial customs, and ornaments in an effort to distinguish one ethnic group from another and to construct more detailed cultural chronologies. Items of technology that appeared to have spread rapidly from one society to another, such as more effective tools and weapons, were considered unsuitable for this purpose but were used, as were trade goods, to assign neighbouring prehistoric cultures to the same time period. This preoccupation with style resulted in increasing intellectual self-sufficiency. The lack of productive relations with the physical and biological sciences, already noted with Palaeolithic archaeology, intensified and even relations with ethnology became less important. Yet, through the elaboration of their own methodologies, archaeologists made great progress in understanding the past. Artifact typologies were devised, cultures defined, and detailed cultural chronologies constructed. Even today, when archaeologists realize that the relationship between material culture and ethnicity is far more complicated than it was formerly believed to be (Hodder 1982, 1986), the advances that culture-historical archaeologists made in recovering and interpreting spatial as well as temporal variations in the archeological record are of lasting importance.

Archaeologists did not remain content to define

prehistoric cultures and trace their external relations. Beginning in the 1920s a growing number of them became concerned with how individual cultures functioned and how these cultures changed over time. Initially most of this interest was directed towards learning how cultures functioned from an ecological and economical point of view. This was reflected in Cyril Fox's ecological and geographical study The Personality of Britain (1932) and Childe's The Most Ancient East (1928), which examined the economic consequences of bronze working. Later, European archaeologists paid growing attention to reconstructing the political and social aspects of prehistoric cultures, at least in part through the analysis of settlement patterns (Childe 1931, 1942). By the 1950s ecological and settlement studies had begun to replace purely culture-historical archaeology in the United States (Willey and Sabloff 1980: 130-80). For the most part archaeologists sought initially to determine how cultural systems had worked at single points in time (Childe 1956: 111-34). In the early 1960s these functional approaches were superceded by processual analyses which tried to account for how archaeological cultures changed as functioning systems, mainly from an ecological perspective (Willey and Sabloff 1980: 181-210). In the United States, the New (or Processual) Archaeology, in its efforts to be more scientific, adopted an ill-suited and already outmoded hypothetico-deductive positivist approach, which had been formulated primarily with the physical sciences in mind (Salmon 1982). Its deficiencies must, however, be blamed on the philosophers of science who created it, rather than on practising physical scientists.

This interest in prehistoric cultures as functioning systems led to renewed relations between archaeology and the physical and biological sciences. In the late 1940s, for his research on the Mesolithic camp at Star Carr, in Yorkshire, Grahame Clark (1954) enlisted the help of geologists and biologists to analyse findings and determine what use had been made of the site. Robert Braidwood's (1974) Iraq-Jarmo project and Richard MacNeish's (1974, 1978) Tehuacan Valley research pioneered new patterns of interdisciplinary team work aimed at tracing the origins of food production in the Near East and Mesoamerica. Increasingly geologists and biologists sought to become active participants in archaeological field work and were unwilling to continue to restrict their participation to the laboratory analysis of finds that archaeologists brought to them (Reed 1963:205). Even if these efforts at cooperative research now appear to have been less effective than they were initially judged to be, they played a major role in pioneering new forms of interactive, as well as interdisciplinary, studies of archaeological data (Brown and Struever 1973).

Through the efforts of Grahame Clark and Eric Higgs' advocacy of site-catchment analysis (Roper 1979), Cambridge University became a major centre promoting interdisciplinary studies of prehistoric subsistence patterns and palaeoecology in many parts of the world (Higgs 1972, 1975). As these were recognized as major objectives of archaeological investigation, growing attention was paid to the collection and study of plant remains and animal bones and to the elaboration of new techniques for recovering such evidence. The analysis of pollen recovered from soil samples, which the Swedish geologist Lennart von Post had applied to prehistoric sites early in the twentieth century, became increasingly routine in archaeology (Bryant and Holloway 1983). Later the development of flotation permitted the recovery of material that had escaped retrieval by dry-sieving. Coprolite analysis has added a new dimension to the study of prehistoric diet (Callen 1963), while in recent years phytolith studies have provided information about prehistoric plants in contexts where all organic evidence has disappeared (Rovner 1983). Aerial photography and more recently remote-sensing have played a major role in recovering the cultural landscapes of the past (Deuel 1973; Ebert 1984). Among its other significant accomplishments, remote sensing has helped to demonstrate that intensive agriculture as well as swidden cultivation played a major role in the Classic Maya civilization (Flannery 1982).

A second intense focus of interaction, this time exclusively with the physical sciences, has been trace-element analysis, which is used to locate natural sources of different types of widely traded materials, such as clays made into ceramics, turquoise, obsidian, jade, and chlorite (Renfrew et al. 1968; Pires-Ferreira 1976, Hammond et al. 1977; Weigand et al. 1977). This has permitted archaeologists to track the distribution of some of these materials over vast areas and to infer patterns of exchange, often in a quantified fashion. In other cases thin-sectioning and microscopic study by geologists are sufficient to source rocks (Shotton 1963). The physical sciences have also played a major role in studies of prehistoric technology. By learning more about the physical processes involved in stone knapping, metallurgy, and ceramic production, archaeologists can reconstruct these technologies in sufficient detail to identify regional variations in the archaeological record and relate these to economic, social, and historical processes (Wertime and Muhly 1980; Bishop et al. 1982; Sieveking and Newcomer 1987). Technological knowledge also permits archaeologists to understand the manufacturing of perishable materials, such as different kinds of barkcloth, and use this knowledge to gain more detailed insights into culture history (Tolstoy 1966). In addition, physical analyses have long facilitated a more detailed reconstruction of the technical processes employed in producing ancient works of art (Church 1982). On the other hand, architecture and engineering have probably been underemployed by archaeologists as a basis for inferring the technical knowledge that went into erecting ancient structures, whether these were bark-covered houses or the Egyptian pyramids. In general, however, archaeologists recognize that the physical sciences provide a basis for understanding the technological knowledge of ancient peoples. Long ago Childe (1958: 5) predicted that one of prehistoric archaeology's principal accomplishments would be the study of prehistoric technology.

Cooperation between archaeology and the physical and biological sciences is contributing significantly to the understanding of palaeoenvironments, prehistoric subsistence patterns, palaeoecology, prehistoric technology, and patterns of exchange. That leaves many aspects of prehistoric cultures, such as social and political organization, class structure, and ritual behaviour, to be inferred by archaeologists with the assistance of ethnographic analogies. Yet the sustained expansion of cooperation and the constantly growing number of new techniques that facilitated the behavioural interpretation of archaeological findings have resulted in steadily increasing interaction between archaeologists and physical and biological scientists since World War II (Cornwall 1956, 1964; Aitken 1961; Brothwell and Higgs 1963; Pyddoke 1963; Biek 1963; Hodges 1964; Rosenfeld 1965; Dimbleby 1967; Raikes 1967; Allibone 1970).

Another major research area in which there has been growing cooperation between archaeologists and physical scientists is chronology. Prior to 1945 the Scandinavian varve sequence and dendrochronology in the southwestern United States provided the only calendrical dating techniques available to archaeologists, that did not depend upon historical data. These were, however, geographically and temporally extremely limited in their application. Various natural sequences that had been worked out by palaeontologists helped to assign larger numbers of archaeological finds to successive eras. For the most part, however, archaeologists depended upon stratigraphy and seriation to order their material. These techniques provided only relative chronologies, which could not be correlated on a world-wide basis. After World War II radiocarbon dating, potassium-argon ratios, and thermoluminescence, to mention only the most widely applied methods, provided new means for dating archaeological material (Brothwell and Higgs 1963: 21-92). These produced calendrical dates and could be applied to archaeological material from anywhere in the world. Now, for the first time, archaeologists did not have to classify archaeological data primarily in order to work out chronologies. Often in the past this had compelled them to make unwarranted assumptions about cultural processes, especially when they were attempting to correlate archaeological sequences over wide areas. For example, the relative ages assigned to Neolithic and Bronze Age sites in Europe and the Near East by different archaeologists in the late nineteenth and early twentieth centuries have been shown to depend upon their assumptions about whether prehistoric diffusion had mostly carried innovations from Europe to the Near East or in the opposite direction (Renfrew 1973). The new physical dating techniques also provided calendrical estimates that for the first time indicated the duration of prehistoric sequences and hence the rate at which cultural changes had taken place. In most parts of the world, and for both Palaeolithic and more recent periods, it turned out that archaeologists had generally underestimated the duration, and hence overestimated the rapidity, of cultural change in prehistoric times (Renfrew 1973; cf. Ritchie 1944, 1965). It also became possible to compare rates of cultural change everywhere. This chronological revolution played a major role not only in Europe but elsewhere in encouraging archaeologists to pay greater attention to internal factors, rather than to diffusion and migration, as forces bringing about cultural change. That in turn was important in encouraging the development of processual archaeology.

In recent years there has been a trend for archaeologists to supplement the established interests of processual archaeologists in ecology and cultural evolution with renewed attention to cultural specifics. Archaeologists are once more studying style, traditions, and what material culture meant to the people who made and used it (Hodder 1986, 1987a, 1987b). These were concerns of culture-historical archaeology that tended to be lost sight of following the development of functional and processual archaeology. Not surprisingly these particular interests are once again directing archaeologists towards research that does not rely greatly on cooperation with the physical and biological sciences. Yet there is no evidence that these developments are diminishing an interest in the study of

4

palaeoecology, subsistence patterns, and economic behaviour, all of which clearly do depend on such ties.

Archaeologists also are cultivating a growing awareness of the degree to which biases of preservation and recovery limit and distort the archaeological record as a source of information about many aspects of human behaviour (Binford 1977, 1981, 1984). As a result of geological activity the evidence for entire periods and for classes of sites that were restricted to certain locations have failed to survive. Geological studies are therefore essential to understand the limitations of the archaeological record (Butzer 1982). Conversely, bones that were part of the natural background of a site may erroneously be interpreted as evidence of human activity. In an effort to cope with such problems , the field of taphonomy is becoming of great interest to a growing number of archaeologists (Gifford 1981). The understanding of how human material is incorporated into archaeological sites and preserved (or not preserved) for archaeologists to study likewise requires not only ethnological or ethnoarchaeological research but also growing cooperation between archaeologists, biologists, and geologists (Wood and Johnson 1978).

In earlier times archaeology tended to oscillate between phases when its research interests encouraged close contacts with the physical and biological sciences and ones when the questions it asked could be answered either internally or in cooperation with anthropology and the other social sciences. In recent years these oscillations have been giving way to a broader synthesis in which all the basic kinds of questions that were asked in the past become important. In America and western Europe processual archaeology's efforts to interpret cultures as ecologically adaptive systems, explain changes in terms of the internal responses of these systems to the natural environment, and delineated cross-cultural evolutionary regularities in cultural development currently are being modified and supplemented, but not wholly rejected, as the result of a growing interest in cultural specifics, in the role of cultural traditions, diffusion, and migration in bringing about change, and understanding cultures as structurally meaningful configurations. These "new" features were attributes of the cultural-historical approach. Processual archaeology's efforts to explain cultural change wholly in terms of internal responses to ecological factors now appear as limited as the culture-historical approach's attempts to account for it in terms of the influences that neighbouring cultures exerted on one another. It is now acknowledged that cultures must be studied from both inside and outside. More comprehensive interpretations of archaeological data also require ever more detailed chronological controls (Trigger 1984). These developments suggest that a significant number of archaeologists will seek to maintain the closest possible ties with the physical and biological sciences, since these disciplines remain vital for interpreting major sources of data required by archaeologists.

There is also evidence which suggests that this broader synthesis of approaches is not merely a passing fad. Beginning in 1928 Soviet archaeology laid an almost exclusive emphasis on economic and social interpretations of archaeological data. This encouraged many important contributions to the study of human behaviour in prehistoric times, including S.S. Semenov's (1964) pioneering of use-wear analysis on stone and bone tools. At the same time Soviet archaeologists were discouraged from devoting much attention to producing formal classifications of their material or cultural chronologies, since doing so was denounced as a manifestation of "bourgeois formalism". Nor was diffusion or migration thought to be necessary to explain the archaeological record (Miller 1956). In recent years, however, many Soviet archaeologists have been stressing the need for more specific artifact typologies and cultural classifications (to supplement radiocarbon dating), the use of the concepts of diffusion and migration to explain significant aspects of the archaeological record, and the value of cultural ecology. They argue that research along these lines is essential if Soviet archaeology is to produce information about human behaviour that will allow it to make more significant contributions to a Marxist interpretation of prehistory (Bulkin et al. 1982).

This suggests that a basic set of techniques and approaches is emerging that is being recognized by archaeologists around the world as necessary to extract a comprehensive range of information from archaeological finds. The approaches that constitute this package have developed in various sequences in different countries. What is important is not the order in which they are invented or recognized as important but their being identified as part of a comprehensive system that allows meaning to be assigned to archaeological data. Within this package information derived from the physical and biological sciences plays a significant role in helping to establish the limitations of available archaeological data and determine what happened in the past (Trigger 1986). These disciplines do not, however, assist in explaining why things happened, since all such explanations must be framed in terms of human behaviour and perceptions.

IDEAL RELATIONS

What can the history of archaeology tell us about good and bad (productive and unproductive) relations between archaeologists and physical and biological scientists? The structure of these relations is clearly not uniform but varies according to the discipline involved. Physicists who specialize in radiocarbon dating generally seem to prefer to remain in their laboratories, where they study samples collected by archaeologists. It is left to archaeologists to refine collecting techniques in order to determine more precisely to what in the archaeological record radiocarbon dates refer (Browman 1981). On the other hand, as we have already seen, many geologists and biologists maintain that, if they are to contribute effectively to the understanding of the past, they must be involved as full partners in the planning and execution of archaeological research projects. Collaboration of this sort has begun already in the 1840s. Yet only in recent decades has much archaeological research become truly interdisciplinary in its planning and execution.

The most vital issue, from an archaeological perspective, is how archaeologists should assess the findings of other sciences. The techniques that physical scientists and biologists use to interpret archaeological discoveries are often so complex that archaeologists cannot adequately evaluate the theoretical adequacy or methodological skill that goes into such work. Yet they are responsible for integrating these findings into more comprehensive archaeological interpretations. A reliable synthesis of archaeological data requires that every piece of information that is even remotely relevant to a problem should be carefully cross-checked against every other item in order to search for and try to resolve discrepancies. Under these circumstances archaeologists can never consent to be merely consumers of findings made by physical and biological scientists. They must subject their colleagues' conclusions to rigorous review and testing within the general frameworks that they alone have the professional training to construct. Their aim in doing this must be to determine if these conclusions confirm or contradict other findings. In this way archaeologists may be able to contribute to the ongoing refinement of those aspects of physical and biological research that are relevant to their own discipline. I will conclude this paper by examining a number of cases in which this sort of dialogue has been productive of new archaeology and the physical and biological sciences. I will also consider the disastrous consequences of the absence of sufficient dialogue.

A classic example of the benefits of cooperation is the calibration of radiocarbon dating. Historically dated ancient Egyptian objects from as early as 3000 B.C. played an important role in establishing the general validity of the technique of radiocarbon dating (Libby 1955). It soon became apparent, however, that artifacts from Egyptian sites prior to 1500 B.C. yielded radiocarbon dates that were younger than the calendrical dates assigned to them, with the discrepancies becoming increasingly large until at least 3000 B.C. (Libby 1963). The problems involved in calculating precise historical dates for the Old Kingdom and the Early Dynastic Period were (and remain) sufficiently great that it might have been possible for Egyptologists to accommodate their sequence to the new radiocarbon chronology. Yet they had sufficient confidence in the general validity of their historical sequence that instead they questioned the accuracy or relevance of the new radiocarbon chronology prior to 1500 B.C. (Smith 1964). This discrepancy in an important corpus of data led to further technical research that refuted one of the key original assumptions of radiocarbon dating: constancy in the formation of C14. That in turn led to the calibration of radiocarbon dates, so that they now approximate historical ones far more closely than they did previously (Watkins 1975). Being able to trace alterations in the rate of C14 formation has stimulated further scientific research in fields such as climatology and astronomy. While it is likely that radiocarbon dates eventually would have been calibrated even if the discrepancy with the Egyptian historical sequence had not been noted and challenged, the refusal of Egyptologists to compromise their own historically based conclusions clearly accelerated this process and led to results that are of great value to all disciplines concerned with the production and use of radiocarbon dates.

That, however, is not the end of the story. Recently it has been discovered that a large set of calibrated radiocarbon dates, many of them based on short-lived organic materials, recovered from the pyramids appears to be older than the historical dates assigned to these structures (Haas et al. 1988). A hopefully productive new round of dialogue between Egyptologists and radiocarbon experts appears to be beginning. Whatever the true dates for the Old Kingdom turn out to be, the first cycle of Egyptological resistance clearly benefitted radiocarbon dating.

Ursula Franklin, a physical scientist familiar with the social sciences, has demonstrated how to derive behavioural conclusions from technological data. In her studies of Shang bronze casting she has used archaeological data and a detailed understanding of technological processes to reconstruct the technical skills, organization of labour, and problems involved in procuring raw materials. Her inferences about the organization of labour and broader social and political relations for the most part flow directly from archaeological data and metallurgical knowledge (Franklin 1980, 1983). At the same time she has utilized information about traditional Chinese culture to draw significant parallels between early Chinese metallurgical concepts and their cosmological and religious beliefs (Franklin et al. 1985). All of this is accomplished through a detailed contextual interrelating of metallurgical, archaeological, and Sinological data.

There is also growing awareness of the limitations of what can be inferred about human behaviour from physical analyses. Ian Hodder (1984) has pointed out that archaeologists may pinpoint the geological sources of stone axes and trace their distributions by means of petrological analysis. They may also note that the axes get smaller as they turn up farther from these sources. This, however, reveals little about the economic and social mechanisms that produced these distributions. It does not reveal, for example, whether stone axes got smaller as they moved farther from sources because they were easier to transport or because old ones were traded to more distant groups after they had been reduced in size as a result of resharpening. Recently David Gill (1987) has used trace-element analysis of an Etruscan painted cup to raise the possibility that pottery clays as well as finished vessels might have been traded in the Mediterranean region, thus creating new problems for the interpretation of archaeological ceramic distributions. In these cases at least part of the problem is the lack of sufficient archaeological data to reduce the range of alternative possibilities (Chamberlin 1944). Archaeologists may not even be aware of important alternatives. The precision with which the findings of physical scientists can be used to resolve archaeological problems depends on the realization that these findings relate only to part of a more complex situation in which behavioral issues play a important role. Many archaeologists and their collaborators in the physical sciences still have to learn that they must delineate precisely what questions physical science data can answer if such information is to be use effectively.

In other cases archaeologists have been slow to recognize how different their data are from those of other sciences. It is generally assumed that the basic principles of stratigraphy were borrowed from geology. Some archaeologists have referred to the rule of superposition as "Steno's law" in honour of the seventeenth century geologist who first articulated it (Heizer 1962: 4-10). It seems likely, however, that early antiquarians, such as Olof Rudbeck (Klindt-Jensen 1975: 30) and William Stukely (Piggott 1985: 67) independently concluded that underlying structures or deposits were earlier than ones found on top of them. In spite of this, the main development of stratigraphy as an archaeological dating technique took place in the nineteenth century, when Palaeolithic archaeologists hailed it as the application to their field of a dating device developed by geologists. Yet in their excavations archaeologists habitually encountered features of a sort rarely, if ever, found in natural stratigraphy: pits, wells, foundation trenches, basements, deliberate levelling, deposits from earth re moval, terracing, and building new walls on top of old ones. Generally, individual instances of these process were interpreted on the basis of common sense. Nevertheless it was not until 1979 that Edward Harris clearly enunciated the ways in which human stratigraphy differed from natural stratigraphy and formulated a set of rules that has facilitated the systematic analysis of very complex stratified sites. The prestige that archaeologists accorded to an analytical method derived from the physical sciences seriously inhibited the conceptual adaptation of that method to the needs of their own discipline. While this was perhaps not a very serious loss, it exemplifies the problems that any science encounters when it applies the principles of another discipline without rethinking and, if necessary, reformulating them.

The relationship between archaeology and astronomy provides some extremely unedifying chapters in the history of interdisciplinary studies. At the same time it teaches some salutary lessons. Astronomical phenomena loom large in the archaeological record: in the orientation of structures, lines of sight, calendrics, and religious symbolism. To infer astronomical knowledge in ancient times, archaeologists must depend upon astronomers for detailed information about stellar and planetary positions at specific times in the past. In return they sometimes recover written texts that contain information about astronomical events, such as the appearance of supernovas, that is of interest to astronomers. While archaeologists generally acknowledge that they cannot handle astronomical data without astronomical expertise, some astronomers, such as J. Norman Lockyer (1894), Gerald Hawkins (1965), and Fred Hoyle (1966), have attempted to interpret prehistoric structures without learning enough about the history of their construction or the societies that produced them. The result has been amateurish and often misleading work done by eminent scientists (Chippindale 1983: 216-35). On the other hand, archaeologists and astronomers, taking account of each other's expertise, have inferred astronomical knowledge that is of great importance for understanding ancient cultures. Nowhere is this currently more true than in studies of ancient Mesoamerica (Aveni 1975, 1977, 1981). By reconstructing this knowledge it becomes possible to understand not only an important intellectual achievement of these cultures but also how astronomical lore was integrated into their religious beliefs, architecture, and settlement patterns (van Zantwijk 1985).

CONCLUDING REMARKS

It is clear that archaeology depends upon the closest possible cooperation with the physical and biological sciences to achieve a rounded understanding of the past. The history of this cooperation reveals that to be effective it must be based on mutual respect and on an effort by the participants to understand the problems and limitations, as well as the potential, of each discipline. This cooperation must involve a determination to regard the other discipline not merely as a source of interesting questions and answers but also as a challenge to further scholarly enquiry. Geologists and biologists have responded to this challenge by becoming actively involved in archaeological

fieldwork. Archaeologists have not been slow to reject radiocarbon dates that displeased them, often without adequate justification. Yet, on the whole, they tend to accept the findings of the "hard sciences" with undue passivity. Only by subjecting the conclusions of physical and biological analyses to a critical review can archaeologists engage in a productive dialogue. Since archaeologists are generally poorly equipped to criticize the techniques used by other sciences, this involves cross-checking the findings of these disciplines with what else they know about the past to determine if the whole makes - or might make - sense. Finally, archaeologists must strive to determine precisely what archaeological questions the physical and biological sciences can answer and not try to use them to resolve other questions. Archaeologists and their colleagues in the physical and biological sciences have been striving, slowly and often discontinuously but also increasingly effectively, to define a positive working relationship, from which archaeologists generally have been the main beneficiaries. Enough has been learned about the problems and promises of this relationship for both parties to look forward to ever more productive interaction, which is threatened mainly by governments reducing their financial support for all our disciplines.

ACKNOWLEDGEMENTS

A preliminary version of this paper was read to the Archaeology Seminar, McGill University, 8 October 1987.

REFERENCES

Aitken, M.J., 1961, Physics and Archaeology, London: Interscience.
Allibone, T.E., (ed.), 1970, The Impact of the Natural Sciences on Archaeology, Oxford: Oxford University Press.
Aveni, A.F., (ed.), 1975, Archaeoastronomy in Pre-Columbian America, Austin: University of Texas Press.
Aveni, A.F., (ed.), 1977, Native American Astronomy, Austin: University of Texas Press.
Aveni, A.F., 1981, Archaeoastronomy, Advances in Archaeological Method and Theory, 4, 1-77.
Berger, R., 1970, Scientific Methods in Medieval Archaeology, Berkeley: University of California Press.
Bibby, G., 1956, The Testimony of the Spade, New York: Knopf.
Biek, L.,1963, Archaeology and the Microscope, London: Lutterworth.
Binford, L.R., (ed.), 1977, For Theory Building in Archaeology, New York: Academic Press.
Binford, L.R., 1981, Bones: Ancient Men and Modern Myths, New York: Academic Press.
Binford, L.R., 1984, Faunal Remains from Klasies River Mouth, New York: Academic Press.
Bishop, R.L., R.L. Rands, and G.R. Holley, 1982, Ceramic compositional analysis in archaeological perspective, Advances in Archaeological Method and Theory, 5, 275-330.
Braidwood, R.J., 1974, The Iraq Jarmo project, in Archaeological Researches in Retrospect, (ed., G.R. Willey), pp. 59-83, Cambridge: Winthrop.
Brothwell, D. and E. Higgs, (eds.), 1963, Science in Archaeology, New York: Basic Books.
Browman, D.L., 1981, Isotopic discrimination and correction factors in radiocarbon dating, Advances in Archaeological Method and Theory, 4, 241-95.
Brown, J.A. and S. Struever, 1973, The organization of archaeological research, in Research and Theory in Current Archaeology, (ed., C.L. Redman), pp. 261-80,

New York: Wiley.

Bryant, V.M., Jr. and R.G. Holloway, 1983, The role of palynology in archaeology, Advances in Archaeological Method and Theory, 6, 191-224.

Bulkin, V.A., L.S. Klejn, and G.S. Lebedev, 1982, Attainments and problems of Soviet archaeology, World Archaeology, 13, 272-95.

Butzer, K.W., 1982, Archaeology as Human Ecology, Cambridge: Cambridge University Press.

Callen, E.O., 1963, Diet as revealed by coprolites, in Science in Archaeology, (eds., D. Brothwell and E. Higgs), pp. 186-94, New York: Basic Books.

Chamberlin, T.C., 1944, The method of multiple working hypotheses, Scientific Monthly, 59, 357-62.

Childe, V.G., 1925, The Dawn of European Civilization, London: Kegan Paul.

Childe, V.G., 1928, The Most Ancient East, London: Kegan Paul.

Childe, V.G., 1929, The Danube in Prehistory, Oxford: Oxford University Press.

Childe, V.G., 1931, Skara Brae: A Pictish Village in Orkney, London: Kegan Paul.

Childe, V.G., 1942, The chambered cairns of Rousay, Antiquarian Journal, 22, 139-42.

Childe, V.G., 1956, Piecing Together the Past, London: Routledge and Kegan Paul.

Childe, V.G., 1958, Valediction, Bulletin of the Institute of Archaeology, University of London, 1, 1-8.

Chippindale, C., 1983, Stonehenge Complete, London: and Hudson.

Church, A.H., 1892, The Chemistry of Paints and Painting, 2nd ed., London: Seeley.

Clark, J.G.D., 1954, Excavations at Star Carr, Cambridge: Cambridge University Press.

Clarke, D.L., 1973, Archaeology: the loss of innocence, Antiquity, 47, 6-18.

Cornwall, I.W., 1956, Bones for the Archaeologist, London: Phoenix.

Cornwall, I.W., 1958, Soils for the Archaeologist, London: Phoenix.

Cornwall, I.W., 1964, The World of Ancient Man, London: Phoenix.

Daniel, G., 1967, The Origins and Growth of Archaeology, Penguin.

Daniel, G., 1975, A Hundred and Fifty Years of Archaeology, London: Duckworth.

Dimbleby, G.W., 1967, Plants and Archaeology, London: Baker.

Deuel, L., 1973, Flights Into Yesterday: The Story of Aerial Archaeology, Harmonsworth: Penguin.

Ebert, J.I., 1984, Remote sensing applications in archaeology, Advances in Archaeological Method and Theory, 7, 293-362.

Flannery, K.V., (ed.), 1982, Maya Subsistence: Studies in Memory of Dennis E. Puleston, New York: Academic Press.

Fox, C., 1932, The Personality of Britain, Cardiff: National Museum of Wales.

Franklin, U.M., 1980, The beginnings of metallurgy in China: a comparative approach, in The Great Bronze Age of China, (ed., W. Fong), pp. 94-9, New York: Knopf.

Franklin, U.M., 1983, On bronze and other metals in early China, in The Origins of Chinese Civilization, (ed., D.N. Keightley) pp. 279-96, Berkeley: University of California Press.

Franklin, U.M., J. Berthrong, and A. Chan, 1985, Metallurgy, cosmology, knowledge: the Chinese experience, Journal of Chinese Philosophy, 12, 333-69.

Gellner, E., 1985, Relativism and the Social Sciences, Cambridge: Cambridge University Press.

Gifford, D.P., 1981, Taphonomy and paleoecology: a critical review of archaeology's sister disciplines. Advances in Archaeological Method and Theory, 4, 365-438.

Gill, D.W., 1987. Metru.menece: An Etruscan painted inscription on a mid-5th-century BC red-figure cup from Populonia, Antiquity, 61, 82-7.

Gräslund, B., 1974, Relativ Datering: Om Kronologisk Metod i Nordisk Arkeologi, Uppsala: Tor, 16.

Grayson, D.K., 1983, The Establishment of Human Antiquity, New York: Academic Press.

Haas, H., M. Lehner, R. Wenke, and W. Wölfli, 1988, A radiocarbon chronology for the Egyptian pyramids, Archaeometry (in press).

Hammond, N. et al., 1977, Maya jade: source location and analysis, in Exchange Systems in Prehistory, (eds., T.K. Earle and J.E. Ericson), pp. 35-67, New York: Academic Press.

Harris, E.C., 1979, Principles of Archaeological Stratigraphy, New York: Academic Press.

Hawkins, G.S., with H.B. White, 1965, Stonehenge Decoded, Garden City: Doubleday.

Heizer, R.F., (ed.), 1962, Man's Discovery of his Past: Literary Landmarks in Archaeology, Englewood Cliffs: Prentice-Hall.

Higgs, E.S., (ed.), 1972, Papers in Economic Prehistory, Cambridge: Cambridge University Press.

Higgs. E.S., (ed.), 1975, Palaeoeconomy, Cambridge: Cambridge University Press.

Hodder, I., 1982, Symbols in Action: Ethnoarchaeological Studies of Material Culture, Cambridge: Cambridge University Press.

Hodder, I., 1984, Archaeology in 1984, Antiquity, 58, 25-32.

Hodder, I., 1986, Reading the Past: Current Approaches to Interpretation in Archaeology, Cambridge: Cambridge University Press.

Hodder, I., (ed.), 1987a, The Archaeology of Contextual Meanings, Cambridge: Cambridge University Press.

Hodder, I., (ed.), 1987b, Archaeology as Long-Term History, Cambridge: Cambridge University Press.

Hodges, H., 1964, Artifacts: An Introduction to Early Materials and Technology, London: Baker.

Hoyle, F., 1966, Stonehenge - an eclipse predictor, Nature, 211, 454-6.

Hunter, M.C., 1971, The Royal Society and the origins of British archaeology: I and II, Antiquity, 65, 113-21, 187-96.

Klindt-Jensen, O., 1975, A History of Scandinavian Archaeology, London: Thames and Hudson.

Kossinna, G., 1911, Die Herkunft der Germanen, Leipzig, Kabitzsch.

Libby, W.F., 1955, Radiocarbon Dating, 2nd ed., Chicago: University of Chicago Press.

Libby W.F., 1963, The accuracy of radiocarbon dates, Science, 140, 278-9.

Lockyer, J.N., 1894, The Dawn of Astronomy, London: Cassell.

Lubbock, J., 1865, Prehistoric Times, London: Williams and Norgate.

Lynch, B.D. and T.F. Lynch, 1968, The beginnings of a scientific approach to prehistoric archaeology in 17th and 18th century Britain, Southwestern Journal of Anthropology, 24, 33-65.

MacNeish, R.S., 1974, Reflections on my search for the beginnings of agriculture in Mexico, in Archaeological Researches in Retrospect, (ed., G.R. Willey), pp. 205-34, Cambridge: Winthrop.

MacNeish, R.S., 1978, The Science of Archaeology? North Scituate, Duxbury Press.

Miller, M.O., 1956, Archaeology in the U.S.S.R., London, Atlantic Press.

Morlot, A., 1861, General views on archaeology, Washington: Annual Report of the Smithsonian Institution for 1860, 284-343.

Nilsson, S., 1868, The Primitive Inhabitants of Scandinavia, London: Longmans, Green.

Piggott, S., 1950, rev. ed., 1985, William Stukeley: An Eighteenth-Century Antiquary, London: Thames and Hudson.

Pires-Ferreira, J.W., 1976, Obsidian exchange in formative Mesoamerica, in The Early Mesoamerican Village (ed., K.V. Flannery), pp. 292-306, New York: Academic Press.

Pyddoke, E., 1963, The Scientist and Archaeology, London: Phoenix.

Raikes, R., 1967, Water, Weather and Prehistory, London: Baker.

Reed. C., 1963, Osteo-archaeology, in Science in Archaeology, (ed., D. Brothwell and E. Higgs), pp. 204-16, New York: Basic Books.

Renfrew, A.C., 1973, Before Civilization: The Radiocarbon Revolution and Prehistoric Europe, London: Cape.

Renfrew, A.C., J.E. Dixon, and J.R. Cann, 1968, Further Analyses of Near Eastern obsidians, Proceedings of the Prehistoric Society, 34, 319-33.

Ritchie, W.A., 1944, The Pre-Iroquoian Occupations of New York State, Rochester: Rochester Museum of Arts and Sciences, Memoir, 1.

Ritchie, W.A., 1965, The Archaeology of New York State, Garden City: Natural History Press.

Roper, D.C., 1979, The method and theory of site catchment analysis: a review, Advances in Archaeological Method and Theory, 2, 119-40.

Rosenfeld, A., 1965, The Inorganic Raw Materials of Prehistory, London: Weidenfeld and Nicolson.

Rovner, I., 1983, Plant opal phytolith analysis: major advances in archaeobotanical research, Advances in Archaeological Method and Theory, 6, 225-66.

Salmon, M.H., 1982, Philosophy and Archaeology, New York: Academic Press.

Schiffer, M.B., 1976, Behavioural Archaeology, New York: Academic Press.

Schiffer, M.B., (ed.), 1978-86, Advances in Archaeological Method and Theory, Vols. 1-9, New York: Academic Press.

Semenov, S.A., 1964, Prehistoric Technology, London: Cory, Adams and Mackay.

Shotton, F.W., 1963, Petrological examination, in Science in Archaeology, (eds., D. Brothwell and E. Higgs), pp. 482-8, New York: Basic Books.

Sieveking, G. de G. and M.H. Newcomer, (eds.), 1987, The Human Uses of Flint and Chert, Cambridge: Cambridge University Press.

Smith, H.S., 1964, Egypt and C14 dating, Antiquity, 38, 32-7.

Sollas, W.J., 1911, Ancient Hunters and their Modern Representatives, London: Macmillan.

Sperber, D., 1985, On Anthropological Knowledge, Cambridge: Cambridge University Press.

Tolstoy, P., 1966, Method in long range comparison, Congreso Internacional de Amercanistas, 36, 69-89.

Trigger, B.G., 1986, Prospects for a world archaeology, World Archaeology, 18, 1-20.

van Zwantwijk, R., 1985, The Aztec Arrangement: The Social History of Pre-Spanish Mexico, Norman: University of Oklahoma Press.

Watkins, T., 1975, Radiocarbon: Calibration and Prehistory, Edinburgh: Edinburgh University Press.

Weigand, P.C., G. Harbottle, and E.V. Sayre, 1977, Turquoise sources and source analysis: Mesoamerica and the southwestern U.S.A., in Exchange Systems in Prehistory, (eds., T.K. Earle and J.E. Ericson), pp. 15-34, New York: Academic Press.

Wertime, T.A., and J.D. Muhly, 1980, The Coming of the Age of Iron, New Haven: Yale University Press.

Willey, G.R., and J.A. Sabloff, 1980, A History of American Archaeology, 2nd ed., San Francisco: Freeman.

Wood, W.R. and D.L. Johnson, 1978, A survey of disturbance processes in archaeological site formation, Advances in Archaeological Method and Theory, 1, 315-81.

2. Roman Moulds from Castleford, West Yorkshire

P. BUDD

Department of Archaeological Sciences, University of Bradford, Bradford, West Yorkshire, England, BD7 1DP.

J. BAYLEY

Ancient Monuments Laboratory, English Heritage, Fortress House, 23 Savile Row, London, England, W1X 2HE.

ABSTRACT: *Two large groups of fragments provide evidence for the construction and use of Roman moulds. The first was for casting spoons in multiples. The second group was for casting sections of enamelled vessels.*

INTRODUCTION

Castleford lies between the major Roman centres of York and Lincoln about 30 km south of York (See Figure 1). The site is located at the confluence of two rivers and is thought to be an important staging point during the Roman period. Excavations, directed by Mr. Phil Abramson of West Yorkshire Archaeology Service, started in 1974 in advance of a phased re-development of the town centre (Abramson forthcoming).

Initial occupation of the site was military and two forts have been identified, the first established in the 70's A.D. and the second in the late first or early second century. A civilian vicus developed and flourished until at least the mid second century. The late third century saw a re-occupation of the later fort after a period of disuse, and it was in a pit cut from this level that the bulk of the spoon mould fragments were found. The vessel mould fragments were recovered from a nearby pit of uncertain date, but possibly belonging to the late first century.

THE SPOON MOULDS

A total of almost 800 fragment from a number of clay moulds used to cast copper alloy spoons were recovered from the upper fill of the third century pit. Typical examples are shown in Plate 1. Uniquely identifiable portions have been counted and represent a minimum number of at least 52 moulds. No other evidence of metalworking (e.g., slag, ingots, or crucibles) was found with the moulds although some crucible fragments have been recovered from other areas of the site.

After their initial recognition, the moulds were examined in detail at the Ancient Monuments Laboratory. An initial description was published (Bayley and Sherlock 1986) and a full report drawn up for inclusion in the excavation report (Bayley and Budd 1987).

Although it was not possible to reconstruct any of the moulds in full, the partial reassembly of many has provided details of their design. Figure 2 is a reconstruction drawing showing one of the spoons. Note that the spoons are purse-shaped with a medial rib running along the back of the bowl. The handle makes a 10-15° angle with the plane of the bowl and has a raised collar or knob.

The great majority of the moulds were made either from one model or from several intended to be identical. A few moulds for a second design of spoon have been identified, their only significant difference being the lack of a medial rib.

Each spoon was cast in a two-piece, or bi-valve, mould. The moulds were made by pressing the back of a model spoon into a roughly shaped lump of clay and then pressing a second piece of clay over the front and down into the bowl. The two valves were then taken apart, the model carefully removed, the mould reassembled, and the join sealed (luted) with extra clay. This system allowed the model spoon to be removed and used to make many moulds. No vents or runners were provided and the casting was made by feeding the molten metal into an in-gate at the handle end and letting it run down the spoon handle to the bowl. The porosity of the mould fabric must have been sufficient to allow any trapped gases to escape.

The fabric of the moulds is tempered with abundant fine quartz grains and some mica. It fires pale pink to pale grey. The modelled surfaces and adjacent areas are always reduced fired from contact with the molten metal, however the bulk of the mould fabric is frequently oxidized-fired.

Before the moulds were used they were assembled into multiples for casting. Virtually all of the fragments have some evidence of a thick layer of coarser clay which was added to their sides, often over the thin luting clay layer. There are no examples where this thick "packing clay" layer has been added to the mould backs or fronts, and from this it seems clear that the moulds were assembled edge on rather than back-to-back or front-to-front. A number of the surviving pieces remain attached to one another in this way. Some examples of this are illustrated in Plate 2. From these examples it is clear that the moulds were assembled into a composite so that all the handle ends were close together and the spoon bowls were virtually touching. Surviving fragments show that a single sprue cup was added to the composite mould at the end of the handles.

Given that the moulds were assembled side-by-side with the handles and bowls touching two arrangements were possible for the composite mould, a fan shaped or a cone-shaped array. A number of features suggest that the latter is more likely. Firstly a cross-sectional view of the two mould fragments illustrated at the bottom of Plate 2 shows that the mating surfaces of these moulds, which were adjacent in the composite, are not level, but meet at angles of 20-30°. This suggests that the moulds originally formed a circle. Secondly, remaining fragments of sprue

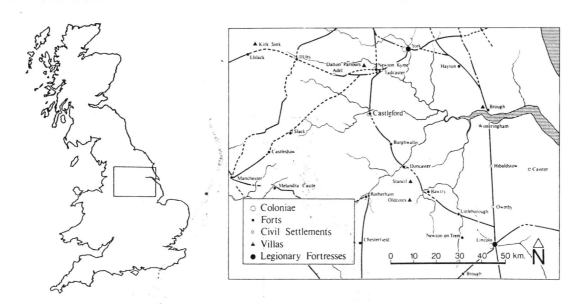

Figure 1. Castleford in relation to main Roman roads and military bases.

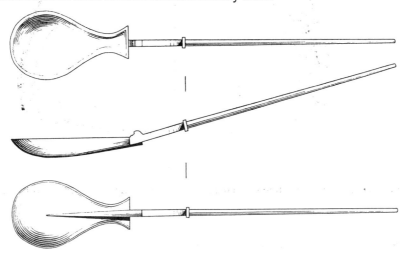

Figure 2. Reconstruction drawing showing the design of the spoons cast in the Castleford moulds (Scale 1:1.5).

cup show that it was circular in form and not rectangular or oval which would have been expected if a fan-shaped assembly had been used. Thirdly, the surface of the clay added to the handle ends, presumably to support the sprue cup, is circular in shape. Finally, there are no definite "end" moulds, with packing clay extending from only one side, as would be expected for the moulds at the extreme end of a fan-shaped assembly.

A reconstruction drawing of the cone-shaped composite mould is shown in Figure 3. Estimates of the number of moulds which were arranged in the composite have been made, based on calculations of the diameter of the supposed circle of handle ends at the apex of the mould. This put the number between 8 and 18, with the best estimate at 16. This would present a maximum angle to the incoming metal during casting of 30° from vertical. It must be stressed that these Figures are no more than a rough guide to the number of moulds which may have been arranged in this way since the data used in these estimates was extrapolated from only a few small diagnostic fragments.

Two mould fragments had traces of corroded metal on fractured surfaces, presumably where metal had run into cracks in the moulds. These were analysed qualitatively by X-ray fluorescence (XRF). The metal was a lead gunmetal, a quaternary alloy (Cu-Zn-Sn-Pb) suitable for casting. Apart from these two fragments only slight copper alloy traces were detected by XRF and it is assumed that the two metal samples were representative of the alloy from which all of the spoons were made.

The spoon moulds from Castleford are so far unparalleled in the western Roman Empire. There is some evidence for the manufacture of spoons at Augst in Switzerland where the back valve of a two part marble mould was found, as were four unfinished cast spoons (Rhia and Stern 1982). Other unfinished metal spoons have been found in France (ibid) and recent excavations at Wroxeter in England have produced a failed casting for a spoon with a leaf-shaped bowl made in a two piece mould.

Although no other examples of composite Roman spoon moulds are known, one composite mould intended for casting fibulae has recently been identified among the finds from a first century B.C. context at Bibracte, France (Beck et al. 1983/83). The mould was unused and so remains almost complete. In this example, the individual moulds were investment moulds rather than piece moulds.

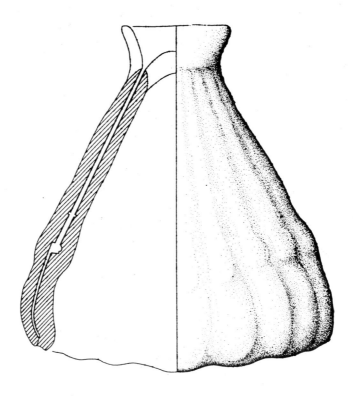

Figure 3. A reconstruction drawing of the cone shaped composite into which the moulds were assembled for casting. (Scale 1:2).

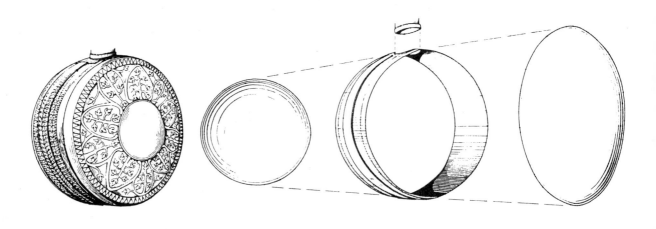

Figure 4. Probable reconstruction of one of the vessels cast from the Castleford vessel moulds. The reconstruction shows how the individually cast components were assembled to make the vessel. (Scale 1:3.3).

However, there are similarities with proposed Castleford arrangement in that the twelve moulds were arranged in a conical shape with molten metal fed to each from a common sprue cup at the apex. Also, as with the Castleford moulds, no vents were provided.

THE VESSEL MOULDS

Over 1000 clay fragments were recovered from the first century pit. The fragments were from numerous moulds used to cast copper alloy vessels with champlevé fields which were intended to take enamel. These mould fragments are currently the subject of detailed examination at the Ancient Monuments Laboratory and a full report is in preparation for inclusion in the excavation report (Bayley forthcoming A). This paper is an interim statement of evidence drawn from this investigation.

The vessels were assembled from a number of components which were cast individually and then attached to one another, probably by riveting or soldering. The main components were a shallow open-ended cylinder, which is pierced by a circular orifice, and two slightly convex, circular "end plates". In addition there are a number of fragments from moulds used to make small circular castings of similar diameter to the orifice in the central cylinder-shaped piece which may have formed a collar. These components are illustrated in the reconstruction drawing Figure 4.

In most cases, the moulds used to cast the central cylinder were of complex, multi-piece construction. This was necessary to ensure that the model from which they were made could be removed and re-used. A few fragments have no visible edges and so cannot definitely be said to be from piece moulds. It is however, unlikely that some would be piece moulds and some investment moulds.

Some fragments of cylinder mould are illustrated in Plate 3 which also shows the way in which the mould pieces were assembled. The mould has a hollow inner core with a modelled exterior surface forming the inner wall of the casting. Fitted round the core were a number of mould pieces designed to mate together, carrying the relief decoration on modelled inner surfaces. Plate 3 clearly shows how clay locating lugs at the base of the patterned pieces kept them correctly aligned. Traces of a layer of extra clay on the outside of the mould fragments indicate that the pieces were luted together to form a seal prior to casting.

The absence of undecorated fragments of cylinder mould suggests that the designs were virtually continuous, running most of the way around the cylinder. One fragment shows a termination of the design and it is probable that the blank area was left on which the vessel stood or to which a base was attached. On a few fragments the design was interrupted by a raised circular area in the centre of the band which would have produced a hole in the wall of the finished casting as mentioned above.

Details of the in-gates on the cylinder mould are not yet fully understood although a few fragments suggest that metal may have been fed to a blank area in the design or to a circular moulding to which a base was attached.

The moulds used to manufacture the end plates were less complex, two-piece designs. Examples of fragments from some of these are illustrated in Plate 4. They consist of a circular valve with a smooth, undecorated, convex surface forming the inner wall of the casting, mating with a second valve carrying the decoration on a concave surface, with a built-in in-gate.

The reconstruction drawing Figure 5 shows how the two valves were fitted together. As with the cylinder

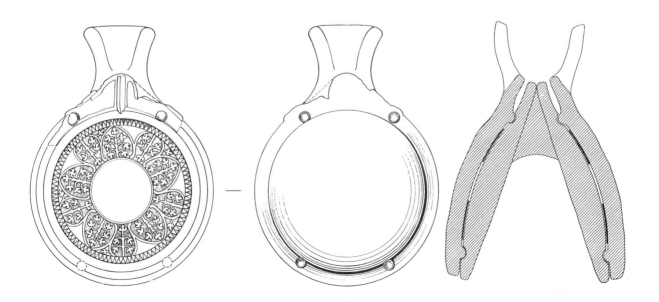

Figure 5. Reconstruction drawing showing how the end plate moulds were assembled and used. (Scale 1:3.1).

moulds they were kept correctly aligned by clay lugs and then sealed with luting clay, traces of which remain attached to many fragments. A sprue cup made of the luting clay was added to the in-gates. The end plates were probably cast as pairs. The evidence for this is the characteristic wedge-shaped pieces of packing clay, circular in cross-section, which have distinctive dark coloured, reduced fired centres corresponding to markings on the mould backs.

A selection of the designs examined are shown in Figure 6. Two groups of designs have been identified, stylized foliage and geometric patterns. The foliage patterns are not common on Roman enamelwork although geometric designs are frequently found.

No other clay mould fragments from cast Roman vessels are known. The authors are aware of only one vessel in the form reconstructed from the Castleford moulds, this is from Pinguente in Istria, Yugoslavia and is said by Henry (1933) to be in Vienna. She describes it as enamelled in red, blue and orange.

CONCLUSIONS

Clay piece moulds were the normal type of mould used to cast small objects in Roman Britain (Bayley, forthcoming B) and in the first to third centuries A.D. in the Roman provinces north of the Alps (Drescher 1973). The unusual aspect of the Castleford moulds, particularly the spoon moulds, is their assembly into composites for casting. This is a facet of Roman mass production which has not previously been recorded in Britain, perhaps because most of the finds of clay moulds have been restricted to small groups of fragments so that the evidence has not been available.

There is no evidence that any of the moulds were used more than once. The saving of the relatively small amount of effort required to form the clay around the model would not have justified the increased risk of a re-used mould fracturing and spoiling the casting. In any case even careful removal of the mould pieces after casting would probably have resulted in damage to the fine detail of the mould surface rendering the mould unusable.

The Castleford moulds are, for the moment, unique. However, it is not their manufacture but their survival which is unusual. Given the large number of Roman castings still in existence, one might expect large numbers of moulds of all sorts to be found. That they are not is due in part to the sorts of sites which are chosen for excavation, but more to the innate fragility of clay moulds. They are not normally as well fired as pottery and their soft fabrics combined with their odd shapes make them liable to breakage and disintegration. The friable mould fragments would not have lasted long on the workshop floor so the survival of so much material on this site must be due to the deliberate dumping of the fragments into pits soon after use. There is little sign of abrasion or weathering on the majority of the fragments.

ACKNOWLEDGEMENTS

We would like to thank West Yorkshire Archaeology Service for kindly allowing these details to be presented prior to publication of the full excavation report and for their permission to reproduce Figure 1. Thanks also to Professor R. Tylecote for drawing our attention to the moulds from Bibracte and Sarnia Butcher for providing the information on enamelled vessels, especially that from Pinguente. The drawings are the work of Margaret Mahoney and Miranda Schofield and the photographs were taken by Louis Woodman of English Heritage. Finally we would like to thank the Science and Engineering Research Council for a generous grant which allowed these results to be presented at the conference.

REFERENCES

Abramson, P. (forthcoming) Excavations at Roman Castleford.

Bayley, J. (forthcoming A) Roman vessel moulds from Castleford, West Yorkshire. Ancient Monuments Laboratory Report Series.

Bayley, J. (forthcoming B) Non-metallic evidence for metalworking. Proc. 25th Symposium on Archaeometry, Athens, 1986.

Bayley. J. and Budd, P. (1987) Late Roman spoon moulds from Castleford, West Yorkshire. Unpublished Ancient Monuments Laboratory Report No 161/87.

Bayley, J. and Sherlock, D. (1986) Roman spoon moulds from Castleford, West Yorkshire. Antiquaries Journal 66(2), 382-384.

Beck, F. Monthel, G. and Rabeisen, E. (1982/3) Note sur un mould a fibules de Bibracte. Antiquitiés Nationales 1982/3 14/15, 78-85.

Drescher, H.(1973) Der Guss von Kleingerät, dargestellt an Funden aus provizialrömischen werkstätten. Early Medieval Studies 6 (Antikvariskt arkiv 53), 48-62.

Henry, F. (1933) Emaillears d'occident. Prehistoire.2, 65-146.

Riha, E. and Stern, W.B. (1982) Die romischen Löffel aus Augst und Kaiserangst Forschungen in Angst, Band 5.

PHOTOGRAPHS

Plate 1. A selection of spoon mould fragments from both the front and back valves.

Plate 2. Some of the fragments of moulds which were adjacent to one another in the composite and which still remain attached. Note that both the handle ends and the spoon bowls were touching.

Plate 3. Typical fragments from the moulds used to cast the central cylinder of the vessels. Note the complex construction of the mould and the clay peg used to align the mould pieces correctly.

Plate 4. Fragments of the moulds used to cast the vessel end plates. Note the runners which would have fed molten metal to the edge of the casting.

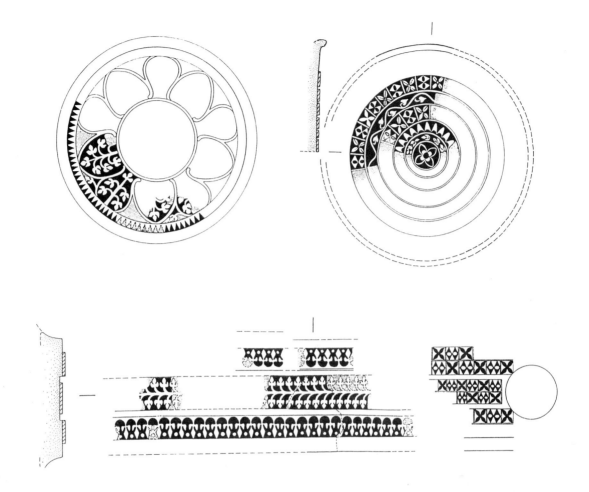

Figure 6. A selection of the champlevé designs found on the Castleford vessel moulds. (Scale 1:2.5).

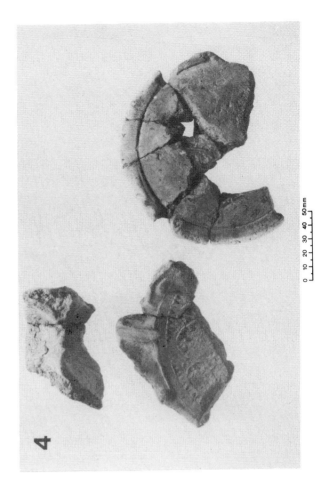

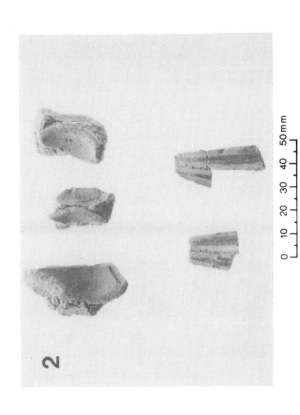

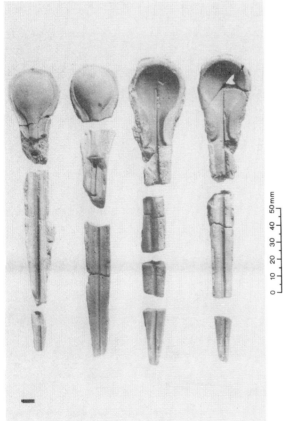

16

3. Stoneware from 3rd Millennium B.C.:
Investigation of a Metal-Imitating Pottery from Northern Mesopotamia

G. SCHNEIDER

Arbeitsgruppe Archäometrie, Freie Universität Berlin, W-Germany

ABSTRACT: *Chemical and mineralogical investigations of potsherds are used to define a stoneware-like ceramic which was made from uncalcareous high-flux clay fired between 1000 and 1100 °C.*

INTRODUCTION

Most distinctive for the remains of the Early Dynastic to Akkadian periods in Northern Mesopotamia (about 2800-2300 B.C.) is an extraordinary pottery which is found in Northeast Syria and the neighbouring areas of Turkey and Iraq (Figure 1). This pottery is very fine, wheelmade, well fired, and characterized by the stone like appearance of the fracture, its hardness (the "metallic clink" of sherds when knocked together), by a special surface treatment and by a limited variety of forms. It is called "Metallic ware" (Kühne 1976), "Stoneware" (Fielden 1977; Oates 1982) or North-Mesopotamian Stoneware (this paper).

Its most characteristic form is a round based globular jar as shown in Figure 4. The colour of the fracture is mostly grey, but surface colours range from dark grey to brilliant red, sometimes on the same pot, and there is also a pale olive "Green stoneware". This latter group seems to have been used preferably for beakers and bowls and probably is Akkadian in its majority.

The use of a fast wheel and of advanced kilns with two chambers allowing a controlled firing at high temperatures was known in northern Mesopotamia before the 3rd millennium B.C. The development of a hard and dense ceramic ware in the Early Bronze Age, however, would have been stimulated by the competition of the coming material, metal.

North-Mesopotamian stoneware is an important indicator for chronology and trade. Imports were found as far away as in Troy (Kühne 1976). From this series of analyses a sherd found in Uruk was chemically identified to be imported at this site. (More detailed information on the general background is given by Kuhne and Schneider 1987).

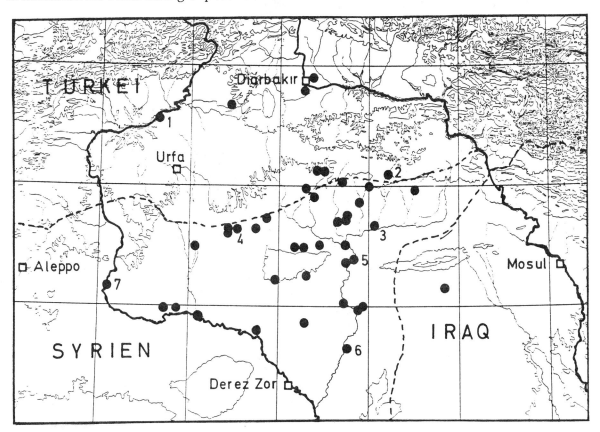

Figure 1. Archaeological sites from which samples of North-Mesopotamian stoneware have been analysed. Numbers refer to excavations mentioned in the text: 1 Lidar Höyük, 2 Girnavaz, 3 Tell Brak, 4 Tell Huera, 5 Tell Bderi, 6 Tell Sheh Hamad, 7 Halawa.

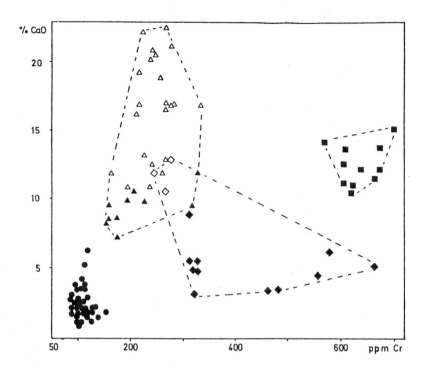

Figure 2. Variation of calcium and chromium in sherds from North-Mesopotamian Stoneware showing a clear distinction between groups.

- Group A and B, calcareous Stoneware (• pale green colour),
- Stoneware from Lidar Höyük (◊ pale green colour),
- Grey Spiral Ring Burnish ware from Halawa and Tell Heura.

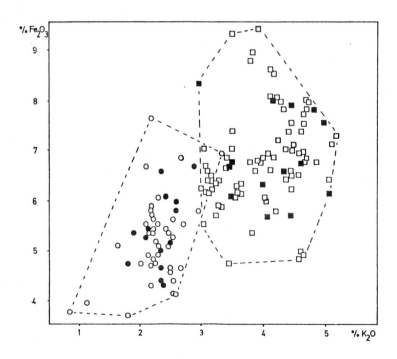

Figure 3. Variation of iron and potassium in uncalcerous North-Mesopotamian Stoneware.
- ○ Group A (• samples from Tell Huera),
- □ Group B (■ samples from Tell Brak).

PROBLEM DEFINITION

(1) Many names were given to this pottery by different authors and at different sites, e.g., black or grey burnished ware, stoneware, metallic ware, clinky ware. We wanted to know whether this is always the same pottery and also which varieties must be included and which excluded to define one North-Mesopotamian stoneware.

(2) What are the significant criteria to define a ceramic ware, technology, colours, or provenience as shown by main or trace element composition?

(3) What are the manufacturing methods: choice and preparation of the raw materials, techniques of forming and surface treatment, firing, innovations?

(4) Does the North-Mesopotamian stoneware fit the criteria for a stoneware in a modern technological sense?

SAMPLES

One hundred and eighty eight samples of North-Mesopotamian stoneware from 44 archaeological sites were analysed. The sherds originated from excavations of 3rd millennium sites in NE-Syria (17 samples from Tell Huera, 22 samples from Tell Brak) and in SE-Anatolia (12 samples from Lidar Höyük) or from surface finds. The samples cover the main area where North-Mesopotamian stoneware is found (Figure 1), not including rare instances of imports out of this area. About 500 analyses of common pottery and geological clays from a larger study of North-Mesopotamian pottery were available for comparison.

METHODS OF INVESTIGATION

Chemical composition: wavelength-dispersive X-ray fluorescence (Phillips PW1400). After removing the outer layers of a fragment of a sherd and grinding, 1 g of the powdered and ignited sample is mixed with 4 g of a flux (Merck Spectromelt A12) and fused to obtain a 32 mm ø glass disc. Twenty nine elements were measured (the determinations of S, Cl, Co, Cu, Nb, Sn, La, Pb, Th are less accurate and therefore not included in Table 1).

Mineralogical composition: polarizing microscopy of thin sections, X-ray diffraction (Philips APD20).

Firing temperature: refiring of sherds and investigation of the changes by X-ray diffraction and scanning electron microscopy (SEM; Cambridge Stereoscan 90).

Other methods: water absorbing capacity, Moh's hardness.

DATA AND INTERPRETATION

Chemical composition

Most of the analysed samples of North-Mesopotamian stoneware fall within a low calcium and chromium group (Figure 2) and are very different from calcareous stoneware, from a Lidar Höyük group of stoneware and from a third homogeneous group formed by samples of "metallic ware painted in horizontal stripes" (Kühne 1976). The samples

from Lidar Höyük seem to represent a local variety of North-Mesopotamian stoneware. This is, however, different in composition to local pottery and clays from this site and is therefore suspected to be an import (Klenk 1988). The third group in Figure 2 should not be taken as a subgroup of North-Mesopotamian stoneware for compositional and technological reasons. Only the uncalcareous groups A and B and the calcareous varieties from NE-Syria will be considered in the following.

The uncalcareous stoneware can be divided into two compositional groups A and B (Figure 3) supplying significant information to the still unresolved question of provenience: 14 uncalcareous samples from Tell Huera belong to group A, where as 14 uncalcareous samples from Tell Brak are within group B (whereas only 3 samples of each of these sites belong to the respective other group. The remaining samples from Huera and Brak are calcareous stoneware). The compositions of A and B are similar to each other but very different from the calcareous stoneware (Table 1).

Calcium contents above 3 % CaO found in some sherds of group A and B (Figure 2) are caused by calcite deposits from burial. This is clear from microscopic investigation, X-ray diffraction and high ignition losses. The uncalcareous composition group A and B sherds is very unusual among Mesopotamian pottery until Byzantine times. This is also confirmed by analyses of local clays from many sites in NE-Syria which always have a high calcium, chromium and nickel content. A compositional overlap only exists between common wares and calcareous Stoneware.

Calcareous Stoneware does not form a homogeneous chemical group (therefore only a compositional range is given in Table 1) and probably represents minor local products made from ordinary calcareous clays. The distinction of calcareous Stoneware from overfired Fine ware (Fielden 1977) is still not clear and needs further investigation.

Mineralogical composition and firing temperatures

Sherds of groups A and B are characterized by a very high amount of quartz (30 to 40 %, by volume) with particle sizes of about 50 µm as a natural tempering material. Mica, only in low fired sherds, and plagioclase are minor constituents. Mullite was detected by X-ray diffraction in most samples of A and B. Hercynite which forms in a reducing atmosphere above 900°C was found in nearly all grey sherds from group B but very rarely in those from group A. K-feldspar is present only in group B sherds (e.g., in Figure 5) resulting in higher potassium and rubidium contents.

A few red or pale grey sherds of group A and B not containing mullite must have been fired below 950°C. From the typical phase assemblage of the lower fired sherds of A and B (mullite, mica, K-feldspar) the original firing temperature of these sherds must have been about 1000°C. Therefore refiring to 1000°C does not change the original vitrification stage (Figure 6). The vitrification increases continuously with temperature (Figure 7). The upper limit of firing temperatures is demonstrated by a light, porous sherd of group B which probably is an overfired waster (Figure 8). However, its original firing

Main elements (%, by wt.):	SiO_2	TiO_2	Al_2O_3	Fe_2O_3	MnO	MgO	CaO	Na_2O	K_2O	P_2O_5
group A (n=54) mean	67.0	1.30	21.5	5.21	0.009	0.88	1.59	0.08	2.29	0.09
std.dev.	±2.5	±0.66	±1.9	±0.85	±0.004	±0.13	±0.60	±0.04	±0.39	±0.03
group B (n=95) mean	63.1	1.22	21.8	6.84	0.012	1.16	1.67	0.11	4.01	0.12
std.dev.	±2.3	±0.05	±1.4	±0.98	±0.005	±0.22	±0.99	±0.05	±0.59	±0.05
calcareous Stone ware (n=32) range: min.	47.0	0.72	12.7	6.70	0.068	3.8	6.9	0.07	0.69	0.15
max.	62.0	1.12	16.1	9.55	0.162	10.7	22.9	1.42	3.35	0.52
Trace elements (ppm, by wt.):	V	Cr	Ni	Zn	Rb	Sr	Y	Zr	Ba	Ce
group A (n=54) mean	113	105	31	33	88	161	31	290	301	104
std.dev.	±15	±9	±8	±9	±18	(±257)	±8	±30	±76	±19
group B (n=95) mean	138	107	35	48	153	191	34	250	474	106
std.dev.	±15	±12	±9	±11	±21	±93	±10	±32	±69	±20
calcareous Stone ware (n=32) range: min.	122	155	105	69	25	284	18	112	110	32
max.	205	333	334	125	100	1160	32	225	556	86

Table 1. Mean chemical composition of uncalcareous North-Mesopotamian Stoneware group A and B and compositional range of calcareous Stoneware (not including the "Lindar-group" and the "Grey Spiral Ring Burnish ware").

temperature must have been below 1150°C. This can be seen from the higher vitrification stage developed in a fragment of this sherd if refired to 1150°C (Figure 9).

Firing of the calcareous Stoneware was done in the same of slightly lower range of temperatures, so concluded from vitrification stages and from phase compositions. Typical phases in sherd with CaO contents above 20 % are diopside and gehlenite along with some secondary calcite and very few residual quartz particles. Gehlenite was not detected in sherds with lower calcium contents. Hercynite was found in pale olive sherds thus indicating a reducing firing atmosphere. Mullite did not develop in the calcareous Stoneware.

Porosity measurements

Water absorbing capacity is a simple measure for the open porosity of ceramic materials. Modern Stoneware is defined by a water absorbing capacity not exceeding 2 %. In an investigation of 20 sherds from Tell Huera, all from 3rd millennium but representing different wares, this limit was used by Fitz (1984) to characterize three sherds as a "Stoneware from Tell Huera". In 185 samples of North-Mesopotamian Stoneware we found a variation from 1 to 14 % with a maximum at about 6 %. So the 2 % limit cannot be used to define this ware. The grey sherds are generally denser and harder than the red varieties.

Colours

Surface colours of the North-Mesopotamian Stoneware are grey to brown-orange, rarely brick red. In the latter case the colour of the fracture can also be red. In most sherds, however, there is a grey core resulting from firing in a reducing atmosphere and a diffusion controlled red layer on one or both sides which had developed during a short reoxidation stage. The characteristic dull glossy, grey-red surfaces or patterns were produced by wet-smoothing, horizontally or spiral pattern burnishing or incising in burnished surfaces, repeatedly changing the kiln atmosphere and applying high firing temperatures. This special surface treatment and firing would have been used deliberately to produce colours imitating the appearance of used copper jars. This again shows a relationship to metal jars of the same time from Tell Huera which are similar in their form (Kühne 1976).

Pale olive colours occur in sherds with contents of more than 10 % CaO. However, there was also one group A sherd with less than 1 % CaO showing the same colour (Munsell Soil Colour Chart 5Y7/1). Obviously colours can not unequivocally distinguish between compositional groups of North-Mesopotamian Stoneware.

RESULTS AND CONCLUSIONS

(1) Analyses of samples from many different sites show that the different ware names were not related to chemical or technological groups. The majority of North-Mesopotamian Stoneware falls into only two homogenous compositional groups which are very similar to each other. One group seems to be characteristic for Tell Huera, the other group for Tell Brak. The calcareous varieties seem to be minor and of local production. All other grey or black pottery of the area, as far as we know, is very different in technique as well as in composition and should not be included as a subgroup of North-Mesopotamian Stoneware.

(2) The basis for the definition of a North-

Mesopotamian Stoneware is its highly developed technology comprising the selection of uncalcareous raw materials and a special manufacturing technique. On the other hand, the calcareous Stoneware in some cases can only be identified by chemical analysis and should be included. A large variation occurs in firing temperature and atmosphere resulting in a wide range of porosity and colour. Therefore the most distinctive classification is done by chemical composition.

(3) Firing techniques were well developed by the 3rd millennium, but making a dense pottery was limited by the use of highly calcareous raw materials. This give an extensive vitrification at temperatures below 1000°C. However, calcareous clays are sensitive to overfiring above 1000°C as indicated by many finds of overfired wasters of common wares which in Mesopotamia always seem to be calcareous.

To produce a Stoneware one needs clays with a high amount of flux which withstand high temperatures without warping and slumping. The first condition is achieved by a high amount of potassium (or sodium) and iron, and firing in a reduced atmosphere, the second condition by a high amount of very fine grained quartz. Such raw materials have been used to make North-Mesopotamian Stoneware which was fired in a controlled kiln atmosphere at 1000 to 1100°C.

(4) The third millennium North-Mesopotamian Stoneware is not Stoneware in a modern technological sense but this would also be true for many other historical "Stonewares". Obviously a Stoneware technology was applied and the water absorbing capacities are very low in comparison to other wares. Therefore I would accept the term "Stoneware", even in its technological meaning of Stoneware. The term "North-Mesopotamian Metallic ware" (Kühne) expressing the relationship of this ceramic ware to metal work is retained as a synonym to "North-Mesopotamian Stoneware" (Oates).

ACKNOWLEDGEMENTS

This investigation is part of a study of Northern Mesopotamian pottery with special regard to the material from the excavations at Tell She Hamad and Tell Bderi, NE-Syria (supported by the German Research Foundation DFG and the Free University Berlin). I am particularly grateful to H. Kühne for initiating this project and introducing me to the archaeological problems. I am further indebted to H. Erkanal, H. Hauptmann, K. Kohlmeier, U. Moortgat-Correns, D. and J. Oates, W. Orthmann and E. Strommenger who kindly provided material from their excavations or surveys. I thank also H. Dohmann and P. Pfälzner for their helpful assistance and H. Ghobarkar for the SEM-photo-micrographs.

REFERENCES

K. Fielden (1977). Tell Brak: The Pottery, Iraq 39, 245-255.

S. Fitz (1984). Steinzeug vom Tell Huera: Das früheste Beisiel für die Herstellung dichtgebrannter Keramik, Zeitschrift für Assyriologie 74, 123-132.

G.B. Klenk (1987). Geologisch-mineralogische Untersuchungen zur Technologie frühbronzezeitlicher Keramik von Lidar Höyük (Südost-Anatolien), Münchner Geowissenschaftliche Abhandlungen 3, 1-64.

H. Kühne (1976). Die Keramik vom Tell Chuera, Berlin.

H. Kühne and G. Schneider (1987). Neue Untersuchungen zur Metallischen Ware, Damaszner Mitteilungen 3, in press.

J. Oates (1982). Some Late Early Dynastic III Pottery from Tell Brak, Iraq 43, 205-219.

FIGURE CAPTIONS FOR THE NEXT PAGE

Figure 4. Characteristic form of North-Mesopotamian Stoneware (Metallic ware) from Tell Huera (by courtesy of H. Kühne).

Figure 5. Thin section photomicrograph of a typical sherd of uncalcareous Stoneware (Tell Brak, group B), containing very fine grained quartz. In the middle an unusual large grain of microline surrounded by a cavity can be seen. Crossed polarizers.

Figure 6. SEM photomicrograph of a fresh fracture surface of uncalcareous North-Mesopotamian Stoneware group A showing extensive vitrification (refired at 1000°C).

Figure 7. SEM photomicrograph of a group A sherd refired at 1150°C.

Figure 8. SEM photomicrograph of an overfired (?) group B sherd.

Figure 9. SEM photomicrograph of the same sherd as in Figure 8, refired at 1150°C.

Figure 4

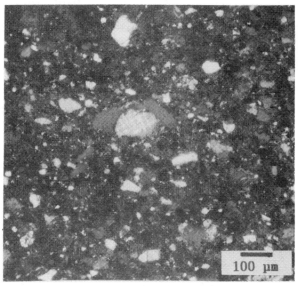

Figure 5

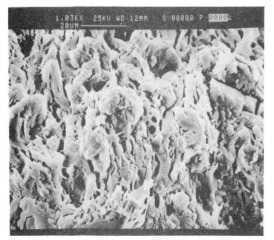

Figure 6

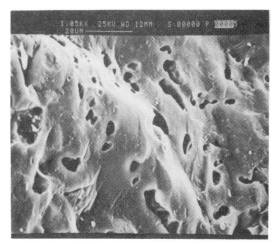

Figure 7

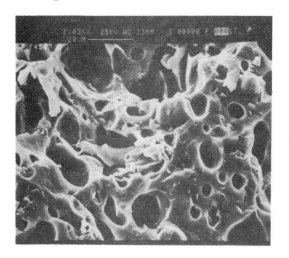

Figure 8

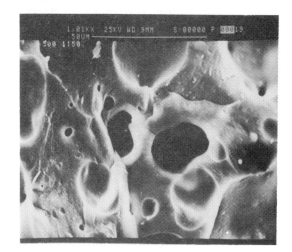

Figure 9

4. The Effects of Surface Treatment on Permeability and Evaporative Cooling Effectiveness of Pottery

M. B. SCHIFFER
Laboratory of Traditional Technology, Department of Anthropology
University of Arizona, Tucson, AZ 85721, U.S.A.

ABSTRACT: *Experiments were carried out on 27 miniature ceramic vessels to ascertain the effects of traditional surface treatments on permeability and evaporative cooling effectiveness.*

After cooking, probably the most common use of pottery is water storage. In arid lands, especially, clay pots are sometimes preferred for storing water even when substitutes of metal and plastic are available. The reason is clear: the walls of low-fired pots are permeable, and the film of water that continuously evaporates from the exterior surface cools the vessel and its contents.

Occasionally it has been proposed that potters pick particular tempers to facilitate evaporative cooling (e.g., Matson 1965). Recent experiments have shown that temper type can indeed affect permeability, but differs in the degree of evaporative cooling (i.e., evaporative cooling effectiveness). In the laboratory Skibo et al. (n.d.) found that vessels having horse manure, sand, and no temper cooled water to the same temperature despite differences in permeability. On the other hand, when stressed by heat guns that simulate extreme environmental conditions, the more permeable vessels had greater evaporative cooling effectiveness. These experiments indicate that the effects of temper on evaporative cooling effectiveness are more complex than had been thought because they are influenced by environmental conditions.

Investigators also suggest that surface treatments such as burnishing and polishing can affect a vessel's permeability (e.g., Bronitsky 1986:226; Henrickson and McDonald 1983; Raab 1973; Rice 1987:231; Scott 1954:381). Presumably aware of these effects, potters could choose a specific surface treatment to provide an appropriate degree of permeability for water cooling. Although plausible, the purported linkages between surface treatments, permeability, and evaporative cooling effectiveness have not been demonstrated experimentally. The present paper reports a series of controlled laboratory experiments that explored the effects of traditional, non-glaze surface treatments—interior and exterior—on permeability and evaporative cooling effectiveness.

The permeability of a ceramic vessel (cf. Rice 1987:351-352) is defined here as the rate that water or another specified liquid passes through the vessel wall from the interior to exterior surface under constant pressure. (Permeability is clearly liquid-specific; the present study treats only permeability to water.) Permeability varies in response to characteristics of the ceramic, including paste composition, degree of sintering and glass formation, and surface treatments like glaze. In principle, permeability should also vary with traditional surface treatments such as polishing, slipping, and smudging because they affect grain density and orientation. In addition, conditions of the use environment, including temperature, air velocity, and relative humidity, can be expected to influence permeability.

In much of the archaeological and ethnographic literature it is assumed that evaporative cooling effectiveness is a simple and direct function of permeability. As already noted, the experiments of Skibo et al. (n.d.) contradict this view. To explain their findings, these investigators argue that the maximum temperature drop is achieved, under given environmental conditions, when permeability exceeds a critical threshold (that is required to maintain a continuous film of water on the exterior surface). Permeability above this level is deemed "excess", but nonetheless may help to maintain cooling effectiveness under more stressful conditions or over longer periods of use as pores become clogged. The present study sheds additional light on the complex relationships between permeability and evaporative cooling effectiveness.

THE EXPERIMENTS

Twenty-seven miniature vessels in the shape of deep bowls were made in molds with a heavily tempered paste (see Appendix A). Pots are 4.2 cm high and 6.9 cm in maximum diameter (at the rim). The first 20 vessels represent all combinations of 4 interior and 5 exterior surface treatments. Specific treatments were chosen to approximate extremes in permeability found among low-fired vessels. Interior treatments are (1) finger smooth, (2) polish, (3) low-iron (LFe) slip and polish, and (4) LFe slip, polish, and smudge. Treatments applied to exteriors are (1) textured, (2) finger smooth, (3) polish, (4) LFe slip and polish, and (5) LFe slip, polish, and smudge. After these vessels had been made, it was discovered that a high-iron (HFe) slip can sometimes produce a surface of very low permeability and so 6 vessels were made with this surface treatment. Regrettably, the number of vessels with HFe slip is insufficient to permit many direct comparisons with the other surface treatment types. Finally, a pot having an impermeable resin (polyurethane varnish) on the interior was included as a control. Table 1 displays the interior and exterior surface treatments applied to each pot.

Initial Absorption Tests

When a porous (and permeable) sherd is pressed against the tongue, it absorbs saliva; its degree of adhesion is a gross measure of a ceramic's initial absorption. A test with greater objectivity than the tongue test, employed on bricks and concrete (e.g., McCurrich et al. 1985), has been

Table 1. Interior and Exterior Surface Treatments for Experimental Vessels.

Pot No.	Interior Treatment	Exterior Treatment
1	Finger Smooth	Textured
2	Finger Smooth	Finger Smooth
3	Finger Smooth	Polish
4	Finger Smooth	LFe Slip and Polish
5	Finger Smooth	LFe Slip, Polish, and Smudge
6	Polish	Textured
7	Polish	Finger Smooth
8	Polish	Polish
9	Polish	LFe Slip and Polish
10	Polish	LFe Slip, Polish, and Smudge
11	LFe Slip and Polish	Textured
12	LFe Slip and Polish	Finger Smooth
13	LFe Slip and Polish	Polish
14	LFe Slip and Polish	LFe Slip and Polish
15	LFe Slip and Polish	LFe Slip, Polish, and Smudge
16	LFe Slip, Polish, and Smudge	Textured
17	LFe Slip, Polish, and Smudge	Finger Smooth
18	LFe Slip, Polish, and Smudge	Polish
19	LFe Slip, Polish, and Smudge	LFe Slip and Polish
20	LFe Slip, Polish, and Smudge	LFe Slip, Polish, and Smudge
21	HFe Slip and Polish	Textured
22	Finger Smooth	HFe Slip and Polish
23	HFe Slip and Polish	HFe Slip and Polish
24	HFe Slip, Polish, and Smudge	Textured
25	Finger Smooth	HFe Slip, Polish, and Smudge
26	HFe Slip, Polish and Smudge	HFe Slip, Polish, and Smudge
27	Varnish over LFe Slip	Polish

Table 2. Summary Data on Initial Absorption Tests

Surface Treatment	Sample Size	Initial Absorption (Mean, in grams)
Interior		
Finger Smooth	7	2.80
Finger Smooth (excluding vessels 22, 25)	5	2.86
Polish	5	2.52
LFe Slip and Polish	5	1.83
LFe Slip, Polish, and Smudge	5	.91
HFe Slip and Polish	2	1.98
HFe Slip, Polish, and Smudge	2	1.22
Exterior		
Textured	7	5.45
Textured (excluding vessels 21, 24)	5	5.58
Polish	5	4.21
LFe Slip and Polish	5	3.26
LFe Slip, Polish, and Smudge	5	2.70
HFe Slip and Polish	2	3.63
HFe Slip, Polish, and Smudge	2	2.53

Table 3. Mean Water Temperature and Weight Loss Data For the Steady-State Test (43 hrs.).

Surface Treatment	Sample Size	Water Temperature (°C)	Weight Loss (g)
Interior			
Finger Smooth	5	18.6	12.88
Polish	5	18.8	12.76
LFe Slip and Polish	5	18.7	12.90
LFe Slip-Polish-and Smudge	5	18.8	13.56
Exterior			
Textured	4	18.4	13.30
Finger Smooth	4	18.5	13.72
Polish	4	18.6	13.62
LFe Slip and Polish	4	18.5	13.71
LFe Slip-Polish-and Smudge	4	19.7	10.79

modified for use here. There are versions for interior and exterior surfaces. The interior test begins with a dry vessel, which is weighed to the nearest 0.01 g on a Setra 1000 scale and filled with 15 ml of distilled water. After 60 seconds, the water is poured out, the interior quickly wiped with a paper towel and the vessel reweighed. To measure exteriors, one begins with a small plastic cereal bowl, partially filled with 200 ml of distilled water, having a metal washer resting on the bottom. The dry vessel is weighed and a pebble added for ballast. Next, the vessel is deftly placed on the washer where it sits for 60 seconds. After immersion, the pot is wiped and reweighed. In both tests, weight gain is used as an index of initial absorption.

Because the absorption tests lack standardization for surface area, interior and exterior values are not equivalent. Of interest here, however, is the _relative_ performance of different surface treatments. Consistent with previous beliefs, it can be seen (Table 2) that traditional surface treatments have a large effect on initial absorption. Finger smooth and textured surfaces absorb the most, and slip-polish-smudge surfaces the least. The summary data in Table 2 also disclose much variability within generic categories of surface treatment, such as "slipping" or "smudging".

The initial absorption test is easy to carry out and provides definitive results, but its relationship to permeability and evaporative cooling effectiveness remains undemonstrated. I now turn to a number of _behaviourally relevant_ (cf. Schiffer and Skibo 1987) tests that explore these relationships while revealing more about the effects of surface treatment.

TESTS OF PERMEABILITY AND EVAPORATIVE COOLING EFFECTIVENESS

The Cool-Down Test

The first test determines which surface treatments provide the most rapid cooling. Testing was carried out in the laboratory under conditions of low stress (i.e., still air, temperature of about 23°C). Thirty ml of distilled water (at 23°C) is placed in the vessel and temperature is recorded at various intervals thereafter. For this and remaining tests, vessels sit on metal washers and are covered by lids. Vessels are filled and temperatures monitored at 30 second intervals to insure a constant elapsed time for tests of short duration. Temperature is measured by a mercury thermometer, which gently stirs the water.

The first observations (see Appendix B) at 27 minutes (.5 hr), indicate that evaporative cooling has progressed substantially; all vessels have cooled the water at least 2.0°C below the control (pot 27). When these data are aggregated by treatment type (Figure 1), one observes that all interior surfaces produce essentially the same temperature drop. On the other hand, LFe slip-polish-smudge appears to lag slightly among the otherwise uniform exterior surfaces (Figure 2).

A second set of temperature observations for the cool-down test, at 94 minutes (1.5 hrs), reiterates patterns already seen (Figures 1 and 2): (1) interior surface treatments do not influence evaporative cooling effectiveness, (2) the exterior surface having the lowest initial absorption (LFe slip, polish, and smudge) also produces the smallest temperature drop; the others perform about the same, and (3) under low-stress conditions, there is no overall correlation between initial absorption rate and evaporative cooling effectiveness or between surface treatment and evaporative cooling effectiveness. By 1.5 hrs, these small vessels have already reached the minimum temperature under prevailing conditions. Although larger vessels would take longer to achieve complete cooling (because of their lower ratio of surface area to volume), it is doubtful that the effects of surface treatments on full-size vessels would differ.

Steady State Tests

In summers, drinking water from streams and wells is apt to be cooler than ambient air, and so rapid cooling is really not the most important function of a water-storage vessel; rather, it is maintaining cooling effectiveness over a longer time. A test that simulates steady-state cooling was carried out next. Actually, it was conducted in the laboratory as a continuation of the cool-down test. At 20.5 hours, pots were "topped off" with distilled water; at 14 and 43 hours, water temperatures were measured. Mean values computed for interior and exterior treatments yield unsurprising results (Figures 1 and 2), as previously observed patterns persist. Indeed, there are no detectable differences in the results at 1.5, 14, and 43 hours.

After temperatures were recorded at the end of the 43-hour period, vessels were reweighed and weight losses computed (Appendix B). Clearly, the weight loss figures directly indicate permeability, since most of the water passed through the vessel wall. When the weight loss data are aggregated by treatment type, a familiar pattern emerges (Table 3): interior surfaces have little influence on water loss, whereas one exterior surface, LFe slip-polish-smudge, shows a reduced water loss. That very same treatment also produced less effective cooling. In this case permeability and evaporative cooling effectiveness are related. What is surprising about these results, however, is that—with but one exception—permeability and evaporative cooling effectiveness do not vary with surface treatment: nearly all vessels cooled water about equally well.

These findings can be accommodated by the threshold model. Once a vessel achieves or surpasses a particular value (or threshold) of permeability under given environmental conditions, providing a continuous film of water to the vessel's exterior, the degree of evaporative cooling cannot further improve. When environmental conditions become more stressful (i.e., higher temperatures, lower humidity, faster air movement), fewer and fewer vessels surpass the new threshold, and so their performance is impaired. Indeed, under quite stressful conditions, one can anticipate that the threshold value will be met by no vessels. It is then—and only then—that one can expect to find a correlation among surface treatments, permeability, and evaporative cooling effectiveness.

High Stress Test

In order to evaluate these predictions of the threshold

25

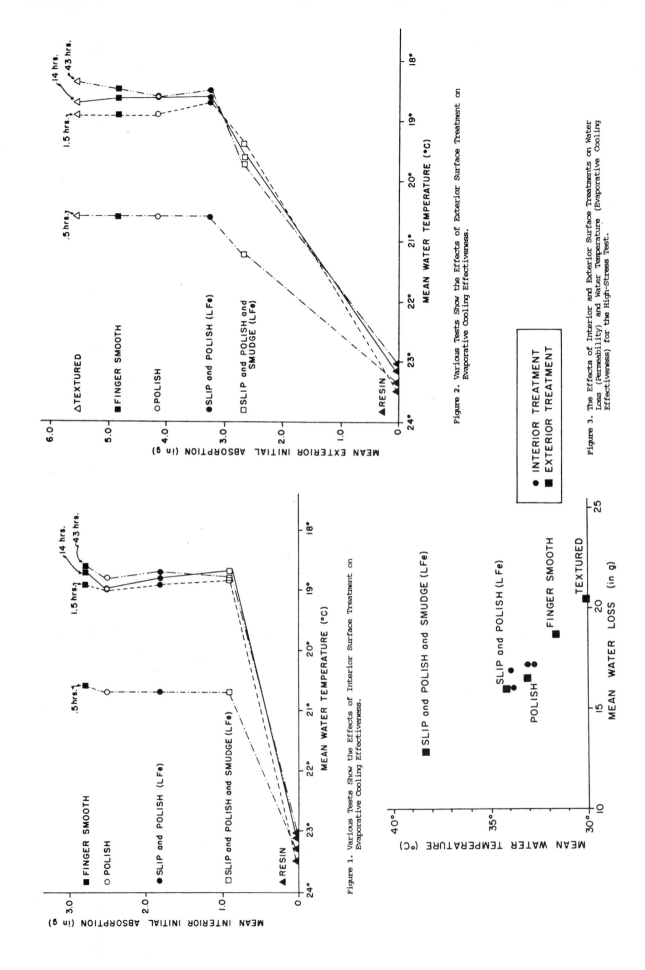

Figure 1. Various Tests Show the Effects of Interior Surface Treatment on Evaporative Cooling Effectiveness.

Figure 2. Various Tests Show the Effects of Exterior Surface Treatment on Evaporative Cooling Effectiveness.

Figure 3. The Effects of Interior and Exterior Surface Treatments on Water Loss (Permeability) and Water Temperature (Evaporative Cooling Effectiveness) for the High-Stress Test.

26

model, a high-stress test was conducted. Vessels are "topped off" with distilled water, weighed, covered, and placed in a Despatch Digitronic oven at 60°C for 4 hours. This oven contains a circulating fan, which adds to the stress on the pots. Vessels are removed from the oven and monitored as quickly as possible for temperature and weight loss. However, because the pots and water are gradually cooling during the transfer and recording period, these data contain random errors. Nonetheless, the results are quite definitive.

Water temperatures rose considerably after oven exposure, to a mean of 32.7°C (n=26). The control vessel—the hottest by far—reached 48.8°C. In conformity with patterns documented above, interior and exterior surfaces differ in their influence on permeability and evaporative cooling effectiveness. Interior surfaces had scarcely a discernible influence on water loss or temperature (Figure 3); in contrast, both variables are correlated with exterior surface treatment (Figure 3). In conformity with the threshold model, surfaces of lowest exterior absorption (12.8 g) had the highest water temperature (38.4°C). Vessels with more absorptive exteriors (textured and finger smooth) were able to maintain lower water temperatures (30.0°C and 31.7°C, respectively) through greater water loss (20.5 g and 18.4 g, respectively). These patterns support the prediction that when no vessels in a set meet the threshold value of permeability, there will be a correlation between permeability and evaporative cooling effectiveness.

In addition to stressful environmental conditions, vessels are exposed during use to dissolved ions, organic molecules, particulate matter, and microorganisms in the water. A variety of mechanisms, including precipitation of salts during drying or high stress, could lead to the deposition of substances in vessel walls, contributing to degraded performance over the long run. Additional experiments, lasting months, will be required to detect these predicted effects.

DISCUSSION

These experiments have shown that surface treatments affect permeability and evaporative cooling effectiveness, but only under relatively stressful conditions. Some environments, like the laboratory during the steady-state test, promote relatively low evaporation rates and thus do not tax the water-transport capability of most permeable vessels. However, when evaporation rates increase, as in the high-stress test, water is not supplied to the exterior surface fast enough to maintain the film of water needed for maximum evaporative cooling. The steady-state and high-stress tests ostensibly bracket the range of environmental conditions likely to be encountered in societies that use clay pots for storing and cooling water. Thus, it should be possible to develop some very general implications of the present study for understanding the design of such vessels.

One surprising implication is that potters using trial-and-error methods would have quickly arrived at vessel designs that could achieve maximum cooling effectiveness (under most conditions). The reason is that any heavily tempered vessel that is simply scraped or finger smoothed on the exterior will provide very high permeability. Ironically, the greatest short-term problem may be that in

low-stress environments vessels lose water too rapidly by leakage and dripping. In previous experiments, Skibo et al. (n.d.) found that the most permeable pots rested in puddles of water. Perhaps potters sometimes selected surfaces that reduce permeability!

Surface treatment choices also might have been affected by the long-term problem of pore clogging, which can in principle be caused by a variety of use-related factors. Vessels that achieve maximum cooling effectiveness in the short-term could be less effective in the long-term; and vessels suitable for the long haul may leak excessively at first. As a result, surface treatment (and temper) choices will sometimes be compromises conditioned by a host of local factors. The latter need to play a prominent role in the explanation of surface treatment choices in particular cases.

CONCLUSIONS

Experiments have shown that the effects of surface treatment on permeability and evaporative cooling effectiveness are strongly mediated by environmental conditions. Under low-stress conditions, most vessels perform at about the same level, with little variation in temperature drop of amount of water loss despite vast differences in surface treatment. When conditions are drastically altered in the high-stress test, however, large differences in performance appear, as does a correlation between exterior surface treatments, permeability, and evaporative cooling effectiveness. The surface treatments tested here are not intended to represent fully those particular treatments as found in archaeological and ethnographic contexts. There is simply too much variation in the execution of such treatments to expect the present findings to be applicable in detail. However, the more general relationships uncovered can be presumed to hold widely. As additional experiments are carried out and integrated with archaeological and ethnographic cases, a better understanding will emerge about why people apply to their water-storage pots particular surface treatments.

ACKNOWLEDGMENTS

I thank Setra Systems, Labline, Inc., and IBM for donations of equipment used in these experiments. Annette Schiffer assisted with the high-stress tests, and I appreciate her help. I am also grateful to W. David Kingery for advice on ceramic drying. R. B. Heimann provided helpful suggestions on an earlier draft.

REFERENCES

Bronitsky, G. (1986). The use of materials science techniques in the study of pottery construction and use. In Advances in Archaeological Method and Theory, Vol. 9, edited by M. B. Schiffer, pp. 209-276. Academic Press, Orlando.

Henrickson, E. F., and M. A. McDonald. (1983). Ceramic form and function: an ethnoarchaeological search and an archaeological application. American Anthropologist 85:630-643.

Matson, F. R. (1965). Ceramic ecology: an approach to the study of early cultures of the Near East. In Ceramics and Man, edited by F. R. Matson, pp. 202-218. Aldine, Chicago.

McCurrich, L. H., A. R. Archer, P. B. Bamforth, R. Cather, J. N. Clarke, G. P. Daw, C. D. Lawrence, M. Levitt, and P. L. Walton. (1985). Permeability testing of site concrete—a review of methods and results. In Permeability of Concrete and its control, pp. 1-68. The Concrete Society, London.

Raab, L. M. (1973). AZ AA:5:2: a prehistoric cactus camp in Papagueria. Journal of the Arizona Academy of Science 8 (3):116-118.

Rice, P. M. (1987). Pottery analysis: a sourcebook. University of Chicago Press, Chicago.

Schiffer, M. B., and J. M. Skibo. (1987). Theory and experiment in the study of technological change. Current Anthropology 28:595-622.

Scott, L. (1954). Pottery. In A history of technology, Volume I, edited by C. Singer, E. J. Homyard, A. R. Hall, E. Jaffe, R. H. G. Thompson, and J. M. Donaldson, pp. 376-412. Clarendon Press, Oxford.

Skibo, J. M., M. B. Schiffer, and K. C. Reid. (n.d.). Organic tempered pottery: an experimental study. American Antiquity (in press).

Vaz Pinto, I., M. B. Schiffer, S. Smith, and J. M. Skibo. (1987). Effects of temper on ceramic abrasion resistance: a preliminary investigation. Archaeomaterials 1:119-134.

APPENDIX A. TECHNIQUES OF VESSEL MANUFACTURE

PASTE COMPOSITION AND VESSEL FORMING

In order to replicate the coarse textures often found in water-storage jars, a heavily tempered paste was formulated. The recipe is as follows: (1) 3000 g premoistened clay (Westwood EM210); for some compositional information on this clay, see Vaz Pinto et al. (1987), (2) 342 g 16 mesh Ottawa quartz sand, (3) 362 g 30 mesh Ottawa quartz sand, (4) 321 g 60 mesh Ottawa quartz sand, and (5) 120 ml distilled water.

Vessels are made in plaster molds, the template for which was the blunt end of a L'eggs pantyhose plastic container. Forming uses 95.0 g of paste. In making vessels, one encounters two major problems: (1) controlling wall thickness and (2) ensuring that the paste is pressed tightly against the mold. These problems are ameliorated by applying the paste in small dabs, each one being pressed and smeared. This process begins at the bottom of the mold, spirals upward, and is repeated. When the last layers are applied, the rim is thickened somewhat to prevent cracking during surface treatment. The vessel interior is smoothed with thumb and index finger; a needle is used to gauge approximate thickness at the base. Despite efforts to maintain uniform walls, all vessels have thick and thin spots. In the last stage of forming, the rim is slightly moistened with a small sponge, then flattened and smoothed with a plastic guitar pick and fingers; the interior of the rim is rounded slightly to prevent chipping during polishing. Finally, the vessel number is impressed twice on opposite sides of the rim. To prepare vessel interiors for polishing and slipping, surfaces are smoothed after forming

with a shiny pebble. Vessels shrink free of the mold in about two hours when the paste is leather hard. Because of the laminated structure of the paste, small bits of vessel wall sometimes stick to the mold. The pits are patched with fresh paste and guitar pick. This problem can be minimized by making the first layer of paste a bit thicker (ca. 3-4 mm). After these minor repairs, the exterior rim is beveled slightly with a guitar pick, then moistened and finger-smoothed. Vessel exteriors to be slipped or polished are smoothed with a polishing pebble.

SURFACE TREATMENTS

Textured. This rough surface has a large area similar to the stamped and impressed vessels of the eastern United States and corrugated pots of the Southwest. This treatment, used only on vessel exteriors, is made by rolling and rocking the threads of a large stove bolt against the surface. The texture is applied from rim to base and covers the entire surface.

Finger-Smoothed. On vessel interiors a finger smooth surface results from the basic forming process; no additional treatment is needed. Larger temper particles protrude from this surface, and there are some minor undulations. Leather-hard vessel exteriors are moistened with a sponge and smoothed using first sponge then finger in a circular motion. The result is a surface with some temper drags and only slight protrusion of temper. Obviously, interior and exterior versions of this treatment differ slightly. Nonetheless, in smoothness and surface area both versions fall between textured and polished surfaces.

Polish. Smoothing of the surface before and during the leather-hard stage does not produce a lasting polish. To create the latter, small areas of the vessel surface (ca. 5-6 cm^2) are rewet and vigorously polished with a pebble. On slipped vessels, polishing follows the "grain" of the slip.

Slip. The two slips used in this study, low iron (ca. 0.5 percent) and high iron (ca. 26 percent), are prepared as follows: Low iron: (1) 75 g dry, pulverized clay (Westwood EM210), (2) .40 g iron oxide (Fe$_2$O$_3$) powder, and (3) 65 ml distilled water. High iron: (1) 19.27 g dry, pulverized clay (Westwood EM 210), (2) 5.00 g iron oxide (Fe$_2$O$_3$) powder, and (3) 27 ml distilled water. Slip is applied to the dry vessel with a wiping motion of the index finger. These finger wipes, which overlap somewhat, are done quickly. After drying for a few minutes, both interior and exterior surfaces are given a second coat. This technique produces and uneven slip, with shallow grooves, that is difficult to polish well.

Smudge. Smudging was applied to polished as well as slipped and polished vessels. Interiors, exteriors, or both were smudged. Slightly different smudging techniques were employed in these cases, which has inflated the variability observed in the tests described above. That trivial differences in smudging technique lead to appreciable differences in performance suggest that any generalizations about the effects of "smudging" be carefully qualified.

Three conditions are necessary to produce a good smudge: (1) the vessel must be hot, preferably near its maximum firing temperature, (2) plant material must be present to serve as a source (preferably by smoke but also by contact) of pyrolyzed organic matter, and (3) the hot vessel and organic matter must come into contact in an oxygen-starved atmosphere. To provide these conditions the following procedures are employed. Vessels are placed in a Neycraft automatic furnace and refired at 725°C. Total firing time is one hour, which includes a 40-minute soak at 725°C. Smudging is accomplished by removing the vessel from the furnace at the end of the soak and bringing it into contact, usually in a larger container, with bran. Entire vessels are plunged into a jar containing bran. The jar is immediately covered to restrict oxygen. Heat from the vessel causes the bran to smoke profusely, thereby smudging the entire vessel. To smudge only exteriors, vessels are placed—open side down—on a bed of dry fire clay mixed with 60 mesh sand, which rests on the bottom of the smudging container. This mixture seals off the vessel interior from the smoke. Bran is added immediately and the jar covered. Interiors are smudged by placing the hot vessel upright and adding a small amount of bran and a cover to the vessel itself.

FIRING

Before firing, pots are heated in a Labline Imperial III oven at 70°-80°C for at least 10 hours. Firing takes place in a Paragon electric kiln fitted with an Orton Computer. The temperature is raised at a medium rate to 750°C and soaked for 1 hour. The rate of temperature increase is 208° per hour.

Appendix B. Raw Data for Tests of Permeability and Evaporative Cooling Effectiveness

Pot No.	Int. Abs. (in g)	Ext. Abs. (in g)	Cool-Down .5 hr (in °C)	Cool-Down 1.5 hrs (in °C)	Steady-State 14 hrs (in °C)	Steady-State 43 hrs		High-Stress	
						(in °C)	(in g)	(in °C)	(in g)
1	2.92	5.64	20.7	19.1	18.8	18.5	12.91	29.4	20.60
2	2.81	5.01	20.5	18.9	18.6	18.4	12.81	30.0	19.05
3	2.98	4.11	20.5	18.8	18.4	18.5	13.04	34.1	15.84
4	2.81	3.16	20.6	18.6	18.3	18.5	13.97	36.5	15.32
5	2.78	2.80	20.9	19.0	19.0	19.2	11.65	33.6	15.06
6	2.61	5.55	20.5	18.9	18.5	18.4	12.45	32.8	18.05
7	2.43	4.73	20.6	18.9	18.5	18.5	13.71	30.9	19.73
8	2.63	4.31	20.4	19.0	18.6	18.5	14.45	35.0	17.81
9	2.47	3.33	20.7	18.9	18.5	18.7	13.63	31.6	16.17
10	2.47	2.72	21.2	19.5	19.8	19.9	9.58	40.4	12.89
11	1.85	5.42	20.6	18.8	18.3	18.2	13.59	29.2	18.61
12	1.98	4.26	20.4	18.8	18.3	18.4	14.15	34.8	16.58
13	1.83	4.20	20.8	18.8	18.6	18.7	13.34	33.3	16.30
14	1.81	3.25	20.6	18.7	18.3	18.5	13.24	33.2	17.15
15	1.69	2.63	21.3	19.5	19.7	19.9	10.20	39.1	11.89
16	.56	5.69	20.4	18.7	18.2	18.4	14.25	28.8	24.79
17	.89	5.38	20.8	18.8	18.4	18.7	14.19	31.2	18.42
18	.62	4.20	20.7	18.6	18.4	18.6	13.64	29.5	15.99
19	.93	3.31	20.6	18.4	18.2	18.4	14.01	35.6	15.28
20	1.55	2.66	21.2	19.5	19.6	19.7	11.71	40.4	11.46
21	1.97	5.37	20.9	19.0	18.7	18.8	12.94	29.4	20.84
22	2.63	3.63	20.5	18.8	18.6	18.6.	13.89	35.8	19.45
23	1.98	3.62	20.1	18.3	18.2	18.3	14.69	33.8	17.26
24	.86	5.03	20.1	18.4	18.2	18.3	15.07	31.4	18.99
25	2.67	3.02	20.9	19.1	19.0	19.4	11.96	38.9	13.40
26	1.57	2.03	20.2	18.3	19.2	19.5	12.47	38.2	17.66
27	—	—	23.3	23.5	23.1	23.1	.53	48.8	1.64

5. Inter-Relationship Between Chinese and Islamic Ceramics from 9th to 16th Century A.D.

M.S. TITE
British Museum Research Laboratory, London WC1B 3DG, U.K.

ABSTRACT: *Production technologies employed for Chinese imports and Islamic imitations during Tang, Sung and Yuan/Ming dynasties are investigated and compared.*

INTRODUCTION

As recently summarised by Watson (1987), it is generally accepted that the main impact of imported Chinese ceramics on the development of Islamic ceramics occurred in three phases. First, in response to the import of Tang dynasty white-bodied wares in the 9th century, Islamic potters turned to the use of tin-opacified glazes. Second, in response to the import of Sung dynasty yingqing porcelain in 12th century, the Islamic potters revived the use of quartz-frit bodies. Finally, in response to the import of Yuan/Ming dynasty blue-and-white porcelains in 14th/15th century, a wide range of imitations again mainly based on quartz-frit bodies were produced.

In the present project, the production technology employed for both the Chinese imports and the Islamic imitations have been investigated in order to obtain a better understanding of the inter-relationship between these two ceramic groups. The study has been based on the examination in the scanning electron microscope (SEM) of polished sections through the glazes and bodies prepared from small samples removed from the ceramics. The bulk chemical composition of the bodies and glazes were determined using the energy dispersive X-ray spectrometer attached to the SEM (Table 1).

For each ceramic type, the nature of the body (i.e., earthenware, porcelain or quartz-frit) and the glaze (i.e., over-, on- or underglaze) has been determined.

TANG DYNASTY IMPORTS

The Tang dynasty whitewares, which were exported from, for example, Gong Xian to the Near East during 9th century have bodies made from high alumina clays (~30 per cent Al_2O_3) containing low lime (<1 per cent CaO) and low iron (~1 per cent FeO) but significant titania (~1 per cent TiO_2). The compositions of these bodies are therefore typical of the overall range of greenware and porcelain bodies produced in northern China. The bodies are coated first with a slip layer (~500 μm thick) which is finer textured than, but similar in composition to the bodies and secondly with a transparent lime-alkali glaze. The firing temperatures were such as to produce a more-or-less continuous glass matrix within the body (Figure 1a) which, for the high alumina clays used, suggests a temperature in the range 1150 - 1200°C.

The contemporary Islamic potters of the Abbasid period in Iraq were not able to match these hard white bodies because they lacked both the necessary clays and the firing technology. They therefore continued to make their bodies from the locally available calcareous earthenware clays (~15 per cent Al_2O_3 and ~20 per cent CaO) which contained high iron (~7 per cent FeO). No slip layer was applied but the bodies were coated with glaze opacified by the addition of tin oxide which is present as a high concentration of clusters of particles up to 10 μm across (Figure 1b). The firing temperatures were such as to produce an open network of interconnecting glass/relict clay within the body which, for the calcareous clays used, suggest a temperature in the range 850 - 1050°C. The glazes used are of the alkali-lime type with the addition of small amounts of lead (up to 2.5 per cent PbO). The whiteness of the glaze varies according to the tin oxide content which ranges from less than 2 per cent to about 7 per cent SnO_2.

A further Islamic development during this period was the use of cobalt-blue pigment in the decoration of the ceramics. The pigment was applied onto the powdery surface of the unfired glaze and then became fused into the glaze during the firing. This method of decoration onto a tin-opacified glaze, subsequently spread through the Near East and along North Africa reaching Europe by the 13th century where it took the form of Hispano-Moresque lustreware and Italian maiolica.

SUNG DYNASTY IMPORTS

The Sung dynasty yingqing porcelain from southern China which was imported to the Near East during the 12th century has bodies made from silica rich clays (75-80 per cent SiO_2), again containing low iron (<1 per cent FeO). The low alumina contents (~15 per cent Al_2O_3) of these bodies as compared to the Tang whiteware bodies (~30 per cent Al_2O_3) reflect the use of porcelain stone (alteration product of quartz-feldspar rocks) in southern China instead of the kaolinitic clays used in northern China (Tite et al. 1984). These bodies are again coated with a transparent lime-alkali glaze, but without any intermediate slip layer. The firing temperatures were such as to produce a fully vitrified body with a continuous glass matrix which suggests a temperature in the range 1200 - 1250°C.

On this occasion, the contemporary Islamic potters responded by reviving the use of quartz-frit bodies which derive ultimately from the material referred to as Egyptian faience and which had had a very long history extending back to the 4th millennium B.C. in Egypt and the Near East. These bodies consist of unreacted or partially reacted quartz particles bound together by varying amounts of interstitial glass (Figure 1c). They have a low iron content (<1 per cent FeO), and hence they are normally white

30

throughout. They have therefore been glazed using transparent alkali-lime glazes with the decoration painted directly on the body (i.e., underglaze decoration) as well as tin - opacified lead alkali glazes with the decoration applied to the surface of the glaze (i.e., over-or on-glaze decoration).

A very wide range of ceramics based on the use of quartz-frit bodies was produced throughout the Islamic world from the 12th century onwards until the present day. An example of such ceramics produced during the 12th and 13th centuries is the lustreware made at Kashan in Persia, the production of which is described in a Persian treatise on pottery manufacture written by Abu' l-Qasim in 1301 (Allan 1973). In the case of a lustreware tile fragment dating to about 1300, the quartz particles in the body are more-or-less surrounded by glass and somewhat rounded as a result of solution in the glass (Figure 1c). The glass phase is clearly inhomogeneous but typically contains some 8 per cent each of alumina and alkali (soda plus potash) together with the order of 0.5 per cent of lead oxide. According to the description given by Abu' l-Qasim, the bodies were made from ground quartz to which was added small amounts of a white clay to give plasticity and a frit to form on firing the bonding glass. The frit itself was prepared by firing a mixture of ground quartz and alkali in the form of plant ash. Therefore, assuming equal parts by weight of silica and alumina in the clay and, as described by Abu' l-Qasim, equal parts of silica and alkali in the frit, it is estimated from the analytical data that the quartz-clay-frit mixture contained between 5 - 10 per cent each of clay and frit. This estimate is in agreement with the description given in Abu' l-Qasim's treatise of a body made from 10 parts quartz, 1 part clay and 1 part frit. The degree of reaction between the quartz grains and the body glass indicates that the firing temperature employed was almost certainly in excess of 1000°C.

The lustreware glaze is of the lead-alkali type with medium lead content (~20 per cent PbO). It has been opacified by the addition of tin oxide (~10 per cent SnO_2) which is present as a high concentration of particles a few microns across. According to Abu 'l-Qasim, the glaze was prepared by the addition of a lead and tin oxide mixture to the alkali-based frit. The observed proportions of lead and tin oxides in the glaze (about 2 parts PbO and 1 part SnO_2) are again consistent with the recipes given in the treatise. The very low lead content of the body glass (~0.5 per cent PbO) probably represents contamination from the glaze rather than the deliberate addition of lead to the body. This interpretation is also consistent with Abu' l-Qasim's treatise from which the implication is that no lead was added to the body.

After application of the glaze, the ceramic would have been fired at a temperature almost certainly in excess of 1000°C. Subsequently, a metal containing mixture would have been applied to the surface of the glaze (i.e., overglaze) and the ceramic refired at a considerably lower temperature to form the lustre (Kingery and Vandiver 1986). Since the metal phase associated with lustre is concentrated in a very thin surface layer (<0.5 µm), this phase was not detected in the SEM examination.

YUAN/MING DYNASTY IMPORTS

The final phase of Chinese influence on Islamic ceramics occurred with the import of Yuan/Ming dynasty blue-and-white porcelain to the Near East. The production of blue-and-white porcelain was well established in China by the mid 14th century, but apparently this porcelain was not exported until towards the end of the 14th century, with exports really only gaining momentum in the early 15th century. As with the Sung dynasty yingqing porcelain, the bodies of the blue-and-white porcelain were made from silica-rich clays (70 - 75 per cent SiO_2) containing low iron (<1.5 per cent FeO). The alumina content (~20 per cent Al_2O_3), however tends to be slightly higher than that of the yingqing porcelain (~15 per cent Al_2O_3), possibly because of the addition of a kaolinitic clay to the porcelain stone used to make the blue-and-white bodies (Tite et al. 1984). The glaze is again of the transparent lime-alkali type with the decoration painted directly onto the body using a cobalt-blue pigment (ie., underglaze), the ore for which almost certainly coming from Persia at this period.

The import of Chinese blue-and-white porcelain stimulated the production during the 15th century of numerous local imitations in Egypt and to a lesser extent, Syria and Persia (Rogers and Ward 1988). These imitations were normally based on the use of transparent alkali-lime glazes with underglaze decoration applied to either quartz-frit or earthenware clay bodies. In the later case, the bodies were coated with a white-firing low iron quartz-based slip. In addition, however, tin-opacified lead glazes with on-glaze decoration were sometimes used, again in conjunction with either quartz-frit or clay bodies.

Ottoman Turkey was a comparative latecomer both with regard to the acquisition of Chinese blue-and-white porcelain and to the production of Isnik ware which represents the local imitation. However, although the production of blue-and-white Isnik ware only became prolific during the late 15th and early 16th century, it was technologically vastly superior to the earlier imitations produced in Egypt, Syria and Persia.

The Isnik ware bodies consist of angular quartz particles bonded together but only partially surrounded by a fairly extensive glass phase (Figure 1d). The glass phase contains some 5 - 7 per cent each of alumina, alkali (soda plus potash) and lead oxide. Therefore, as for the Kashan lustreware, the Isnik bodies were made from ground quartz to which was added 5 - 10 per cent each of white clay and frit. There were, however, differences between the Kashan and Isnik bodies. First, the clay content tended to be higher than the frit content in the Kashan bodies, whereas the opposite was the case for the Isnik ware. Second, the frit used for the Isnik body contained similar amounts of both alkali and lead, whereas the frit used for the Kashan body contained only alkali (N.B., in order to estimate the amount of frit added to Isnik bodies, it is necessary to assume that the frit contained equal parts by weight of silica and of alkali-plus-lead oxide). Further, because the quartz grains in the Isnik bodies are more angular than those in the Kashan bodies and because the glass phase has a lower melting point, the firing temperature for the Isnik ware was probably less than 1000°C and certainly less than that used for the Kashan ware.

The Isnik ware glaze is again of lead-alkali type with a medium lead content (~30 per cent PbO). The lead-to-alkali ratio is about 3:1 by weight which compares with an approximately 1:1 ratio for the body glass indicating that frits of different composition were used for the glaze and the body. The glaze contains significant tin-oxide (4 - 7 per cent SnO_2), but is still more-or-less transparent since the majority of the tin remains in solution, and there are only occasional tin-oxide particles in the glaze. The decoration, for which a cobalt-blue pigment was used, was therefore applied under the glaze. Intermediate between the body and the glaze is a slip layer, typically 200 - 500 µm thick (Figure 1d). This slip has a comparable quartz-glass microstructure to the body, but contains slightly less glass and was produced from a purer and finer textured quartz such that the bulk iron oxide content is less than 0.3 per cent as compared to ~1 per cent in the body. The application of this layer thus achieved a fully white appearance without tin-oxide opacification, and at the same time minimised the use of the more expensive pure, fine textured quartz.

CONCLUSIONS

The above results indicate that the Islamic potters used a number of different methods in order to overcome the problem of replicating the hard white Chinese porcelain bodies without having either abundant supplies of the necessary white-firing clay or the associated high temperature technology. One approach was to coat the buff-coloured earthenware clay bodies with a white tin-opacified lead-based glaze. A second approach was to use a low iron quartz-frit body instead of a clay body in which case a transparent glaze could be applied. Finally, a third approach was to coat either an earthenware clay body or an off-white quartz-frit body with a thin layer of a white-firing slip before applying a transparent glaze. The slip could itself be either a clay or quartz-based mixture with low iron content.

Using the different approaches the Islamic potter was thus able at successive periods to respond to the pressure created by Chinese imports for more abundant and thus more generally available imitations. At the same time, he himself initiated developments in decorative methods including the use of cobalt-blue pigment, lustre decoration and underglaze painting which not only significantly extended his own decorative repertoire but also influenced in due course the decoration of Chinese porcelain.

Although a basic framework for the inter-relationship between Chinese and Islamic ceramics is now established, further more detailed work is clearly necessary in order to fully define this inter-relationship and to determine more precisely when and where the various technological developments (eg., tin oxide opacification, quartz-frit bodies, underglaze decoration, etc.) first occurred.

ACKNOWLEDGEMENTS

I am indebted to Mrs. J. Rawson and Mr. M. Rogers of Department of Oriental Antiquities for providing the sherds examined and for helpful discussion during the course of the work. Miss M. Bimson is thanked for her most valuable advice and comments.

REFERENCES

Allen, J.W. (1973). Abu' l-Qasim's treatise on ceramics. Iran 11: 111-120.

Kingery, W.D. and Vandiver, P.B. (1986). Ceramic Masterpieces. New York: Free Press: 111-121.

Rogers, J.M. and Ward, R.M. (1988). Suleyman the Magnificent. London: British Museum Publ.: 186 - 188.

Tite, M.S., Freestone, I.C. and Bimson, M. (1984). A technological study of Chinese porcelain of the Yuan dynasty. Archaeometry 26: 139 - 154.

Watson, O. (1987). Islamic pots in Chinese style. Burlington Magazine 129: 304 - 306.

TABLE 1

TYPICAL CHEMICAL COMPOSITIONS FOR CHINESE AND ISLAMIC CERAMICS

Pottery type	Period	Oxide concentrations (per cent wt)								
		SiO_2	Al_2O_3	Na_2O	K_2O	CaO	MgO	FeO	PbO	SnO_2
BODY										
Gong Xian whiteware	Tang	64	30	0.5	2.2	0.4	0.5	1.1	–	–
Yingqing porcelain	Sung/Yuan	79	16	0.8	2.8	0.7	0.2	0.6	–	–
Blue-and-white porcelain	Yuan	72	21	1.9	3.4	0.1	0.1	1.2	–	–
Islamic tin-glazed	9th cent	47	12	2.1	1.0	22	6.9	6.7	–	–
Persian lustreware	c 1300	91	3.5	2.7	0.9	1.1	0.6	0.5	–	–
Isnik – body	16th cent	87	2.6	2.5	0.7	2.4	1.2	1.0	2.1	–
– slip		92	1.8	2.1	0.5	1.0	0.5	0.3	1.4	–
GLAZE										
Gong Xian whiteware	Tang	64	18	0.8	2.1	13	1.4	0.6	–	–
Yingqing porcelain	Sung/Yuan	65	14	0.9	1.9	16	0.5	0.7	–	–
Blue-and-white porcelain	Yuan	67	16	2.8	3.5	9.4	0.4	1.3	–	–
Islamic tin-glazed	9th cent	66	1.9	7.0	4.1	6.7	2.8	0.8	2.4	~7
Persian lustreware	c 1300	50	1.6	8.0	1.5	3.1	1.5	0.9	22	~10
Isnik	16th cent	49	0.6	9.2	0.9	1.0	0.1	–	33	4-7
BODY GLASS										
Persian lustreware	c 1300	77	7.7	6.1	2.4	1.6	1.5	0.9	0.7	–
Isnik – body	16th cent	72	6.2	5.6	1.8	3.8	2.6	2.3	5.1	–
– slip		73	5.7	5.3	1.7	2.5	1.0	0.4	5.7	–

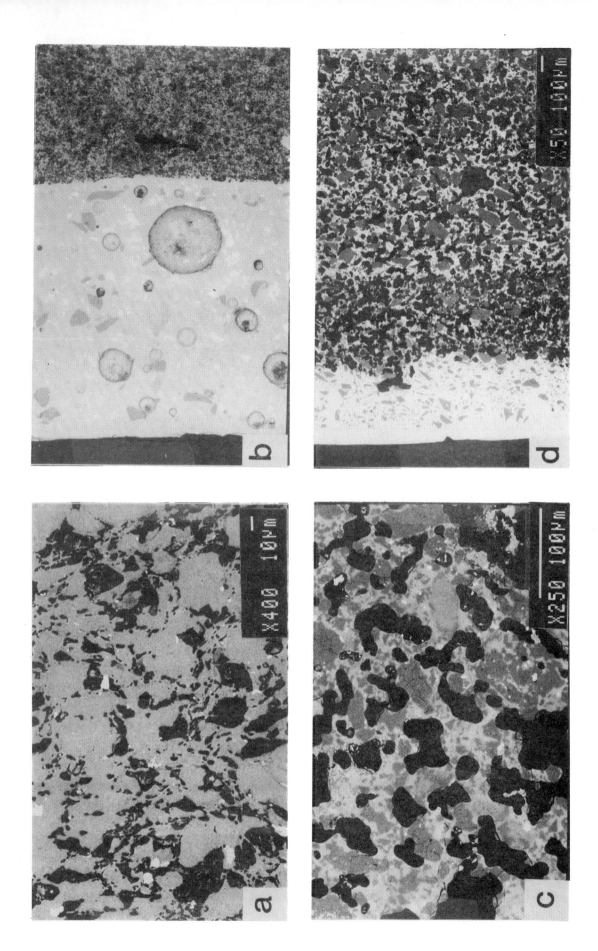

Figure 1 SEM photomicrographs of sections through (a) body of Tang dynasty whiteware showing more-or-less continuous glass matrix; (b) glaze and body of Abbasid blue-decorated sherd from Iraq showing tin oxide particles (white) in glaze; (c) body of Kashan lustreware showing rounded quartz particles (dark grey) surrounded by glass (light grey); (d) glaze, intermediate slip layer and body of Isnik ware showing quartz particles (grey) bonded together by glass (white) in body and slip.

6. First Results of a Mössbauer and Neutron Activation Analysis Study of Recent Ceramic Finds from Montegrande, Peru

U. WAGNER, S. v. BRANDIS, C. ULBERT and F.E. WAGNER
Physik-Department, Technische Universität München, D-8046 Garching, FRG.

H. MÜLLER-KARPE
Kommission für Allgemeine und Vergleichende Archäologie des Deutschen Archäologischen Institutes (KAVA), D-5300 Bonn, FRG.

J. RIEDERER
Rathgen-Forschungslabor, Staatliche Museen Preussischer Kulturbesitz, D-1000 Berlin, FRG.

M. TELLENBACH
Seminar für Völkerkunde, Universität Bonn, D-5300 Bonn, FRG.

ABSTRACT: *Recent ceramic finds from the settlement of Montegrande, Peru, were studied by neutron activation analysis, thin section microscopy and Mössbauer spectroscopy. The cluster analysis of the NAA data yields two major groups. This result is confirmed by thin section microscopy and shows ample agreement with the typology of the sherds. In addition a classification of the material according to the pattern of the Mössbauer spectra is attempted. For the assessment of the firing conditions, systematic laboratory firing experiments in oxidizing and reducing atmospheres were performed on mud recovered from the wattle and daub wall of an excavated house.*

INTRODUCTION

The settlement of Montegrande in the Jequetepeque valley in northern Peru was excavated under the direction of the German Archaeological Institute (KAVA) during the years 1980-1983. The excavation was carried out over a total area of 10 000 m², which was subdivided into squares of 10 x 10 m. The remains of about 200 small houses and 3 ceremonial platforms were discovered (Tellenbach 1987 and references therein). Two phases of settlement can be distinguished. Fine ware, bottles and cups of different shapes were found together with large amounts of everyday ware, most of them decorated with incisions and applications, or by stamping and polishing. The systematic documentation of the excavation describes about 4000 rim and bottom sherds and their location. Ninety of these sherds, representing the different types of vessel shapes, were studied by neutron activation analysis (NAA), Mössbauer spectroscopy (MS) and thin section microscopy (TSM). This information is intended to be used as reference in a future interpretation of the total material from Montegrande, and for comparison with other formative ceramics recently excavated in the northern Andean region, on the coast, e.g., in Purulén (Alva 1987; Wagner et al. 1987), and in the highlands at Udima (Alva 1987), Pandanche (Kaulicke 1981) and Huacaloma (Terada and Onuki 1982 and 1985).

NEUTRON ACTIVATION ANALYSIS AND THIN SECTION MICROSCOPY

Seventeen trace and 4 major element concentrations were determined by NAA of two independent samples taken from each sherd. Prior to irradiation, the powdered samples were heated to 850°C for 24 h (Kilikoglou et al.

1988). The logarithms of the mean values of each pair of samples were used in the cluster analysis. The dendrogram obtained by the weighted average linkage method is shown in Figure 1, together with the TSM results. The dendrogram remains unaltered after the application of the hillclimbing procedure (Fahrmeir et al. 1984).

The cluster analysis reveals two major groups, cluster 1 and cluster 3. The hatched columns on the left of the dendrogram illustrate the extent to which the results of NAA and TSM agree with each other and with the archaeological typology of the vessels. The samples marked by dotting in Figure 1 show a behaviour that deviates from the major NAA clusters. The observed types of vessels are round jars with (2b) and without (3a - d) neck, carinated bowls with concave, straight and convex upper parts (4a - c), bottles (1), big cups (5) and special forms (6). For demonstration, the drawings of reconstructed vessels are presented in Figure 1. The big clusters 1 and 3 contain distinctly different types of vessels, which represent two "sets" of household ware.

For cluster 1 the results of NAA and TSM agree well with the typology. In TSM all samples of cluster 1 are characterized by the presence of quartz and of large amounts of coarse inclusions of plagioclase of volcanic origin as indicated by its zone structure. Black or red colour of the main part of the sherds is marked, respectively, as 1a or 1b in the TSM column of Figure 1. No traces of weathering or reconversion into clay minerals is visible. Plagioclase inclusions have also been observed in 11 of 14 surface finds from Huacaloma, which were at our disposal. Material from Huacaloma in the Cajamarca valley has been studied in detail (Ninimiya et al. 1982). The authors have used X-ray radiography and X-ray diffraction to identify the mineral composition of their material. They

Figure 1. Dendrogram obtained by the cluster analysis of the NAA data. The sample numbers are given in the NAA column; the sample without a number is the mudplaster described in the text. The results of TSM and the archaeological typology are displayed in the left TSM and Type column (6) comprises various special forms, which are not shown. The different vessel shapes are depicted on the right.

designates members of cluster 1 in NAA, high plagioclase content in TSM and various types of vessel shapes which can be compared to highland ware.

designates members of cluster 2 in NAA, not distinguished from cluster 3 in TSM.

designates members of cluster 3 in NAA, high content of clay nodules in TSM and characterizes various types of vessel shapes which are considered as local ware.

designates members of a small cluster in NAA, so far uninterpreted.

designates samples which exhibit deviant behaviour.

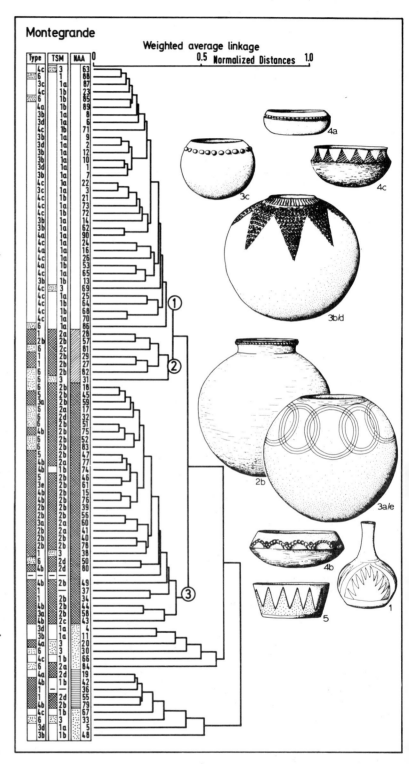

observe large amounts of feldspars, but do not distinguish plagioclase. Although we have only TSM results on some surface finds from Huacaloma, we feel that the occurrence of plagioclase in ceramics from Montegrande as well as in the early Huacaloma material deserves further attention, especially since the vessel shapes are also similar.

The material falling into cluster 3 is mainly characterized by the presence of a high percentage of clay nodules. Four subgroups can be distinguished in TSM. Group 2a contains predominantly clay nodules, while in group 2b quartz is present additionally. Group 2c contains small amounts of fine plagioclase, while in group 2d the clay nodules are fewer. Mudplaster recovered from the wattle and daub walls of one of the Montegrande houses is also a member of cluster 3. Material in cluster 3 is therefore considered as local. The mudplaster was used in our laboratory firing experiments. After ultrasonic extraction and separation (Kilikoglou et al. 1988), the fine and coarse fractions of the mudplaster still join in cluster 3. The small cluster 2 cannot be distinguished from cluster 3 by TSM. At the bottom of the dendrogram, one finds a number of samples that differ from those in clusters 1 through 3, while the fairly well defined group of five samples with horizontal hatching may expand into a bigger cluster as more samples will be studied. The other samples in this range do not exhibit much likeness in their trace element content.

MÖSSBAUER SPECTROSCOPY

Mössbauer spectroscopy provides information on the chemical and physical state of the iron present in the

ceramics. The most relevant parameters are the quadrupole splitting and the isomer shift. They fall into characteristic regions and give information on the valence state of the iron and on the local symmetry around the iron atoms. Additionally oxidic phases can be identified on account of magnetic ordering phenomena (Wagner et al. 1986a and references therein).

Carefully separated material from the outer layers and inner cores of all sherds was measured at RT in transmission geometry with an intensity of at least 2 million counts per channel in 1024 channels. In a few cases a pigment could be scraped off the surface, and measured separately. Such a situation is represented in Figure 2, where the pigment shows the six line pattern of haematite, while the interior of the sherd contains mainly divalent iron. All spectra were fitted with a superposition of Lorentzian lines. It was attempted to use the smallest necessary number of lines. The fitted components often have rather broad lines and therefore must be regarded as representing the maxima of distributions of magnetic fields or quadrupole splittings.

Six different types of Mössbauer spectra can be distinguished in the Montegrande ceramics (Figure 3). The correlation of these types with the results from the NAA and TSM as given in Figure 1 is shown in Figure 4 for material from the outer layers and the core of the sherds. In Table 1 the group averages and standard deviations of the fitted parameters are compiled for the different types of spectra. Spectra of type 1 show mainly a Fe^{3+} quadrupole doublet with a small splitting, due to the presence of a high amount of paramagnetic and superparamagnetic species as well as the magnetic pattern of haematite, and an additional distribution of magnetic fields presumably due

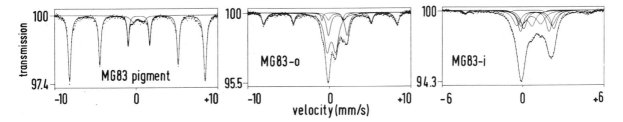

Figure 2. Mössbauer spectra of the surface pigment, the outer layer and the inner core of sherd MG83 (cluster 3) measured at room temperature with a $^{57}CoRh$ source. Note the different velocity scales; o = outer layer, i = inner core.

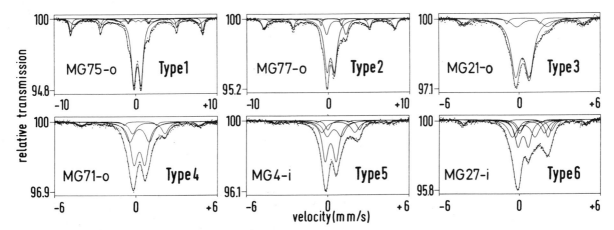

Figure 3. The six different types of Mössbauer spectra observed in the Montegrande ceramics at RT. Note the different velocity scales; o = outer layer, i = inner core.

Type	No.		H (T)	A_{Mag} (%)	QS (mm/s)	SQ (mm/s)	WQ (mm/s)	AQ (%)
1	13	Fe^{3+}	18.6–49.8	38.2(13.9)	0.99(5)	0.25(1)	0.82(6)	61.8(13.9)
2	36	Fe^{3+}	27.3–50.3	29.8(5.8)	0.96(7)	0.26(2)	0.81(6)	58.1(6.4)
		Fe^{2+}			2.47(24)	0.91(9)	0.82(7)	12.1(6.1)
3	13	Fe^{3+}	49.0(1.3)	22.2(14.2)	0.98(7)	0.27(3)	0.81(9)	66.7(13.8)
		Fe^{2+}			2.39(15)	0.92(8)	0.87(9)	11.1(5.7)
4	55	Fe^{3+}	47.9(2.1)	17.4(9.5)	0.79(6)	0.25(2)	0.61(5)	41.4(7.9)
					1.38(15)	0.34(9)	0.76(7)	25.8(8.2)
		Fe^{2+}			2.45(15)	0.92(7)	0.68(7)	15.4(7.7)
5	37	Fe^{3+}	46.8(2.2)	14.0(7.6)	0.80(8)	0.26(5)	0.60(6)	36.2(7.0)
					1.37(25)	0.38(8)	0.71(7)	19.0(7.7)
		Fe^{2+}			2.23(21)	0.85(8)	0.69(7)	17.5(7.0)
					2.45(14)	1.05(8)	0.53(7)	13.3(6.0)
6	18	Fe^{3+}	47.9(1.5)	8.4(2.9)	0.73(14)	0.29(7)	0.60(6)	21.1(4.8)
					1.23(24)	0.48(11)	0.77(8)	16.5(5.5)
		Fe^{2+}			1.99(32)	0.85(4)	0.65(9)	17.7(3.7)
					2.19(17)	1.06(16)	0.52(7)	16.3(6.2)
					2.45(14)	0.93(14)	0.55(7)	20.0(6.6)

Table 1: Group averages and standard deviations (in parentheses) of the Mössbauer parameters observed for the different types of Mössbauer spectra, measured at RT. No. is the number of samples. The parameters are given as measured against a source of ^{57}CoRh. H is the magnetic hyperfine field, A_{Mag} is the fractional area of the magnetically ordered part of the spectrum. The maximum and minimum magnetic fields are listed in cases where a distribution of 4 to 9 magnetic fields was needed to fit the spectra. QS, SQ and WQ are the quadrupole splittings, isomer shifts and experimental full linewidths at half maximum. The AQ are the fractional areas of the Fe^{3+} and Fe^{2+} quadrupole doublets.

to oxidic components with varying particle sizes and Fe substitution. Type 2 spectra contain additional Fe^{2+}. Type 3 is best fitted with one Fe^{3+} and one Fe^{2+} doublet and some magnetic oxide. Type 4 is a pattern common in Montegrande ceramics. It is a superposition of two Fe^{3+} doublets with a small and a big quadrupole splitting, one Fe^{2+} doublet and again a small amount of oxidic species. In types 5 and 6 the increasing amounts of Fe^{2+} had to be fitted with two of three doublets, respectively. The distinction between Mössbauer spectra with a distribution of magnetic fields and a reasonably well defined single field becomes more difficult as the oxidic fraction decreases. Magnetite was occasionally observed in spectra with complicated patterns of magnetic field distributions and high amounts of Fe^{2+} components.

In Figure 4 all studied sherds are classified according to the type of Mössbauer spectra observed for their outer layer and inner core. The NAA cluster to which the samples belong is indicated by the hatched column on the left of the graph as in the dendrogram displaying the cluster analysis. The original firing conditions which the sherd has experienced become increasingly reducing from the left to the right columns in Figure 4. A rather uniform firing process appears to have been applied in the production of ceramics in cluster 1. Generally the outer layers exhibit Mössbauer spectra of type 4, while the cores are of type 5 or 6 with about twice as much Fe^{2+} as in type 4 spectra. The difference between outer layer and core is often insignificant in this group, presumably because there was only a short period of oxidation at the end of the firing cycle.

Members of cluster 3 have experienced a variety of firing conditions, though oxidized material prevails. The results of our laboratory firing experiments, which will be discussed below, suggest that the original firing was reducing with a deliberate or incidental oxidation step at the end of the firing cycle. The studied bottles are brown or red on the outside and contain large amounts of Fe^{2+} in their core and inner surface, indicating that the inside of the bottles was not reached by the air entering the kiln during the last stage of the firing. The colours of the different layers of the sherds are manifold, but they do not necessarily reflect the concentrations of the various components as observed in the Mössbauer patterns. Polished surfaces can be distinguished from applied surface pigments by TSM.

FIRING EXPERIMENTS

Mud plaster from the wattle and daub wall of one of the excavated houses was the best material available for systematic Mössbauer studies after laboratory firing experiments. In the mudplaster 10 % of the total iron is in form of magnetically ordered haematite. The intensity of such haematite does not increase on lowering the measuring temperature to 4.2 K (Figure 5). The amount of paramagnetic Fe^{3+}, however, decreases from 76 % at RT to 41 % at 4.2 K, while a sextet with a small and poorly defined field, probably representing ferrihydroxides, appears. Thus about 40 % of the iron appears to be incorporated in clays or other minerals still paramagnetic at 4.2 K. Samples of

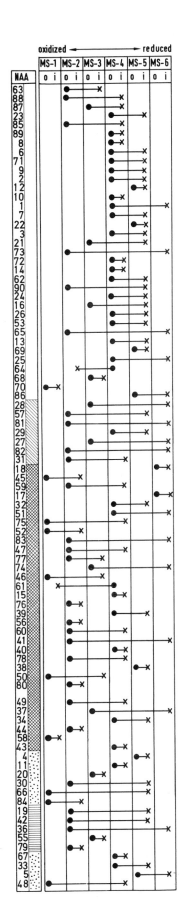

Figure 4. Mössbauer patterns (MS types) of the outer layers and inner cores (X) of all study sherds. The sherds are listed in the sequence established by the cluster analysis (Figure 1), the hatching on the left has the same meaning as in the NAA column of Figure 1.

this material were fired in air at increasing temperatures for 48 h with (-RO-) and without (-O-) previous reduction with charcoal for 3 h. In a third series of experiments, samples were only reduced (-R-) at increasing temperatures with charcoal for 3 h. For the series fired in air Mössbauer spectra were taken at RT and also at 4.2 K. The fitted curves are shown in Figure 6, which also gives the temperature dependence of some relevant parameters.

During firing in air (-0-) the quadrupole splitting in the mudplaster increases with temperature due to the distortion of the lattice during dehydroxylation of octahedral layers of the clay minerals (Wagner et al. 1986a). Fe^{2+} is oxidized around 400°C. Above 800°C haematite forms from iron liberated during the breakdown of the clay lattice. Most of the Fe^{3+} doublet observed at RT is caused by small particle oxides which yield magnetic patterns at 4.2 K due to blocking of the super paramagnetism. Even at 4.2 K the order is not yet complete (Wagner et al. 1988). We still observe magnetic field distributions, as can be seen from the contour plot. Above 1000°C vitrification begins and the quadrupole splitting increases again when spinel-type compounds are formed. After a preceding reduction, firing in air (-RO-) is dominated by the oxidation of the Fe^{2+} species which is complete near 600°C. Up to this temperature, two weak Fe^{2+} components can be distinguished. Such spectra are characteristic for the oxidation of clays previously fired in a reducing atmosphere (Wagner et al. 1986b). They are of type 4 (Figure 3) and common in ceramics from Montegrande (Figure 4). At higher oxidizing temperatures the spectra do not differ much from those observed after direct oxidization. The reduction with charcoal (-R-) becomes effective only above 450°C. Then the Fe^{2+} content increases dramatically. Oxidic phases are not stabilized; the iron appears to dissolve in the silicate matrix. Metallic iron formed near 1000°C can easily be distinguished by its small magnetic field of 33 T.

LABORATORY EMULATION OF THE FIRING OF MONTEGRANDE CERAMICS

The majority of the ceramics from Montegrande have been fired in a reducing environment. To simulate these conditions, we have tested different laboratory firing cycles (Figure 7). The results are compared with selected spectra of ceramics. On top of Figure 7 the spectrum of mudplaster reduced with charcoal at 800°C, is compared with that of the core of sherd MG25. Below two spectra of mudplaster first reduced at 800°C and then refired at 400 and 550°C in air are compared with the cores of sherds MG41 and MG60. If oxidizing refiring is incomplete, sherds with brick-coloured outer layers and gray inner parts result. Such material is frequent among Montegrande ceramics. Finally the spectra of mudplaster fired in air at 1000°C and 1100°C and then reduced at 800°C are compared with those of the core of sherd MG37 and of the outer layer of sherd MG42. Spectra like that of MG37 are scarce in Montegrande ceramics, but were frequently encountered in ceramics from Chavin (Wagner et al. 1987). The outermost

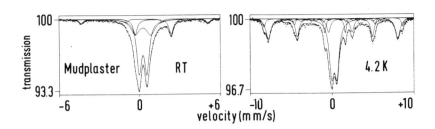

Figure 5. RT and 4.2 K Mössbauer spectra of the mudplaster used in our library firing series. The [57]CoRh source was at the same temperature as the absorber.

Fe^{2+} doublet in the mudplaster in row 5 is rather unstable and disappears already after reoxidation between 200 and 300°C. The ceramics often contain somewhat more Fe^{3+} species than the model samples, but generally their Mössbauer spectra could be emulated quite well by the laboratory firings. The spectra of the Montegrande ceramics cannot be emulated by purely oxidative firing (Figure 6, top). To explain the observed complicated patterns, one has to assume firing cycles with changing atmospheres. Reduction followed by oxidation would correspond to firing in reducing kiln atmosphere with an oxidizing step at the end, while the oxidation followed by reduction at a lower temperature would mean that the kiln was covered completely only after the heat had already reached its maximum.

CONCLUSIONS

The studied ceramics from Montegrande were classified by NAA and TSM into two major groups. The archaeological typology is in good agreement with the physical analyses. A relation between the ceramics from the highlands and the Montegrande material in cluster 1 is suggested by the high content of plagioclase in both and by striking similarity with the typology of the early Huacaloma ceramics. The given classification is also supported by the result of the Mössbauer measurements. Comparison with laboratory firing experiments on mudplaster shows that reducing fire was predominant. However, firing cycles involving changing kiln atmospheres must be assumed to explain the complicated Mössbauer patterns observed in the Montegrande ceramics.

ACKNOWLEDGEMENTS

We wish to thank Mrs. M. Bartel and Mr. J.E. Punsch for their untiring help in preparing the samples and conducting the experiments. The work was supported by the Deutsche Forschungsgemeinschaft. For this we are very grateful.

Alva Alva, W. (1987). Resultados de los excavaciones en el Valle Zaña, Norte del Peru. In: W. Bauer, ed., Archäologie in Peru - Archäometrie,: 61-79. Konrad Theiss Verlag Stuttgart.

Fahrmeir, L., A. Hammerle, (1984). Multivariate statistische Verfahren. Walter de Gruyter, Berlin, New York 1984.

Kaulicke, P. (1981). Keramik der frühen Initialperiode aus Pandache, Depto. Cajamarca, Peru. AVA-Beiträge. Bd.3: 363-389.

Kilikoglou, V., Y. Maniatis and S.P. Grimanis, (1988). The Effect of Purification and Firing of Clays on Trace Element Provenance Studies, Archaeometry, 30:37-46.

Ninimiya, S., T. Kishimoto, K. Kimizuka, T. Matsuzawa, M. Osawa, (1982). Chemical Studies on Pottery Sherds from the Huacaloma Sites. In: Report 2 of the Japanese Scientific Expedition to Nuclear America, University of Tokyo Press: 269-287.

Tellenbach M., (1987). Die Ausgrabungen in der formativzeitlichen Siedlung Montegrande, Jequetepeque-Tal, Nord Peru. AVA-Materialien 39. München.

Tereda, K., and Y. Onuki, (1982). Excavation at Huacaloma in the Cajamarca Valley, Peru 1979. Report 2 of the Japanese Scientific Expedition to Nuclear America. University of Tokyo Press.

Tereda, K., and Y. Onuki, (1985). The formative period in the Cajamarca Basin, Peru. Excavations at Huacaloma and Layzón, 1982. Report 3 of the Japanese Scientific Expedition to Nuclear America. Tokyo.

Wagner, U., F.E. Wagner, J. Riederer, (1986a). The Use of Mössbauer Spectroscopy in Archaeometric Studies. In Olin, J.S. and M.J. Blackman, eds., Proc. of the 1984 Symposium on Archaeometry, Washington D.C., Smithsonian Institution Press: 129-142.

Wagner, U., F.E. Wagner, A. Stockklauser, R. Slazar, J. Riederer, F. Kauffmann-Doig, (1986b). Mössbauer Analysis of Recent Finds from Chavin. Hyperfine Interactions, 29:1113-1116.

Wagner, U., W. Alva, F. Kauffmann-Doig, J. Riederer, R. Salazar, M. Tellenbach, C. Ulbert, J.M. Vreeland, F.E. Wagner, H. Müller-Karpe, (1987). In W. Bauer, ed., Archäologie in Peru - Archäometrie, p. 167-184. Konrad Theiss Verlag Stuttgart.

Wagner, U., W. Knorr, A. Forster, E. Murad, R. Slazar, F.E. Wagner, (1988). Mössbauer Study of Illite Associated with Iron Oxi-Hydroxides. Hyperfine Interactions, 41:855-858.

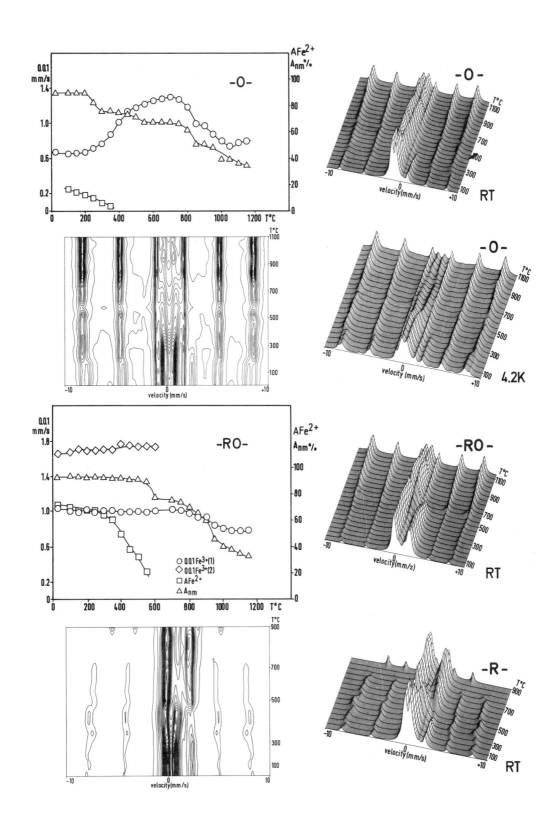

Figure 6. Dependence of Mössbauer spectra (right) and some relevant Mössbauer parameters on the firing temperature of mudplaster from Montegrande. From top to bottom, the series are: Firing in air (-O-), firing in air after preceding reduction at 800°C (-RO-) and firing in reducing environment (-R-). The samples fired in the air were measured at RT as well as 4.2 K. For the latter and the R-series, the data are also presented as contour plots. QQ1 is the quadrupole splitting of the Fe^{3+} doublet(s); A_{nm} and A_{Fe2+}, respectively, are the content of nonmagnetic iron (Fe^{2+} plus Fe^{3+}) and of nonmagnetic Fe^{2+} alone.

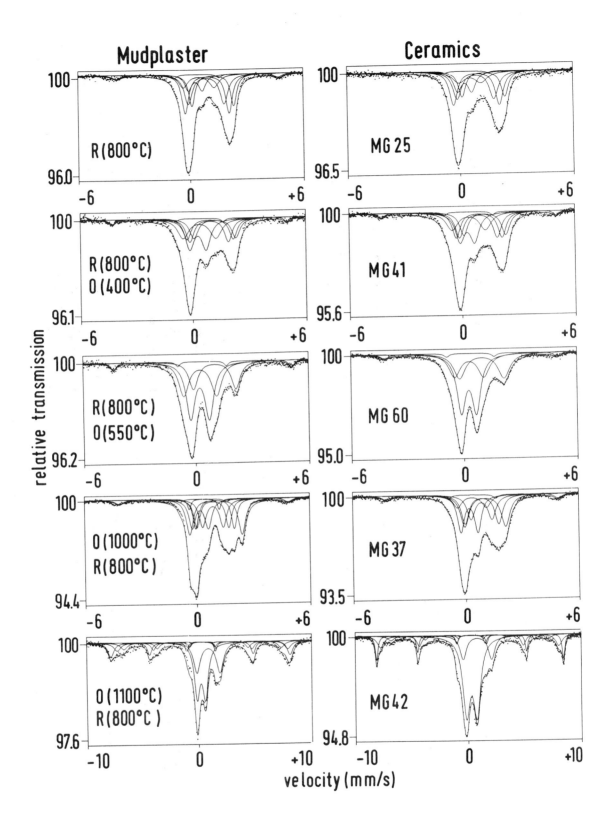

Figure 7. Comparison of the RT Mössbauer spectra of the laboratory fired mudplaster (left) with selected spectra of Montegrande ceramics (right). The sequence of oxidizing (-O-) and reducing (-R-) treatments of the mudplaster is indicated. Reductions with charcoal took place at the given temperatures for 3 h, oxidation in air for 48 h. Note changes in velocity scales.

7. Technological and Organizational Change in the Godin III Pottery Tradition of Western Iran (2600-1400 B.C.)

R. C. HENRICKSON

West Asian Department, Royal Ontario Museum, Toronto, Ontario, Canada M5S 2C6.

ABSTRACT: *Radiographic examination of Iranian Bronze Age pottery distinguishes vessel forming methods and allows tracing of changes within and between ceramic wares during a 1000-year cultural period.*

INTRODUCTION

The millennium-long Godin III buff ware tradition of western Iran, dating to 2600-1400 B.C., allows investigation of long-term technological and other developments within a single ceramic tradition. Excavations at Godin Tepe in central western Iran yielded a long sequence of well-stratified material. The ceramic assemblage was predominantly buff ware, some with monochrome painted decoration (dark brown to black). Distinctively coloured wares (red, grey and grey-black) formed a minor component (see Table 1). Both professional "workshop" and non-professional "household" potters used a number of vessel forming and finishing methods, singly or in various combinations. The range of techniques used and their relative importance changed with time and varied depending on the type of potter and the ware produced.

METHODS

Xeroradiographic, macroscopic and low-power microscopic examinations of vessels and sherds have identified various vessel forming and finishing methods. Patterns and natures of breaks provide further evidence (Rye 1981). Ethnographic data aids inferences as to the possible organization, or "mode", of production on the basis of production techniques used (van der Leeuw 1984). This permits tracing of both technological and related socio-cultural developments of the assemblage and the society using it.

DISCUSSION

Preliminary results of work in progress offer insights on two levels: 1) change within the core buff ware tradition, such as shifts in modes of production, and 2) paths of adoptions and (subsequent) adaptations of techniques, ideas, or attributes from other ceramic traditions.

Professional potters, probably working in small workshops, produced the monochrome painted buff common ware which was the hallmark of the assemblage (Henrickson 1986). Carinated pots and jars in a wide range of sizes and proportions were the characteristic vessel form of the painted buff ware. Additional buff ware vessels, primarily bowls and beakers, were decorated simply (Henrickson 1984, 1987). Despite the workshop mode of production, the potter's wheel was not an important tool. It was used only for production of small painted vessels, mostly carinated forms, all of whose maximum diameter was <16 cm. Not even all such vessels were wheelmade.

This suggests that the potter's wheel had severe technological limits. Potters used various types of slab construction and coiling, with finishing on a tournette, for making most vessels (Henrickson 1986, 1989).

In addition, wares distinguished by their colour and surface finish form a minor component of the assemblage (Table 1). Buff Coarse wares were used in less skilled production of some utilitarian pottery. Simpler modes of production, based within the household, may have been used for some of these (Henrickson 1988).

Through the first two phases of the Godin III tradition (III:6-5) during the third millennium B.C., professional potters made an appreciable part of the assemblage (e.g., Buff Common ware [>60% in Table 1]). At the end of the third millennium (Godin III:4), however, fundamental changes in modes of production occurred. The importance of Buff Common ware fell markedly (from 68% to 27% [Table 1]). Production of Red Slipped (handmade using slab and coiling with coarsely tempered clay, [self]-slipped) and Buff Coarse ware increased dramatically (Table 1). The forming and finishing methods suggest simpler modes of production, some perhaps within households (Henrickson 1988, 1989). As use of Red Slipped ware expanded, such vessels filled not only the traditional functional niches for coloured wares in the assemblage (vessels for food service and consumption), but also duplicated all standard Buff Common ware forms, including carinated pots and jars of all sizes (Henrickson 1984, 1988, 1989).

By the early second millennium (Godin III:2), poorly formed and finished Buff Coarse ware became predominant (83% [Table 1]). Although still the product of professional potters, painted Buff Common ware fell to only 2% of the assemblage. Household or simple cottage industry (van der Leeuw 1984) production of Buff Coarse ware essentially supplanted the previously important workshop industry of skilled artisans. Thus even shifts in ware frequencies, illuminated by study of the forming methods used for each ware group, provide evidence for changes in the organization of pottery production.

Patterns of adoption and adaptation provide further insights into the development of the Godin III tradition. Forming methods provide clear evidence for connections between wares and considerable continuity within the tradition. Three processes will be reviewed here: 1) interrelated changes in vessel form and forming methods; 2) the persistence of forming methods in production of a vessel class; and 3) sustained isolation of a new ware in the assemblage.

Study of forming methods clarifies the relationship between the Godin III:6-5 Grey-black and Godin III:5-4 Red Slipped wares (cf. Table 1). The development of the typical bowl provides a good example. The use of burnished Grey-black pottery is an adoption from the assemblage of the previous period in the valley (Godin IV). Despite the almost complete replacement of the local ceramic assemblage, other archaeological data such as settlement patterns suggest continuity of the human population. Cultural and economic factors account for the change of ceramic assemblage (Henrickson 1988).

The shallowness of the typical Godin III:6 Grey-black bowl (Figure 1.5), essentially featureless radiographs, and the radial pattern of breakage all suggest clay was pressed into an external mould to form the bowl. Later in Godin III:6 slab-like elements instead were sometimes pressed into such a mould (Figure 1.4). Finally only the base and lower curve of the wall were formed in a mould; a slab of clay added to this rounded base then formed the majority of the height of the bowl wall (Figure 1.3). The abandonment of moulding the entire bowl required that the sides of the bowl become more nearly vertical to prevent sagging of unsupported everted upper walls during forming. After this final change in forming methods, the firing atmosphere was changed from reducing to oxidizing, yielding Red Slipped ware by Godin III:5 (Figure 1.1-2).

This sequence of changes — introduction of forming by addition of successive slab-like or strip elements within a mould, making the walls nearly vertical to allow use of a single slab for the majority of the wall height, and the shift to an oxidizing atmosphere — all brought the distinctive Grey-black ware ever closer to the production norms of the dominant buff ware assemblage: slab or coiled construction and an oxidizing firing atmosphere (Henrickson 1988). In this way the minor coloured ware was assimilated into the dominant tradition in the course of two or three centuries.

Forming methods also link Godin III:5-4 Red Slipped ware to Godin III:3-2 Buff Coarse ware. In Godin III:5-4 large carinated painted Buff ware jars were made by coiling (Figure 2). At the same time, however, similar jars in Red Slipped ware were made using large slab-like elements (Figure 3). Later, in Godin III:2, Red Slipped ware jars had disappeared, but Buff Coarse ware jars are made using slab-like elements (Figure 4); the baggy form with a shoulder ridge had developed from the earlier carinated vessels (Henrickson 1987). The techniques used to make painted Buff Common ware vessels, however, remained unchanged from Godin III:5-2 (Henrickson 1989). Thus the approach to production of a specific vessel type remained constant not only through time but also between wares as even the vessel form changed.

Finally, also in Godin III:2 there is a well-made Grey ware, unrelated typologically or technically to either any other part of the contemporary assemblage or the earlier Grey-black ware (Henrickson 1984, 1987, 1989). Typology suggests tenuous links to both southwestern and northeastern Iran (Henrickson 1987). The only indication of assimilation to the Godin III buff tradition is rare replication of the typical painted Buff Common ware ridge-shouldered vessel in a rather coarse and dark grey fabric (Figure 5, cf. Henrickson 1989).

In this case the isolation of the Grey ware in the assemblage is noteworthy, particularly given the earlier convergences between wares. The low frequency of both Grey and painted Buff wares, the only likely products of skilled potters in the assemblage, suggest a decline in the ceramic component of the regional economy. Almost all of the assemblage is the simple, rather crude Buff Coarse ware which is most likely produced in households or a cottage industry. The earlier workshop mode of production is almost absent.

CONCLUSIONS

The more than 1000-year span of the Godin III tradition affords rich opportunity to study the long-term dynamics and technological development of a regional ceramic tradition. Study of the use of various vessel forming and finishing techniques yields both synchronic and diachronic links between wares within the tradition. Integration of results of these and further analyses with other archaeological data from the site and region should provide not only a greater understanding of why the ceramic tradition developed as it did but also of the people and society who made and used it.

ACKNOWLEDGEMENTS

All of the radiographic work has been done in the Radiology Department of Women's College Hospital (Toronto) through the generosity of Dr. T. Connor, Radiologist-in-Chief.

REFERENCES

Henrickson, R.C. (1984). Godin Tepe, Godin III, and Central Western Iran ca. 2600-1400 B.C., Ph. D. Dissertation, University of Toronto.

Henrickson, R.C. (1986). Craft Specialization and Pottery Production in Bronze Age Central Western Iran. In Technology and Style (Ceramics and Civilization II), edited by D. Kingery (Columbus: American Ceramic Society): 53-85.

Henrickson, R.C. (1987). The Godin III Revised Chronology for Central Western Iran, ca. 2600 - 1400 B.C. Iranica Antiqua XXII: 33-115.

Henrickson, R.C. (1988). The Buff and the Grey: Ceramic Assemblages and Cultural Process in the Third Millennium B.C. Central Zagros, Iran. In Cross-Craft and Cross-Cultural Interactions in Ceramics (Ceramics and Civilization IV), edited by M.R. Notis and P.E. McGovern (Westerville, Ohio: American Ceramic Society), in press.

Henrickson, R.C. (1989). Painted Decoration, Vessel Function, and Stylistic Regionalism. In The Changing Roles and Functions of Ceramics in Society (Ceramics and Society V), edited by W.D. Kingery (American Ceramic Society), in press.

Rye, O.S. (1981). Pottery Technology: Principles and Reconstruction. Washington: Taraxacum.

van der Leeuw, S.E. (1984). Dust to Dust: A Transformational View of the Ceramic Cycle. In (S.E. van der Leeuw and A.C. Pritchard, eds.) The Many Dimensions of Pottery. Amsterdam: Universiteit van Amsterdam, 707-774.

Table 1. Frequencies by phase for Godin pottery (sherds from trash and floor deposits).

Date	2600-	2300-	2100-	1900-	1500-	B.C.
Ware			III:			N =
Group	6	5	4	3	2	1	
B Com	62.5	68.4	26.6	14.5	8.8	15.5	3427
B Cs	27.1	18.2	46.8	71.8	83.2	78.0	5282
RS	0.9	12.6	25.3	12.0	5.6	5.3	1140
GB	9.5	0.8					268
Grey			1.3	1.7	2.5	1.1	124
Temper							
Coarse	32.7	31.2	72.9	84.6	87.9	80.5	6545
Common	67.3	68.8	27.1	15.4	12.1	19.5	3696
Decoration							
Painted	15.7	21.0	6.5	5.6	3.6	3.6	926
N =	2769	715	3211	234	2867	445	10241

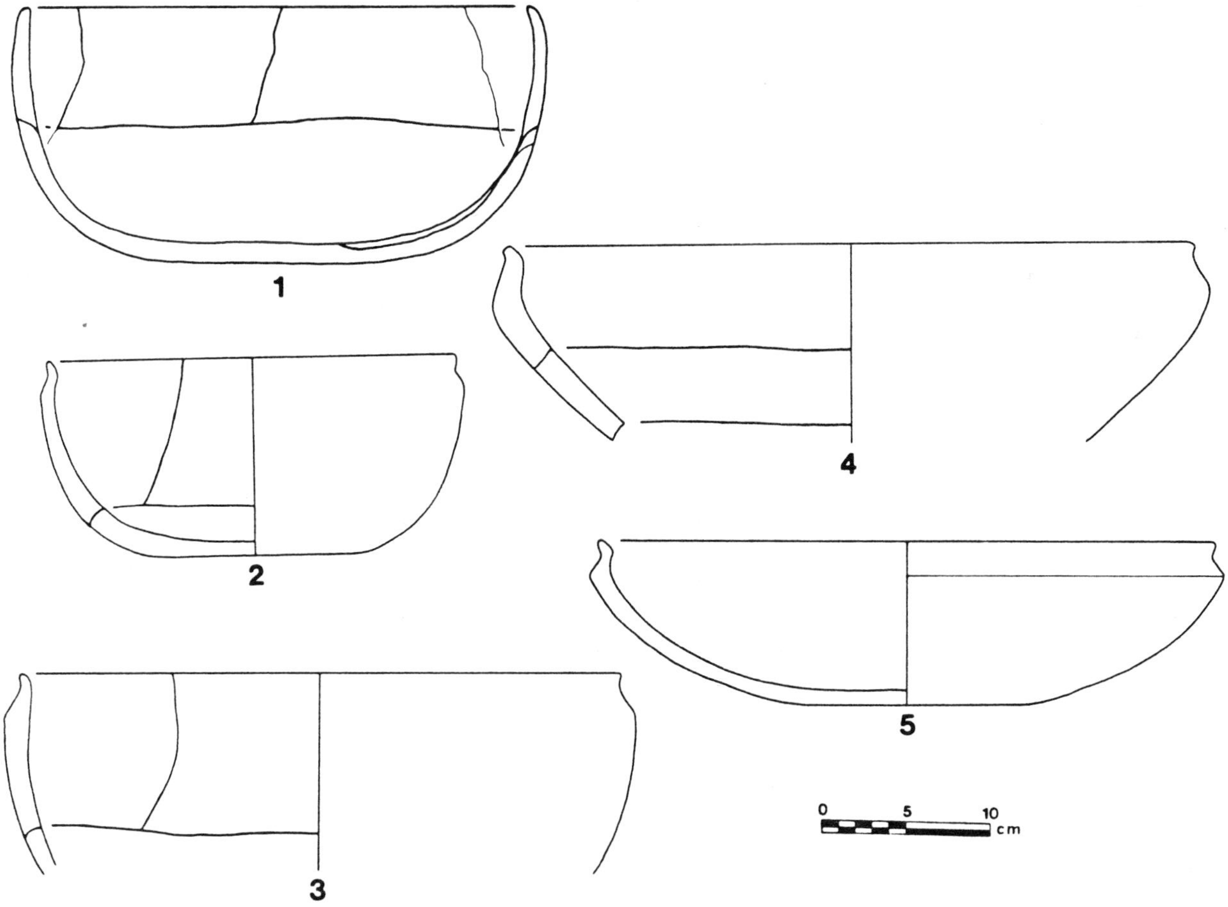

Figure 1. Forming methods used for Godin III:6 Grey-black (3-5) and Godin III:5-4 Red Slipped (1-2) bowls.

45

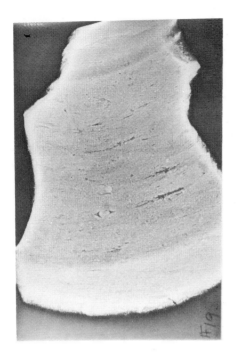
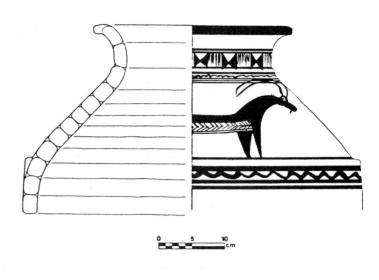

Figure 2. Xeroradiograph and schematic drawing of a large Godin III:4 coiled jar.

Figure 3. Construction of Godin III:4 Red Slipped jar.

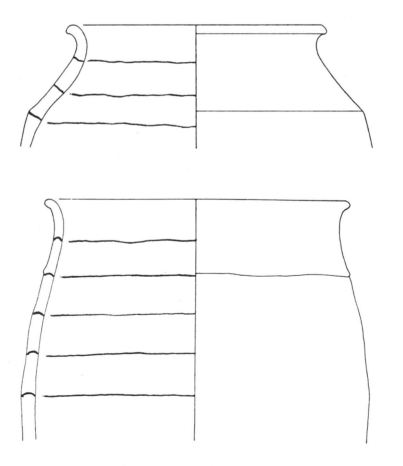

Figure 4. Construction of Godin III:2 Buff Coarse jar.

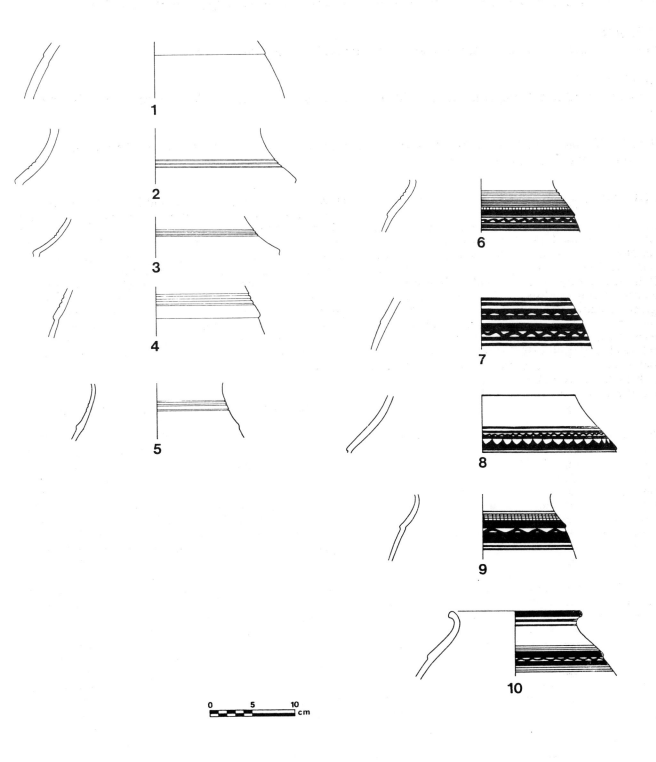

Figure 5. Godin III:2 Grey (1-5) and painted and incised (6-10) ridged jars.

8. Burnt Stones from Ancient Fires

F.T. HEDGCOCK
H. MARSHALL
Department of Physics, McGill University, 3600 University St., Montreal, P.Q., Canada H3A 2T8.

G.W. BERGER
Department of Physics, Simon Fraser University, Burnaby, B.C. Canada V5A 1S6.

P.E.L. SMITH
Département d'Anthropologie, Université de Montréal, C.P. 6128, Succursale A, Montreal, P.Q. Canada. H3C 3J7.

ABSTRACT: *Thermoluminescence of limestone and visual inspection of chert confirms previous heating in neolithic sites and provides evidence for fireplaces.*

INTRODUCTION

Ganj Dareh Tepe is a small mound in the Zagros Mountains of western Iran. It has a sequence of five principal Neolithic occupations, and was abandoned in about 7000 B.C. The earliest occupation, Level E, represents a small human group without solid architecture; the subsistence economy was based on hunting and gathering, although some cultivated barley was present. The most characteristic features are at least thirty shallow basins dug into the virgin soil, some containing limestone cobbles and fragments of chert (Smith 1978, 1983). Such round or oval depressions have been uncovered at a number of Near Eastern sites of the Neolithic period. They frequently contain ashes and burnt stones, and occasional organic debris.

These basins have been called "fire-pits." Confirming that their contents have been subjected to the heat of fires would be a step towards determining their function. If the stones found in the pits were in place and heated in the ninth millennium B.C., the effects of this heating should be detectable. Thermoluminescence analysis has been used successfully to date pot-stones, fireplaces, and ovens (as reviewed by Wintle 1980) so it is reasonable to expect to see evidence for the heating of a stone at a known date.

The stones taken from in and near Ganj Dareh pits are of fairly hard limestone, mostly calcite itself, containing very little magnesium. There have been TL analyses of flowstones and stalagmitic calcite (e.g., Wintle 1978 and Debenham 1983) but few of heated limestones; Wintle (1974) reports a fine-grain analysis of a heated soft limestone, and Prescott (1982) describes analysis of calcrete ovenstones. Carbonates occur as chunks rather than as aggregates, and are thus difficult to crush; slices of calcite are difficult to produce (Wintle 1978), and, in general, cutting and drilling have been found to alter the natural TL signal from calcite (Wintle 1975 and Chapman and Walton 1982). The effects of spurious TL can be controlled for large grains (Wintle 1975), but may be more troublesome in measurements from fine grains (Wintle 1980). Prescott (1982) worked around the problems of studying calcite itself by recovering the crystalline silicate grains included in a carbonate matrix, but these may occur in such small numbers that hundreds of grams of carbonate sample would be required for useful TL measurements. Wintle

(1978) uncovered further difficulties in the dating of stalagmites and flowstones, stemming from the inhomogeneous distribution of uranium within the samples. In the present instance, such local variations are unlikely, but would be averaged by taking a bulk sample. Indeed, even the average uranium concentration need not be known precisely. Since we must only distinguish between limestones which are probably several million years old and similar limestones which may have been heated in the Holocene, we are faced only with discriminating between TL signals from ionization damage accumulated over millions of years and over thousands of years.

THERMOLUMINESCENCE MEASUREMENTS

Five stones were selected for analysis: three from positions directly over pits, laboratory sample log numbers 60, 62Ai, and 62B, one from the ground next to a pit, number 61L, and a hammerstone from a later occupation of the site, number 73. These stones were crushed to produce unstressed grains, as described elsewhere (Berger and Marshall 1984). Briefly, the rind of each stone was cut off with a carborundum blade and the fresh surfaces hand-lapped and acid-rinsed to remove the layer damaged by cutting, and cleaned pieces of hearthstone were shattered in a percussion mortar, the debris being sifted after each blow to collect all sub-millimetre grains and protect them from further damage. This sub-millimetre debris was then separated into size fractions, and the 2-11µ grains and 8-25µ grains rinsed with very dilute acetic acid. The fine grains were used for TL measurements of all samples, and measurements were made on some large-grain samples to check for alteration of the natural TL signal caused by the crushing; the signal emitted by the large grains would be less disturbed by any surface effects. Subsamples of the fine- and large-grain fractions were mounted on aluminum discs for TL analysis, the fine grains by settling from methanol suspensions, the coarse grains by sprinkling over lightly oiled discs.

The TL analyses were carried out using the fast photon counting equipment described by Wintle and Huntley (1980), with a low-pressure flow of purified argon through the sample chamber (Berger et al. 1982). The samples were heated at 5 deg s⁻¹, and the signal integrated over ten degree intervals. Since the thermoluminescent emission from calcites is in the yellow-green region, with a maximum at 550 nm (Medlin 1968; Debenham et al. 1982; and Chapman and Walton 1982), all samples were glowed under a filter with a transmission peak at 550 nm and a window of ~ 100 nm (Spectrocoat Monopass, Optics Technology Inc.). On some samples, measurements were also made in the blue region (Berger and Marshall 1984).

The equivalent dose for each sample was estimated by the additive dose technique (the adaptation to TL measurements of the method of standard additions), using a cobalt-60 gamma-cell as a radiation source. Where supralinearity was evident, the extrapolation was carried out from a quadratic curve. The fine-grain subsamples, weighing ~ 0.5 mg, can be assumed to be identical. The signals from the coarse-grain subsamples were weight-standardized, but the correction factors were not large, as it was possible to select subsamples which fell within a weight range of ± 10%. The peak at 260C was assumed to be thermally stable, and free from anomalous fading (Wintle 1978, or Debenham 1983).

The glow curves of these calcite samples show peaks at 260C and 340C; the signal intensity is very reproducible, and there is little evidence of spurious signal.

Figure 1 shows the additive-dose curves for two of the samples, and clearly illustrate the reproducibility of the signal. The equivalent doses derived from the additive - dose curves are given, for all the samples in the Table below.

It is clear from the accumulated results for samples 60 and 61L, considering the data from both peaks, both grain sizes, and both wavelengths, that the behaviour of the

large grains does not differ from that of the fine grains, and so we can deduce that none of the material suffered local or surface effects during the sample preparation.

The equivalent dose for samples 60 and 61L are consistent with the dose that could be expected since the occupation of the site; the stones contain very little thorium or potassium and about 3ppm uranium and, buried, would have received a total dose of a few Grays per thousand years. Samples 62Ai and 62B display equivalent doses almost one hundred times greater, as does the hammerstone, sample 73, suggesting that these stones have, over several million years, reached thermal equilibrium with their natural environment. It is also notable that the natural TL from these stones is much brighter. This suggests that, if the sensitivities of the several samples of calcite are similar, the first two stones record a much shorter history. In sum, both the intensity of the natural TL signals and the extrapolated values of the equivalent dose suggest that 60 and 61L have been heated and 62Ai and 62B have not, and as further evidence supporting this conclusion, the behaviour of 62Ai and 62B resembles that of sample 73, a stone from an environment which was assumed never to have been heated.

EVIDENCE FROM CHERT

Pieces of apparently heated chert are found among the debris in the supposed fire-pits. We set out to discover whether the change in the appearance of chert was dependent on the actual temperature of heating, and, if so, whether this dependance was so strong that a usefully narrow difference in temperatures could be observed by eye, without recourse to instrumental techniques of measurement. When this proved to be the case, we

Table 1.

Natural TL signals and ED values

Sample	size	wavelength (nm)	Natural TL at 260C $\left(\frac{photons}{degree}\right)$	Equivalent Dose (Gy) 260C	340C
60	fine	550	500	6	20
	coarse	550		10	10
	fine	425		23	10
61L	fine	550	400	16	10
	coarse	425		18	10
62Ai	fine	550	18 000	650	> 1 400
62B	fine	550	25 000	1 200	> 1 800
73	fine	550	130 000	560	> 830

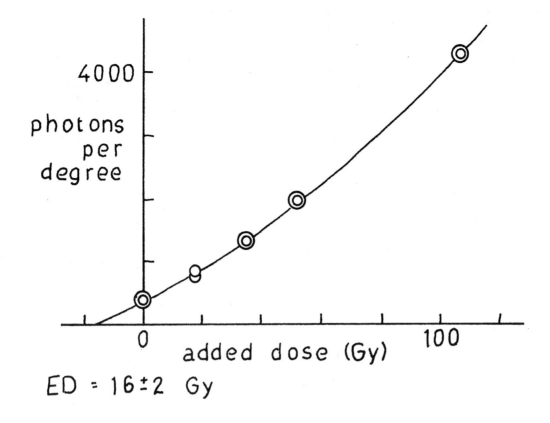

ED = 16±2 Gy

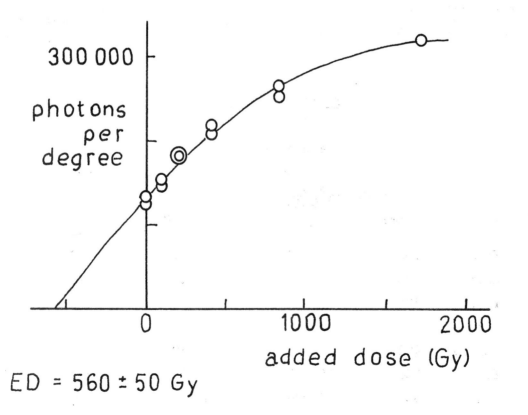

ED = 560 ± 50 Gy

Figure 1. Additive-dose curves for (top) sample 61L, found adjacent to a fire-pit, and (bottom) sample 73, a hammerstone.

estimated the temperature of the previous heating of two flints from a fire-pit, and of two flints from the later conflagration that destroyed the dwellings of Level D of the site (and preserved their ruins).

Two quite different cherts, a grey European flint and a dark reddish-brown chert from the surface of Ganj Dareh Tepe, were used to illustrate the effect of heat on flint. With two different raw cherts, we hoped to isolate effects from any reactions peculiar to one specimen. The two cherts were broken up, and pieces were heated in a tube furnace to temperatures between 300C and 1000C, under mildly oxidizing or reducing conditions, for 1 day (23-25 hr), to determine the effects of temperature and electrochemical environment. There was no visible difference between the results of oxidizing or reducing firings, for either type of flint, and subsequent firings were done under mildly oxidizing or neutral conditions.

The most visible change in flint on heating is a change of phase to an opaque ceramic, which took place at a temperature just over 500C for both of these samples. More subtle changes are also apparent for other firing temperatures. The grey flint was a lustrous, translucent, charcoal grey which gradually lost its luster and became murky as the firing temperature was raised from 300C to 500C. At 550C the translucent material was converted to an opaque state, resembling a fine grey porcelain. The grey became lighter at even higher temperatures, and the material became more brittle, spalled during the firing, and was more easily broken by handling. The flint from Ganj Dareh is a deep reddish-brown. The colour became thinner as the firing temperature was increased, and the material lost its luster to show a flat surface at 600C. The whitish cast of this ceramic became more and more evident at higher temperatures. A further change phase, giving the appearance of a glaze, takes place between 900C and 1000C, and at this point there does seem to be a difference between the reduced and the oxidized pieces, but such high temperatures were not of concern here, and this was not considered further.

The firing time of one day had been chosen for convenience, and some tests were then done to see whether the effects of heat were independent of firing time. Chunks of the grey flint were heated at 500C for three days, and were not discernably different from those heated at the same temperature for (the usual one day). Chips heated at 600C for only 2.5 hours were, however, slightly darker than those heated at the same temperature for 23 hours. From this we concluded that a firing time of several hours is necessary, but further prolonged heating has no additional effect.

These observations agree with those of Mandeville (1973) and Purdy (1971, 1974), Inter alia. In general, chert shows a decrease in density and in refractive index as it is heated, and drastic structural changes, between 400C and 600C and above 1000C. Free water is driven off at low temperatures, though there is no visible alteration, bound water is lost at 300 - 400C, and carbon dioxide, from the matrix, at about 600C. After heating to about 400C, the chert is stronger, and breaks in the manner of glass, a glossy vitreous scar is said to be characteristic of heated chert. Mandeville (1973) suggests the matrix fuses to form a more homogeneous glue to bind quartz cryptocrystals

more firmly; Purdy (1971) suggests the matrix acts as a flux to fuse a surface layer of the quartz grains, to the same effect. Changes in colour, like the colour of raw chert itself, are so dependent on the actual impurities, that no one colour can be characteristic of the heated material.

Since there are progressive changes in appearance of flint on heating (including cloudiness, loss of luster, loss of colour, and further whitening, or loss of chroma, after the phase transition), it should be possible to estimate the temperature of a previous firing by heating the flint until a further change occurs, concluding that the original firing was to a lower temperature. Even if the effects are too subtle to be visible in the waxy mineral, an upper limit can be placed on the original temperature by determining the transition temperature; the same may be true for firings above the first phase transition temperature, but below the second.

The flints from the firepits were broken up and the pieces were heated to different temperatures to see if any change was observed. Sample 80.1 has a dark slate skin, but broken surfaces are close to the colour of strong cocoa. Pieces of this sample which have been heated to 300C and 350C look the same as the untreated piece, but a piece heated to 400C is slightly redder. This suggests that the sample had previously been heated to a temperature exceeding 350C, but not to 400C. Similarly, a piece of sample 80.2 which was heated to 300C is the same dark-reddish brown of the original sample, but a sample heated to 350C is slightly lighter, and one heated to 400C is very much redder, suggesting this sample was previously heated to a temperature between 300C and 350C. Together, these suggest the available temperature within a fire built in the pit was about 350C. If the cherts were exposed only briefly to heat in the pit, the actual temperature could have been somewhat higher than the temperature estimated here from the effects of 23-hour firings, but such a brief heating seems unlikely.

The temperature of the fire could not be estimated from the thermoluminescence data alone, but this temperature of 350C is consistent with the complete zeroing of the TL signal represented in the two peaks of the glowcurves from the limestone cobbles, samples 60 and 61L.

Two flints from Level D, the hamlet destroyed by fire, were handled in the same way. Sample 78.1 is coarsely granular, it resembles red granite but is almost friable, and has clearly been heated beyond the phase transition. The fabric became greyer and more fragile on heating, and the results indicate that it has been heated previous to a temperature greater than 500C, but less than 700C. Sample 79.1 is flat orange-beige with grey mottling. Chips heated to 500C and 600C are not visibly different, but a piece heated to 700C is slightly pinker, and a piece heated to 900C is decidedly pink, implying that it was heated to about 700C. Together, these samples suggest the temperature reached almost 700C in at least two places during the conflagration, a temperature much hotter than that in controlled fires.

CONCLUSIONS

With careful sample preparation, even hard limestones can yield reliable and reproducible thermoluminescent data.

The changes in chert on heating are visible, and differences in temperature of 50 or 100 degrees can be noted. Destructive analysis of chert samples can yield an estimate of the temperature to which they have been heated.

Examination of limestone cobbles and chert fragments from the fire-pits of Ganj Dareh indicates the stones were indeed heated; the inferred temperature of 350C is reasonable for a domestic Neolithic fire.

ACKNOWLEDGEMENT

We are grateful to Professor David Huntley for his generous offer of access to the facilities of his laboratory at Simon Fraser University, and for his ready advice.

REFERENCES

Berger, G.W., T.A. Brown, D.J. Huntley, and A.G. Wintle, 5 spurious tidbits, Ancient TL, 18 (1982): 7-10.

Berger, G.W., and H Marshall, The TL behaviour of some limestone rocks, Ancient TL, 2 (1984): 1-6.

Chapman, G.N. and A.J. Walton, Spectral studies of the light emitted on cutting minerals with a diamond saw, PACT (Journal of the European Study Group on Physical, Chemical, and Mathematical Techniques Applied to Archeology), 6 (1982): 533-538.

Debenham, N.C., Reliability of thermoluminescence dating of stalagmitic calcite, Nature, 304 (1983): 154-156.

H.S.T. Driver, and A.J. Walton, Anomalies in the TL of young calcites, PACT, 6 (1982): 555-562.

Mandeville, M.D. A consideration of the thermal pretreatment of chert, Plains Anthropologist, 18 (1973): 177-202.

Medlin, W.L., The nature of traps and emission centres in thermoluminescent rock minerals, in Thermoluminescence of Geological Materials, D.J. McDougall (ed.), Academic Press, New York (1968).

Prescott, J.R., TL dating of calcrete ovenstones, Ancient TL, 17 (1982): 7-8.

Purdy, B.A., and H.K. Brooks, Thermal alteration of silica minerals: an archaeological approach, Science, 173 (1971): 322-325.

Purdy, B.A., Investigations concerning the thermal alteration of silical minerals: an archaeological approach, Tebiwa, 17 (1974): 37-66.

Smith, P.E.L., An interim report on Ganj Dareh Tepe, Iran, American J. Arch., 82 (1978): 538-540.

Smith, P.E.L., Ganj Dareh: an early Neolithic site in Iran, Archiv für Orient forschung, XXIX (1983): 300-302.

Wintle, A.G., Factors determining the thermoluminescence of chronologically significant materials. D. Phil. thesis, University of Oxford, Linacre College, (1974).

Wintle, A.G. , Effects of sample preparation on the thermoluminescence characteristics of calcite, Modern Geology, 5 (1987): 165-167.

Wintle, A.G., A thermoluminescence dating study of some Quaternary calcite: potential and problems, Can. J. Earth Sci. 15 (1978): 1977-1986.

Wintle, A.G., Thermoluminescence dating: A review of recent applications to non-pottery materials, Archaeometry, 22 (1980): 113-122.

Wintle, A.G and D.J.H. Huntley, Thermoluminescence dating of ocean sediments, Can. J. Earth Sci. 17 (1980): 348-360.

9. Developments in Accelerator Mass Spectrometry (AMS) at the IsoTrace Laboratory

W.E. KIESER, R.P. BEUKENS, R.G. CRESSWELL, L.R. KILIUS, A.E. LITHERLAND and J.C. RUCKLIDGE
IsoTrace Laboratory, University of Toronto, 60 St. George Street, Toronto, Canada M5S 1A7.

ABSTRACT: *Developments in Radiocarbon AMS with respect to the range of analysed materials, minimum sample size and precision of measurement are reported; the extension of AMS to other chronometers is discussed.*

INTRODUCTION

On examining the radiocarbon analysis statistics for the third year of operation of the IsoTrace Laboratory, improvements can be noted in three areas: a) an extension of the range of sample materials from which sufficient carbon can be extracted to perform a measurement, b) a decrease in the minimum amount of various sample materials required for a successful analysis, while avoiding the introduction of contamination during the chemical preparation and c) an increase in the output of the spectrometer ion source, which yields higher precision for a per unit analysis time.

In addition to radiocarbon analysis, it has been the mission of IsoTrace since its inception to explore the feasibility of AMS analysis of other rare isotopes and elements, an endeavour which has largely been directed by requests from potential users. The need in the earth science community to analyze radioiodine and the platinum group elements has lead to the construction of a new post-accelerator analysis section for the spectrometer, suitable for a wide range of heavy element analysis. Among these elements is included thorium-230 with a half life of 75,000 years. This isotope may prove to be a useful chronometer for the dating of objects of interest to archaeologists and anthropologists.

RANGE OF RADIOCARBON SAMPLE MATERIALS

Table 1 shows the type of materials analyzed during the 1987-88 fiscal year (May 1 to April 30). While shell, wood and charcoal continue to be the most popular materials, the increasing percentage of samples submitted as CO_2 gas is indicative of an emerging capability on the part of submitters to perform the first stages of the chemical pre-treatment themselves, and thus save expenses and decrease the turn-around time. (Most of the waiting time in the IsoTrace queue is due to variabilities and difficulties in the first stage of preparation, particularly in samples such as sediment or bone.)

The analysis of small samples of earthenware artifacts has been shown to be feasible wherever sufficient organic temper was present in the artifact to yield an analyzable quantity of carbon. The inorganic fraction is dissolved in a 54% HF solution over a period varying from 2 days to 2 weeks, following which a standard acid-alkali treatment is used on the residue. From an abandoned Neolithic village

Table 1. Samples analyzed, arranged by materials submitted 1987-88 fiscal year.

Material	Number	Percent
Shell	151	33.3
Wood	71	15.6
CO_2 - Atmosphere, Hydrology	55	12.1
CO_2 - Meteorites	49	10.8
Charcoal	41	9.0
Peat, Soil or Sediment	33	7.3
Bone (Collagen)	15	3.3
Carbonates (from groundwater)	14	3.1
Earthenware (pottery, mud bricks)	11	2.4
CO_2 (testing of extraction from iron)	7	1.6
Shell Protein (periostracum)	5	1.1
CO_2 (testing of extraction from zeolite)	2	0.4
	==	
	454	

in Yugoslavia, three mud brick samples tempered with straw required an average of 135 g of brick to yield 5 mg of carbon in the form of CO_2, although the actual requirements ranged from 5 to 350 g, indicating considerable inhomogeneity in the brick. In an attempt to correlate the ages obtained from a suite of seven Japanese pots with cultigens associated with them, the density of recoverable carbon was higher but the inhomogeneity was almost as large: for an average of 127 mg of pottery required to yield 5 mg of carbon, the actual requirements ranged from 33 to 250 mg. The actual sample sizes in both these cases have been normalized to a 5 mg carbon yield for the purpose of comparison; however there is no correlation between the smaller actual size and lower yield, so there is no indication of a lower efficiency for the extraction process for smaller samples.

The further analysis of iron artifacts, reported last year [1], is proceeding now that the origin of a troublesome contamination, at a level of 25,000 BP as measured in low carbon steel (which should have an infinite age as coke is used in the iron production) has been found. This required an investigation of all the new materials used in preparation procedure one at a time; the contamination was found in a cylinder of medical grade oxygen.

The presence of limestone near a site in which shells were recovered makes interpretation of their analysis problematic. An alternative shell-related material which can be analyzed is the periostracum, or protein sheath covering the shell. Aside from the fact that the very presence of this physically rather fragile material is indicative that the shell has not experienced significant movement and is thus most likely to be indigenous to the site in which it was found, the protein material is not affected by the presence of transient carbonates after its growth period. While this is not a new material for earth scientists, it may be of use for archaeological investigation as shown by the three samples analyzed for the Joint Physics and Archaeology course at the University of Toronto.

MINIMUM SAMPLE SIZE

The quantity of sample which we would like to receive, if possible, is indicated in Table 2, along with the smallest samples which we have so far successfully analyzed. The lack of an entry in this latter column simply means that no

Table 2. sample size requirements.

submitters have so far wished to attempt the analysis of a sample significantly smaller than the preferred size. These "smallest" sample sizes themselves do not necessarily represent a fundamental limit, but are largely artifacts of the design of our CO_2 processing equipment to work with 18 mg of CO_2 (i.e., 5 mg of carbon). Design work on smaller system will begin this summer, but when it is available tests on the pre-CO_2 stages with smaller amounts will have to be carried out to ensure the absence of contamination.

The availability of smaller sample analyses will change the way in which the archaeologist selects samples at the site. A paper presented in the Memorial Session at the beginning of this conference [2], aside from indicating clearly that sample selection must include detailed consideration of the environment, shows the efficacy of analyzing samples that otherwise might be rejected, for example, a single pine needle. Another type of sample which might be overlooked is a single seed. Both of these small samples give sufficient carbon for analysis and appear to be well isolated from the environmental contamination through their post depositional history.

The absence of any weights in Table 1 for bone is an indication of the extreme variability in the preservation of collagen in bones. This problem exists because preservation depends upon the environment to which the bone was subjected, which can often be largely unknown. The extraction of collagen from bone by acid and alkali extraction [3] has been the focus of much of our development effort in sample preparation. The purchase of a high speed centrifuge in early 1987 to reduce the preparation time required, (and the potential for atmospheric CO_2 contamination) during the various extraction phases has allowed us to increase the efficiency of collagen recovery and this year's purchase of a freeze dryer will reduce the time the sample spends at an elevated temperature during drying, another possible source of contamination.

MEASUREMENT PRECISION

The precision obtained for all the samples measured in the 1987 calendar year is plotted as a function of sample age in Figure 1. The precision is calculated from the ^{14}C counting errors and the ^{12}C and ^{13}C current measurement errors for both the sample and the associated standards [4]. Seven targets (machine ready samples) two of which are

Material	Preferred Sample Weight (mg)		Smallest Successfully Analysed Weight (mg)	
CO_2	18	(9 ml STP)	2	(1 ml STP)
Wood	25			
Seeds	25		7	
Charcoal	20		1.5	
Shell	180		18	
Carbonate	100			
Bone		as much as possible		

standards (NBS Oxalic acid I), are loaded into the ion source for each 9 hour analysis period; thus each target is analyzed for approximately 75 minutes. The solid curve in Figure 1 indicates the results expected for a "normal" precision analysis in which two targets for each sample are analyzed on different occasions. Higher precision can be obtained simply by analyzing more targets and many of the points significantly below the line represent four target analyses. The points substantially above the line represent samples for which insufficient material was submitted, usually less than 30% of the preferred sample weight (Table 2). A recent improvement in which the target size for such small samples is reduced from 3 mm to 2 mm diameter and the caesium primary beam current is reduced to prevent premature destruction of the thin carbon layer has improved the precision which can be obtained in these cases.

For normal targets, increasing the carbon ion current from the source can, for the fixed analysis time described above, increase the precision obtained. In the past year we have been testing the doubling of the ion source current from 5 to 10 μa. However further testing will be required to ensure that the fractionation changes resulting from the more rapid changes in target properties and geometry [5] does not cancel any gain in precision. We continue to find that the measurement of all three isotopes improves the quality of the radiocarbon dates.

HEAVY ELEMENT ANALYSIS EQUIPMENT

The need to analyse ^{129}I in order to trace groundwater flow, especially in the regions around prospective nuclear waste storage sites, and requests from economic geologists for a simple method for detecting the presence of, and even

for assaying platinum group elements in natural ore material, have long supported efforts to analyse heavier elements at IsoTrace. The magnets on the post-accelerator section used for ^{14}C do not have sufficient bending power to analyse elements much over mass 27 in an efficient manner, although a scheme using a foil after the accelerator to change the heavy ions to a higher charge state so that the ions have less rigidity, was tested successfully for platinum isotopes [6]. However, the installation of the extra equipment for this procedure interfered with normal ^{14}C analysis and thus did not prove practical as a routine analytical tool. A separate analysis line, built around a 30 year old 90° magnet was then assembled, and early in 1987 was used to demonstrate detection limits below 0.1 parts per trillion (1 part in 10^{+13}) for ^{129}I [7].

Even as this demonstration was taking place, negotiations were being completed with Atomic Energy of Canada (Chalk River) for a long term loan of an unused analyzing magnet with 10 times the bending power of the older magnet. This 16 ton magnet arrived in the laboratory in late summer and was installed in early 1988. However, one of the electrical coils had been damaged in storage and leaked water profusely and so another delay was encountered while funds to repair the coil were sought. Yale University came to the rescue with the loan of an identical pair of coils which were installed at the end of April. Other analysis elements and the connecting vacuum lines are now being put in place and a repeat of the ^{129}I test is scheduled for early June.

Just as in the post-accelerator section, sharing of the pre-accelerator section with ^{14}C analysis will probably cause a loss in efficiency. Work has begun on the construction of second ion source, beams from which can be switched into the inflection magnet using a rotatable

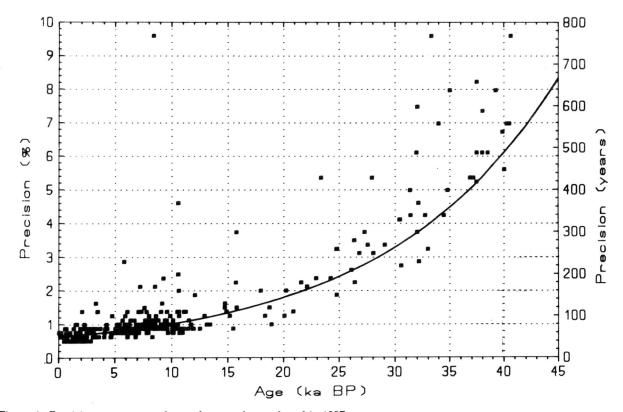

Figure 1. Precision versus sample age for samples analyzed in 1987.

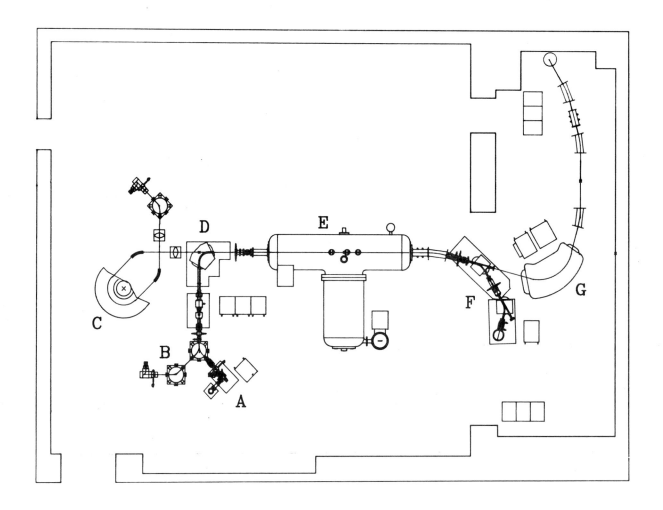

Figure 2. Configuration of the IsoTrace AMS system with the heavy ion equipment in place. A is the 14C ion source, B the new heavy ion source, C the Oxford inflection magnet, D the existing inflection magnet, E the accelerator, F the 14C analysis line, and G the Chalk River magnet.

electric analyzer. In the longer term plans, we have also received a 13 ton inflection magnet from Oxford University, which is far more suitable for heavy ions than the one currently used for 14C. Figure 2 shows a possible configuration of the system after this magnet is installed.

THE THORIUM-230 CHRONOMETER

Even at the first stage of completion of the heavy ion system, with only the Chalk River magnet and associated analysis systems installed, the development of analytical procedures for many other elements, one of which will include thorium, will be possible. Recent work by G. Wasserburg and his collaborators [8] has shown that by using conventional mass spectrometric techniques, samples of coral can be dated to a significantly better precision by using ^{230}Th than by using ^{14}C in the age range from 50 to 50,000 BP, and with a half life of 75,000 years, measurements on corals up to 500,000 years old can be made. The use of this isotope has also been suggested by H. Schwarcz for dating sites in which artifacts are embedded in calcium carbonate layers which have been deposited from an aqueous carbonate solution [9].

The use of this isotope in a more general range of archaeological materials will require further study of the mechanism by which ^{230}Th and its progenitor ^{238}U enter each material form the environment. However, unlike the radiocarbon case, where one is dependent upon a constant production of ^{14}C by cosmic radiation, and an even distribution throughout the biosphere, ^{230}Th is produced at one of the stages in the decay of ^{238}U which is widely distributed in the earth's crust [10]. Another isotope of uranium, ^{235}U is also present at a level of 0.72% of the abundance of ^{238}U. This decays by alpha and beta emission to ^{231}Pa which has a half life of 32,800 years. Since the uranium parents are soluble, and the thorium and protactinium are insoluble, both decay chains behave in a similar fashion in the environment and so the ^{235}U -> ^{231}Pa chain can be used as a check on ^{230}Th measurements. For typical abundance levels of uranium in a sample (~ 3 parts per million) the equilibrium levels of ^{230}Th and ^{238}Pa are approximately 42 and 0.84 times the concentration of ^{14}C in modern carbon. Such concentration levels should be well within the capability of the new heavy element analysis system, thus affording the opportunity for detailed studies of the distribution mechanisms of these chronometers in archaeological materials.

ACKNOWLEDGEMENTS

Research work reported in this paper has been supported by the Natural Sciences and Engineering Research Council (NSERC) of Canada, Energy, Mines and Resource Canada and the University of Toronto. The operation of the accelerator mass spectrometer is also partially funded by NSERC Infrastructure grant, and partially by the many sample submitters who have paid for radiocarbon analyses at IsoTrace. One of us (WEK) would like to thank Mr. L. Pavlish for helpful discussions about this manuscript.

REFERENCES

1. Cresswell, R. (1987). Iron Comes of Age, in Program Abstracts, Society for American Archaeologists 52nd Annual Meeting, p. 62 and MSc Thesis, University of Toronto.

2. MacDonald, G.M. (1988). New Insights on the Chronology of the Western Canadian 'Ice-Free' Corridor, this conference, session M2 and MacDonald, G.M., Beukens, R.P., Kieser, W.E. and Vitt, D.H. (1987) Comparative Dating of Terrestrial Plant Macrofossils and Aquatic Moss from the 'Ice-Free Corridor' of Western Canada, Geology vol 15 p.837.

3. Gurfinkel, D.M. (1985). Carbon 14 Sample Preparation, in 1984 Annual Report, IsoTrace Laboratory p. 5.

4. Beukens, R.P., Gurfinkel, D.M. and Lee, H.W. (1986). Progress at the IsoTrace Radiocarbon Facility, Radiocarbon vol 28 p. 229.

5. Nadeau, M.J., Kieser, W.E., Beukens, R.P. and Litherland, A.E. (1987). Quantum Mechanical Effects on Sputter Source Isotope Fractionation, Nuclear Instruments and Methods vol B29, p. 83

6. Kilius, L.R., Rucklidge, J.C., Wilson, G.C., Lee, H.W., Chang, K.H., Litherland, A.E., Kieser, W.E., Beukens, R.P. and Gorton, M.P. (1984). Charge Ratio Mass Spectrometry of Heavy Elements, Nuclear Instruments and Methods vol B29 p. 185

7. Kilius, L.R., Rucklidge, J.R., and Litherland, A.E. (1987). Accelerator Mass Spectrometry of ^{129}I at IsoTrace, Nuclear Instruments and Methods vol B29 p. 72

8. Edwards, R.L., Chen, J.H., Ku, T.L. and Wasserburg, G.J. (1987). Precise Timing of the Last Interglacial Period from Mass Spectrometric Determination of Thorium-230 in Corals, Science vol 236 p 1547

9. Schwarcz, H.P. (1980). Absolute Age Determination of Archaeological Sites by Uranium Series Dating of Travertines, Archaeometry vol 22 pp. 3-24

10. Ahrens, L.H. (1965). Distribution of the Elements in our Planet McGraw Hill, New York.

10. Radiocalcium (^{41}Ca) Dating: Recent Developments and Current Issues

R.E. TAYLOR and P. J. SLOTA, Jr.
Radiocarbon Laboratory, Department of Anthropology, Institute of Geophysics and Planetary Physics, University of California, Riverside, CA 92521. U.S.A.

W. HENNING
Gesellschaft für Schwerionenforschung, Darmstadt, Federal Republic of Germany.

W. KUTSCHERA
Physics Division, Argonne National Laboratory, Argonne, IL, 60439. U.S.A.

M. PAUL
Racah Institute of Physics, Hebrew University, Jerusalem, Israel.

ABSTRACT: *The general feasibility of employing radiocalcium (^{41}Ca, $t_{1/2}$ = ca. 10^5 years) to infer the age of bone and other calcium-bearing materials in the temporal range of up to ca. 1 million years is being evaluated.*

INTRODUCTION

The possible use of ^{41}Ca as a means of dating calcium-containing sample materials such as bone was first pointed out by Yamaguchi (1963). Raisbeck and Yiou (1979) provided a more detailed outline of a dating model for the radiocalcium method. With a half-life of about 10^5 years, ^{41}Ca could potentially be employed to infer age for calcium-containing samples over about the last 10^6 years. Like ^{14}C, ^{41}Ca is produced by cosmic-ray neutron secondaries. However, the bulk of the isotope is not produced in the atmosphere as is the case with ^{14}C. Rather, it is produced primarily in the upper meter of the soil profile by neutron capture on ^{40}Ca. The cosmic-ray produced ^{41}Ca is mixed with the other naturally occurring calcium isotopes into the surface soils and is taken up into the plant tissue. Radiocalcium would then be incorporated into bone mineral through ingestion of plant materials. Figure 1 summarizes the basis of the method (Taylor 1987).

A ^{41}Ca/Ca equilbrium ratio would be maintained in living organisms by exchange and metabolic processes. In contrast to ^{14}C dating, where the death of an animal or plant and the isolation of a sample from one of the carbon reservoirs constitutes the t=0 event, zero B.P. in the ^{41}Ca method would occur when a sample is permanently shielded from the effect of the cosmic-ray produced neutron irradiation. This could be accomplished either through burial or placement in a cave/rock shelter environment to a sufficient depth. The required depth would vary as a function of the surrounding soil or rock media. In addition, ^{41}Ca produced through neutrons generated by natural radioactivity (uranium and thorium) in the burial environment must be negligible. Age inferences would be based on the measurement of the residual ^{41}Ca with respect to the stable isotopes of Ca. The decay of ^{41}Ca to ^{41}K takes place by electron capture and the emission of a neutrino.

To be able to employ directly changes in the ^{41}Ca/Ca ratios to infer an age for calcium-containing samples with some degree of accuracy, a series of conditions would need to hold. They include: (i) that the initial concentration of cosmogenic ^{41}Ca in samples has remained essentially constant over the projected ^{41}Ca time scale (or appropriate corrections can be made for documented variations); (ii) that the ^{41}Ca/Ca ratio in a sample has not been altered except by ^{41}Ca decay since the sample was shielded from the effects of neutron irradiation, e.g., no postdepositional exchange/contamination of the in situ ^{41}Ca has occurred; (iii) that mixing of cosmogenic ^{41}Ca in the source of calcium for a sample has occurred over a relatively short period of time as compared to the ^{41}Ca half-life; (iv) that the half-life of ^{41}Ca is accurately known; and (v) that the natural levels of ^{41}Ca can be measured within reasonable levels of uncertainty (Taylor et al. n.d.).

It should be emphasized that the projected ^{41}Ca method carries with it potentially serious deficits that could easily put quite rigid constraints on the types of depositional environments that can be expected to give straightforward results. The fact that lithospheric rather than atmospheric production predominates raises the strong possibility that localized mixing and erosional effects may cause significant variations in initial ^{41}Ca/Ca ratios in many environments. In addition, since samples which have not been buried deeply enough will continue to be subject to ^{41}Ca formation from the cosmic-ray generated neutron secondaries, the burial histories of samples may affect ^{41}Ca concentrations. Localized variations in uranium concentrations would also perturb ^{41}Ca levels particularly in bone which can concentrate uranium over time. Also, one might reasonably expect post-depositional exchange of calcium isotopes in some samples through various effects. These and other factors suggest that samples from each site or locality might exhibit unique initial ^{41}Ca concentrations. An additional complicating issue is that the current precision with which the half-life of ^{41}Ca is known is estimated to be on the order of ± 30%.

MEASUREMENT OF RADIOCALCIUM AT NATURAL LEVELS

To develop a practical method of employing ^{41}Ca concentrations in calcium-containing samples to infer age and to determine the degree of general applicability, a series of studies must be undertaken that, in broad outline, would parallel the initial set of experiments which established the utility and accuracy of the ^{14}C method. All of the experiments which would be needed to demonstrate the general usefulness of the ^{41}Ca method would require the existence of a practical and effective means of measuring natural ^{41}Ca in terrestrial samples.

Since 1980, several groups have examined various approaches to the measurement of ^{41}Ca at natural concentrations. Initial experiments have been summarized in Taylor et al. (n. d.). The first direct measurement of the ^{41}Ca terrestrial concentration in natural samples was accomplished at the Argonne National Laboratory using the Argonne Tandem Linac Accelerator System (ATLAS) following the pre-enrichment of the ^{41}Ca employing a Calutron isotope separator at the Oak Ridge National Laboratory (Helling et al. 1987). These experiments indicated that ^{41}Ca/Ca ratios down to about 6×10^{-14} can be unambiguously measured with this AMS system. Using pre-enriched samples with more than 2 orders of magnitude enrichment, ^{41}Ca/Ca ratios below this value could be inferred down to about 5×10^{-16}.

Pre-enriched bone, surface and deeply-buried limestone samples exhibited ^{41}Ca/Ca ratios well above the limit observed with the background sample. The inferred ^{41}Ca/Ca ratio measured in modern bone was $2.0(\pm 0.5) \times 10^{14}$. This is somewhat higher than the secular equilibrium value [ca. 8×10^{-15}] estimated by Raisbeck and Yiou (1979). There was the initial expectation that the surface limestone would exhibit about the same ^{41}Ca/Ca ratio as the modern bone sample and the 11-metre limestone several orders of magnitude below this. However, both limestone samples, within error, showed about a factor of 2-3 lower ^{41}Ca concentrations. There are a number of possible explanations that would account for these results. For example, the high ^{41}Ca/Ca ratio in contemporary bone may indicate a contribution of anthropogenic ^{41}Ca originating from the nuclear weapons test era prior to 1963, similar to the effects observed for ^{36}Cl (Elmore et al. 1982; Bentley et al. 1982).

EXAMINATION OF DATING MODEL

The development of an effective method of measuring natural ^{41}Ca concentrations in terrestrial samples will permit a critical examination of the ^{41}Ca dating model. A series of interrelated issues needs to be addressed to determine the practical feasibility of the method. These issues would involve investigations relating to: (i) variations in ^{41}Ca/Ca values between modern samples and samples of "infinite age" ($>10^6$ years) as far as their cosmogenic ^{41}Ca content is concerned; (ii) variations in the ^{41}Ca content in contemporary samples exhibiting ideal preservation histories (i.e., no post-depositional exchange of calcium) from a variety of geographical areas; (iii) ^{41}Ca variability in samples which have been subjected to varying degrees of calcium exchange and; (iv) differences in the ^{41}Ca content of contemporary samples recovered from a range of biogeochemical environments (Taylor et al. n.d.).

Unfortunately, there appears to be little fractionation of Ca isotopes in the contemporary natural marine and terrestrial environments (Russell et al. 1978) as well as in fossil bone (D.A. Papanastassiou, California Institute of Technology, personal communication, 1987). Stable Ca isotope analysis thus will not be useful in identifying post-depositional isotopic exchange in fossil bone samples.

If variations in contemporary ^{41}Ca concentrations are found to be within a relatively narrow range, then one will be able to infer the age of samples without a detailed knowledge of the geochemicial status of the calcium source(s). The current expectation, however, is that there may be significant variations in contemporary ^{41}Ca content as well as varations in ^{41}Ca content as a result of diagenetic processes. Because of this, it may be necessary to treat each contextual situation (e.g., cave, rock shelter, sedimentary deposit) as a separate geochemical system. Because of the potential complexity of the factors which can influence the ^{41}Ca content of samples, we are currently operating under the assumption that the technique needs to be developed under circumstances where the accuracy of the ^{41}Ca age estimates can be rigorously gauged and tested.

Once the basic parameters of the method are defined, it will be necessary to examine a series of bone and other calcium-bearing samples from long stratified sequences that extend from upper layers datable by the ^{14}C method (either by decay or direct counting) down into older portions of the deposit currently off the ^{14}C scale. An evaluation of results from several localities with contrasting ground water conditions, types of soils, and other geochemical environments would be required to permit critical judgments to be made of the general applicability of the method.

CURRENT STUDIES

Currently, the most important issue in advancing the radiocalcium method is the developing of the routine ability to measure ^{41}Ca/Ca ratios at natural terrestrial concentrations without pre-enrichment. This primarily involves the improvement of the overall detection efficiency. The major limitation has been the relatively low yield of negative ions from the Cs-beam sputter source.

Encouraging results have been reported by the University of Pennsylvania group (Middleton 1986; Sharma and Middleton 1977) who observed CaH_3^- currents from freshly prepared CaH_2 materials which were one to two orders of magnitude higher than previously obtained. Very recently, AMS groups at both Argonne and the University of Pennsylvania (Fink et al. 1988) have succeeded in measuring ^{41}Ca/Ca ratios in bone and other calcium-bearing materials without pre-enrichment. At Argonne, we have very preliminary results on three ^{14}C-dated bone specimens from tar pit environments (reducing likelihood of diagenetic effects) indicating ^{41}Ca/Ca ratios in the low, middle and high 10^{-15} range for bone samples with ages of about 1600, 10,000 and >40,000 ^{14}C years. [The sample with an indicated ^{14}C age of >40,000 years has been assigned an age of > 1 million years on geologic criteria.] These results may indicate effects of ^{41}Ca build-up due to high uranium and thorium content. Additional ^{41}Ca/Ca measurements and a uranium analysis of these bone samples are currently underway.

SUMMARY

The ability to provide an independent temporal scale for the Middle and early Late Pleistocene comparable to that established for the Early Pleistocene by K/Ar values and for terminal Pleistocene with ^{14}C data, would clearly be of major significance in providing critical data that would impinge on several important debates currently underway among archaeologists and palaeo-anthropologists. Over the next half-decade, experiments now underway should determine the general feasibility and practicality of utilizing ^{41}Ca to provide a chronometric scale for this time period.

ACKNOWLEDGEMENTS

The research of the UCR Radiocarbon Laboratory is supported by a National Science Foundation grant BNS 8603478 (Anthropology Program) with additional funds supplied by UCR Chancellors Theodore L. Huller and Rosemary S.J. Schraer. Radiocalcium measurements are supported by the U.S. Department of Energy, Nuclear Physics Division, under contract W-31-109-ENG-38. We are indebted to D.A. Papanastassiou (California Institute of Technology) for his collaboration. This is contribution 88/21 of the Institute of Geophysics and Planetary Physics, University of California, Riverside.

REFERENCES

Bentley, H.W., F.M. Phillips, S.N. Davis, S. Gifford, D. Elmore, L.E. Tubbs and H.E. Gove (1982). Thermonuclear ^{36}C1 pulse in natural water. Nature, 300: 737-740.

Elmore, D., L.E. Tubbs, D. Newman, X.Z. Ma, R. Finkel, K. Nishiizumi, J. Beer, H. Oeschger, and M. Andree (1982). ^{36}C1 bomb pulse measured in a shallow ice core from Dye 3, Greenland. Nature, 300: 735-737.

Fink, D., Middleton, P. Sharma, and J. Klein, (1988). AMS measurements of ^{41}Ca in terrestrial samples without pre-enrichment. Abstract of paper presented at Goldschmidt Conference, May 11-13: 1988.

Henning, W., W.A. Bell, P.J. Billquist, B. Glagola, W. Kutschera, S. Liu, H.F. Lucas, M. Paul, K.E. Rehm and J.L. Yntema, (1987). Calcium-41 concentration in terestrial materials: prospects for dating of Pleistocene samples. Science, 236: 725-727.

Middleton, R., (1986). Highlights of ion source development at the University of Pennsylvania. Workshop on Techniques in Accelerator Mass Spectrometry, Oxford, June 30 - July 1, 1986, R.E.J. Hedges and E.T. Hall, Eds.: 82-89.

Raisbeck, G.M. and F. Yiou, (1979). Possible use of ^{41}Ca for radioactive dating. Nature, 277: 42-44.

Russell, W.A., D.A. Papanastassiou, and T.A. Tombrello (1978). Ca isotope fractionation on the Earth and other solar system material. Geochemica et Cosmochimica Acta, 42: 1075.

Sharma, p. and R. Middleton, (1987). Sample preparation and production of negative ions of calcium hydride for ^{41}Ca AMS. Nuclear Instruments and Methods in Physics Research, B29: 63-66

Taylor, R.E., (1987). Dating Techniques in archaeology and paleoanthropology, Analytical Chemistry, 59: 317A-331A.

Taylor, R.E., P.J. Slota, Jr., W. Henning, W. Kutschera and M. Paul, n.d. Radiocalcium (^{41}Ca) dating: potential applications in archaeology and palaeoanthropology. In Archaeological Chemistry IV, R.O. Allen, Ed., Washington, D.C.: American Chemical Society. In press.

Yamaguchi, Y., (1963). Possible use of Ca^{41} in nuclear dating. Progress of Theoretical Physics, 29: 567.

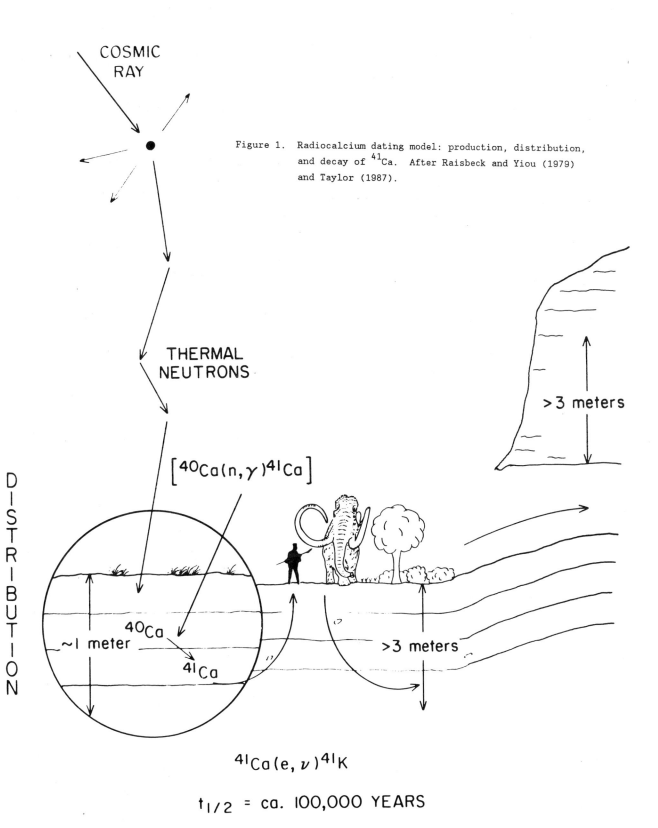

PRODUCTION

DISTRIBUTION

DECAY

COSMIC RAY

Figure 1. Radiocalcium dating model: production, distribution, and decay of ^{41}Ca. After Raisbeck and Yiou (1979) and Taylor (1987).

THERMAL NEUTRONS

$$\left[^{40}Ca(n,\gamma)^{41}Ca\right]$$

>3 meters

~1 meter

^{40}Ca

^{41}Ca

>3 meters

$$^{41}Ca(e,\nu)^{41}K$$

$$t_{1/2} = ca.\ 100,000\ YEARS$$

11. Relative Dating of Burials by Fluoride and Nitrogen Analysis

M. MARCHBANKS

Texas Archeological Research Laboratory, University of Texas at Austin, Balcones Research Center #5, 10100 Burnet Road, Austin, TX 78758. U.S.A.

ABSTRACT: *Fluoride and nitrogen analysis provide an inexpensive way to determine the interment sequence of burials at prehistoric cemeteries.*

INTRODUCTION

Traditionally, archaeologists have relied on stratigraphic and burial positions to try to estimate temporal placement of burials. Clusters of burials were assumed to have been interred during the same time period. Some temporal distinctions could be made, however, when it was clear that a more recent interment cross-cut an older one. Radiocarbon dating cannot be utilized because it is not discreet enough to show temporal distinctions.

Fluoride and nitrogen analysis can be utilized as an inexpensive and sensitive method for determining temporal distinctions between the burials and can generate a workable interment sequence.

There were several general questions addressed with the information provided by the fluoride and nitrogen analyses at most of the sites that were tested. First, was there a relationship between the stratigraphic depth and relative age of the burials, as indicated by the fluoride and nitrogen analyses? If the cemetery was utilized over an extended period of time, a deposition of debris and soil might occur, which would cover up the burials and result in the deeper burials being older interments than more shallow ones. If the cemetery was utilized over a short period of time, though, there might be little or no relationship between the depth and relative age and stratigraphic depth of burials within individual time periods or clusters (provided by the fluoride and nitrogen analysis). This, of course, depends on many cultural and environmental factors. Several factors include the geomorphology of the site (might enhance or prohibit the deposition of debris and soil), the cultural and soil deposits (might vary depending on what type of activities occurred at the site), and the nature of the culture. Different amounts and types of deposition would be expected in midden burials, than in an isolated hilltop cemetery.

Secondly, the results of the fluoride and nitrogen analysis were used to check for change in possible "burial patterns" and skeletal positions through time. The term "burial patterns" was defined as similar aspects between different burials that could include location, caches, and the position in which the burial was interred. This information was determined by checking for clusters of burials according to their relative age, their locations within the cemetery, and the stratigraphic level in which they were buried, then comparing any changes with associated features such as caches and other burial associations. This information can be used to infer culture changes over time and, perhaps, different cultural groups utilizing the cemetery. If there were specific relative age clusters in which specific burial patterns were being used, this information can potentially be used to link uncertain caches or features to the proper burial.

METHODOLOGICAL THEORY

The basis of the fluoride analysis is the replacement of the hydroxl ion (OH) in hydroxyapatite $[Ca_5 (OH) (PO_4)_3]$ by a fluoride ion (F^-) forming the compound fluroapatite $(Ca_5(F)(PO_4)_3)$ (Haddy and Hanson 1982). Fluoride is accumulated in the bone by ground water (containing fluoride) moving through the soil matrix and making contact with the bone. As such, the rate of the fluoride uptake is dependent on the local groundwater chemistry and many other environmental factors such as the type of soil, elevation, soil pH, and soil temperature.

Nitrogen is present within the bone protein. After death, the protein in the bone is hydrolyzed into peptides which then break down into their component amino acids (Ortner, VanEndt and Robinson 1971). The rate of protein degradation is varied by the local groundwater chemistry, soil temperature and pH. Therefore, as with the fluoride analysis, nitrogen analysis is very dependent on the environmental conditions in which the bone is buried.

Because the local microenvironments and/or groundwater chemistry change, the rates of nitrogen depletion and fluoride absorption are not constant and, as such, cannot be used as an absolute dating technique. They can be used for relative dating, however, because the older the bone is, the longer it has been exposed to the environmental conditions and different rates of depletion (nitrogen) and absorption (fluoride), resulting in the oldest interments having more fluoride and less nitrogen than the more recent ones until the bone reaches the saturation or depletion point.

EXPERIMENTAL METHODOLOGY

The basis for the fluoride methodology was the procedure described by Singer and Armstrong (1968). However, to overcome fluctuating electrometer readings several adaptions had to be made: the samples were mixed (1:1 mixture) with Total Ionic Strength Adjustment Buffer (TISAB) to prevent aluminum and iron interference; the pH of the sample was balanced by adding potassium salts, using bromomethyl blue as an indicator; and the sample was centrifuged before conducting electrometer measurements to reduce the number of undissolved particles in the sample that might cause a distortion of the millivolt potential.

The nitrogen analyses were conducted using the micro-Kjeldahl technique described by Ortner and Von Endt (1972). In this methodology, a sample of bone is digested in sulfuric acid converting all the nitrogen into ammonium ions. Nessler's reagent is added to the sample and combines with the ammonium ions to form a yellow complex. This is quantified with a spectrophotometer. To reduce the turbidity of the sample, EDTA was added, and then it was centrifuged.

To indicate that the fluoride methodology was accurate, fluoride analysis was conducted on a sample of fresh animal bone provided by the International Atomic Energy Agency (IAEA, 1982). This is the standard bone sample Number H-5 in which the levels of several elements have been calculated by several labs, and their values published. The IAEA bone had a mean calculated fluoride value (from two laboratories) of 451 ppm. This methodology calculated the fluoride content of the fresh bone as 433 ppm of fluoride, very close to the IAEA calculation and well within the 95% confidence level of 321-581 ppm of fluoride (IAEA 1982), indicating this procedure to be a viable, working method for determining the fluoride level in bone. Other checks for the consistency of the fluoride analysis included comparing the relative age of the burials as indicated by both the fluoride and nitrogen analyses.

BLUE BAYOU SITE

The Blue Bayou Site (41VT94) was a prehistoric cemetery on DuPont Chemical Co. property in Victoria County, Texas. The site was exposed after the topsoil was removed, by a heavy earth mover, from a sandy hillside for the construction of a new DuPont plant entrance.

It was impossible to determine any burial pit outline, due both to sandy soil (with clay lenses) and intrusive burials; therefore, each skeleton or portion of a skeleton was catalogued as a burial. The relationships between the burials and the interment sequence could not be determined from the stratigraphic evidence, such that fluoride and nitrogen analysis was conducted to chemically determine the interment sequence of the burials. It must be mentioned, however, that the Blue Bayou Site was only partially excavated and, as such, no statistical analysis can be justified, only general and probable trends noted.

This site provided an excellent opportunity to test the utility of the interpretation of the fluoride and nitrogen analysis as indicators of the burial interment sequence. Out of the 30 excavated burials, 24 had enough non-diagnostic bone present to conduct the analysis. Thirteen of the 24 tested burials were either above, below, or cross-cutting other burials, such that their relationships allowed for an interment sequence to be inferred. The interment sequence provided by the fluoride and nitrogen analyses (Figure 1) was compared to the inferred interment sequence indicating either agreement, or providing help in understanding the uncertain interment sequence between the burials. The interactions between the burial interments were explained by the fluoride and nitrogen analysis (Huebner 1988). On a larger time scale (300-600 plus years) the validity of the fluoride and nitrogen analyses was also verified by the radiocarbon dates. Although there is no space to discuss it in detail in this report, the average of the fluoride concentration in the bone, and the radiocarbon dates had almost a perfect relationship to each other (Marchbanks 1987).

In plotting the burial positions it became clear that different areas of the cemetery were used at different time periods (Figure 2). The more recent interments were concentrated at the southern part of the cemetery, while the older interments were mostly in the northern part. There were also clusters of burials that were separated enough in time, yet spatially close enough together, to indicate that the Indians may have been marking the graves with some kind of perishable material.

Although there is much more data concerning this site, it will not be included in this report. This site is currently being written up by Jeffrey Huebner.

COLHA, NORTHERN BELIZE

Four burials were uncovered beneath the Main Plaza at the Colha Site in Northern Belize (Anthony 1987). The burials are Middle Preclassic (Preclassic from 900 B.C. to A.D. 250), associated with Structure I, and predate the second construction phase. All four individuals occupied simple midden graves, buried almost in a straight line. The adult individuals, 54 and 63, were extended on their backs with their heads to the west. The young child, 57, and the adolescent, 59, however, were in a tightly-flexed sitting position, 57, and a semi-flexed position, respectively.

Both burial 54 and 59 had bowls placed over their heads. These bowls were from the Bolay Complex (Anthony 1987) one being a Consejo Red and the other a Ramgoat Red type. Both of these bowls had evidence of use wear indicated by slip erosion along the bases and rims.

Because the burials were spatially so close to each other, they were assumed to have been interred during a relatively short time. However, the fluoride and nitrogen analyses indicated that the two burials with the bowls over their heads (54 and 59) were interred significantly earlier than the other two burials (Figure 3). This could be an indication of burial pattern change, but there were only four burials in the midden. More studies need to be conducted to determine if this is a consistent pattern.

LOMA SANDIA SITE

The Loma Sandia Site (41LK28) was a prehistoric cemetery in Live Oak County in southern Texas, excavated by State Department of Highways and Public Transportation (SDHPT) archaeologists during 1977-1978. The cemetery was radiocarbon dated to ca. 850-600 B.C., and contained skeletal remains of between 110-191 individuals with numerous grave associations.

The fluoride and nitrogen analysis was conducted on 141 burial features at the site to provide relative dates. A detailed copy of the analysis, complete with statistical analysis, is being published in the site report (Taylor 1988). Francis Meskill utilized the relative dates of the burials provided by the fluoride and nitrogen analysis to look for patterns in the burial sequences and clusters (Taylor 1988).

Another application of the fluoride and nitrogen tests at Loma Sandia was comparing results from the burial features within the main cemetery to burials found by a backhoe trench cut outside the main cemetery. The area discovered by the backhoe was called Area Q and contained

Figure 1.

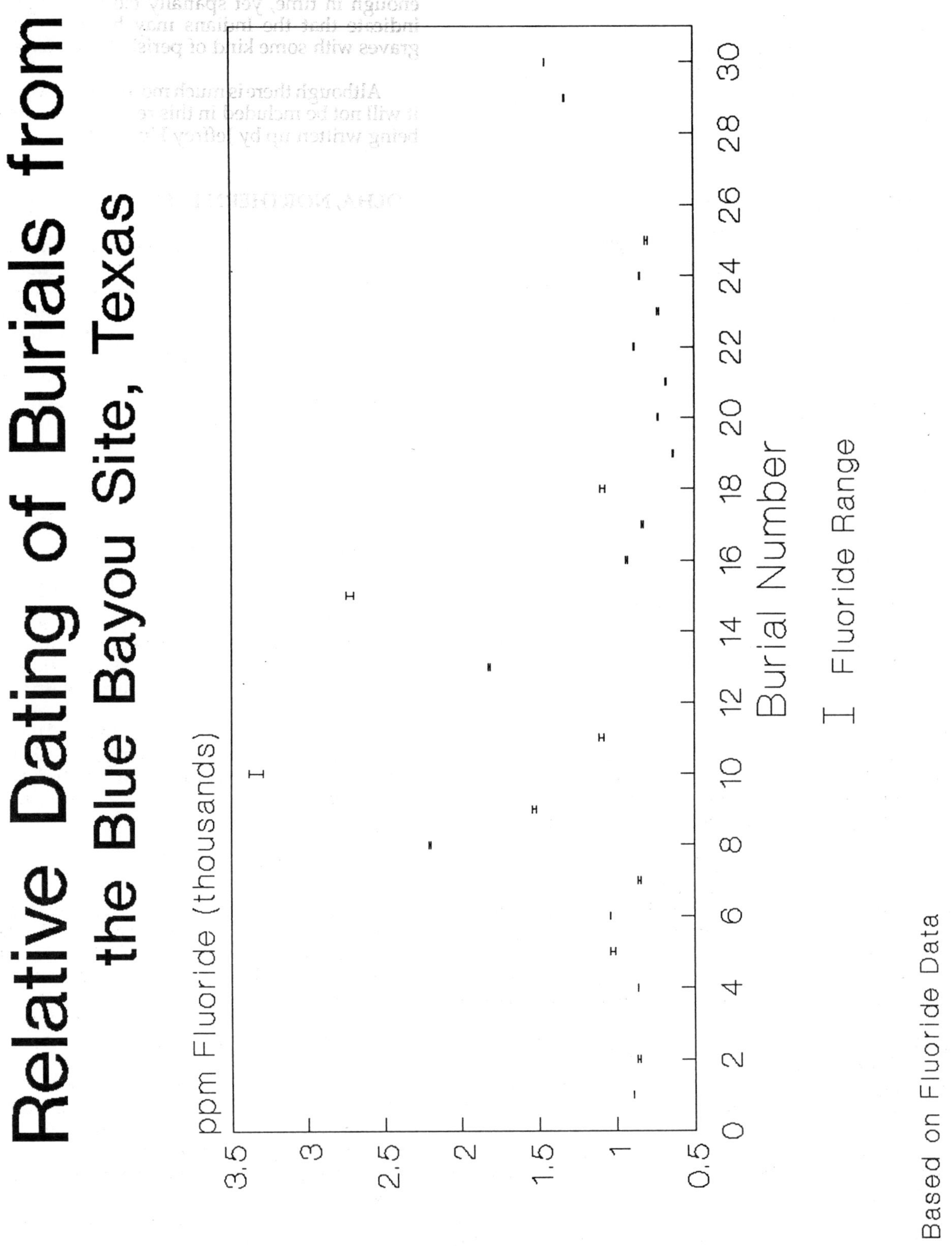

Relative Dating of Burials from the Blue Bayou Site, Texas

ppm Fluoride (thousands)

3.5

3

2.5

2

1.5

1

0.5

0   2   4   6   8   10   12   14   16   18   20   22   24   26   28   30

Burial Number

I Fluoride Range

Based on Fluoride Data

Figure 2.

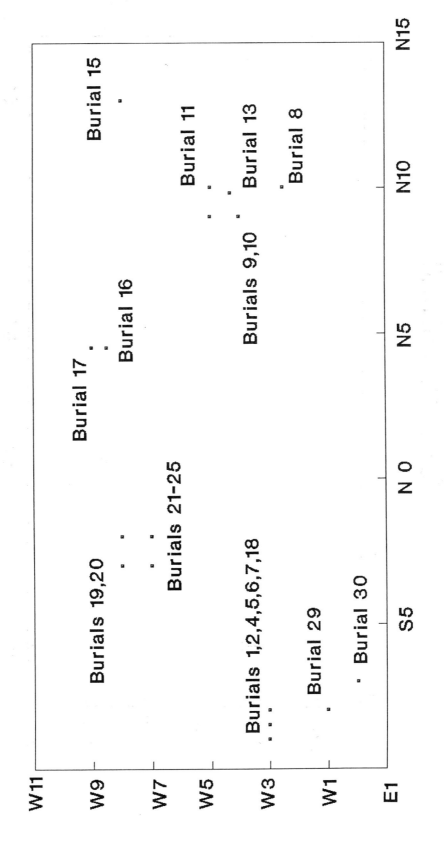

Blue Bayou Site
Burial Position and Number

Positions Based on Field Notes

Figure 3.

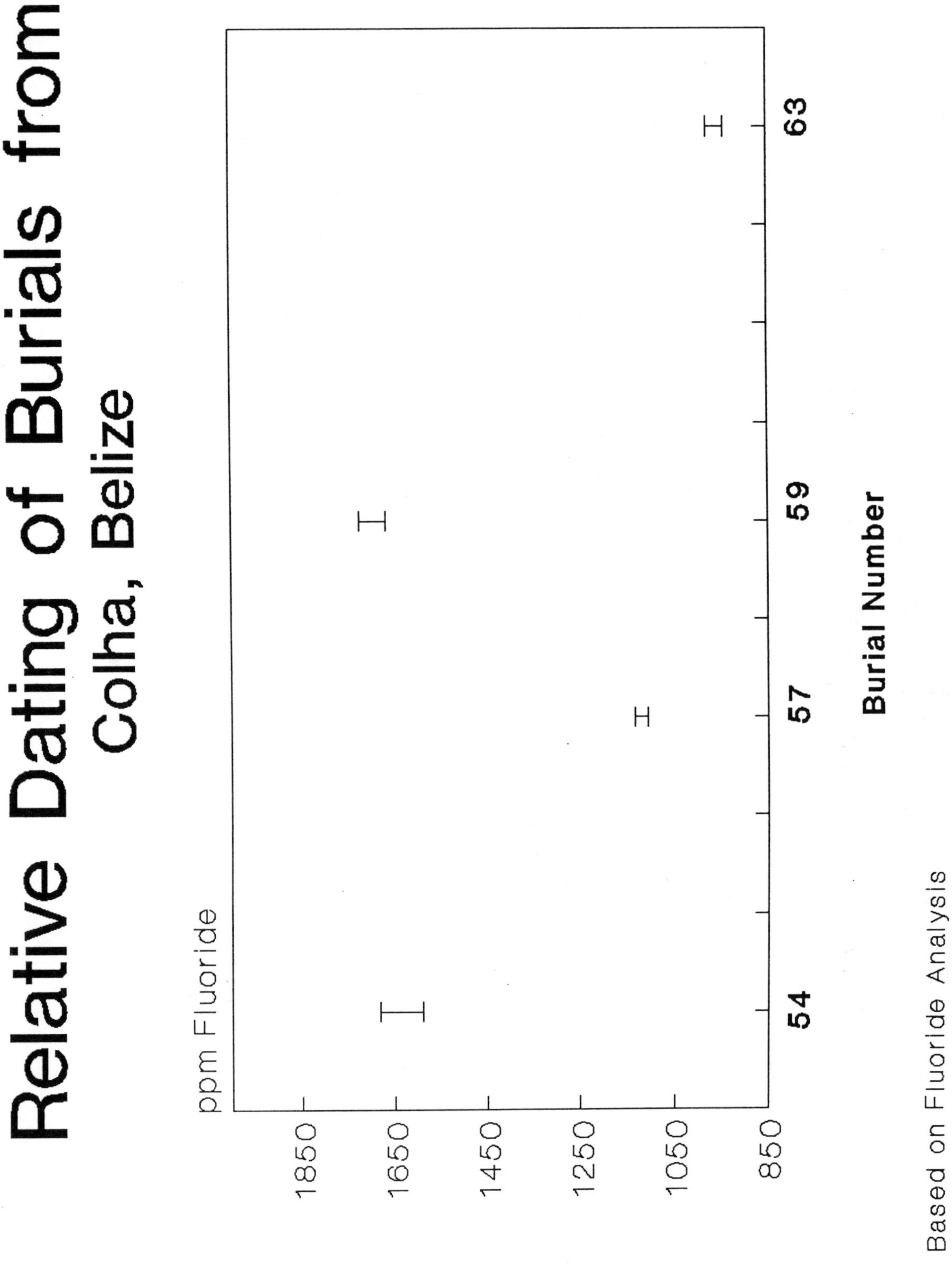

Relative Dating of Burials from
Colha, Belize

Based on Fluoride Analysis

Features 13 (F.13) and F.13-B. A Morhiss projectile point was found with a burial (F.13) in Area Q; Morhiss points were also with F.119 and F.200, caches within the main cemetery. Since the Morhiss point dates to the Middle Archaic (L. Highley, in Taylor 1988) and the radiocarbon dates indicate the cemetery dates to, roughly, 850 - 600 B.C. (late Middle Archaic) this implies that the burials from both Area A and Q were interred during the same time period. This data indicates that there could have been a continuation of the cemetery, between the main cemetery (Area A) and Area Q, which was not excavated.

REFERENCES

Anthony, D. S., (1987). An Analysis of the Preclassic Households Beneath the Main Plaza at Colha, Belize. Masters Thesis. On file at the University of Texas at Austin.

Haddy, A. and A. Hanson, (1982). Research Notes and Application Reports: Nitrogen and Fluorine Dating of Moundville Skeletal Samples. Archaeometry, 24 (1):37-44.

Huebner, J. (1988). The Archaeology of Blue Bayou Site: A Late Archaic/Late Prehistoric Cemetery Site in Victoria, Texas. Master Thesis. Manuscript in process. Will be on file at the University of Texas at San Antonio in Fall 1988.

International Atomic Energy Agency (1982). IAEA Animal Bone (H-5) Provisional Certificate of Analysis. Vienna, Austria.

Ortner, D.J., D.W. VonEndt, and M.S. Robinson (1972). American Antiquity, 37:514.

Parker, R.B., J.W. Murphy, and H. Toots (1974). Fluorine in Fossilized Bone and Tooth: Distribution Among Skeletal Tissues. Archaeometry, 16:98-109.

Singer, L., and W.D. Armstrong (1968). Determination of Fluoride with the Fluoride Electrode. Analytical Chemistry, 40(3): 613-614

Taylor, A.J. (1988). Archaeological Investigation at the Loma Sandia Site (41LK28): A Prehistoric Cemetery and Campsite in Live Oak County, Texas. Manuscript in progress. Center for Archaeology Research, University of Texas at San Antonio.

12. Archaeomagnetism as a Dating Method

M. KOVACHEVA

Geophysical Institute, BAS, 1113 Sofia, Bulgaria.

ABSTRACT: *Three examples for dating of archaeological sites by the archaeomagnetic method are discussed. Some requirements for applicability of the method for dating purposes are considered.*

INTRODUCTION

In the Proceedings of the 1986 International Symposium on Archaeometry the methodology of the archaeomagnetic studies in Bulgaria is given (Kovacheva in press). The important feature of our studies is that we deal with the three geomagnetic characteristics: declination (D), inclination (I) and intensity ratio F^A/F^D. The effectiveness of archaeomagnetic studies for dating purposes depends very much on the exactness of a previously obtained archaeomagnetic scale for the given geographical region. This scale must be elaborated on the basis of a great number of samples from each dated site and after averaging between the synchronous archaeological sites in the geographical region under consideration.

METHOD AND REFERENCE CURVES

As it was mentioned above we will not discuss the method used which is described in detail elsewhere. We will mention only that the elaborated reference curves (Kovacheva 1980) are still in use for dating purposes, Figure 1. They are in the continuous process of specification and filling up the gaps. We consider our scale more or less completed for the last 3000-4000 years. The newly examined collections from the Neolithic past will help us to specify this part as well. The results filling up the millennium around 3500 B.C. are shown in our previous paper (Kovacheva, in press).

DATING

In our long practice many datings have been done, some of them reported in previous symposia. We cannot say that an unambiguous answer could be reached in all cases. There are numerous causes of systematic character which can worsen the experimental results, but fortunately these causes influence the various geomagnetic elements in a different manner. In this way many successful datings and synchronizations have been appreciated by the archaeologists. We will discuss here three examples from our recent practice.

A small collection has been gathered from a medieval sanctuary. The question was to find out if it was from early medieval age or from the late medieval one. The three geomagnetic elements have been examined. Their values are shown in Table 1, given in the Appendix. The dating procedure is shown in Figure 2. Here only a part of our archaeomagnetic scale is taken (the last 2000 years). The obtained average values of the geomagnetic elements are written at the bottom of the graph. The intensity result is converted in terms of F/F_o and gives three possible solutions: 6, 9 and 12 c. A.D. They are seen in Figure 2: the three arrows obtained from the

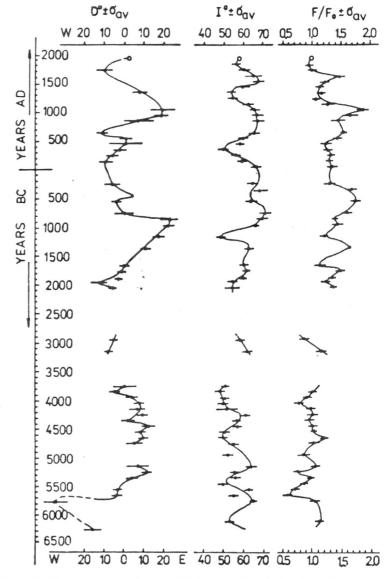

Figure 1. The curves of variation of D, I and ration F/F_o, where F_o is the present day geomagnetic intensity at the sampling place. The points are 100 years averages between synchronous archaeological sites. All data comes from Bulgaria.

intersection of the solid line (the intensity result) and the variation curve at the bottom. We take the declination result (see the middle variation curve in Figure 2), which brings us again to the 6 and 9 c.A.D. - the very beginning of them. At the same time it does not agree with the 12 c.A.D. Finally the inclination value of 57.7° resolves the ambiguity. It gives two possibilities, seen at the top of the Figure. They are again 6 and 12 c.A.D., but now 9 c.A.D. is rejected. Thus we consider that the appropriate dating is the first half of 6 c.A.D., as the three geomagnetic characteristics suggest.

Next, two Thracian sites from northeastern Bulgaria, which are not very far apart from each other will be considered. Let us call them Thracian site No 1 and Thracian site No 2. The two collections examined were big enough and many Thellier's experiments (Thellier et Thellier 1959) have been made, but their quality was not always as good as usual. This reflects the least square estimates σ of the individual results, given in Table 2 and Table 3 (see the Appendix). The technique for chemical cleaning (Roy and Park 1974; Sakai and Hirooka 1986) did not help us essentially. That is why we augmented the number of specimens studied. One of more or less successful results for the intensity ratio determination is shown in Figure 3. The Arrai diagram (straight line) in this case is the best fitted line between all experimental points from 20° to 550°C. The second horizontal axis is for the curves of demagnetization (solid line) and remagnetization (dashed line).

The dating procedure of Thracian site No 1 is demonstrated in Figure 4.

Again, a part of our archaeomagnetic scale is taken, covering the time period of interest. At the bottom of the figure the directional and intensity results are indicated. The numbers in the circles give the number of examined samples. These results are demonstrated on the graph by the vertical dashed lines.

The intensity ratio gives two solutions (dotted lines): 4 and 9 c.B.C. The inclination result shows even a triple (dashed lines) possibility: 3, 7 and 10 c.B.C. At the end we use the value of declination which definitely narrows the interval (see solid lines) between the very end of the 3 and 6 c.B.C. We consider the most probable age of this site to be 4 c.B.C.

In Figure 5, the Thracian site No 2 is considered. The archaeomagnetic results are also written at the bottom. The double age obtained from the intensity ratio value is the 4c. and the very beginning of the 9 c.B.C. (dotted lines). Fortunately, here the higher value of inclination shows a single solution: 8 c.B.C. (dashed line). The declination is considerably higher than those obtained from the previous site and brings the solution here to the almost maximum in the declination curve. This determines the dating as the second half of the 8 and first half of the 9 c.B.C. for the Thracian site No 2.

We would like to emphasize here, that if we have not had at our disposal the third geomagnetic element-declination, we could hardly distinguish the two Thracian sites, because the other two elements have very close values.

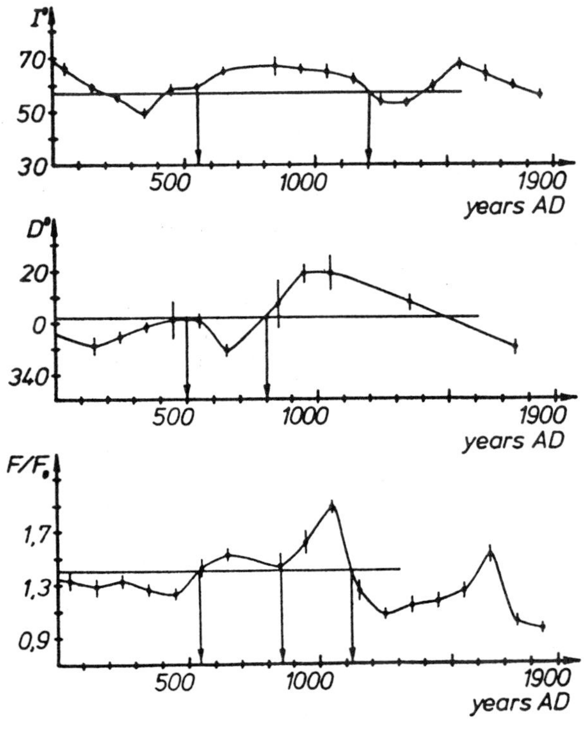

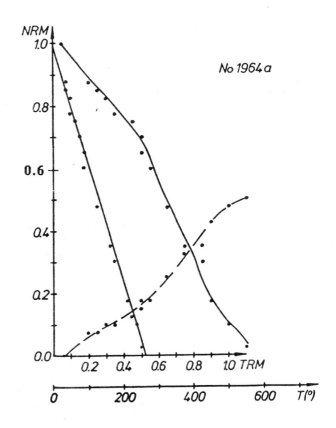

Figure 2. The dating procedure of the medieval sanctuary. The archaeomagnetic results are: I=57.7°, D=1.5°, F/F° =1.408.

Figure 3. The Thelliers' experiment.

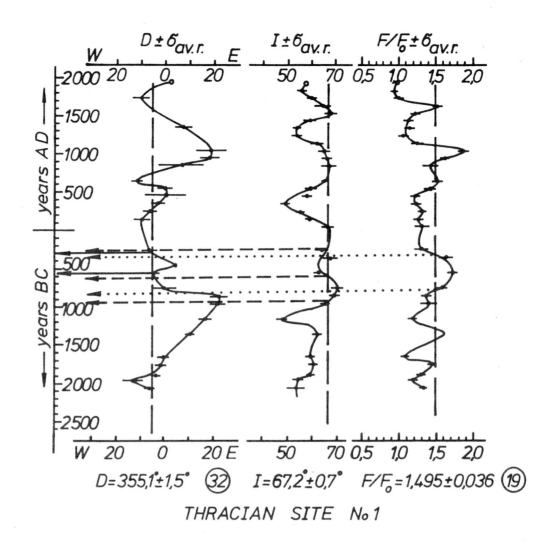

Figure 4. The dating procedure of Thracian site No 1.

CONCLUSIONS

We have always underlined the necessity of the three geomagnetic elements for dating purposes. It is mainly caused by the complex character of variation in geomagnetic elements. The different quasiperiods of changes in their trend help the unambiguity in dating.

On the other hand we were very pleased to obtain this high value of declination, confirming the external value in the declination curve, which is also observed in similar studies in Ukraine and has always been a striking feature (Figure 6) (Rusakov and Zagniy 1973; Kovacheva 1982).

The intensity ratio results obtained from the two Thracian sites are in a good agreement also with Prof. Aitken's results from Crete, Egypt and Mesopotamia (Aitken et al. personal communication). These facts are of great importance for the geomagnetism.

In this way archaeology helps geophysics through archamagnetic studies, and vice versa, the latter can help archaeology for dating as shown. This interdisciplinary character is a common feature of science today.

In this connection we hope to make our scale similarly

exact and for the more remote past (Aeneolithic and Neolithic age). We take as a basis the calibrated radiocarbon dates with the inevitable help of the relative chronology of the prehistoric cultures. It is clear that physics, dendrochronology, archaeology and geophysics are in deep interaction for the elaboration or specification (in our case) of archaeomagnetic variation curves. Thus archaeomagnetism can be considered as an absolute dating method.

At the end it should be concluded that obviously we cannot date if we have no good reference curves for the region. We cannot date also on the basis of an insufficient number of samples measured. We have the conviction that the three geomagnetic elements are necessary for unequivocal archaeomagnetic dating.

REFERENCES

Aitken, M., and Bussel G.D. (personal communication). Archaeo-intensity results from Crete, Egypt, Mesopotamia.

Kovacheva M. (1980). Summarized results of the archaeomagnetic investigation of the geomagnetic field variation for the last 8000 years in South-eastern Europe.

Geophysical J.R. Astr. Soc.,61:57-64.

Kovacheva M. (1982). Archaeomagnetic investigations of geomagnetic secular variations. Phil. Trans. R. Soc., London, A306:79-86.

Kovacheva M. (in press). Archaeomagnetic studies as a dating tool and some considerations on the archaeomagnetic methodology. Proceedings of the 1986 International Symposium on Archaeometry, Athens.

Roy J.L. and Park J.K. (1974). The magnetization process of certain red beds: Vector analysis of chemical and thermal results, Can. J. Earth Sci., 11: 437-471.

Russakov O.M. and Zagniy G.F. (1973). Archaeomagnetic secular variation study in the Ukraine and Moldavia. Archaeometry, 15: 153-157.

Sakai H. and Hirooka K. (1986). Archaeointensity determinations from Western Japan. J. Geomag. Geoelectr., 38: 1323-1329.

Thellier E. et Thellier O. (1959). Sur l'intensité du champ magnétique terrestre dans le passé historique et géologique. Ann. Géophys., 15: 285-376.

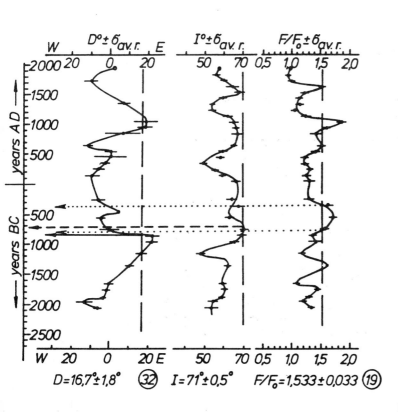

D=16,7°±1,8° (32)   I=71°±0,5°   F/F₀=1,533±0,033 (19)

Figure 5. The dating procedure of Thracian site No 2.

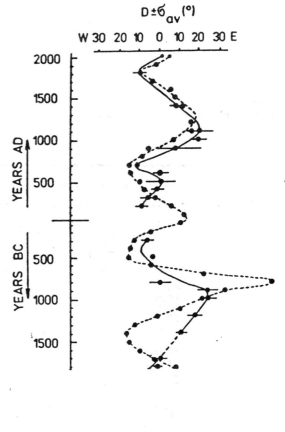

Figure 6. Declination results from Bulgaria and Ukraine.

71

Table 1
The directional and intensity results from individually orientated samples. The Fisher's estimates are: K=187.9, I=57.8°, D=1.5° and α_{95}=3.5°. Weighted average for F^A/F^D is: 1.371 ± 0.045.

Medieval sanctuary GORANOVCI					
Field No	No of speci- mens	I(°)	D(°)	F^A/F^D	σ
1933	1	54.7	352.7		
1934	1	52.9	1.1	1.487	0.043
1935	2	55.9	11.8	1.477	0.044
1936	2	60.2	3.0	1.477	0.048
1937	1	63.9	7.3		
1938	1	63.6	5.1	1.272	0.048
1939	1	53.7	3.2		
1940	1	64.7	356.0		
1941	1	55.8	354.1	1.379	0.057
1942	2	51.4	1.6	1.263	0.030

Table 2
As in Table 1. Fisher's estimates are: K=259.9, I=67.3° D=354.7°. α_{95}=1.5°. Weighted average for F^A/F^D is: 1.461 ± 0.035.

Thracian site No 1: DEMIR BABA					
Field No	No of speci- mens	I(°)	D(°)	F^A/F^D	σ
1879	2	69.5	1.6	1.204	0.074
1882	1	72.6	7.3	1.391	0.105
1883	1	73.0	351.3		
1884	1	62.3	345.7		
1887	1	71.5	357.6	1.359	0.110
1888	1	71.8	354.0	1.268	0.103
1889	1	67.0	353.9	1.148	0.053
1890	1	72.6	345.3	1.211	0.077
1891	1	72.9	7.4		

Continuation of Table 2.

Field No	No of specimens	$I(^\circ)$	$D(^\circ)$	F^A/F^D	σ
1895	1	64.0	355.2	1.386	0.140
1896	1	67.5	355.7	1.296	0.086
1918	2	69.2	353.6	1.364	0.088
				1.325	0.178
1920	2	64.2	343.1	1.420	0.105
1923	1	63.7	11.9	1.362	0.088
1924	1	73.9	11.0		
1925	1	67.9	346.5	1.432	0.046
1926	1	63.7	339.6		
1988	3	66.7	347.5		
1987	3	66.3	350.8		
1990	2	66.9	0.2		
1991	2	62.5	357.4		
1992	6	67.9	355.3		
1993	2	65.7	354.4	1.254	0.024
1994	2	71.1	356.3	1.316	0.043
1995	5	61.1	357.3		
1996	5	67.7	2.1	1.536	0.067
1997	4	64.4	351.1		
1998	4	59.7	351.7	1.274	0.041
1999	4	61.3	344.4	1.463	0.086
2000	3	65.0	10.3		
2001	2	68.0	349.6		
2002	5	67.4	353.9	1.620	0.136

As in TABLE 1. The Fisher's estimates are: $K=259.9$, $I=67.3^\circ$, $D=354.7^\circ$, $\alpha_{95}=1.5^\circ$. Weighted average for F^A/F^D is: 1.461 ± 0.035.

Table 3.

Thracian site No 2: KAMEN RID					
Field No	No of specimens	$I(^\circ)$	$D(^\circ)$	F^A/F^D	σ
T1/1	1	71.2	9.5	1.888	0.106
T1/5	2	68.0	23.2	1.889	0.077
T2/3	1	73.0	17.9	1.857	0.092
T3/3	2	R	R	1.392	0.115
				R	

Continuation of Table 3 As in Table 1. Fisher's estimates are: $K=388.6$, $I=71.3°$, $D=16.9°$, $\alpha_{95}=1.2°$. Weighted average for F^A/F^D is: 1.499 ± 0.032. R means that the result is rejected.

Field No	No of specimens	$I(°)$	$D(°)$	F^A/F^D	σ
1901	Without	orientation		1.418	0.123
1903	"	"		1.689	0.146
1905	"	"		1.253	0.150
1910	"	"		1.955	0.180
1912	"	"		1.807	0.209
1911	"	"		R	
1951	1	70.8	17.7		
1960	5	69.9	24.6		
1961	1	70.6	15.9	1.521	0.055
1962	4	69.9	29.4	1.531	0.040
1963	3	68.3	9.1		
1964	5	65.1	10.9	1.503	0.030
1965	2	68.4	25.7		
1966	1	67.6	19.3	1.510	0.054
1967	6	71.6	0.1	1.492	0.038
1968	3	70.0	10.6	1.464	0.037
1969	2	69.1	4.0		
1970	4	73.3	20.5		
1971	4	70.3	21.9		
1972	8	70.3	11.1	1.352	0.053
1973	1	74.9	359.7		
1974	3	72.2	9.5		
1975	3	72.3	8.4		
1976	6	74.2	18.0		
1977	1	68.2	17.7		
1978	7	76.3	31.3		
1979	2	76.1	25.0	1.359	0.055
1980	4	69.9	26.7		
1981	5	71.1	24.5		
1982	2	71.3	13.5		
1983	7	71.4	22.0		
1984	5	69.8	17.0	1.374	0.031
1985	7	69.8	28.7	1.682	0.048
1986	8	76.1	345.7		
1987	4	72.1	34.3		

13. Secular Variation and Magnetic Dating of Fired Structures in Greece

M.E. EVANS
Institute of Earth and Planetary Physics, University of Alberta, Edmonton, Canada.

M. MARESCHAL
Centre Géologique et Géophysique, U.S.T.L., Montpellier, France

ABSTRACT: *New Archaeomagnetic results help define geomagnetic secular variation in antiquity and provide constraints on the ages of certain structures and events including the destruction of Minoan civilization by volcanic activity.*

INTRODUCTION

It is now more than twenty years since archaeomagnetic studies in Greece were pioneered by Belshé et al. (1963). However, out of 31 features investigated, they assessed only 2 results as "good" (in a four-fold classification: good, fair, poor, useless). Several reasons could be responsible for this rather disappointing outcome, but the most likely is the lack of an adequate number of samples at each site. The largest number of samples studied was 8 (from a kiln in Athens, site HD), but 21 of their results are based on less than 5 samples. Except under very favourable circumstances such small numbers will inevitably lead to large statistical uncertainty in the final results. For example, Thellier (1981) rejects results for which α_{95} (the semi-angle of the 95% cone of confidence for a Fisherian distribution of unit vectors) exceeds 3°, and if this is done for the early Greek work, only three sites survive.

In view of these problems and bearing in mind the advances made during the last two decades, in particular the renewed interest in the secular variation brought about by limnomagnetic research, a new effort to obtain reliable archaeomagnetic directions from Greek sites seemed worthwhile.

Table 1. Summary of the archaeomagnetic directional results.

Site	Lat	Long	N	Dec	Inc	k[1]	α95
1. Palaikastro(PK)	34.94	26.28	13	005.9	49.3	305	2.4
2. Stylos(SY)	35.42	24.10	14	003.5	55.1	293	2.3
3. Corinth(CR)	37.92	22.92	16	352.8	60.1	538	1.6
4. Cnossus(KN)	35.32	25.26	9	352.4	58.8	244	3.3
5. Corinth(CO)	37.92	22.92	11	353.6	57.2	1726	1.1
6. Kalochorio(KC)	35.10	25.71	20	357.7	43.0	304	1.9
7. Gortyn(GO)	35.05	24.95	13	357.6	45.0	222	2.8
8. Argos(AG)	37.63	22.70	17	358.6	54.8	776	1.3
9. Delos(DE)(A)	37.38	25.29	8	354.5	55.2	476	2.5
10. Delos(DE)(B)	37.38	25.29	10	352.1	47.1	373	2.5
11. Delos(DE)(C)	37.38	25.29	5	001.9	51.9	998	2.4

[1] Fisherian precision parameter, k=N-1/N-R (where N is the number of samples).

SAMPLING AND RESULTS

Orientated samples were collected from 9 sites, either by drilling small (25 mm diameter) cores using a gasoline - powered drill or by bonding small plastic plates (20 mm x 20 mm) onto in situ material. In all cases orientation was by means of solar bearings. Standard laboratory procedures were followed; commercially available spinner magnetometers (Schoenstedt and Molspin) were used for determination of remanence vectors, and magnetic stability was tested by alternating field demagnetization. In some cases, thermal demagnetization was carried out. The oven used is located in a magnetically - shielded room in which the field is less than 50 nT, and in which the samples were stored when not directly under investigation.

In common with earlier studies of fired archaeological material it was found that most samples carried a strong and stable remanence. There are exceptions, but little is to be gained by discussing every anomalous sample. Some of these are unsuitable by virtue of lithology (e.g., calcareous stones used in kiln construction), some appear to have been peripheral to the main heating area (these carry an overprint as described in a detailed study recently reported by Evans and Mareschal (1986); further work is necessary to extract the underlying original magnetization but at this stage this has not been carried out since in all cases other

samples from the same site provide a well-defined result), still others carry a stable magnetization that diverges strongly from the group of vectors obtained from other samples at the same site (these have apparently suffered some form of displacement since the feature in question was last fired). In any case, whatever the cause, these samples are excluded in an attempt to obtain the most reliable estimate of the ancient field direction at each site. There remain 136 samples, the results of which are summarized in Table 1.

DISCUSSION

It is convenient to divide the results into separate time intervals in order to facilitate comparison with other results from Greece and elsewhere:

(a) Minoan Crete; The sudden destruction of Cretan sites by volcanic activity of Santorini was first suggested by Marinatos (1939) and has been the subject of debate ever since (e.g., Page 1970; Pichler & Schiering 1977; Blong 1980). Preliminary palaeomagnetic studies by Wright (1978) and Tarling (1980) were inconclusive, but subsequently a very detailed study of volcanic material and archaeological remains on Santorini itself and of several archaeological sites on Crete was published by Downey

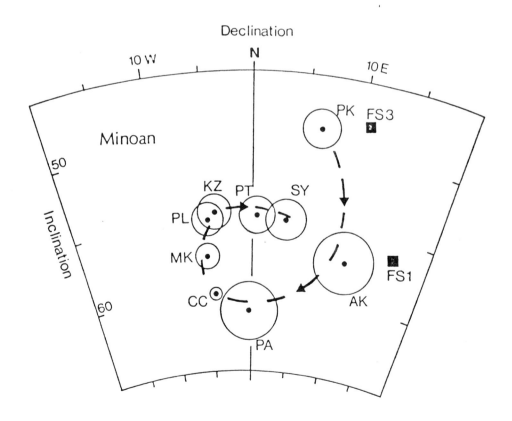

Figure 1. Declination - Inclination plot of results from Crete and Santorini. The identifying letters are explained in the text; the new data reported here are PK (Palaikastro) and SY (Stylos). Circles represent the circular standard error (α_{63}), the corresponding α_{95} values being given in Table 1. No errors are shown for Thomas' Phaestos results as they are based on only two samples each.

and Tarling (1984). In their discussion, these authors choose to concentrate on the angle of inclination (i.e., the angle between the magnetic vector at a site and the horizontal), but it is both necessary and desirable to consider also the declination (i.e., the angle in the horizontal plane between true north and the observed magnetic vector). This is done in Figure 1 which shows that the Santorini volcanics (PA = Plinian Ashfall; PT = Paroxysmal Tephra) have declinations close to zero whereas the Cretan destruction levels all yield values about 5 degrees west of north. Figure 1 also includes our own results from the kilns at Stylos (SY) and Palaikastro (PK). Our Palaikastro result is easterly and of shallow inclination and differs markedly from the Palaikastro result (PL) reported by Downey and Tarling (1984). Our samples were collected from the kiln described by Davaras (1980), for which age control is almost entirely lacking, whereas the data of Downey and Tarling refer to burnt walls and floors attributed to the Late Minoan IB (LMIB) destruction level of the town itself. Davaras' kiln lies some 300 m to the southeast of the town site. Both archaeomagnetic results are of high quality and they differ from one another by several times their associated statistical errors; thus the archaeomagnetic data indicate that whatever the actual ages of the two sites are, they are not contemporaneous. At present the archaeomagnetic database cannot resolve this problem, but existing Greek limnomagnetic and Bulgarian/Russian archaeomagnetic data indicate that shallow inclinations occurred in Middle Minoan times around 2000 B.C. (see Kovacheva 1983, Figure 3-8 and Creer et al. 1981, Figure 11). Furthermore, some preliminary data from two kilns at Phaestos (Thomas 1981) are compatible with the interpretation illustrated in Figure 1; FS3 represents the result she obtained from a kiln belonging to the First Palatial Period, whereas FS1 belongs to the Second Palatial Period. She reports thermoluminescence dates of 1834±206 B.C. and 1516±240 B.C. for FS3 and FS1 respectively.

Next we move to the Akrotiri result (AK) which pre-dates the Plinian ash fall. From there we suggest the sequence indicated by the arrows in Figure 1, ignoring for the moment the palaeomagnetic data from the volcanic deposits themselves. Thus we follow Downey and Tarling in placing the LMIB destruction levels in central Crete (CC represents the average of the seven sites studied) before the destruction levels in eastern Crete (PL and KZ). But we have left Makrygialos (MK) in an intermediate position as its magnetic result suggests, rather than associating it with the time of destruction in eastern Crete as was done by Downey and Tarling. The sequence then ends with Stylos (SY) which is thought to be LMIIIB (Davaras 1972a). This sequence forms a pattern of magnetic vectors suggestive of an open clockwise loop which is typical of geomagnetic behaviour, as seen for example in the historically observed record over the last 3 or 4 centuries in western Europe.

But what of the palaeomagnetic results from the Santorini volcanics, and of the much-discussed connection between eruptive events and the widespread destruction on Crete? Despite the fact that all the geological field evidence suggests a single eruptive cycle, the magnetic investigation yields two distinct vectors. Downey and Tarling interpret this as indicating two eruptive events separated by an interval of perhaps 20 years. They further argue that the similarities of the inclinations suggest that the earlier ashfall (PA: I =61.1°) corresponds to the LMIB destruction levels in central Crete (CC: I=60.0°) whereas

the paroxysmal tephra (PT: I=54.8°) corresponds to the destruction in eastern Crete (Palaikastro, PL: I=55.1°, Kato Zakro, KZ: I=54.6°). Even if we set aside the problem of the intermediate inclination value at Makrygialos (MK: I=57.5°), which does not fit this scheme, we are still faced with the difficulty of explaining the volcanic declinations, which stubbornly remain about 5° east of the archaeological results. Added to the geological evidence favouring a single eruption, these shortcomings cast some doubt on the Downey and Tarling hypothesis. Sparks (1985) has suggested that the PT result corresponds to a later time due to a very slow cooling of the accumulated pyroclastics, but one also wonders if other distorting mechanisms have affected this result, such as anisotropy due to rock fabric or depositional inclination error. A renewed inquiry is urgently required to settle the matter.

(b) Fourth century B.C.; three kilns were sampled, two at Corinth and one at Knossos. All three exhibit declinations about 7° west of north, and inclinations range from 57.2° to 60.1°. But since the sites are at different latitudes it is necessary to make a correction before a proper comparison can be made. The dipole gradient causes the angle of inclination to increase as one moves northwards (by approximately 1 degree for every degree of latitude in mid-latitudes), hence the Knossos result (entry 4 in Table 1) corresponds to an inclination of 61.4° at Corinth. The archaeomagnetic data therefore yield a sequence of decreasing inclinations from Knossos (61.4°) via Corinth kiln CR (60.1°) to Corinth kiln CO (57.2°). This trend is comparable to that deduced from contemporaneous Italian sites (see Evans and Mareschal 1988, Figure 2), which also yield declinations west of north. Previously, kiln CR was undated, but Cook (1961) lists it as "presumably earlier than" the other Corinth kiln (CO). The latter is a much more elaborate structure and is dated as fourth century B.C. in Cook's list. In fact, it most likely belongs to the late fourth century (C. Williams, pers. comm.). On the other hand, Cook lists the Knossos kiln as early to middle fourth century. The magnetic data therefore imply a mid-fourth century date for the last firing of Corinth kiln CR.

At this early stage, there is very little other data to which these results can be usefully compared. However it is worth noting that a kiln in the Phoenician settlement at Motya in western Sicily (12.50°E, 37.83°N) dated to the first half of the fourth century B.C. yields a result (D = 352.2°, I = 61.3°, α_{95} = 2.2°; Evans and Mareschal 1988, Table 1, entry 2) almost identical to the latitude corrected Knossos vector.

(c) Roman sites; Samples were collected from Argos, Gortyn, Kalochorio and Delos. At Argos, on the mainland, the material sampled came from the furnaces associated with the Roman baths (Thermes A), and a tight group of directions was obtained with a mean declination slightly west of north and a mean inclination of about 55° (Table 1). At Gortyn, in Crete, the furnaces serving the Megali Porta Baths were sampled, and a mean vector slightly west of north was also obtained but this time with an inclination of only 45°. If the Gortyn result is corrected for latitude then the inclination would correspond to a value of 47.5° at Argos. The Gortyn baths are thought to be 2nd century A.D. (Sanders 1982) whereas those at Argos seem to have continued in use until the 4th century (Aupert 1973). The magnetic data thus implies a steepening of the ambient field vector similar to that reported by Aitken and Weaver (1962) for the later Roman period in Britain (see their

Figure 2). Their increase amounts to some 10° and ends up about 3° shallower than the inclination of a theoretical axial dipole field. The situation in Greece is very comparable, the observed increase being about 8° ending up about 2° shallower than the reference dipole field. The British declinations are also biased to the west of north.

Our Kalachorio samples represent the pottery kiln described in detail by Davaras (1973b). There is very little archaeological dating evidence for this structure, but Davaras claims that the potsherds found in association with the kiln indicate a Roman age. The magnetic result is very close to that obtained from the baths at Gortyn (Table 1), which implies a date in the 2nd century A.D.

Finally, we turn to the data obtained from the island of Delos. Three structures were sampled, a kiln in the "Quartier du Lac" (DE)(A), and a series of fireplaces in what is traditionally interpreted as a restaurant in the "Quartier du Stade" (DE)(B), and the burnt walls of the "Maison des Sceaux" (DE)(C). These three features each yield their own characteristic magnetic vector, which suggests that they are not all contemporaneous. However the result from the burnt walls is based on only five samples, two of which come from the same block. In fact, a total of eleven samples were collected from this house - which was destroyed when the island was sacked in 69 B.C. - but the other six samples seem to have escaped complete reheating. They do yield magnetic vectors loosely grouped around the mean of the five samples quoted in Table 1 (entry 11), but a more detailed investigation, preferably involving further sampling, is necessary to obtain a really convincing result. The kiln (DE)(A) probably fell into disuse shortly after 69 B.C. as the island was gradually deserted (Bruneau and Ducat 1983). Certainly this agrees very well with our magnetic data from Apani in Italy (Evans and Mareschal 1988, Table 1, entry 6). This latter kiln is attributed to the first half of the 1st century B.C. and it yields a declination of 356.7° and an inclination of 58.9°, which is 1.8° less than a dipole field. The Delos kiln yields D=354.5° and I=55.2°, which is 2.0° less than the dipole inclination. The result from the restaurant is puzzling due to its shallowness, I being 47.1° compared to a dipole value of 57.2°. As noted above in connection with the data from Gortyn, one expects shallow inclinations sometime in the first few centuries A.D. (in Britain, for example, a minimum occurs in the first half of the third century). Taken at face value therefore the (DE)(B) result suggests that the restaurant was re-used as late as about 200 A.D.; as Plassart (1916) points out, this is a very pleasant spot, having a disposition both "élégante et spacieuse".

CONCLUSIONS

The main conclusions can be briefly summarized as follows:

(i) The new results from Crete, in conjunction with a reappraisal of data already published, do not support the idea that the eruption of Santorini directly caused the downfall of Minoan civilization, either as a single event or as two separate outbursts;

(ii) The kiln (PK) that we sampled near the town of Palaikastro in eastern Crete seems to be somewhat earlier than the LMIB destruction levels in the town itself;

(iii) The kiln CR at Corinth yields a magnetic direction intermediate between those obtained from the kiln at Knossos and kiln CO at Corinth and therefore appears to have last been used in the mid-fourth century B.C. The magnetic vectors from these three kilns are compatible with those from southern Italy, and confirm the westerly declination swing seen there, but absent from the British lake sediment record;

(iv) The data from the baths at Gortyn (GO) and Argos (AG) record the same inclination increase seen in the British data between the 2nd and 4th centuries A.D.;

(v) The kiln (DE)(A) on the island of Delos yields a direction consistent with that from Apani in Italy and thus with a date in the first half of the 1st century B.C.;

(vi) The data from the restaurant (DE)(B) in the "Quartier du Stade" on Delos are puzzling since they imply use, or re-use, as late as 200 A.D.

REFERENCES

Aitken,M.J. & Weaver,G.H.(1962). Magnetic dating: some archaeomagnetic measurements in Britain. Archaeometry, 5: 4-22.

Aupert,P.(1973). Argos, Thermes A. Bull. Corr. Hellénique, 98: 764-774.

Belshé, J.C., Cook, K. & Cook, R.M.(1963). Some Archaeomagnetic Results from Greece. Ann. Brit. School Athens,58: 8-13.

Blong, R.J.(1980). The possible effects of Santorini tephra fall on Minoan Crete. In (C.Doumas,ed.) Thera and the Aegean World II: 217-226.

Bruneau, P. & Ducat, J.(1983). Guide de Delos. Ecole Franc. Athènes, 280 pp.

Cook, R.M.(1961). The 'Double Stoking Tunnel' of Greek Kilns. Ann. Brit. School Athens, 56: 64-67.

Creer,K.M.,Readman,P.W.& Papamarinopoulos,S.(1981). Geomagnetic secular variations in Greece through the last 6000 years obtained from lake sediment studies in Greece. Geophys.J.R.Astr. Soc.,66: 193-219.

Davaras, C. (1973a). A Minoan pottery kiln at Stylos Hania. AE(Archaeological Ephemeris): 75-80.

Davaras, C. (1973b). A pottery kiln at Istrona in eastern Crete. A.Delt.(Archaeological Bulletin) ,28: 110-115.

Davaras,C. (1980). A Minoan pottery kiln at Plaikastro. Ann. Brit. School Athens, 75: 115-126.

Downey, W. & Tarling, D. (1984). Archaeomagnetic dating of Santorini volcanic eruptions and fired destruction levels of late Minoan civilization. Nature, 309: 519-523.

Evans, M.E. & Mareschal, M. (1986). An archaeomagnetic example of polyphase magnetization. J. Geomag. Geoelec., 38: 923-929.

Evans, M.E. & Mareschal, M.(1988). Secular variation and magnetic dating of fired structures in southern Italy. Proc. 25th Int. Symp. Archaeometry. (in press).

Kovacheva, M. (1983). Archaeomagnetic data from Bulgaria and southeastern Yugoslavia. In (Creer, K.M. et al. eds.) Geomagnetism of baked clays and Recent sediments, Amsterdam: Elsevier: 106-110.

Marinatos, S. (1939). The volcanic destruction of Minoan Crete. Antiquity, 13: 425-439.

Page, D.L. (1970). The Santorini volcano and the desolation of Minoan Crete. London: Society Promotion Hellenic Studies: 45 pp.

Pichler, H. & Schiering, W. (1977). The Thera eruption and Late Minoan destructions on Crete. Nature, 267: 819-822.

Sanders, I.F. (1982). Roman Crete. Warminster, England: Aris & Phillips, 185 pp.

Sparks, R.S.J. (1985). Archaeomagnetism, Santorini volcanic eruptions and fired destruction levels on Crete, Nature, 313: 74-75.

Tarling, R.S.J. (1980). Magnetic studies of the Santorini tephra deposits, In (C. Doumas, ed.) Thera and the Aegean World I: 195-201.

Thellier, E. (1981). Sur la direction du champ magnétique terrestre, en France, durant les deux derniers millenaires. Phys.Earth Planet. Int., 24: 89-132.

Thomas, R.C. (1981). Archaeomagnetism of Greek pottery and Cretan kilns. Ph.D. thesis, Univ. Edinburgh.

Wright, J.V. (1978). Remanent magnetism of poorly sorted deposits from the Minoan eruption of Santorini. Bull. Volcanol., 41: 131-135.

14. Physical Characteristics of Amber

C.A. WERT

Department of Materials Science and Engineering and Materials Research Laboratory, University of Illinois, 1304 W. Green St., Urbana, IL 61801 U.S.A.

M. WELLER

Max-Planck Institute fur Metallforschung, Institute fur Werkstoffwissenschaften, 92 Seestrasse, 7000 Stuttgart, West Germany.

ABSTRACT: *Acoustical absorption and dielectric loss verifies polymeric character of amber.*

INTRODUCTION

Amber and jet are often found in important archaeological sites. They are usually well preserved since they are resistant to oxidation and corrosion. They carve well and were used frequently for ornamentation. Finds of amber are cited in many references (Beck 1986; Rice 1980; Soffer 1985; Hunger 1979 and Fraquet 1987). Of great import is the establishment of trade routes, especially of Baltic amber. Also of value is `the dating of amber in geological time. Collections of amber from early times exist in many museums of Europe. The Romans also used amber extensively. Jet has also been found extensively in graves and living sites. Muller (1987) describes both artefacts and possible sources of material.

The composition of amber and jet can be measured easily. Their composition is roughly 75 wt% C, 5 to 10 wt% hydrogen and the balance oxygen. Sulfur comprises about 0.5% of amber and somewhat more of jet. About 0.5 to 1% of nitrogen is found in each, and smaller concentrations of metallic elements such as Al and Si. These numbers vary somewhat, but the composition of both is close to that of bituminous coal. A large compilation of elemental compositions of ambers is given by Schmid (1931). It shows variation of ± 5% in carbon concentrations from amber to amber, with corresponding adjustment of the other elements. For jet, the data are fewer, but two published values agree: Muller (1987) and Traverse and Kolvoord (1968).

We have examined amber and jet by two techniques of materials science, acoustical energy absorption and dielectric loss, to deduce details of the hydrocarbon structure. Our work on jet is yet fragmentary, so we concentrate here on amber.

The chemistry of amber has been investigated by infrared spectroscopy (Beck 1986), by mass spectrometry (Eichoff and Mischer 1972) and by combined gas chromatography mass spectrometry (Mills, White and Gough 1984/85). Carbon-13 NMR has been found by Lambert and Frye (1982) and Lambert, Frye and Poinar (1985) to permit identification of organic functional groups. These papers and others yield the following picture: the hydrocarbon matter is comprised both of some loosely held organic units, which can be dissolved by mild organic reagents, and a less soluble polymeric portion of linked aromatic structure termed labdane. Thus, it is similar to bituminous coal, which commonly has 40% "volatile" carbon (i.e., loosely held organic constituents) and 60% "fixed" carbon (a crosslinked macromolecular structure) (van Krevelen 1981).

Table 1. The elastic constants of "polymeric materials" and iron.

PARAMETER	AMBER[a]	COAL[b]	PE[c]	IRON[d]
YOUNG'S MODULUS	4.45 ± 0.19 GPa	5.3	5.05	205
SHEAR MODULUS	1.65 ± 0.07 GPa	2.0	1.92	82
POISSON'S RATIO	0.35 ± 0.006	0.33	0.33	0.29

a. Present work. b. van Krevelen (1981). c. Odajima and Maeda (1966). d. Handbook, American Institute of Physics, 3rd Ed. McGraw Hill, Gray (1972).

a. Present work. b. van Krevelen (1981). c. Odajima and Maeda (1966). d. Handbook, American Institute of Physics, 3rd Ed. McGraw Hill, Gray (1972).

EXPERIMENTAL TECHNIQUE AND RESULTS

Synthetic polymers are characterized by viscoelastic behaviour under stress. Their elastic modulus is low, i.e., they deform easily: Young's modulus for polyethylene is only 3% of that for iron at room temperature, for example. In addition, they readily convert vibrational energy to heat, i.e., acoustical waves are rapidly damped by the material. Both effects are a result of the folded configuration of the macromolecular structure. Under stress, elongation or shear takes place primarily by rearrangement of the coils, an event easier than direct stretching of the atom-to-atom bonds—hence the modulus of elasticity is low.

We have measured the modulus of elasticity of a Dominican amber by ultrasonic means: Ledbetter, Frederick and Austin (1980) and Ledbetter, Chevacharoenkul and Davis (1986). The results are shown in Table 1, along with values for polyethylene, coal and iron. Young's modulus and the shear modulus of the first three are similar, and are much lower than that of iron, a result of the polymeric character of the amber, coal and polyethylene. Poisson's ratio is in the "normal" range for all four.

The energy-dissipative feature of macromolecular solids can readily be demonstrated. Let a sinusoidal stress be applied to a solid: stress = A sinωt. Strain results, but it may not be in time-phase with a stress. If it is out of phase by an angle δ, strain = A' sin(ωt + δ). The rate of energy dissipation is tangent of δ.

Several ways exist to measure δ. One may propagate an acoustical wave through the solid and measure the reduction of A' with a distance. One may set up standing waves in a rod and measure their resonance characteristics—this is equivalent to measuring the Q of an equivalent electrical unit. Or one may measure the decay of the amplitude of free oscillator system, thereby determining δ. We used the last method.

A thin rod of amber is made and is suspended on a torsional system whose amplitude oscillation can be followed by an optical lever. The specimen is enclosed in a vacuum so that energy loss is that of the amber rod. A dewar allows the specimen to be maintained below room temperature; a small furnace permits heating above room temperature. The value of sigma is measured as the specimen slowly warms from low temperature. All ambers were supplied by Dr. Schlee of the Rosenstein Museum, Stuttgart, and are identified by the site in that collection.

A measurement for a specimen of Baltic Amber is shown in Figure 1. The rate of energy dissipation is low, near absolute zero, goes through several maxima and increases rapidly as the temperature is raised above room temperature. The maximum near 200 K consists of 2 peaks, one at 200 K and a smaller peak near 140 K, as the lines sketched-in show. The computer controlled data acquisition system takes points every degree, so that energy absorption lines are smooth. For convenience of presentation, all curves in other figures are drawn with smooth lines.

The similarity of the macromolecular character of the amber to a common polymer is shown by the second curve in Figure 1. One sees a low temperature peak and a rapidly rising energy absorption above room temperature.

Ambers of other origins show a similar energy absorption character (Figure 2). Measurements for a Dominican amber, a Japanese amber and a Mexican amber have peaks in the same temperature regime. Although the magnitudes of the peaks vary somewhat, reflecting slightly different macromolecular detail, the general molecular character of ambers of different origin is about the same. Thus, our hope that these viscoelastic features might differentiate among ambers is not fulfilled. This difficulty exists in other spectroscopies, see Beck (1986) for example.

The rate of polymerization of resins during fossilization is of importance. Heated disputes exist over changes in chemistry which occur during fossilization (Beck 1986; and Rottländer 1970). Our viscoelastic measurements cannot describe specific chemical species, but they do show how rapidly fossilization has occurred. Figure 3 shows measurements for three copals of different origins. Their absorption spectra are similar to those of Figures 1 and 2, indicating that the polymerization must occur early—copals are hundreds of thousands of years old , where ambers may be 50 million or more years old.

These observations do not imply, though, that polymerization of the copals, as they are found, is complete. On the contrary, heating of copals at modest temperatures may produce additional polymerization. This is shown for a Kenya copal in Figure 4. After a first measurement, the specimen was held for a few minutes at 360 K. A second measurement, upper curve, showed larger absorption peaks, indicating additional polymerization. Heating to still a higher temperature would not necessarily produce further changes, since the copals and amber undergo large irreversible glass to rubber changes above 400 K.

The ambers and copals are not the only natural hydrocarbon materials to display the viscoelastic effects. Similar effects are found in coal, wood and oil shale. See Weller and Wert (1984a), Wert, Weller and Caulfield (1984) and Wert and Weller (1985). An example of measurements may be seen in Figure 5. These natural hydrocarbon solids apparently posses a polymeric structure, as does amber.

ELECTRICAL MEASUREMENTS: TECHNIQUES AND RESULTS.

Amber is a superb dielectric material. Consequently, measurements of its dielectric properties are instructive and simple. Reported values of its dielectric constant are reviewed by Schmid (1931); an average value relative to vacuum is about 2.85. Later measurements, including some of our own, (Weller and Wert 1984b) agree.

Its excellent dielectric characteristics do not preclude the possibility that it displays dielectric loss, indeed it does. The phenomenon is simple to understand; it is analogous to mechanical loss described in the preceding section. Let a sinusoidal electric field be impressed on a specimen: E = Constant*sinωt. An electric polarization P, results with same frequency, ω. But P may not be in time-phase with E, so that P = Constant* sin(ωt + θ). That part of P which is in-phase with E yields the dielectric stated above. That part of P which is 90° out of phase is the dielectric loss; numerically it is the tangent of θ.

We have measured dielectric loss of many ambers; an

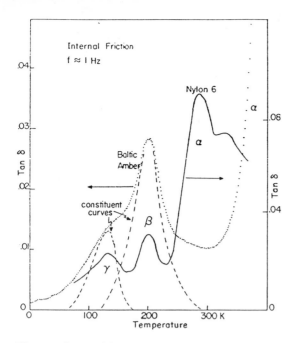

Figure 1. Internal friction of Baltic amber and nylon.

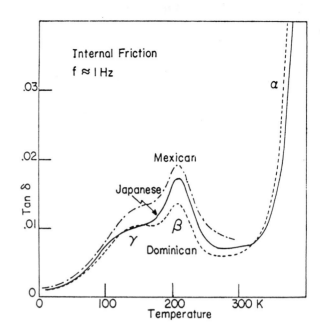

Figure 2. Internal friction of three additional ambers.

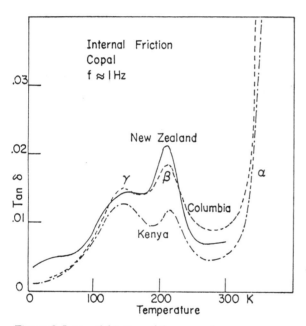

Figure 3. Internal friction of three copals.

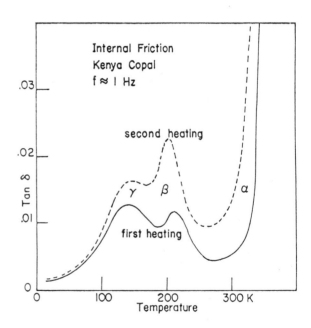

Figure 4. Polymerization of a Kenya copal after heating.

example is given in Figure 6, for a frequency of 1000 Hz. Two peaks are seen, one near 230 K, other above room temperature. The first is the dielectric analog β-peak of Figure 1; the second is the dielectric analog of the sharp rise in the mechanical loss above room temperature. Similar measurements have been made for other ambers and copals; the results will be reported separately. For clarification of the interpretation given in the next section, we show similar measurements for a jet-like coal in Figure 7. Again a dielectric loss peak just above 230 K is seen; it corresponds to the mechanical β-peak. The higher temperature peak is the dielectric loss, labelled α, corresponding to the mechanical α-peak. But there is no dielectric loss peak for the γ-peak for coal, as is also true for amber. This absence for both materials is crucial for the

molecular model we propose.

INTERPRETATION OF THE MEASUREMENTS.

These results can be used to infer a picture of the macromolecular structure. For this purpose we rely heavily on the polymer literature. From books such as McCrum et al (1967), Murayama (1978), Blythe (1979) and Daniel (1967) one can establish the following general picture:

1. All of these loss peaks have their origin in the rearrangement, under stress, of the segments of the intertwined network of the macromolecular solid. For a mechanical stress, such rearrangement allows an additional

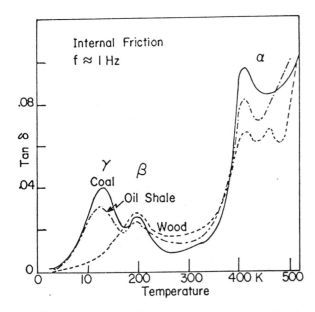

Figure 5. Internal friction of natural macromolecules.

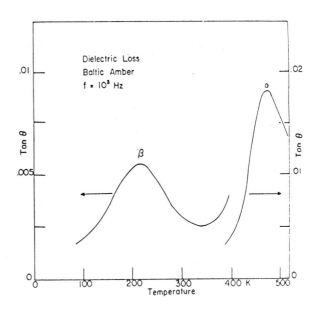

Figure 6. Dielectric loss of Baltic amber.

strain to occur over that which would be allowed by a strict Hooke's law extension of the interatomic bonds. That is, the twisting, flexure or uncoiling of the macromolecular chain allows an additional strain to occur over the strictly interatomic strain. The dielectric phenomenon has an analogous interpretation. In an imposed electric field, two types of response are allowed. The first is an electric polarization which occurs instantly and reversibly—it is measured by the real part of the dielectric constant. The second part of the polarization is a time-dependent component which results from a rearrangement in space of permanent electric dipoles. Since the rearrangement may not be instantaneous, energy may be transferred from the source to heat, resulting in dielectric loss. Understanding of this phenomenon dates back many decades (Debye 1929; Daniel 1967; and Blythe 1979). From this perspective of materials structure, the problem then resolves into one of relating the observed effects to a particular macromolecular structure.

2. The mechanical loss peak at lowest temperature labelled γ in Figure 1, results from a small-scale twisting or

bending under stress of the backbone macromolecular chain. In the case of the amber, this would be the "labdane carbon skeleton" described by Beck. Such a structure exists in both ambers and copals, so that it must develop early in the fossilization process. No γ-peak exists in the dielectric loss, so that macromolecular units which relax must possess no permanent electric dipole moment.

3. The loss peak which occurs near 200 K, labelled β in Figure 1, is apparently caused by reorientation, under stress, of a side chain. It also causes dielectric loss, so that the relaxing unit must possess a permanent electric dipole moment. A likely candidate is an O-H or CH_2OH unit which is either part of the volatile, easily removed constituent of amber or appended to the labdane skeleton. See the sketches in the article by Beck (1986) or that by Mills, White and Gough (1984/85).

4. The loss peak above room temperature, labelled α in Figures 4 and 5, is somewhat more difficult to interpret. It

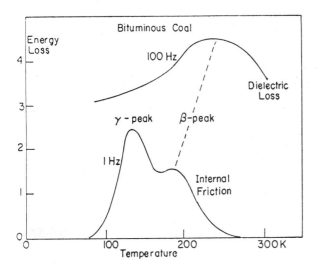

Figure 7. Dielectric loss of a Jet-like coal.

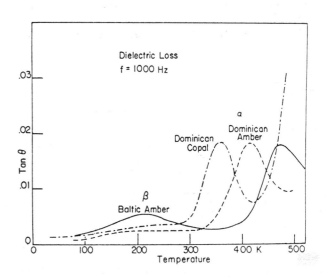

Figure 8. Dielectric loss of copal and amber.

has commonly been described as a glass-transition point, a temperature at which large scale, more or less free motion of macromolecules occurs upon heating. It is clearly associated with the rapid softening in amber which occurs upon heating. The effect, in fact, may be one of the most reliable ways of differentiating among the ambers and copals. We have measured the α-peak for several ambers and copals; the results are presented in Figure 8. Wide variation in the position of the peaks in temperature is observed, implying that the glass-transition temperature has wide variation among the fossil resins. If this effect has general validity, it might be a more promising method of differentiating the source ambers.

SUMMARY

Amber and jet are important materials for decoration, both being heavily used in modern times for jewelry and art objects. But both have been used heavily in the past, as well, and they are important in archaeology. They are hydrocarbon solids of about the same chemical composition, nearly the same, in fact, as bituminous coal. They are fossilized plant material, amber having its origin in resins and other exudants from trees and jet from woody matter. Amber has been extensively studied by chemical means and the general character of its structure is known—it consists partly of volatile organic molecules easily dissolved by mild reagents and partly of a cross-linked hydrocarbon skeleton of greater stability. Thus, it has many features of synthetic polymers. This paper reports on the examination of that polymeric character using both viscoelastic mechanical measurements and dielectric loss measurement. These materials indeed have polymeric character. Both amber and the younger copals show prominent loss peaks similar to those observed in polymers, peaks at about 130 K, 200 K and 400 K for frequencies in the range 1 to 1000 Hz. Models have been proposed which interpret these phenomena in terms of small-scale main-chain motion under stress, motion of appended polar side-units, and the glass transition change characteristic of the change from the glassy state to a rubbery state.

The measurements show that fossilization occurs rapidly with time, since the loss peaks are similar in magnitude for ambers and copals. The temperature of the glass-transition shows considerable temperature variation, though, and the possibility exists that it may be a way of differentiating among the ambers and the copals, as well as between the natural fossil resins and the many fakes and synthetic materials.

ACKNOWLEDGEMENTS

We acknowledge the support of the Alexander von Humboldt Stiftung, Bonn, and the Max Planck Society for support of the work. The support of the Department of Energy, USA, is acknowledged for C. Wert during the preparation stages of the manuscript, Division of Materials Science, Contract DE-ACO2-76-ER-1198. Dr. Dieter Schlee, Staatlisches Museum fur Naturkunde, Stuttgart, supplied us with reliable samples and gave us helpful advice. Measurements were carried out by Mr. Rahn and Miss Hamm of the laboratory in Stuttgart. Measurements of elastic constants were made by Dr. Hassel Ledbetter, NBS, Boulder, Colorado; his results will be reported in more detail later.

REFERENCES

Beck, C. (1986). Spectroscopic Investigations of Amber, Applied Spectroscopy Reviews, 11: 57-110.

Blythe, A.R. (1979). Electrical Properties of Polymers, Cambridge University Press, Cambridge, England.

Daniel, V.V. (1967). Dielectric Relaxation, Academic Press, New York.

Debye, P. (1929). Polar Molecules, Dover Publications, New York.

Eichholf, E.J. and Mischer, G. (1972) Massenspektrometrische and Emissionsspektrometrische Untersucherungen an Bernstein zur Herkunftsbestimmung, Z. Naturforsch. B27: 380-386.

Fraquet, H. (1987). Amber, Butterworths, London.

Gray, D.E. (1972). American Institute of Physics Handbook, 3rd Ed. McGraw Hill, New York.

Hunger, R. (1979). The Magic of Amber, Chilton Book Co., Radnor, PA, USA.

Lambert, J.B. and Frye, J.S. (1982). Carbon Functionalities in Amber, Science, 217: 55-57.

Lambert, J.B., Frye, J.S. and Poinar, Jr., G.O. (1985) Amber from the Dominican Republic: Analysis by Nuclear Magnetic Resonance Spectroscopy, Archaeometry, 27: pp. 43-51.

Ledbetter, H. M., Frederick, N.V. and Austin, M.W. (1980). Elastic Constant Variability in Stainless Steel 304, J. of Appl. Phys., 51: 304-305

Ledbetter, H.M., Chevacharoenkul, S. and Davis, J. (1986). Monocrystal Elastic Constants of NbC, J. Appl. Phys., 60: 1614-1617.

McCrum, N.G., Read, B.E. and William, G. (1967). Anelastic and Dielectric Effects in Solids, Wiley, New York.

Mills, J.S., White, R. and Gough L. J. (1984/85). The Chemical Composition of Baltic Amber., Chem. Geol., 47:15-39.

Muller, H. (1987). JET, Butterworths, London.

Murayama, T. (1978). Dynamic Aspects of Polymeric Material, Elsevier, Amsterdam, New York.

Odajima, A. and Maeda, T. (1966). Calculation of the Elastic Constants and the Lattice Energy of the Polyethylene Crystal, J. Polymer Science C, 16: 55-73.

Rice, P. (1980). Amber, The Golden Gem of the Ages, van Nostrand Reinhold, New York.

Rottländer, R.C.A. (1970). On the Formation of Amber from Pinus Resin. Archaeometry, 12: 35-51.

Soffer, O. (1985). The Upper Paleolithic of the Central Russian Plains. Academic Press, New York.

Schmid, L. (1931). "Bernstein", section in Handbook der Mineralschemie, Band IV, eds. C. Doelter and H. Leitmeier, Verlag von Theodor Steinkopff, Dresden and Leipzig: 842-943.

Traverse, A. and Kolvoord, R. (1968). Utah Jet: A Vitrinite with Aberrant Properties, Science, 159: 302-305.

Van Krevelen, D.W. (1981). Coal, Elsevier, Amsterdam, New York.

Weller, M. and Wert, C. A. (1984a). Cross-Linking of Macromolecules in Coal, Fuel, 63: 891-986.

Weller, M. and Wert, C.A. (1984b). Neue Physikalische Untersuchungen zur Strucktur der Moleküle im Bernsteing, Bernstein Neuigkeiten, Stuttgarter Beiträge zur Naturkunde, Serie C, No. 18: 85-100.

Wert, C.A., Weller, M. and Caulfield, D. (1984). Dynamic Loss Properties of Wood, J. Appl. Phys., 56: 2435-2458.

Wert, C.A. and Weller, M. (1985). Structure of Natural Macromolecular Solids, J. de Physiqe, 46, C10: 561-564.

15. The Analysis of Organic Archaeological Residue: an Evaluation of Thin Layer Chromatography

D.M. GURFINKEL
U.M. FRANKLIN
Department of Metallurgy and Materials Science, University of Toronto, Toronto, Canada M5S 1A4

ABSTRACT: *If thin layer chromatography is to be useful in the analysis of organic archaeological residue then separation of polar constituents must be achieved.*

INTRODUCTION.

Thin layer chromatography (TLC) is a widely used procedure for the separation and identification of organic substances (Stahl 1969; Touchstone and Rogers 1980). Examples of its application to archaeological material include Gurfinkel and Franklin (1988) and Lubec and others (1987). TLC is appealing because it is inexpensive and can easily be set up in the laboratory. The purpose of the present study is to determine if TLC can be used to identify organic archaeological material.

A small number of archaeological pot residues, believed to be either food or resinous material, were obtained, along with food and resin samples (resins from Sigma Chemical Co.) These known samples were heated for eight months at 105°C attempting to simulate the degradation that occurs in an archaeological context. This degradation is twofold: that which occurs during material use, e.g., cooking food and then that which occurs after burial.

Comparison of artifact chromatograms with those of the known samples is reported here.

METHODS

For each sample two chemical fractions were prepared:
a) chloroform extract (CE) for the isolation of any lipid constituents (Figure 1).
b) acid precipitates (AP) for the isolation of protein and/or humic acids (Figure 2).

Thin layer chromatography was performed in the following manner: A sample solution (2 μl) was spotted on the bottom of a 5 cm x 5 cm silica-coated plate (0.2 mm Polygram silica gel N-HR plastic sheets from Macherey Nagel & Co). A solvent or solvent mixture was allowed to run up the plate by capillary action. The relative attraction of sample constituents for silica compared to the solubility in the solvent system determined how far they migrated up the plate. Polar compounds remained near the origin (i.e., site of sample application) while less polar substances migrated up the plate. After development, plates were dipped in a visualization reagent. For the CE chromatogram antimony pentachloride (20% in $CHCl_3$) was used. This reagent reacted with lipid and resin constituents to produce brown and orange spots when heated (3 min., 105°C). The detection limit was approximately 0.1 μg (based on oleic acid). For the AP chromatograms, a 1:1 mixture of ferric chloride (2.7 in 2N HCl) and potassium ferricyanide (5%) was found to be a useful visualization reagent. It reacted with samples at room temperature to produce blue-green spots which developed slowly over thirty minutes. The reagent's manufacturer (Sigma Chemical Co.) describes it as detecting aromatic amines and phenolic compounds. The detection limit was approximately 0.1 μg (based on tyrosine).

RESULTS

The CE chromatograms (CEC) and AP chromatograms (APC) are shown in Figures 3 and 4 respectively.

The TLC methods used here were not able to distinguish between individual foods. The CEC and APC of all food samples were similar. While there were differences between CEC of individual fresh resins, these became less pronounced after heat treatment. The APC of all heated resins were identical. There were however, sufficient differences between CEC and APC (both fresh and heated) of food samples as a group and the resins as a group to distinguish between at least broad classifications of materials. Many compound classes will have to be examined to confirm this.

An increase in the presence of polar compounds appeared to accompany the degradation of the organic material. The CEC of the resins and the corn oil sample showed a shift to more polar constituents with heating. The artifacts as a group were generally more polar than either of the heated foods or resins. There were no artifact-known sample CE chromatogram matches to permit identification of artifact residues.

Food APC matched with several artifact samples. Soil samples however, also had similar patterns so that the matches were not meaningful. A large portion of all AP samples appeared to remain at the origin and presumably unseparated. The TLC methodology must be further developed to separate these polar compounds, thereby increasing the possibility of material identification.

CONCLUSIONS

Further methodological development must focus on the separation of polar sample constituents.

More samples must be examined to confirm that TLC can be used for identification at least at a broad classification level.

ACKNOWLEDGEMENTS

The authors wish to thank the University of Toronto and the Natural Sciences and Engineering Research Council for financial support, the Department of Anthropology for providing laboratory space, and J. Holladay, R. Nash, F. Stewart, and C. Stimmell for providing the archaeological samples used in this study.

REFERENCES

Gurfinkel D. M. and Franklin U.M. (1988). A study of the feasibility of detecting blood residue on artifacts. J. Arch. Sci., 15: 83-97.

Lubec G., Nauer G., Seifert K., Strouhal E., Porteder H., Szilvassy J., and Teschler M. (1987). Structural stability of hair over three thousand years. J. Arch. Sci., 14: 113-120

Stahl E. (ed). (1969). Thin Layer Chromatography: A Laboratory Handbook., Springer-Verlag., New York.

Touchstone J.C. and Rogers D. (ed). (1980). Thin Layer Chromatography: Quantitative Environmental and Clinical Applications, John Wiley & Sons, New York.

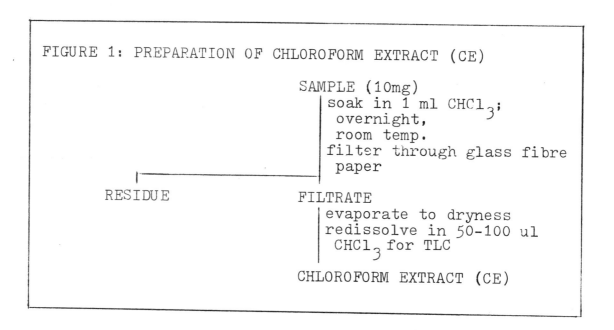

FIGURE 1: PREPARATION OF CHLOROFORM EXTRACT (CE)

SAMPLE (10mg)
soak in 1 ml $CHCl_3$; overnight, room temp. filter through glass fibre paper

RESIDUE | FILTRATE
evaporate to dryness redissolve in 50-100 ul $CHCl_3$ for TLC

CHLOROFORM EXTRACT (CE)

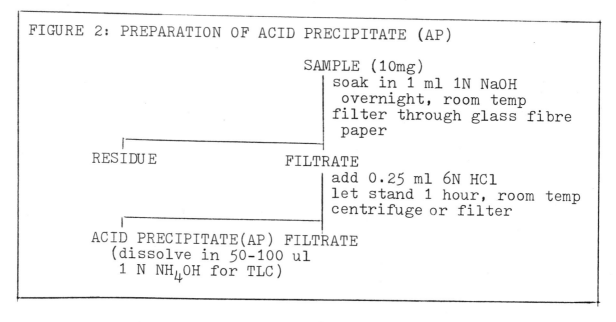

FIGURE 2: PREPARATION OF ACID PRECIPITATE (AP)

SAMPLE (10mg)
soak in 1 ml 1N NaOH overnight, room temp filter through glass fibre paper

RESIDUE | FILTRATE
add 0.25 ml 6N HCl let stand 1 hour, room temp centrifuge or filter

ACID PRECIPITATE(AP) FILTRATE
(dissolve in 50-100 ul 1 N NH_4OH for TLC)

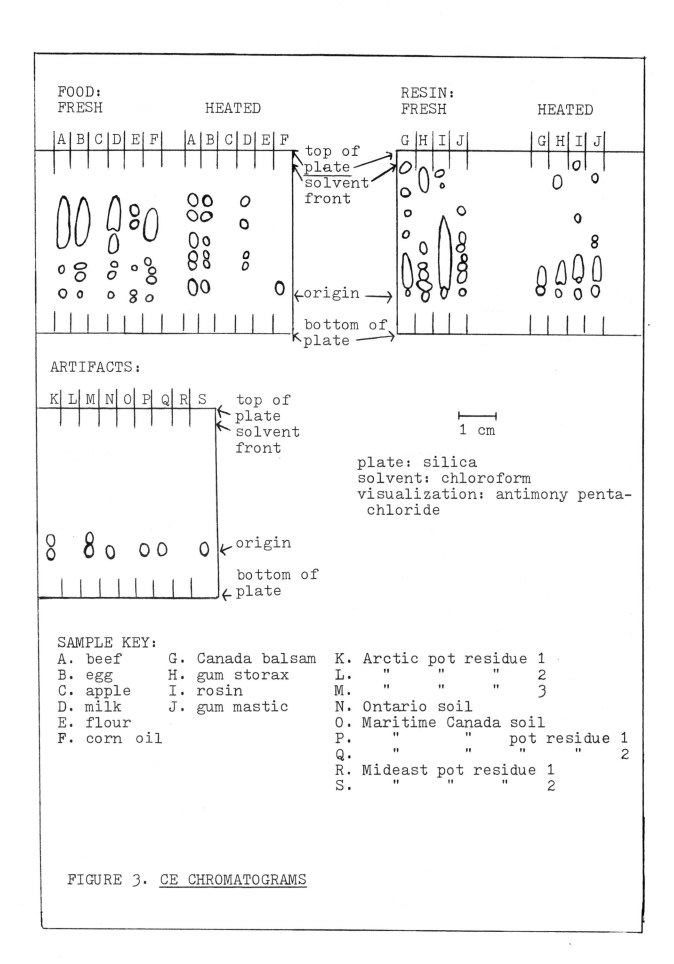

FIGURE 3. CE CHROMATOGRAMS

SAMPLE KEY:
A. beef
B. egg
C. apple
D. milk
E. flour
F. corn oil
G. Canada balsam
H. gum storax
I. rosin
J. gum mastic
K. Arctic pot residue 1
L.   "   "   "   2
M.   "   "   "   3
N. Ontario soil
O. Maritime Canada soil
P.   "   "   pot residue 1
Q.   "   "   "   "   2
R. Mideast pot residue 1
S.   "   "   "   2

plate: silica
solvent: chloroform
visualization: antimony penta-
    chloride

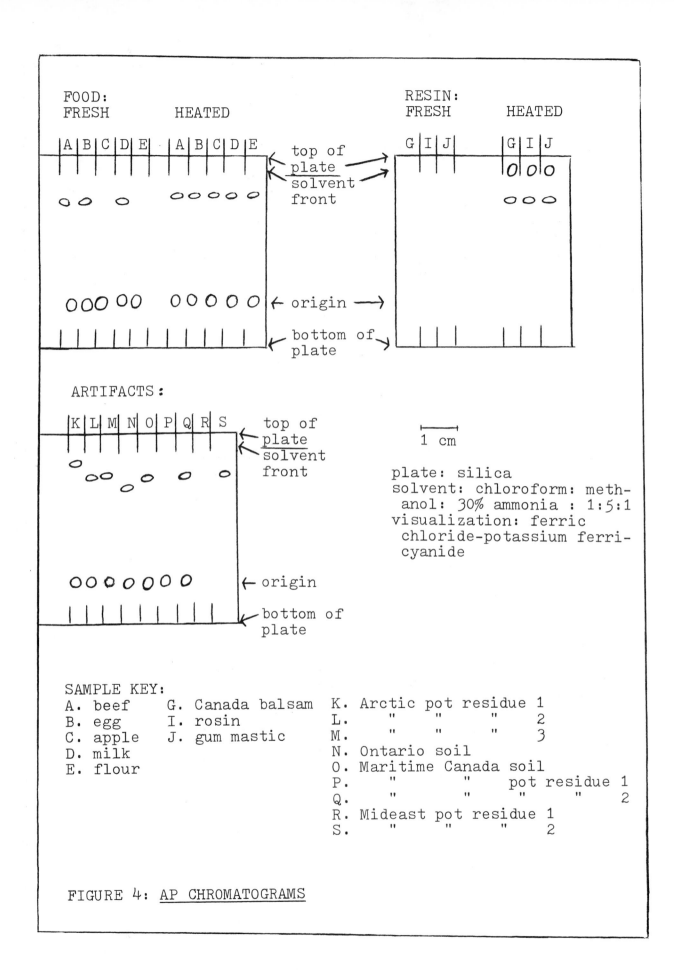

FIGURE 4: AP CHROMATOGRAMS

16. Stable Isotope Analysis of Food Residue from Ontario Ceramics

J.D. MORTON
H.P. SCHWARCZ

Department of Geology, McMaster University, Hamilton, Ontario, Canada L8S 4M1.

ABSTRACT: *Diets of animals and humans can be determined by stable isotopic analyses of bone collagen. Isotopic analyses of residues encrusted on Ontario prehistoric ceramics can provide an interesting comparison to the collagen results.*

INTRODUCTION

It has been previously shown that the onset of maize-based agriculture in southern Ontario can be recognized through shifts in the isotopic composition of human bone collagen from sites dated between 2000 B.C. and 1600 A.D. (Schwarcz et al. 1985). This is consistent with floral analysis studies by Fecteau (1985). He has outlined the arrival and spread of corn and beans with time, as shown by the number of sites on which corn and beans have been found through time. Corn is first found at approximately 500 A.D. and beans at approximately 1000 A.D. His work was based on the floral analyses of 136 archaeological sites in Ontario.

Hastorf and DeNiro (1985) showed that stable carbon and nitrogen isotope analyses of residues on prehistoric ceramics from Peru can provide some information as to what foods were cooked and presumably eaten, in the past. These authors also showed that cooking and carbonization of plants do not change the carbon or nitrogen ratios by any significant amount. The charring does destroy any plant structures within the residues which otherwise could have been identified under a microscope. We have attempted to apply stable isotopic analysis to encrustations on pot sherds from Ontario to test whether the shifts in dietary composition can also be seen in the foods being consumed.

Encrustations of residues commonly appear on the upper inside portions of pots, such as the rim, neck and/or shoulder. These residues are usually thick and flaky, having an appearance resembling charcoal. The residues are also usually very well stuck to the sherd. The residues commonly can be found occurring in a horizontal line, resembling a water line on a jar. Residues can also be found on the exterior surface of a pot. It is possible that exterior residues are due to a meal boiling over. Cooking experiments which we have performed show that thick soups or mashed foods, baked on during use, can result in such residues.

The carbonized nature allows the residues to be somewhat resistant to alteration, and they therefore should still contain some isotopic and chemical evidence of the ingredients that went into making them. If these are indeed food residues, then what better way to study prehistoric food consumption than to study what was cooked and eaten for dinner? Residues may also then provide some evidence of ceramic function.

THEORY OF ISOTOPIC ANALYSIS.

The application of stable isotopes to diet reconstruction is based on the fact that plants can be separated into categories based on their stable carbon and stable nitrogen isotopic ratios. These ratios are of carbon 13 to carbon 12 and nitrogen 15 to nitrogen 14 and are expressed as $\delta^{13}C$ and $\delta^{15}N$ respectively.

Edible plants of Ontario can be divided isotopically into two groups based on the way these plants fix organic carbon during photosynthesis, that is, the photosynthetic pathway. These two groups are C_3 plants and C_4 plants. Most native plants in this area are C_3 plants which use the Calvin pathway and produce organic carbon with mean $\delta^{13}C$ values of -26 per mil with respect to the PDB standard. C_4 plants, including maize, are found in sub-arid, hot regions and use the Hatch-Slack pathway. The $\delta^{13}C$ of these plants average around -12 per mil, but maize is typically about -9 per mil (Schwarcz et al. 1985).

Plants can also be divided into groups based on their nitrogen isotopic ratios ($\delta^{15}N$). Legumes, such as beans, fix their own nitrogen, resulting in $\delta^{15}N$ values similar to that of the atmosphere, for which $\delta^{15}N$ is 0 per mil by definition. Non-legumes obtain inorganic nitrogen from the soil and generally have higher $\delta^{15}N$ values, averaging about +6.2 per mil (DeNiro and Epstein 1981).

Archaeological specimens of plants exhibit isotopic values that differ little from those of corresponding modern plant samples (DeNiro and Hastorf 1985; Schwarcz et al. 1985). Some difference in $\delta^{15}N$ may occur due to modern environmental contamination.

Figure 1 shows the ranges of the various food resources that could have been utilized in prehistoric times. The boxes are constructed by taking the average $\delta^{13}C$ and $\delta^{15}N$ values plus or minus 3 per mil for each food group. These boxes roughly enclose all data for each group.

C_3, C_4 plants and legumes can easily be differentiated isotopically. Terrestrial animals and freshwater fish were also likely significant foods in the diet and can be placed on this graph. The isotopic value of the flesh of an animal is generally close to that of its diet. If C_4 plants are in an animal's diet then its isotopic signature will differ from an animal that prefers wild C_3 plants. This results in two boxes on the graph marked herbivore. The $\delta^{13}C$ for herbivore

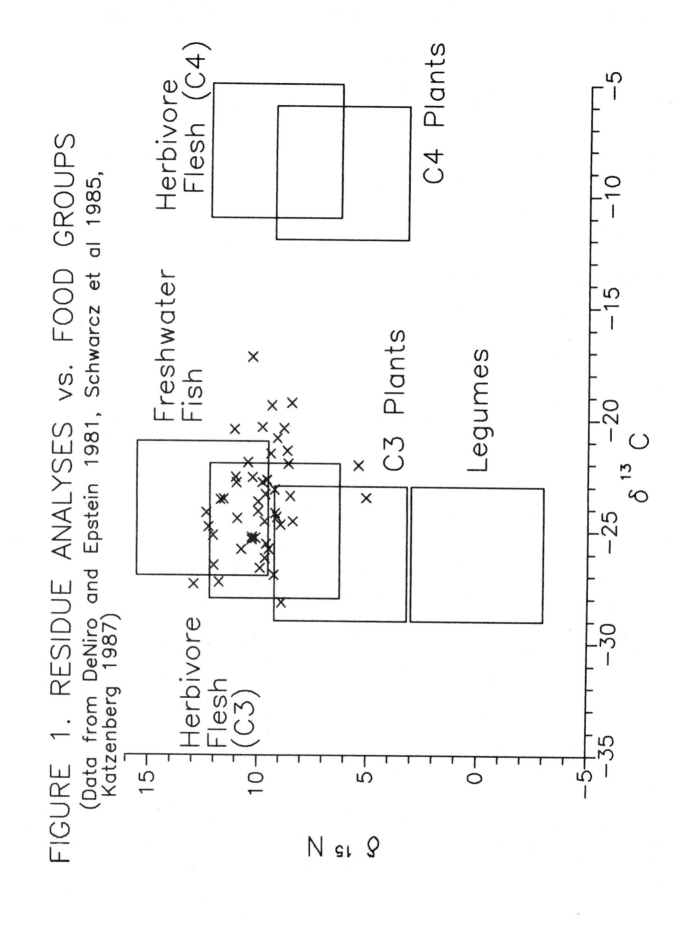

FIGURE 1. RESIDUE ANALYSES vs. FOOD GROUPS
(Data from DeNiro and Epstein 1981, Schwarcz et al 1985, Katzenberg 1987)

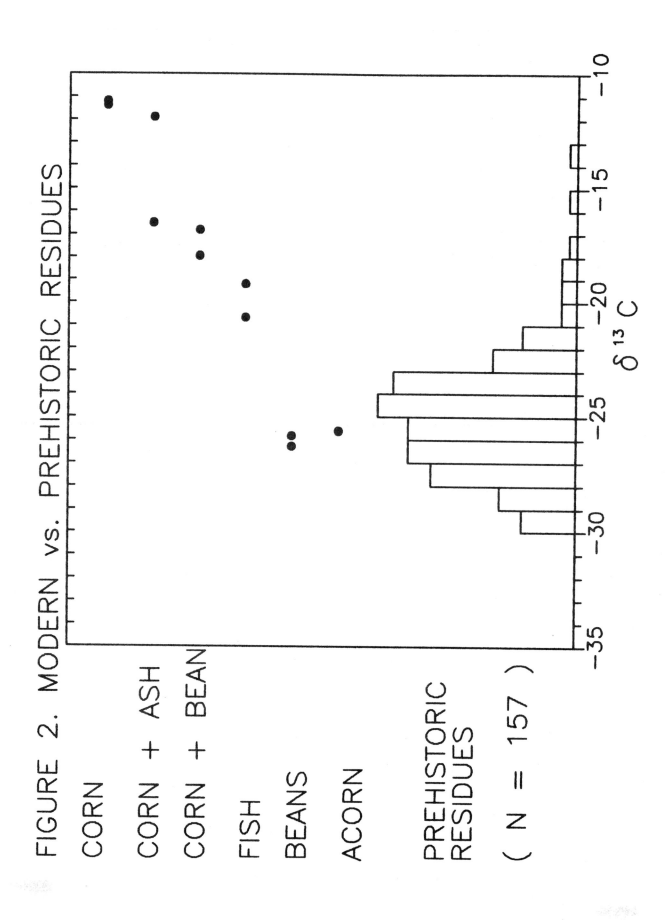

FIGURE 2. MODERN vs. PREHISTORIC RESIDUES

CORN

CORN + ASH

CORN + BEAN

FISH

BEANS

ACORN

PREHISTORIC
RESIDUES

(N = 157)

δ^{13} C

flesh was calculated from the plants in the diet using Schoeninger and DeNiro's (1984) fractionation factors of +1 per mil for $\delta^{13}C$ and +3 per mil for $\delta^{15}N$. The freshwater fish values are collagen values minus the fractionation factor of 3.9 per mil for $\delta^{13}C$ and 2.4 per mil for $\delta^{15}N$ (DeNiro and Epstein 1981).

RESULTS AND INTERPRETATION

For our research, samples of residues were obtained from ceramics from 48 sites, dating from 680 B.C. to 1725 A.D. and encompassing most of the prehistoric cultural periods throughout Ontario. Most of the residues are from southern Ontario sites, with a few from northern Ontario. The rarity of Early Woodland ceramics restricts the number of older residues obtained. Up to ten individual residues were analysed per site.

The analyses of palaeodiet using bone collagen (Schwarcz et al. 1985) showed that corn made up approximately 33% of the diet by 1100-1200 A.D., with a subsequent increase to 50% after this time. There is a time gap in both the bone and the residue analyses dating to the beginning of corn agriculture. Our residues suggest that the content of corn averaged around 9.1% through the interval from 680 B.C. to 1725 A.D., which is substantially less than that shown by the bone analyses.

The carbon isotopic ratio for each sample shows that there is no increase in the $\delta^{13}C$ value with the introduction of corn, nor any significant increase after this. The residues appear to be similar to native C_3 plants both before and after the introduction of corn into this area. The highest value of -12.7 per mil would correspond to a mixture of about 50% C_3 plants and 50% maize, close to the proportions inferred from the analyses of bone collagen by Schwarcz et al. (1985).

This study also involved the analyses of modern foods, before and after cooking. Cooking experiments were performed to reproduce residues on to modern replicas of prehistoric ceramics. Figure 2, comparing $\delta^{13}C$ of the modern residues versus the prehistoric residues, shows that although there is a large range of values for the prehistoric residues, most of the samples are more like C_3 plants. We found that mixtures of C_3 and C_4 plants produce baked-on residues that are substantially richer in ^{13}C than any other prehistoric residues.

The question arises: why is there little evidence of the presence of C_4 plants, namely corn, in the pots ? One possible explanation is that corn was a minor ingredient in the mixtures actually cooked in the pots. The remainder of dietary corn might then have been consumed in a different form, either whole or in some prepared form. The Jesuit Relations, as discussed by Waugh (1973), mention that the Indians were known to have unclean pots commonly encrusted with food. A residue would therefore be a long time accumulation from many meals, and would represent an average value of the food. While this could explain the relatively small spread in $\delta^{13}C$ and $\delta^{15}N$, it cannot account for the low average value, given the common assumption that corn was a food for the native peoples. Another possibility is that the residues have been contaminated by smoke from cooking fires, although this would at least show that corn stalks were not commonly used as fuel.

Partly burnt particles of C_3 plants (wood) present in the pot would lower the $\delta^{13}C$ value of a C_4-rich meal. There are also accounts of hot stones being placed into pots to boil the contents (Waugh 1973), which could provide a further means of transferring charred wood from the fire to the pot. However, it is unlikely that the charred particles constituted more than a few percent of the pot contents. In general, it is safe to assume that corn was likely eaten but it need not have been cooked or cooked in a pot. It could easily have been roasted or made into bread. This contrasts, however, to numerous references by the Europeans to the liquid state of the Indians' meals (e.g., Waugh 1973).

Another question is: how did the residues become carbonized? This may be due to a custom of leaving a pot over the fire for a long time, causing the contents to bake to the pot. Our cooking experiments have shown how easy it is to produce such residues, especially for more viscous mixtures of foods.

Analyses of $\delta^{15}N$ done on the residues also show no shift at the time of the introduction of beans. All the results fall within the range for non-legumes. Beans were expected in the residues since they should be cooked before being consumed. Unless there is another way to cook beans, it would appear that the beans were not a significant component of the diet. These results are very similar to those obtained from human bone in Ontario (Schwarcz et al. 1985), which also showed no shift in $\delta^{15}N$ through time. The necessary protein in the diet may have been supplied by the same sources both before and after the introduction of agriculture, most likely fish and game.

To better understand the results obtained so far in terms of available food resources, the results can be seen on Figure 1. As mentioned earlier, the pot residues do not appear to represent substantial proportions of either corn or beans. They can be accounted for as consisting of mixtures of plants , fish and meat from wild animals. The enrichment in ^{15}N shows the significance of fish in the diet. As Katzenberg (1988) states, it is possible that animal flesh, consumed by the native peoples, contributed to the high $\delta^{13}C$ values in the human bones. Animals could have eaten corn from the fields and if they were in turn eaten by the humans, they would have passed on their high $\delta^{13}C$ values. This effect was apparently a minor one.

DeNiro and Hastorf (1985) presented C:N ratios for both modern plants and prehistoric carbonized plants, and found a large range of values from 6.5 to 131.4 for the prehistoric carbonized plants. Hastorf and DeNiro (1985) obtained C:N ratios from modern meat residues ranging from 4.4 to 6.1. It was therefore hoped that the C:N ratios in the residues might allow us to estimate the proportion of plants to meat. The results which ranged from 18.8 to 39.3, are similar to the values of 18.5 to 32.5 obtained for modern plant residues that were made in our cooking experiments. Residues made from freshwater fish produced a C:N value of 9.1, much lower than that for the plant residues. These data suggest that the prehistoric residues contained substantial amounts of plant matter. The relatively low C:N values confirm that the residues are in fact food burnt to the ceramics and not dominantly wood particles, which was found to have a C:N ratio of 5384. The foods were most likely dominated by C_3 plant matter and not C_4 (corn). The C:N ratios do not require that meat and fish had been ingredients, but this is strongly indicated by the $\delta^{15}N$ values. The proportion of beans were relatively small.

Further chemical analyses of the residues, including gas chromatography of fatty acids, may provide more evidence as to the meals cooked in the past (Patrick et al. 1985; Deal and Silk 1987). Such analyses should be able to distinguish plant from animal matter, and specifically between meat and fish. Further comparisons will also be made with human bone, as well as between different cultural periods in Ontario.

ACKNOWLEDGEMENTS

This research was financed by the Ontario Heritage Foundation and the National Sciences and Engineering Research Council of Canada. We would like to thank all those who generously provided the pot sherd residues. We also thank Martin Kynf for all his patient assistance in the laboratory at McMaster University.

REFERENCES

Deal, M. and P. Silk (1987). Absorption residues and vessel functions: a case study of the Maine- Maritimes region. Ceramica de Cultura Maya. in press.

DeNiro, M. J. and S. Epstein (1981). Influence of diet on the distribution of nitrogen isotopes in animals. Geochimica et Cosmochimica Acta 45: 341-351.

DeNiro, M.J. and C. A. Hastorf. (1985). Alternation of the $^{15}N/^{14}N$ and $^{13}C/^{12}C$ ratios of plant matter during the initial stages of diagenesis. Studies utilizing archaeological specimens from Peru. Geochimica et Cosmochimica Acta 49: 97-115.

Fecteau, R.D. (1985). The Introduction and Diffusion of Cultivated Plants in Southern Ontario. Unpublished M.A. thesis, Department of Geography, York University, Toronto.

Hastorf, C.A. and M.J. DeNiro (1985). Reconstruction of prehistoric plant production and cooking practices by a new isotopic method. Nature 315: 489-491.

Katzenberg, M.A. (1987). Paper presented at the Meeting of the Canadian Association of Physical Anthropologists, Nov 6, 1987. Toronto.

Katzenberg, M.A. (1988). Stable Isotope Analysis of Animal Bone and the Reconstruction of Human Palaeodiet. In Diet and Subsistence: Current Archaeological Perspectives, Proceedings of the Nineteenth Annual Conference of the Archaeological Association of the University of Calgary, eds. B. V. Kennedy, and G.M. LeMoine: 307-314.

Patrick, M., A.J. deKoning and A.B. Smith (1985). Gas-Liquid Chromatographic Analysis of Fatty Acids in Food Residues from Ceramics found in the Southwestern Cape, South Africa. Archaeometry 27: 231-236.

Schoeninger, M. J. and M. J. DeNiro (1984). Nitrogen and Carbon Isotopic Composition of Bone Collagen from Marine and Terrestrial Animals. Geochimica et Cosmochimia Acta 48:625-639.

Schwarcz, H.P., J. Melbye, M.A. Katzenberg, and M. Kynf (1985). Stable Isotopes in Human Skeletons of Southern Ontario: reconstructing Palaeodiet. Journal of Archaeological Science 12:187-206.

Waugh, F.W. (1973). Iroquois Foods and Food Preparation. Canada Department of Mines, Geological Survey Memoir 86(12), Anthropological Series.

17. The Application of Quantitative Structural Image Analysis in the Study of Archaeological Textiles

M. EL-HOMOSSANI
U. M. FRANKLIN.
Department of Metallurgy and Materials Science, University of Toronto, Toronto, Canada.

ABSTRACT *In the course of a study of early compound textiles from Egypt, the authors have developed a systematic protocol for the technical investigation of ancient textiles and the reconstruction of their weaving technologies. To fulfill the protocol requirements, structural image analysis which is non-destructive and quantitative, has been considered.*

INTRODUCTION

The work reported here deals with the application of a quantitative microstructural technique to the characterization and analysis of ancient textiles and their weaving technologies.

Though textiles are of prime importance as historical and cultural sources, the preciousness and fragility of excavated ancient fabrics make the evaluation and comparison difficult. The experimental techniques employed here permit relevant information to be gained from the artifacts themselves. After photographing the objects, specialized measurements can be carried out using only the photographs. No material needs to be removed from the textiles; they are not handled excessively or exposed to uncontrolled atmospheres.

The computerized image evaluation reduces operator error and fatigue and allows for a review and re-examination of all measurements.

The aim of this kind of study is to elucidate the technological weaving details employed in the making of the textiles under study. Materials and weaving technologies in addition to consideration of styles and functions are powerful indicators of cultural contacts and technological innovations.

A research project has been undertaken to technically examine the examples of early compound woven fabrics found in Egypt, generally dated from the 3rd to 8th century A.D., in the Royal Ontario Museum collection. As a result of reviewing the collection, it becomes evident that there are many differences and similarities within the main group of Weft-faced Compound Weave structures. These structural variations demand accumulation of data on a larger scale for reliability and confirmation of results. The data should be based on factual findings resulting from the inner structural analysis of the fabric, and could be of great use in verifying some of the speculations based on theories derived from the outer appearance of the fabric. The existence of so many variables creates a necessity to achieve a suitable methodology which requires development in two areas:

1. establishing a protocol for the reconstruction of weaving technologies from experimental data;

2. applying analytical techniques which are non-destructive and quantitative.

PROTOCOL FOR THE RECONSTRUCTION OF WEAVING TECHNOLOGIES

In the study of archaeological textiles, when the technology becomes obscure due to lack of records or insufficient documentation, the extant product presents the most reliable source for extracting technical information and reconstructing past technology. A systematic analytical scheme as included in the protocol, appearing in Figure 1, recognizes the elements involved in the reconstruction of weaving technologies. The analysis follows a methodology which builds up technical data. This can be employed to characterize indispensible attributes, in order to establish types that can be utilized for tracing cultural influences and to develop logical interpretations for the records of archaeological findings.

The protocol deals with the information and data related to yarn characteristics, fabric construction, weave structures and design execution. The information in this scheme is interdependent and directly affects and contributes to the conclusions to be made, and should be obtained whenever possible. For instance, the fragmentary condition and the absence of selvage in many of the archaeological textiles makes the identification of warp and weft direction difficult. However, data related to yarn properties coupled with an in depth knowledge of weave structures can be utilized to resolve this problem. It is important to understand the interaction between each set of elements and the function of all the constituents incorporated in the weave structure. For example, by developing a new technique to achieve a certain effect in the performance and/or the design of a woven fabric, a new element might be introduced in the weave structure, or, the function of the existing elements could be altered. These changes directly influence the weaving process and require modification of the conventional devices (Looms) to extend their technical possibilities.

Elements such as repetitive order of the pattern unit and its dimensions, the drafts plan (threading order of warp ends), and lifting plan (order and sequence of shed formation), become most relevant to the study of archaeological textiles. This is especially true in the group of Compound Weaves because they give a clearer indication

A PROTOCOL FOR THE RECONSTRUCTION OF WEAVING TECHNOLOGIES: From Experimental Data.

(Fig. 1)

95

of the weaving technology employed in a certain period or region. The weaving technique and possible type of equipment must be explained, evaluated and reconstructed within a framework such as this protocol that allows for a meaningful comparison of data from different investigations, whether they relate to some or all aspects of the study of ancient textiles and their making.

STRUCTURAL IMAGE ANALYSIS

Structural image analysis is an automated analytical technique frequently used in modern material science (1). It is based on the usually computerized point to point evaluation of the microstructural components of a complex object. The quantitative information is obtained from a photograph of the surface under study. This technique has been incorporated into many materials evaluations and test specifications including modern textile testing (2).

While fibres of archaeological textiles have been measured and evaluated microscopically in the past (3), (4), the use of structural *image* analysis, in which the quantitative information is obtained from photographs, does not appear to have been applied to analytical studies in the technology of ancient fabrics.

The analytical scheme presented in the protocol includes parameters which should be quantitatively assessed, e.g., yarn diameter, twist angle, yarn count (linear density) as expressed in textile (g /km) and fabric weight (g/m²); in addition to basic measurements of number of ends and picks per cm. Conventional quantitative methods for measuring the forementioned parameters involve destructive techniques, and require considerable material handling, as well as sufficient sample size. Structural image analysis is non-destructive and avoids as much as possible materials deformation and deterioration.

In the present work, a digitizing tablet was used for the acquisition of data from magnified photographs of yarns making up the structure of archaeological textiles. The data so obtained were transmitted to and stored in an associated graphics microcomputer for subsequent evaluation and calculation, including the assessment of statistical significance.

In this method, a photograph image is projected on the tablet in the form of a slide or negative, and a straight distance between two points across the yarn periphery is traced out point by point, using the cursor of the digitizer. The distance between each two points is automatically determined and stored in the computer. Though the precision of this procedure is limited by the resolution of the tablet and other factors, it was a simple procedure to digitize, for example 40 points on yarns included in an area of one cm² photographed to measure the average yarn diameter. Measuring the number of ends and picks per cm. as well as twist angle is a straightforward procedure which can be done directly from the projected image, thus providing a simple and efficient method. Yarn linear density and fabric weight can be derived by calculations from established formulae (5). Corresponding measurements are carried out to gather data for the subsequent stages of the protocol, including the dimensions of design repeat units, their uniformity and symmetry.

FINDINGS

The testing of the image analyzing techniques and the development of the protocol are part of a larger study centred around the early Compound textiles from Egypt in the Royal Ontario Museum's collection.

The objects are now being studied, and findings listed below are new information on these textiles. They are presented here primarily illustrating the methodology.

Warp vs Weft Determined Patterns

In principle, patterns in early Compound woven fabrics can be either fully or mainly determined by colour arrangement of the Warp, or they can be executed using a variety of Wefts on an essentially plain or uniform Warp.

Ancient Chinese weaving technology has been predominantly *Warp determined* (6), (7). The weaver develops his patterns in the same direction as the user will see it.

Textiles dated to late Roman and Coptic periods (those studied here and many others (8)) exhibit *Weft determined* bands of sophisticated ornamentation. Here the weaver composes the pattern at right angles to the direction the band will appear in the finished object (Figure 2).

These technological alternatives most likely indicate deeply rooted cultural traditions pointing to technical requirements associated with the method of pattern development. Thus, when considering the transmission of technologies and materials it is essential to go beyond style and symbolism to the details of the technical execution of the fabric.

Structural variables within the Textiles Produced in Weft-faced Compound Weaves

Weft-faced Compound weaves are usually classified into two main groups based on the type of weave structure employed for binding the Weft: a) Weft-faced Compound tabby weave; and b) Weft-faced Compound twill weave. Within these two groups, structural variables other than the type of binding weave do exist:
-fibre content: all wool, wool/linen, wool/cotton and silk;
-yarn characteristics: construction (single ply), twist direction (s,z), and the degree of twist angle;
-interlacing order: variation in the ratio of the inner-warp to the binding-warp, 1:1 order and 2:1 order.
Of these, the following features were shown in the image analysis of:

1) ROM, 961.107.5.
Warp: Wool, 2 ply, final twist in S direction,
Weft: wool, single, Z twist,
Binding Weave: tabby, ratio of inner-warp to binding-warp 1:1
The use of 2 ply warp in this context is not known to have been reported, (Figure 3);
2) ROM, 980-78.35.
Warp: wool, single, Z twist,
Weft: wool, two-fold (doubled yarn) per pick, Z twist,

Figure 2. Tapestry band incorporated in a Weft-faced Compound fabric, ROM, 968.323.1.
Notice the pattern shown in the way it is woven, warp in the vertical direction and weft in the horizontal direction. In the finished product the figures will be turned 90°.

Figure 3. Two ply Warp used in a Weft-faced Compound Weave structure, ROM, 961.107.5.

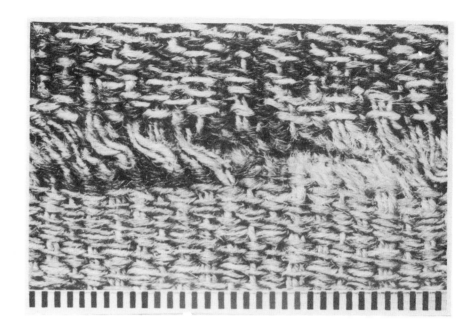

Figure 4. Transition zone from simple weave to Weft-faced Compound weave ROM, 968.323.1.

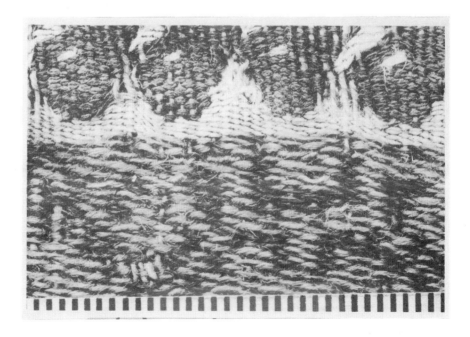

Figure 5. Transition zone from Weft-faced Compound weave to Tapestry weave ROM, 968.323.1.

Binding Weave: twill 1/2, ratio of inner-warp to binding warp 1:1.
3) ROM, 977.173.
Warp: wool, single, S twist,
Weft: cotton, single, S twist; and wool, single, S twist,
Binding Weave: twill 1/2, ratio of inner-warp to binding warp 2:1.

Transition Zones (Figures 4 & 5)

Combination of more than one weave structure in the same fabric can be utilized to depict changes in weaving technologies. The existence of transition zones, resulting from changes in the interlacing order from one weave to another, directly initiates modification in the weaving technique. Hence, loom type, weaving processes and the progress of technology could be reconstructed by detailed analysis of these changes. There is evidence that during this period the weavers were experimenting and developing new techniques to overcome mechanical limitations associated with their weaving devices. Thus the technique has already revealed hitherto unrecorded details which, when properly analyzed and evaluated, may significantly affect the current notions of cultural and technological interplay in the eastern Mediterranean.

ACKNOWLEDGEMENTS

The authors gratefully acknowledge the support, interest and participation of Louise W. MacKie, Curator of the Textiles Department, Royal Ontario Museum.

The work of M. El-Homossani has been supported by the Social Sciences and Humanities Research Council of Canada, the research of U.M. Franklin by the National Science and Engineering Research Council of Canada, which is acknowledged with much appreciation.

REFERENCES

1. Jurgen, P. and Exner, H.E., Recent Development in Automatic Devices for Quantitative Microstructural Analysis, Pract. Met., 23, 1986, pp. 277-86.

2. A.S.T.M., D3510-81, Standard Method for Diameter of Wool and other Animal Fibres by Image Analyzer.

3. Ryder, M.L. and Gabra-Sanders, T., The Application of Microscopy to Textile History, Textile History 16, 1985, pp.123-140.

4. Ryder, M. L. and Gabra-Sanders, T., A Microscopic Study of Remains of Textiles Made From Plant Fibres, Oxford J. of Archaeol., 6, 1987, pp. 91-108.

5. Booth, J.E., Textile Mathematics, Vol.2, The Textile Institute, Manchester, 1975, p.333.

6. Kuhn, D., The Silk-Workshops of the Shang Dynasty, 16th-11th Century B.C., Explorations in the History of Science and Technology in China, Chinese Classics Publishing House, Shanghai, 1982, p.382.

7. Burnham, H.B., Technical Aspects of the Warp-faced Compound Weaves of the Han Dynasty, Bulletin de Liaison, CIETA, No. 22, July 1965, pp. 22-45.

8. Weibel, A.C., Two Thousand Years of Textiles, Publ. for The Detroit Instit. of Arts, Pantheon Books, New York, 1952, p.87 & Figure 37.

SELECTED BIBLIOGRAPHY RELATED TO THE PROTOCOL

Fibres and Yarn Characteristics

Annual Book of ASTM Standards, Vol.07.01 and 07.02., 1986.
    Standard Test Method for Diameter of Wool and other Animal Fibres by Microprojection, D 2130.85.
    Standard Test Method for Diameter of Wool and other Animal Fibres by Image Analyzer, D 3510-81.
    Use of the Tex System to Designate Linear Density of Fibres. Yarn Intermediates, and Yarns, D861-84.
Bellinger, L., Textile Analysis of Early Techniques in Egypt and the Near east, Part I- the four main fibres and the basic weave for each, Workshop Note #2, Textile Museum, Washington D.C. 1950.
Bellinger, L., Craft Habits: Spinning and fibres in Warp Yarns, Part II-Model of Spinner and yarn from the same tomb", Workshop Note #20, Textile Museum, Washington D.C., 1959.
Booth, J.E., Principles of Textile Testing, London, 1970.
Booth, J.E., Textile Mathematics, Vol.2 &3, The Textile Institute, Manchester, 1977.
Crowfoot, G.M., Methods of Hand Spinning in Egypt and the Sudan, Halifax, 1931, Reprinted, 1978.
Hearle, J.W., S., Grosberg, P., and Backer, S., Structural Mechanics of Fibres Yarns and Fabrics, Wiley-Interscience, New York, 1969.
Heyn, A.W.J., Fiber Microscopy: A Text Book and Laboratory Manual, Interscience, New York, 1954.
Hutchings, N. J. and Ryder, M. L., The Automation of the Projection--Microscope Method of Fibre Diameter Measurement, J. Text. Inst., 76, 1985, pp.295-99.
Luniak, B. The Identification of Textile Fibres, Isaac Pittman & Son, London, 1953.
Lutz, H.F., Textiles and Costumes Among the People of the Ancient Near East, Liepzig, 1923.
Matthews, J.M. and Mauersberger, H.R., Textile Fibres, their Physical Microscopical and Chemical Properties, 6th ed., J. Wiley & Sons Inc., New York, 1953.
Pfister, R., Textiles des Palryre, I-III, Paris, 1933, 1937, 1940.
Ryder, M.L. and Gabra-Sanders, T., The Application of Microscopy to Textile History, Textile History 16, 1985, pp. 123-140.
Stove, J.L., Fiber Microscopy, D. van Nostrand Co. Inc., New York, 1958.
Von Bergen, W. and Kraus, W., Textile Fibre Atlas, Textile Book Publishers, Inc., New York, 1949.

Fabric Constructions, Weave Structures and Loom Technologies

Ackerman, P., A Survey of Persian Art, Vol III, Oxford, 1938-39
Allen, H.L., American and European Hand Weaving Revised, College Print. Publ., Madison W.S., 1970.
Bellinger, L., Workshop Notes, Textile Museum, Washington D.C.:
    #3, Textile Analysis: Early Techniques in Egypt and the Near East, Part II: Twill inlay patterns, wool tapestry on linen warp", 1951.
    #6, Textile Analysis: Early Techniques in Egypt and the Near East, Part III: drawloom fabrics with cloth or twill binding; point and comber repeat, 1952.
    #15, Textile Analysis: Developing Techniques in Egypt and the Near East, Part V: expanding use wool weaving traditions, 1957.

#16, Textile Analysis: Developing Techniques in Egypt and the Near East, Part VI: expanding use of linen weaving traditions, 1957.

#19, Craft Habits, Loom Types Suggested by Weaving Details, Part I: model weaving shop and a sheet from the same tomb, 1959.

Burnham, D. K., Warp and Weft, A Textile Terminology, Royal Ontario Museum, Toronto, 1980.

Duncan, J., Practical and Descriptive Essays on the Art of Weaving, Glasgow, 1807-8.

Emery, I. The Primary Structures of Fabrics, The Textile Museum, Washington D.C., 1980.

Emery, I.and and Fiske, P., eds. Irene Emery Roundtable on Museum textiles, 1977, Proceedings: Looms and Their Products, The Textile Museum, Washington D.C. 1979.

Flanagan, J.F., Figured Fabrics, A History of Technology, Vol.3, Oxford University. 1957.

Flanagan, J.F. Figured Silks, in C.F. Battiscombe ed., The Relics of Saint Cuthbert, pp 494-525.

Forbes, R., Studies in Ancient Technology, Vol. 1V, Lieden, 1956.

Geiyer, A., A History of Textile Art, Pasold Research Fund in Association with Sotheby Parker Bernet Publ., London, 1979.

Grosicki, Z.J. Watson's Textile Design and Colour, 7th ed., Newnes-Butterworths, London, 1975.

Grosicki, Z.J. Watson's Advanced Textile Design, 4th ed, Newness-Butterworth, London, 1977.

Guicherd, F., Cours de Theories de Tissage, Editions 7em., Lyon, 1946.

Hooper, L., Hand Loom Weaving, London, 1910, reprinted, 1979.

Hooper, L., Loom and Spindle: Past, Present and Future, Smithsonian Instit., Annual Report for 1914, Washington D.C., pp. 629-79.

Johl, C.H., Die Webestuhle de Grieschen und Romer, Liepzig, 1917.

Ling, R.H. Studies in Primitive Looms, 3rd ed., Halifax, 1950.

Ling, R.H. Ancient Egyptian and Greek Looms, Bankfield Museum Notes, 2nd Series No.2, Halifax, 1951.

Patterson, R., Spinning and Weaving, The Mediterranean Civilizations and the Middle Ages, A History of Technology, Vol. II. Oxford, 1956.

Pfister, R. and Bellinger, L., The Excavation of Dura-Europos, Final Report IV, pt II, The Textiles, Yale University, New Haven, 1945.

Reath, N. A. and Sachs, E.B., Persian Textiles, Yale University, New Haven, 1937.

Robinson, A.C.T. and Marks, R., Woven Cloth Construction, The Textile Institute, 1973.

Schaefer, G. and Born, W., The Loom, Ciba Review, 16, 938. Vocabulary of Technical Terms, Fabrics, CIETA, Lyon, 1964.

Yates, J., Textrenum Antiqorum: An Account of the Art of Weaving Among the Ancient, Taylor & Walton, London, 1843.

Design

Born, W., Textile ornament, Ciba Review, 37, 1941.

Evans, J., Pattern: A Study of Ornament in Western Europe from 1180-1900, Clarendon Press, Oxford, 1931.

Glazier, R., Historic Textile fabrics: A Short history of the tradition and development of pattern in woven and printed stuffs. Chas. Scribner's Sons, New York, 1923.

Grosicki, Z. J. Watson's Textile Design and Colour, Newness-Butterworths, London, 1975, pp. 208-298.

Posselt, E.A., Technology of Textile Design, Henry Carey Baird & Co., Philadelphia, 1889.

Sonday, M., Pattern and Weaves: Sajavid Lampas and Velvet, Woven from the Soul, Spun from the Heart, Textile Arts of Sajavid and Quajar Iran, 16th-9th Centuries, Ed. by C. Bier, The Textile Museum, Washington D.C., 1987.

18. Bone Chemistry and Dietary Reconstruction in Prehistoric Britain: Examples from Orkney, Scotland

S.E. ANTOINE and A. M. POLLARD
Chemistry Department, University College, Cardiff CF1 1XL, Wales, UK.

P.Q. DRESSER
Plant Science Department, University College, Cardiff CF1 1XL, Wales, UK.

A.W.R. WHITTLE
Archaeology Department, University College, Cardiff CF1 1XL, Wales, UK.

ABSTRACT: *Calcium, strontium, zinc and magnesium contents of ashed bones and stable carbon and nitrogen isotope ratios of bone collagen in 159 bone samples from four sites in Orkney, Scotland, were measured. The calcium results show a substantial post-mortem deposition into the inorganic fraction of bone. Those four trace element contents indicate marine subsistence and/or post-mortem deposition from the surrounding environment. Stable carbon isotope ratios did not however indicate a mainly marine diet but rather a mixed marine-terrestrial diet. It is concluded that the palaeodiet of the studied communities is better reconstructed from stable carbon isotopes than from trace element analysis. Stable nitrogen isotope ratios also clearly indicate a mixed marine-terrestrial diet.*

INTRODUCTION

Trace elemental contents in ancient human bone have provided information on the diet of prehistoric communities in Europe, e.g., in the Netherlands (Runia 1987a, b, c), and in the south of England (Antoine et al. 1988) and in the United States and Canada (Beck 1985; Brown 1973, 1974; Fuchs 1978; Gilbert 1975; Hatch and Geidel 1985; Lambert et al. 1979, 1984, 1985; Pate and Brown 1985; Price and Kavanagh 1982; Price et al. 1985b; Schoeninger 1979, 1981, 1982; Sillen 1981; Szpunar 1977 and many others).

Stable carbon isotope ratios of collagen extracted from prehistoric human bone have been used extensively to reconstruct palaeodiet in prehistoric communities in Europe (Tauber 1981; Runia 1978a; Antoine et al. 1988), Africa (Sealey and Van der Merwe 1985; Ambrose and DeNiro 1986) and in America (Chisholm et al. 1982, 1983; Lovell et al. 1986 and other investigators). Stable nitrogen isotope ratios of bone collagen have also received increasing attention over the last decade, though much less than the stable carbon isotope ratios (DeNiro and Epstein 1981; Schoeninger et al. 1982; Nelson et al. 1986; Antoine et al. 1988).

METHODS

A total of 159 human bone samples were obtained from Neolithic burials in the Orkney Islands (Figure 1), of which 97 were from Quanterness, 30 from Isbister Cairn, 22 from Holm of Papa Westray North and 10 samples were from Point of Cott. The types of bone analysed are given in Table 1.

The method for the mineral collagen extraction and measurement of stable isotopic ratios are described in Antoine et al. (1988). Ca, Sr, and Mg were measured by atomic emission; Zn by atomic absorption spectrophotometry.

RESULTS AND DISCUSSION

The range, mean, median, and upper and lower quartiles of the values of mineral content and isotopic ratios of the analysed samples are shown in Figures 2 to 7. The mean and standard deviation of these values and results of F tests are given in Table 2.

Mineral Content

It is clear from Table 2 and Figures 2 and 5 that the calcium, strontium, magnesium and zinc values are markedly high in all four communities which (apart from the calcium) indicates a high marine component in their diet. For example, Kyle (1986) and Runia (1987a) reported that the consumption of sea food will result in high Sr concentrations in bone, since, according to Odum (1957) and Rosenthal (1962), higher Sr levels are found in marine plants and animals than in terrestrial organisms due to the concentrated mineral levels in oceanic waters. Palaeodietary studies of ancient populations from Alaska have indicated that the Sr levels can be used to distinguish the importance of terrestrial versus marine organisms in subsistence (Connor and Slaughter 1984). Other trace elements in bone and minerals are also found in substantial quantities in marine waters. Ultimately marine plants and animals will have higher trace element contents (e.g., Zn and Mg) than terrestial organisms. It should be noted that post-mortem deposition of minerals from the surrounding burial environment might also play an important role in the values obtained from archaeological bone as discussed below.

Table 2 shows significant difference between the concentrations of elements studied, as measured by the F

Table 1. Types of bone analysed.

Source	Femur	Humerus	Ribs	Tibia	Fibula	Radius	Ulna	Meta-tarsals	Unknown
Quanterness	27	2	49	11	–	–	–	–	8
Isbister Cairn	16	12	–	2	–	–	–	–	–
Holm of Papa Westray North	4	1	13	–	1	1	1	1	–
Point of Cott	10	–	–	–	–	–	–	–	–
Total	57	15	62	13	1	1	1	1	8

Figure 1. Map of the study area.

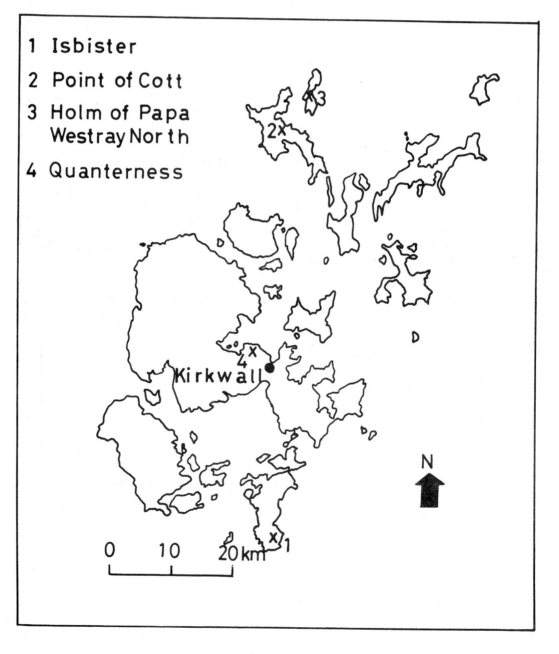

1 Isbister

2 Point of Cott

3 Holm of Papa Westray North

4 Quanterness

Kirkwall

N

0   10   20 km

ratio test. The higher Ca content in the samples compared to that reported for modern bone (Price et al. 1985b) suggests that these bones have been well preserved and that additional post-mortem deposition of Ca has taken place during diagenesis. A similar observation was reported for the Neolithic samples from Hambledon Hill in the south of England (Antoine et al. 1988). The results of this study did not reveal any significant differences in mineral contents of the different types of bone analysed. This agrees with our findings for the Neolithic and Early Bronze Age communities of Wessex in the south of England.

Stable isotope ratios

Table 2 and Figure 6 clearly show that the range and mean values of $\delta^{13}C$ was between that reported indicating a terrestrial diet (-23 to -34°/.., DeNiro and Epstein 1978) and that indicating a marine diet (-10 to -18°/.. DeNiro and Epstein 1978; Tauber 1981). This may indicate the consumption of a mixed marine and terrestrial diet by the Orkney communities, possibly with a higher dependence on marine food in the diet. Table 2 also shows insignificant variations in the isotope ratios between the communities, compared with the highly significant variations shown by the trace elements. Therefore, since stable carbon isotope ratios, as well as stable nitrogen isotope ratios, are not

expected to be subject to such severe diagenetic alteration as that already suggested for the mineral components of the bone, they should be more reliable in palaeodietary reconstruction, particularly in the case of the Orkney samples where the trace elements show a large variation within each site. It is therefore concluded that the palaeodiets of the studied communities are better reconstructed from the stable carbon isotope ratios rather than from the trace element analysis. This conclusion is also reached from our speculation about diagenetic deposition of trace elements and calcium in the buried bones.

The mean and range of $\delta^{15}N$ (Table 2 and Figure 7) of the present study lie between those reported for terrestial animals (mean of +5.3°/..) and that of marine animals (mean of +14.8°/..) Schoeninger and DeNiro 1983). This also suggests that the Orkney diet was a mixed one, and that the reliance on the data provided by the stable isotope ratios gives a better understanding for palaeodiet reconstruction.

REFERENCES

Ambrose, H.S. and M.J. DeNiro (1986). Nature 319:321-324.

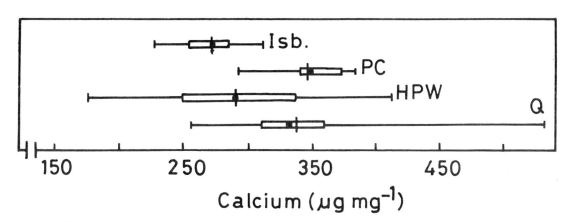

Figure 2. Range, median (bar), mean (closed circle) and upper and lower percentiles of calcium content.

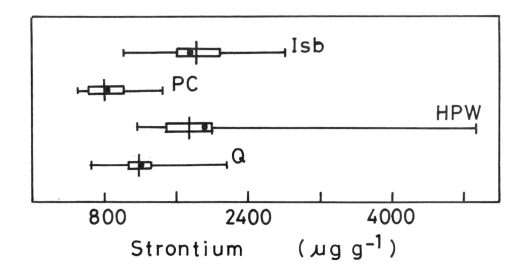

Figure 3. Range median (bar), mean (closed circle) and upper and lower percentile of strontium content.

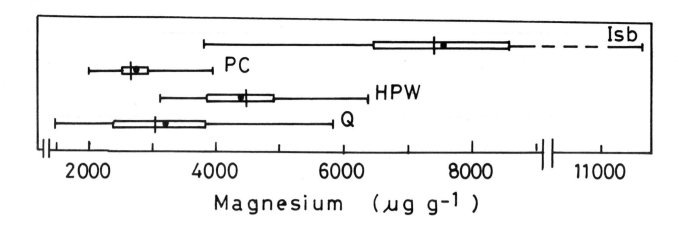

Figure 4. Range, median (bar), mean (closed circle) and upper and lower percentile of magnesium content.

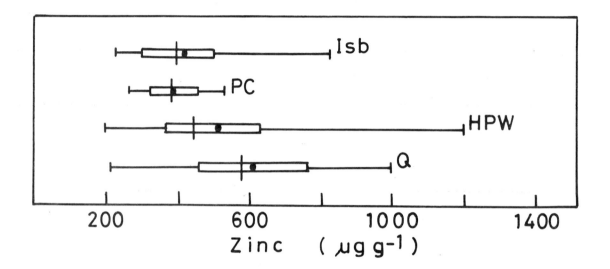

Figure 5. Range, median (bar), mean (closed circle) and upper and lower percentiles of zinc content.

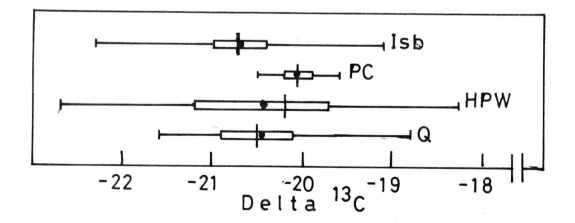

Figure 6. Range, median (bar), mean (closed circle) and upper and lower percentiles of δ ^{13}C values.

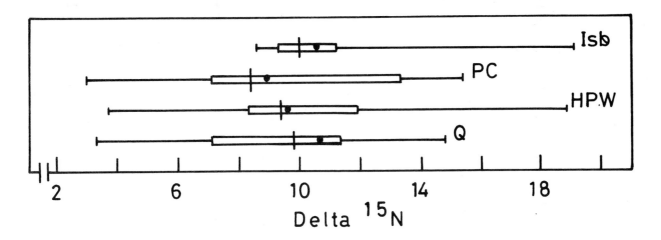

Figure 7. Range, median (bar), mean (closed circle) and upper and lower quartiles of δ ¹⁵N values.

	Isbister Cairn	Holm of Papa Westray	Point of Cott Westray	Quanterness	F
Ca (ug/mg)	272±21	291±60	348±25	334±33	26.2
Sr (ug/g)	1818±389	1931±798	827±261	1200±240	27.1
Mg (ug/g)	7579±1565	4456±873	2744±550	3237±1032	13.3
Zn (ug/g)	417±152	515±227	377±83	611±207	13.0
Delta ^{13}C	-20.7±0.6	-20.4±1.2	-20.1±0.3	-20.6±0.5	2.0
Delta ^{15}N	+10.6±2.1	+9.7±3.5	+9.0±3.9	+10.7±2.4	1.1

Critical F values; for elemental data $(F_{3,150}^{0.05}) = 2.64$

for isotopic data $(F_{3,90}^{0.05}) = 3.25$

Table 2. Detailed comparison of Orkney sites (Means ± 1 standard deviation).

Antoine, S.E., P.Q. Dresser, A.M. Pollard and A.W.R. Whittle (1988). British Archaeological Reports (BAR). In press.

Beck, L.A. (1985) J. of Hum. Evol. 14: 493-502.

Brown, A.B. (1973). Bone Strontium Content as a Dietary Indicator in Human Skeletal Populations. Ph.D Dissertation, University of Michigan.

Brown, A.B. (1974). Conrib. Geol. 13: 47-48.

Chisholm, B.S., D.E. Nelson and H.P. Schwarcz (1982). Nature 216: 1131-1132.

Chisholm, B.S., D.E. Nelson and H.P. Schwarcz (1983). Cur. Anthr. 24: 396-398.

Connor, M. and D. Slaughter (1984). Arctic Anthr. 21: 123-134.

DeNiro, M.J. and S. Epstein (1978). Geochim. Cosmochim. Acta 42: 495-506.

DeNiro, M.J. and S. Epstein (1981). Geochim. Cosmochim. Acta 45: 341-351.

Fuchs, A. (1978). MASCA J. 1: 10-11. (Quoted from Pate and Brown 1985).

Gilbert, R.I. (1975). Trace Element Analyses of Three Skeletal Amerindian Populations at the Dickson Mounds. Ph.D Dissertation, University of Minnesota.

Hatch, J.W and R.A. Geidel (1985). J. of Hum. Evol. 14: 469-476.

Kyle, J.H. (1986). J. Arch. Sci. 13: 403-416.

Lambert, J.B., C.B. Szpunar and J.E. Buikstra (1979). Archaeometry 21: 115-129.

Lambert, J.B., S.M. Vlasak, J.E. Buikstra and D.K. Charles (1984). Analysis of Soils Associated with Woodland Burials. In Archaeological Chemistry. J.B. Lambert (ed). Amer. Chem. Soc.

Lambert, J.B., S.M. Vlasak, C.B. Szpunar and J.E. Buikstra (1985). J. Hum. Evol. 14: 477-482.

Lovell, N.C., D.E. Nelson and H.P. Schwarcz (1986). Archaeometry 28: 51-55.

Nelson, B.K., M.J. DeNiro, M.J. Schoeninger, D.J. De Paolo and P.E. Hare (1986). Geochim. Cosmochim. Acta 50:1941-1949.

Odum, H.T. (1957). Inst. Mar. Sci. Publ. 4: 38-114. (Quoted from Pate and Brown 1985).

Pate, D. and K.K. Brown (1985). J. of Human Evol. 14: 483-491.

Price, T.D. and M. Kavanagh (1982). Mid-Cont. J. Arch. 7: 61-79.

Price, T.D., M. Connor and J.D. Parsen (1985a). J. Arch. Sci. 12: 419-442.

Price, T.D., M.J. Schoeninger and C.J. Armelagos (1985b). J. Hum. Evol. 14: 419-447.

Rosenthal, H.L. (1963). Ann. New York Acad. Sci. 109: 278-293. (Quoted from Price et al. 1985b).

Runia, L.T. (1987a). The Chemical Analysis of Prehistoric Bones. A Palaeodietary and Ecoarchaeological Study of Bronze Age West-Friesland. Bar Internat. Ser. 363. 234pp.

Runia, L.T. (1987b). Archaeometry 29: 221-232.

Runia, L.T. (1987c). J. of Arch. Sci. 14: 599-608.

Schoeninger, M.J. (1979). Am. J. of Phys. Anthr. 51: 295-310.

Schoeninger, M.J. (1981). Palaeorient 7: 73-91.

Schoeninger, M.J. (1982). Am. J. Phys. Anthro. 58: 37-52.

Schoeninger, M.J. and M.J. DeNiro (1984). Geochim. Cosmochim Acta 48: 625-639.

Schoeninger, M.J., M.J. DeNiro and H. Tauber (1982). Geol. Soc. Am. Abstr. Program 14: 611.

Schoeninger, M.J., M.J. DeNiro and H. Tauber (1983). Science 220: 1381-1383.

Sealey, J.C. and N. J. Van der Merwe (1985). Nature 315: 138-160.

Sillen, A. (1981). Am. J. of Phys. Anthr. 56: 131-137.

Spuznar, C.B. (1977). Atomic Absorption Analysis of Archaeological Remains: Human Ribs from Woodland Mortuary Sites. Ph.D Dissertation, Northwestern University.

Tauber, H. (1981). Nature 292: 332-333.

19. Control of Environmental Contamination of Buried Bone

J. B. LAMBERT and LIANG XUE
Department of Chemistry, Northwestern University, Evanston, IL, 60208 U.S.A.

ABSTRACT: *Removal of 1-3 mm of bone surface provides cleaner samples and permits statistical comparisons to determine how levels of specific chemical elements have been altered during burial.*

INTRODUCTION

Extraction of dietary information from buried human bone is one of the most challenging problems in scientific archaeology today. The profile of trace inorganic elements present in bone is taken to reflect the diet of the individual. In order for such data to be validly interpreted, it is of course necessary that the levels of inorganic elements present after excavation be the same as those at the time of death. Unfortunately, there are manifold opportunities for changes to occur. Some elements can exchange chemically with calcium in the hydroxyapatite matrix (heteroionic replacement). Elements also can fill voids, usually formed by the disappearance of organic components, or they may be absorbed onto the bone surface without displacement of calcium (Lambert et al. 1985b). Finally, trace elements already present in bone can be lost through leaching. As reviewed previously (Lambert et al. 1984c, 1985a), several methods have been developed to determine whether levels of specific elements have been altered diagenetically. We will first describe these tests, then we will describe our current efforts to control exchange and contamination.

TESTS FOR DIAGENETIC ALTERATION OF ELEMENTAL LEVELS

As soon as a data set is gathered, the elemental levels may be compared crudely with those in modern bone (Tipton and Shafer 1964). Noticeable differences between modern and ancient levels suggest diagenetic alteration. For example, a modern bone contains 35-36% of Ca. Heteroionic exchange will decrease this value. In our earliest study (Lambert, Szpunar, and Buikstra 1979), we found an average value of 33% for North American Woodland ribs, indicating only minimal exchange. Modern bone contains about 200-500 ppm of Fe, but this same study found 2000-5000 ppm. We concluded that extensive influx of Fe had occurred from the soil.

Contamination, exchange, and leaching should depend on the porosity of bone and hence vary from one skeletal component to another. Parker and Toots (1970, 1980) suggested tests comparing tooth dentine and enamel. We compared a cortical bone (femur) with a cancellous bone (rib) (Lambert et al. 1982) from Woodland sites. Three elements (Sr, Zn, Mg) had statistically identical levels in both bone types. These elements probably were not affected by contamination or leaching. Elements that were significantly lower in the less dense rib (Fe, Al, Mn, Cu, K) were thought to have been contaminated by soil constituents (the rib more so than the femur). Other elements (Na, Pb) showed lower levels in the rib, so that they may have suffered loss through leaching. Grupe (1988) has compared cortical bone (femurs) with trabecular bone (the crista iliaca) for samples from Schleswig (11th and 12th century A.D.) and found significant differences for Ca, P, Sr, Ba, Zn, and Mg. She urged the use of compact bone such as the shaft of the femur or tibia as the best measure of levels in the total skeleton.

Examination of the soil immediately adjacent to buried bone should provide some information about the chemical flux that has occurred, since it is the soil environment that provides the contaminating elements. The great heterogeneity of soil makes such tests both tedious and difficult (Lambert et al. 1984a, 1984b). A study of Woodland burials found the soil closest to bone to be depleted in the elements Fe, Al, and K, since they have partially migrated into the bone. On the other hand, Sr and Zn did not vary with the distance from the bone, suggesting little movement from soil to bone.

The most graphic test, but not always definitive, proved to be scanning electron microscopy (SEM) of the bone surface. Most mechanisms of contamination operate from the surface inwards, so that a gradient should develop. Lack of contamination requires a generally homogeneous distribution (there are small natural gradients probably not visible to the SEM). We found (Lambert et al. 1983, 1984b) that Fe, Al, K, Mn, Cu and Ba have higher concentrations on the surfaces, but that Sr, Zn and Ca showed homogeneous distributions for Woodland samples. The former set of elements clearly is subject to soil contamination, whereas the latter group appears not to have been affected. In these samples, contamination was visible only to a level of about 0.5 mm.

Several other approaches have been developed by other workers. Sillen (1981) has compared elemental levels in herbivores and carnivores. Price et al. (1985) have used white-tailed deer as a point of comparison. Ericson (1985) has examined ratios of the various strontium isotopes. These studies were targeted specifically for Sr and hence are less useful in developing a multivariate approach to diet.

A few reproducible trends have become evident from these studies. Although all elements are subject to diagenetic alteration in samples of extreme degradation, well-preserved samples can yield elemental concentrations that are little altered during burial and hence can give useful information about ancient diet. The element Sr has proved to be reliable by almost all tests. At the other extreme, Fe, Al and Mn, which are major constituents in soil, invariably are contaminating. Numerous other elements (Zn, Mg, Ca, Cu, K, Ba, Pb) may provide reliable data, but their levels have been found to be sensitive to contamination or leaching under some but not all conditions.

Strontium has been used as a rough inverse measure of protein intake, but even this simple approach is vitiated if there is a large shellfish component in the diet (Schoeninger and Peebles 1981). In order to use inorganic analysis of human bone as a measure of diet, it will be necessary to have reliable data on a wide variety of elements. Consequently, it is necessary to develop methods to minimize the effects of diagenesis. The next section describes the approach currently under investigation in our laboratory.

EFFECTS OF SURFACE REMOVAL

It has always been standard procedure to select well-preserved bone samples and to subject them to cleaning prior to analysis. Cleaning might involve brushing of the surface and careful washing, but physical alteration of the bone generally was not performed. Bones cleaned in this fashion showed the characteristic surface concentration of contaminative elements such as Fe, Mn, and Al, when examined by scanning electron microscopy (Lambert et al. 1983). Because contamination visible by SEM was surprisingly superficial (rarely as deep as 0.5 mm), we decided to explore whether removal of a few millimeters of bone would significantly alter the overall composition. We used Middle Woodland Gibson, Late Woodland Ledders, and Emergent Mississippian Helton site samples from west-central Illinois, supplied by J.E. Buikstra of the University of Chicago. The Gibson site dates to about 200 A.D. and the Ledders site to about 1000 A.D. The Helton site is roughly contemporaneous to the Ledders site.

For each of 50 individuals (all adults), we prepared two femoral samples. The first set of samples was cleaned superficially by the usual procedures, examined by SEM, ashed, dissolved, and analyzed by atomic absorption (AA) spectrophotometry. Experimental details are given elsewhere (Szpunar et al. 1978; Xue 1988). Eleven elements (Zn, Sr, Pb, Al, Fe, Mn, Ba, Ca, Mg, K, Na) were analyzed. The second set of femur material from the same individuals was subjected to a procedure for surface removal. At least 1 mm, and usually 2-3 mm, was removed by abrasion with

silicon carbide sandpaper from both the inside and outside surfaces. SEM analysis was carried out after surface removal, and the samples were then analyzed by AA. With only superficial cleaning, Fe, Al, and Mn were visible to the SEM experiment on the surface and in cracks and voids near the surface. After surface removal the distribution of these elements was entirely homogeneous, from one bone surface to the other. At least by this visual criterion, there was no substantial contamination of the abraded samples.

Table 1 presents the results for both sets of analyses (second and third columns). The levels of Ca before abrasion (35%) indicate that the samples indeed are not highly degraded. The fourth column in Table 1 gives the ratios of the means for the two data sets as percentages. Several elements did not change significantly after abrasion, as indicated by percentage ratios of 100 ± 10%, including Na, Ca, Mg, Sr, and Ba. Consequently, there was very little influx of these materials into the bone during burial. The possibility that significant influx had occurred homogeneously throughout the bone is extremely unlikely for samples of this quality of condition. Several elements lost a very considerable amount of their total by removal of the few millimeters of surface, as indicated by ratios much larger than 100%. Thus Zn lost 2/5 of its total, K 1/3, Al 1/2, Fe 3/4, and Mn 2/3. These are very substantial proportions. The means of the cleaned samples in the third column therefore must resemble much more closely the levels present in bone at death, although we do not know if the true antemortem levels have been reached. Interestingly, surface removal increased the amount of Pb, indicating that this element may have leached from the surface of the bone during burial.

The standard deviations are also affected by the process of surface removal, as seen by the figures in the last column of Table 1 (the ratio of standard deviations before and after abrasion). The trends are identical to those for the means themselves: the standard deviations for Na, Ca, Mg, Sr, and Ba are little altered, those for Zn, K, Al, Fe, and Mn increase dramatically, and that for Pb decreases.

These results indicate that for these samples there has

Elem	Mean before abrasion[a]	Mean after abrasion[a]	Ratio(%)	sd/sd
Na	4797±1021	5081±1122	94.4	0.91
Ca[b]	35.07±0.72	35.08±0.80	100	0.90
Mg	3402±1053	3450±1126	98.6	0.94
Zn	200±82	121±38	165	2.2
Sr	173±51	167±50	104	1.0
Pb	13.8±1.2	37.4±11.2	36.9	0.11
K	101±33	64±17	158	1.9
Al	177±57	77±29	230	2.0
Fe	152±64	43±14	354	4.6
Mn	138±104	46±61	300	1.7
Ba	200±99	205±78	107	1.3

Table 1. Effects of Surface Removal. [a]The error is one standard deviation. [b]In percentage; all other concentrations are in ppm. of bone ash.

been little diagenetic alteration of Na, Ca, Mg, Sr, or Ba. Very substantial contamination by Al, Fe, and Mn is indicated, and lesser contamination by Zn and K. Loss of Pb through leaching appears to have occurred. The first set of elements should be reliable measures of antemortem bone composition. The remaining elements are suspect. After cleaning, the levels of K, Zn, and Pb may be reliable indicators of antemortem bone composition, but the high levels of contamination of Al, Fe and Mn may not have been removed entirely by this procedure.

Analysis of variance was carried out for both sets of data. Before abrasion, significant differences are seen between males and females for contaminating elements (Zn, Fe, Mn, but also Pb). The skeletons of females clearly had higher levels of contamination and leaching, possibly as the result of greater brittleness or nonidentical age distributions. After surface removal, all those differences had disappeared.

Comparison of the combined Ledders and Helton groups (between which little difference was seen) with the Gibson samples showed significant differences only with Mg prior to surface removal. At present, it is not known with what dietary components Mg correlates. The significance of the Mg difference is improved on cleaning, and this element is joined by Ca, Pb, K and Sr. Thus, Sr levels decrease with time, although the trend is seen more clearly for the abraded samples. Strontium levels have been considered to be an inverse measure of protein intake. Interpretation of other elements in terms of dietary components is still premature, but progress is being made in our laboratories by means of experiments with live animals.

CONCLUSIONS

Removal of 1-3 mm of bone surface eliminates all visual evidence of contamination according to scanning electron microscopy. Elemental analyses were carried out before and after surface removal. The amounts of Na, Ca, Mg, Sr, and Ba remained unchanged after the cleaning operation. The amounts of Zn and K were modestly lowered, and the amounts of Al, Fe, and Mn were substantially lowered. These five elements constitute contaminants in these samples, with Zn and K less contaminating than the other three, which are major constituents of soil. On the other hand, the amount of Pb increased after surface removal, suggesting that this element was lost in part by leaching during burial. Similar conclusions were reached by examination of the standard deviations of the measurements.

Surface removal eliminated differences between subgroups based entirely on contamination. Differences based on diet were clearly augmented. Consequently, this procedure is recommended in studies of palaeodiet. Conclusions about specific elements for these Woodland sites should not be extended to other sites, whose burials may differ considerably in soil conditions. Thus the depth of contamination should be determined in each case by electron microscopy. It is doubtful that surface removal eliminates all effects of soil contamination, but the process definitely enhances results.

ACKNOWLEDGMENTS

The authors thank the National Science Foundation for support of this work (Grant No. BNS-8711201).

REFERENCES

Ericson, J.E., (1985). Strontium isotope characterization in the study of prehistoric human ecology. Journal of Human Evolution 14: 503-514.

Grupe, G., (1988). Impact of the choice of bone samples on trace element data in excavated human skeletons. Journal of Archaeological Science 15: 123-129.

Lambert, J.B., S.V. Simpson, J.E. Buikstra, and D.K. Charles, (1984a). Analysis of Soil associated with Woodland Burials. In Archaeological Chemistry III J.B. Lambert, Ed. Advances in Chemistry, Series No. 225. Washington, DC: American Chemical Society, pp. 97-113.

Lambert, J.B., S.V. Simpson, J.E. Buikstra, and D. Hanson, (1983). Electron microprobe analysis of elemental distribution in excavated human bone. American Journal of Physical Anthropology 62: 409-423.

Lambert, J.B. C.B. Szpunar, and J.E. Buikstra, (1979). Chemical Analysis of excavated human bone from Middle and Late Woodland sites. Archaeometry 21: 115-129.

Lambert, J.B., S.V. Simpson, C.B. Szpunar, and J.E. Buikstra, (1985a). Bone diagenesis and dietary analysis. Journal of Human Evolution 14: 477-482.

Lambert, J.B., S.V. Simpson, C.B. Szpunar, and J.E. Buikstra, (1984b). Copper and barium as dietary discriminants: the effects of diagenesis. Archaeometry 26: 131-138.

Lambert, J.B., S.V. Simpson, C.B. Szpunar, and J.E. Buikstra, (1984c). Ancient human diet from inorganic analysis of bone. Accounts of Chemical Research 17: 298-305.

Lambert, J.B., S.V. Simpson, S.G. Weiner, and J.E. Buikstra, (1985b). Induced metal-ion exchange in excavated human bone. Journal of Archaeological Science 12: 85-92.

Lambert, J.B., S.M. Vlasak, A.C. Thometz, and J.E. Buikstra, (1982). A comparative study of the chemical analysis of ribs and femurs in Woodland populations. American Journal of Physical Anthropology 59: 289-294.

Parker, R.B., and H. Toots, (1970). Minor elements in fossil bone. Geological Society of America Bulletin 81: 925-932.

Parker, R.B., and H. Toots, (1980). Trace elements in bones as paleobiological indicators. In Fossils in the Making, A.K. Behrensmeyer and A.P. Hill, Eds, Chicago, IL: University of Chicago Press: 197-207.

Price, T.D., M. Connor and J.D. Parsen, (1985). Bone composition and reconstruction of diet: strontium discrimination in white-tailed deer. Journal of Archaeological Science 12: 419-442.

Schoeninger, M.J. and C.S. Peebles, (1981). Effects of mollusc eating on human bone strontium level, Journal of Archaeological Science 8: 391-397.

Sillen, A., (1981). Strontium and diet at Hayonim Cave. American Journal of Physical Anthropology, 56: 131-137

Szpunar, C.B., J.B. Lambert, and J.E. Buikstra, (1978). Analysis of excavated bone by atomic absorbtion. American Journal of Physical Anthropology 48: 199-202.

Tipton, I.H. and J.J. Shafer, (1964). Health Physics Division Annual Progress Report, 31 July. ORNL-3697: 179.

Xue, Liang., (1988). Analytical Chemistry: (I) Multiple Elemental Approach to Dietary Intake of Ancient Human Beings. Ph.D. Dissertation, Northwestern University, Evanston, IL.

20. Expert Systems in Archaeometry

V. VITALI
Department of Metallurgy and Materials Science, University of Toronto, Toronto, Canada M4S 1A4.

ABSTRACT: *This paper assesses the applicability and contribution of expert systems to archaeometric research, and in particular, provenance studies. VANDAL, a prototype of the first expert system to be constructed in archaeometry, is described.*

INTRODUCTION

In recent years a number of newly developed computer methods, as well as those related to computer technology such as quantitative methods, have been applied to archaeological and archaeometric investigations. Developments in the field of artificial intelligence, particularly in the area of expert systems, have provided another important tool for research in archaeometry/ archaeology. This paper will briefly describe the basic characteristics of this new tool, place it within the array of other available computer methods, review some of its applications in archaeology, and assess potential uses in archaeometric investigations.

DEFINITIONS AND CHARACTERISTICS

Expert or knowledge based systems are problem-solving computer programs that can reach a level of performance in a specific domain comparable to that of a human expert. The main features that distinguish such programs from traditional application programs are: a) their capacity to use non-numerical domain-specific knowledge; b) the organization of programs into three parts, namely a knowledge base, which consists of a series of rules or facts that provide a model or description of a specific type of problem in a specified subject domain, a control system or an inference engine, which is a mechanism that performs the reasoning of the system, and a data base, which contains the information concerning a specific problem in the domain under consideration; c) an interactive behaviour with the user in which the expert system explains and justifies the conclusions reached, recognizes absent or contradictory information, and requests further information from the user (Nau 1983). The organization of programs on three levels, rather than the two levels of traditional programs, makes expert systems more flexible and powerful problem solving tools, and much more suitable for dealing with the incomplete and inconsistent knowledge encountered in real-world situations, than the traditional programs. On the other hand, eliciting knowledge from various domain experts and structuring that knowledge is more difficult and time consuming than dealing with traditional programs (Cerri 1987).

Expert systems can perform various functions. These functions can be a single primitive task or a combination of such tasks. According to Reichgelt and van Harmelin (1986) there are four primitive tasks that expert systems perform: a classification or interpretation task, in which the expert system is expected to analyze some data in order to arrive at a higher-level description of the situation (e.g., identification of objects); a monitoring task, in which the expert system iteratively observes the behaviour of some system and extracts features that are essential for the successful execution of that system (e.g., determination of potential flows of a system); a design task, in which the expert system constructs a complex entity that satisfies a number of conditions and constraints (e.g., determination of a spatial configuration of objects); a simulation or prediction task, in which the expert system is expected to infer from a given state and given variables consequences for the functioning of a system (e.g., forecasting).

Expert systems can be constructed using shallow knowledge, that is, only enough knowledge to perform a particular task; or, preferably, expert systems can be designed using deep knowledge, that is to say, they encompass a complete theory of the domain. The nature of the information used can be static, i.e., all constraints of the problem are specified before the session and it is assumed that the problem does not change during the session; or dynamic, where the constraints of the problem cannot be specified before the session. While expert systems can handle both certain and uncertain data and knowledge, the approaches to handling uncertainty remain one of the most important problems to be resolved. For example, expressing uncertainty in a numerical form (such as coefficients of reliability associated either with data or knowledge statements) poses questions about the suitability of this form for expressing likelihood, reliability of numerical values, consistency of assignments, ways of calculating certainty of derived statements, etc. This represents a very important issue, particularly for the use of expert systems in a field such as archaeology (Wilcock 1985).

The modes in which an expert system interacts with the user can be advisory, in which the expert system puts forward possible solutions and the user is asked if the solutions are acceptable; imperative, in which the expert system is the authority for the acceptability of the solution; and criticizing, in which the user presents the system with a problem and a solution and the system analyses and comments on the validity of solution (Reichgelt and van Harmelin 1986).

CONSTRUCTION OF EXPERT SYSTEMS

The development of an expert system usually proceeds in several stages, knowledge elicitation and knowledge representation being the most characteristic phases in the construction of such a system. Knowledge elicitation, a first step, involves the gathering of knowledge from experts and practitioners in a particular field by a knowledge engineer. This is a critical and often the most difficult step. It appears that identifying the expectations for the performance of an expert system, that is, assembling a set of typical, significant questions that should be answered by the system in an ideal case, is the most difficult task that a knowledge engineer has to surmount when dealing with domain (non-computer) experts (Cerri et al. 1987).

Knowledge representation, the next step, involves a description of the elements of the expert system. There are several types of knowledge representation "languages" for both data and knowledge base representations and the choice between those should be made on the basis of the nature of the data and the knowledge. It should be kept in mind that specific choices may also influence the functioning, performance and reliability of the expert system.

Information on the data level, that is, the declarative knowledge, can be represented using logic schemes, frames or semantic network schemes. In logic schemes, facts are presented as a collection of logical formulas composed according to the rules of a specific logic used (e.g., first-order predicate calculus, fuzzy logic, etc.). They are theoretically well-established, relatively simple, easily understood, and are compatible with many types of control mechanisms. However, it appears that the organization of logical formulas within large knowledge bases is not standardized, and the representation of heuristic knowledge is relatively difficult (Hugget and Baker 1985).

Frames are data structures in which all knowledge about a particular object or event is stored together. Many different variants of this type of knowledge representation exist, but most of them propose different types of frames for different types of objects. In such frames, slots (fields) are set to contain information relevant to a particular type of object or event being stored. Semantic networks, like frames, organize knowledge around the object or event being described, but in this case the objects are represented by nodes in a graph and the relations among them are represented by labelled arcs. These forms of representation allow for modularity and the accessibility of knowledge, and particularly in case of networks, are closely associated with search strategies (Nau 1983). However, it appears that there is a lack of standardized approachs for these types of representation.

Domain-specific, problem-solving knowledge is assembled and represented in the knowledge base of an expert system. This knowledge is usually procedural, as it prescribes the steps in data manipulation in order to arrive at a solution to a problem. There are, again, several schemes for the representation of procedural knowledge. Logical schemes using predicate calculus can also be used to express a knowledge base. The best known type of representation is a form of pattern-invoked procedures known as a production system. In this representation, procedural knowledge is expressed as a number of rules of the form IF condition THEN action. While it is argued that this type of representation is the least adequate way of representing complex and large knowledge bases (Doran 1988), the applications of production rules to limited and structured domains of knowledge appears to have been successful (Ganascia et al. 1986).

There are also different strategies in which control systems (inference engines) can evoke the reasoning of the domain-specific knowledge and the choice depends on the nature of the problem and the data. In a forward chaining strategy the process starts with antecedents of the rules and moves to their consequences. Often called a data-driven search, this strategy corresponds to an empirico-inductive approach to interpretation. From a technical standpoint, this strategy may lead to an extremely large number of searches being performed, particularly if combined with backtracking. Backtracking methods explore one path as far as possible, ignoring all other paths. If the path dead-ends or no path is found, the procedure backtracks to a previous stage and chooses a new operator to extend the path in a different direction. A backward chaining strategy involves moving from the consequences of the rules to their antecendents and it corresponds to a hypothetico-deductive approach. This strategy is thought to give a more focussed reasoning. Other strategies, such as problem reduction, also exist (Nau 1983).

There are a number of ways in which one can approach the construction of expert systems. They range from expert system shells to high programming language environments. Expert system shells usually consist of an inference engine, an empty knowledge base, and some primitive debugging and explanation devices. These shells usually result from abstracting the knowledge base from an actual expert system. While shells certainly represent the easiest way to construct an expert system for non-artificial intelligence programmers, their architecture, predetermined by the original problem used in developing the shell, may not be appropriate for the range of tasks and knowledge domains for which a shell may be employed.

On the other hand, high level language programming environments (such as LOOPS or KEE) provide a large number of sophisticated techniques with little instruction for the user. They can be utilized only by experienced, knowledge engineers. Even then, it is argued that certain guidelines related to different tasks and knowledge domains should be established (Reichgelt and van Harmelin 1986).

APPLICATIONS

Expert systems have been developed in various fields and applied to numerous problems - medical diagnosis and consulting, oil and mineral exploration, analysis of electrical circuits and computer configurations, the study of molecular structure, mathematical formula manipulation, etc.

Their suitability for research in archaeology, and their applications in this field have been variously assessed (Wilcock 1985; Hugget and Baker 1985; Ennais 1985; Doran 1986, 1988; Gardin 1987). While most of the expert systems described in the literature have not yet passed the experimental prototype stage, a few are being routinely used.

Expert systems appear to be useful and successful tools in well-defined and structured domains such as archaeological classification. For example, RHAPSODE (Reconnaissance des Haches de l'Antiquite Par un System Organise D'Expertise), successfully classifies and catalogues bronze axes on the basis of their morphological characteristics (Ganascia et al. 1986). Other systems successfully performing essentially classificatory tasks have been developed and reviewed (Hugget and Baker 1985; Wilcock 1985; Lagrange forthcoming).

The most important and successful application of expert systems in archaeology to date has been in the analysis of archaeological reasoning and interpretation (Gardin et al. 1987). Using expert systems to reconstruct a sequence of archaeological reasoning that was employed in presenting certain archaeological findings and then interpreting them, exposes the logical structure of the archaeological interpretation and any flaws that it might have; presents explicitly the premises on which the archaeological interpretations are based; and verifies the conclusions reached.

Expert systems therefore represent a method or set of techniques applicable to and available for archaeological research. They can be viewed as a type of formal method, defined by Doran (1986) as being characterized by a combination of abstraction, systematization and exactness (such as statistical, mathematical or computer-based methods). They can be used to analyse archaeological data, like quantitative data analysis methods, but unlike other formal methods they can play an active role in archaeological interpretations, and not just supply analysed data. As interpretive tools, they can help to construct more powerful and transparent reasoning mechanisms, and provide the development of more rigorous and formalized theories in the domain under consideration. In addition to these principal advantages, expert systems allow for the use of non-numerical data and incomplete knowledge, both very important in archaeology.

On the other hand, building expert systems is a very time consuming task, with the knowledge elicitation and knowledge representation phases also being quite difficult. From the knowledge engineering standpoint, a number of issues still remain to be better resolved: ways of handling uncertainty have to be improved; more suitable solutions for interfacing expert systems with other methods or phases of investigation have to be developed; new approaches to dealing with large and unstructured fields have to be devised.

The potential for the use of expert systems in archaeometric investigation is considerable. As a method, they allow for the use and analysis of numerical and non-numerical data. More importantly, they offer the possibility for knowledge from various disciplines to be assembled and combined in a single technique. On one hand, this permits the cross-verification of results obtained using different techniques; more importantly, it allows for the incorporation of various types of knowledge into a single theoretical framework, resulting in a much more solidly based structure.

A prototype expert system for the determination of the provenance of archaeological ceramics based on instrumental neutron activation (INAA) data, named VANDAL, has already been developed (Vitali and Lagrange 1988). While still in a relatively primitive stage, the VANDAL expert system successfully examines relationships between various groups of archaeological ceramics, makes certain conclusions regarding the production of those ceramics and explains its findings. The starting information used by VANDAL is a mixture of archaeological, chemical, and data analysis information. The archaeological information gives the location (site) where the ceramics were found, the time period to which the ceramics were assigned (based on stratigraphic evidence), their category (type), and the relative percentage of each type of ceramic found at each location. The technical information is based on the chemical composition of the ceramics in terms of their elemental concentration for 15 minor and trace elements. This information was summarized using appropriate data analysis procedures (linear discriminant function and a jackknife procedure for re-classification) and expressed as a misclassification rate.

A comparison of the chemical composition of different archaeological ceramic groups is used throughout the reasoning process to arrive at the different archaeological conclusions, in a manner analogous to the ceramic provenance study by Vitali et al. (1987). The results of a VANDAL run give, for a group of ceramics: (1) a method of production (same as or different from another ceramic group; (2) a geographic origin (local or imported from one site to another, or from a third source); (3) a continuity of production method through two consecutive periods; and (4) a continuity of local production, or import or trade, through two consecutive periods.

While VANDAL successfully performs its essentially classificatory task, its principal success has been in rendering the process of provenance determination based on multidisciplinary information coherent, transparent, and standardized. The premises on which these studies are based are clearly exposed and the conclusions reached specifically justified. Having assembled and structured knowledge from the fields of archaeology, instrumental analysis, materials science and data analysis that is relevant to the task of provenance determination using INAA data, provenance determination can then be performed by an expert system, thereby allowing human experts to turn more of their attention to solving methodological or generic problems.

CONCLUSIONS

Expert systems, as tools, offer a considerable potential in multidisciplinary fields, such as archaeometric research, because of their capacity to combine knowledge from various disciplines. However, their usefulness lies not only in their ability to perform tasks in a standardized manner. More importantly, such systems impose upon the subject the development of a coherent and formalized theoretical framework.

From a technical standpoint, as with all new and sophisticated tools, a number of issues related to their performance still remain to be resolved, and the appropriateness of their applications continue to be of the utmost importance in their assessment and usefulness.

ACKNOWLEDGEMENTS

The author wishes to thank Marie-Salome Lagrange for her invaluable assistance with the development of the VANDAL expert system. Partial support received from

112

C.N.R.S. - E.R. 315, Paris, France, The Archaeometry Laboratory, University of Minnesota - Duluth, and an NSERC grant to Ursula M. Franklin, are gratefully acknowledged.

REFERENCES CITED

Cerri, S.A., P. Landini and M. Leoncini (1987). Cooperative Agents for Knowledge-based information systems: Dialogue about the Archaeology of Rome. Applied Artificial Intelligence, 1: 1-24.

Doran, J. (1986). Formal methods and archaeological theory: a perspective. World Archaeology, 18: 21-37.

Doran, J. (1988). Expert systems and archaeology: what lies ahead? In (C.L.N. Ruggles and S.P.Q. Rahtz) Computer and Quantitative Methods in Archaeology 1987. BAR International Series 393: 237-241.

Ennais, R. (1985). Artificial Intelligence: Applications to Logical Reasoning and Historical Research. Chichester: Ellis Harwood Limited.

Ganascia, J.G., M. Menu and J.P. Mohen (1986). Rhapsode: systeme expert en archeologie. Bulletin de la Societe Prehistorique Francaise, 83: 363-371.

Gardin, J-C., O. Guillaume, P.Q. Herman, A. Hesnard, M-S. Lagrange, M. Renaud and E. Zadora-Rio (1987). Systemes experts et sciences humaines: Les cas de l'archeologie. Paris: Eyrolles.

Huggett, J. and K. Baker (1985). The Computerized Archaeologist: The Development of Expert Systems. Science and Archaeology, 27: 3-7.

Lagrange, M.S. (forthcoming). Expert Systems in Archaeology: A User's View. Computers and the Humanities.

Nau, D.S. (1983). Expert Computer Systems. Computer, 2: 63-85.

Reichgelt, H. and F. van Harmelen (1986). Criteria for Choosing Representation Languages and Control Regimes for Expert Systems. The Knowledge Engineering Review, 1: 2-17.

Vitali, V., J.W. Simmons, E.F. Henrickson, L.D. Levine and R.G.V. Hancock (1987). A Hierarchical Taxonomic Procedure for Provenance Determination: A Case Study of Chalcolithic Ceramics from the Central Zagros. Journal of Archaeological Science, 14: 423-435.

Vitali, V. and M.S. Lagrange (forthcoming). VANDAL: an Expert System for the Provenance Determination of Archaeological Ceramics based in INAA Data. Proc. Computer Applications in Archaeology, University of Birmingham, 23-26 March 1988.

Wilcock, J. (1985). A Review of Expert Systems: Their Shortcomings and Possible Applications in Archaeology. Computer Applications in Archaeology, 13: 139-144.

113

21. Relations Between Elemental Concentrations in Pottery, with Extrapolations and Inferences

O. BIRGÜL
Chemistry Department, Middle East Technical University, Ankara, Turkey. Deceased August 1987

D. DAUTET, H. MARSHALL, and L. YAFFE
Chemistry Department, McGill University, Montreal, P.Q., Canada H3A 2K6.

ABSTRACT: *Definitive linear relationships between correlated elemental concentrations can be calculated with proper attention paid to the uncertainties in both variables.*

INTRODUCTION

The chemical concentrations of trace and minor constituents of pottery and clay are used to fingerprint examples, and thus to indicate provenance. When the concentrations of two elements display a strong linear correlation, it may be useful to discover the coefficients of the linear relationship behind the correlation. Two instances are illustrated in Figure 1.

The upper part of the figure shows the relationship between the lanthanum and iron concentrations in samples of clay from two neighbouring pits, 10 and 11 km upstream from Ikiztepe, northwest of Samsun, in the flood plain of the Kizilirmak, which flows through northern Turkey to the Black Sea, sampled in an effort to characterize the clay available at Ikiztepe. The concentrations of lanthanum and iron are strongly correlated, though not proportional, in each pit. The local geomorphology suggests the clay is reworked, so there is some question whether the deposit is uniform enough to be characterized from a few samples. The lines describing the relationship between the elements in the two pits are different, though the concentrations are very similar, and this forms part of the evidence leading to the conclusion that the underlying deposits are not uniform, and that the clay can be described only in broad terms, with a catalogue of local variations.

The lower part of the figure shows the concentrations of scandium and iron in one of these two clay pits and in Early Bronze Age pottery from Ikiztepe. There is a linear correlation between these elements in the pottery, and it can be argued that the line through the data runs from the point representing the concentrations in the potters clay to the concentrations in the temper. That this line intersects the line of the clay concentration shows, along with other evidence, that clay from such a local pit could have been used in the preparation of these ceramics. It is for arguments such as this that one needs to go beyond the noting of a linear relationship between the variables of a scatter plot, to the definition of the best line through the data in that plot.

TECHNIQUES

The usual approach to the problem of finding the best straight line through scattered data is to minimize the sum of the squares of the deviations of the y-values from the best line,

i.e.,
$$\sum_i (y_i - \hat{y}_i)^2, \qquad (1)$$

to define the coefficients in the expression

$$y = a + bx$$

Implicit in this regression of y on x is the notion of the independent variable: the given values of x are assumed to be free of error, and the scatter of the data due entirely to errors in the values of y, which is clearly not always the case. The regression of x on y, yielding the equation

$$x = \alpha + \beta y, \qquad (2)$$

often recast in the form

$$y = a' + b'x, \qquad (3)$$

is no more satisfactory (see Figure 2).

As the linear correlation between the two variables improves, or r approaches 1, and the data become less scattered, the two regression lines converge to a line of slope $\sqrt{bb'}$, passing through $(\bar{x}, \bar{y})$, yet a third candidate as best line (4). (The linear correlation coefficient, $r = \sqrt{b/b'}$ is a measure of the scatter of the data about this line.) These lines, and others described below, are illustrated in Figure 2.

Rather than minimizing the sum of the squares of the deviations of one variable or the other, one can minimize the sum of the squares of the perpendicular distances from the data points to the line sought. This line is known as the major axis of the data, and is defined by the coefficients

$$\hat{b} = \frac{\sum_i v_i^2 - \sum_i u_i^2 + \sqrt{(\sum_i v_i^2 - \sum_i u_i^2)^2 + 4(\sum_i u_i v_i)^2}}{2\sum_i u_i v_i} \qquad (5)$$

and $\hat{a} = \bar{y} - \hat{b}\bar{x}$,

where $u = x - \bar{x}$ and $v = y - \bar{y}$. This is not generally acceptable as the best line, either, since it is not invariant under a change of scale for either variable. This difficulty can be obviated by converting the variables to dimensionless parameters. If the variables are standardized to the standard deviations of their distributions, that is, the

114

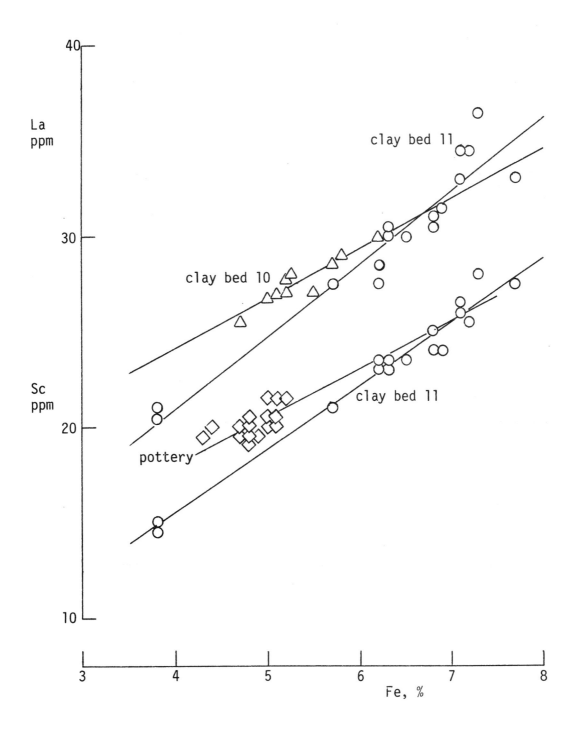

Figure 1. Scattergram for La versus Fe for clay pits 10 and 11 (upper) and Sc versus Fe for ceramics and clays from pit 11 (lower)

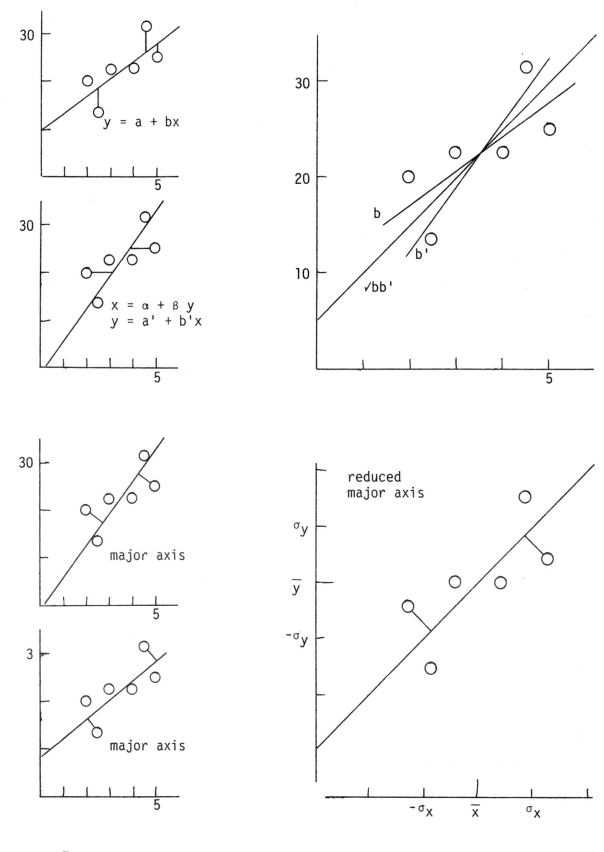

Figure 2.

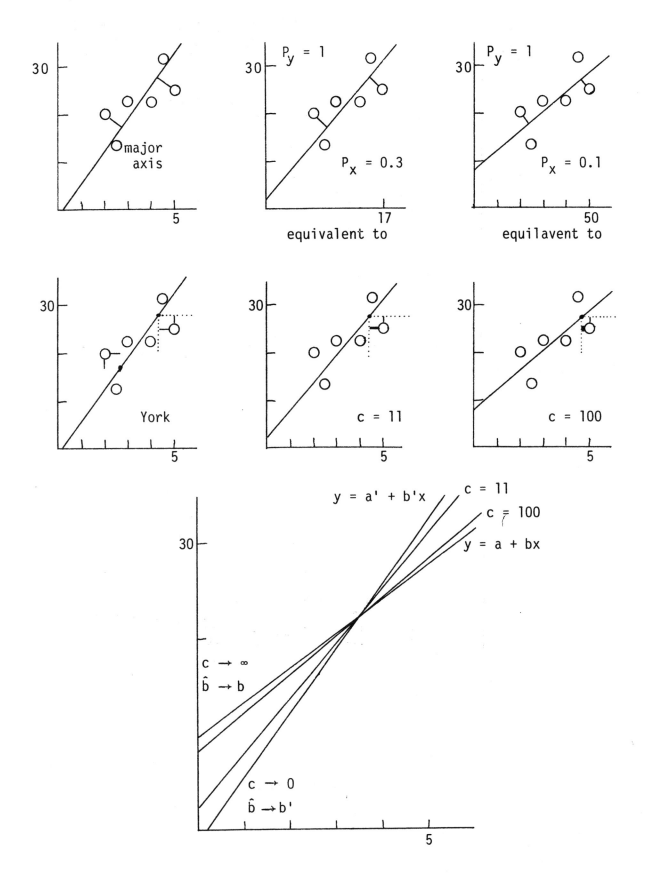

Figure 2. (cont).

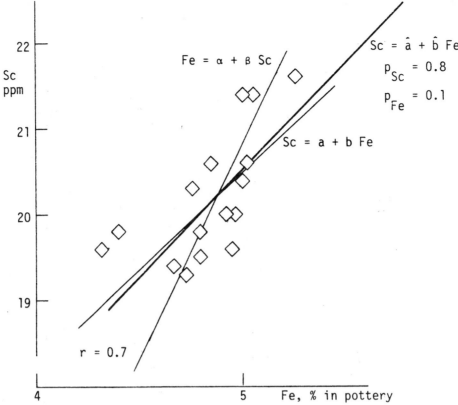

Figure 3. Scattergram at Sc and Fe in Ikiztepe pottery

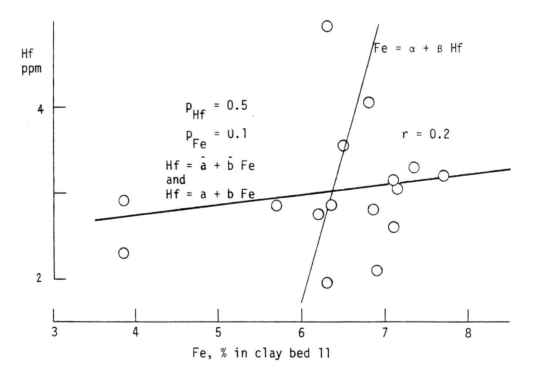

Figure 4. Scattergram of Hf and Fe in clays from pit 11.

co-ordinates are given in terms of (x/σ_x) and (y/σ_y), the coefficients of the major axis (expression 5) are transformed to:

$$\hat{b} = \sigma_y/\sigma_x \text{ and } \hat{a} = \bar{y} - \hat{b}\bar{x}.$$

(6)

The line

$$y = \hat{a} + (\sigma_y/\sigma_x)x,$$

called the reduced major axis, is the same as the line of correlation given above (4).

The variables can be standardized to the probable errors of their measurement, p_x and p_y, rather than the standard deviations of their distributions; with the co-ordinates given in terms of x/p_x and y/p_y, the parameters for the line defined by the minimization of the sum of squared distances become

$$\hat{b} = \frac{\Sigma_i v_i^2 - c\Sigma_i u_i^2 + \sqrt{(\Sigma_i v_i^2 - c\Sigma_i u_i^2) + 4c(\Sigma_i u_i v_i)^2}}{2\Sigma_i u_i v_i}$$

(7)

and $(\hat{a} = \bar{y} - \hat{b}\bar{x}, \text{ where } c = p_y^2/p_x^2)$

(Worthing and Geffner 1946).

Another approach is to minimize the sum of squares of the deviations in x and y at the same time, that is, the sum

$$\Sigma_i((x_i - \hat{x}_i)^2 + (y_i - \hat{y}_i)^2).$$

Just as the deviation of each measurement of y can be weighted in the familiar least-squares calculations of expression (1), the deviation of each measurement of each variable can be assigned a weight in this sum, and the expression to be minimized given by

$$\Sigma_i (w(x_i)(x_i - \hat{y}_i)^2 + w(y_i - \hat{y}_i)^2)$$

where $w(x_i)$ is the weight given $(x_i - \hat{x}_i)^2$, and so forth (Deming 1943). York (1966) has given the general solution for the line satisfying this minimization. In many circumstances it is not necessary to consider different weighting for every point, but only to recognize that the deviations in both variables are included in the calculation, and their relative weights should be considered. That is, the sum to be minimized is

$$\Sigma_i (w_x (w_i - \hat{x}_i)^2 + w_y (y_i - \hat{y}_i)^2)$$

(8)

The general solution reduces to the major axis (expression 5) when $w_x = w_y$, and to the reduced major axis (6) when $w_x = \sigma_x^2$ and $w_y = \sigma_y^2$.

When $w_x = 1/p_x^2$ and $w_y = 1/p_y^2$, the general solution reduces to the solution for the major axis through the variables standardized to their probable errors (expression 7). For convenience, this expression can be recast in terms of b and b':

$$\hat{b} = \frac{b'-c}{2} + \frac{b}{2b|b|}\sqrt{\left(\frac{b'-c}{2}\right)^2 + \frac{c}{2b}}$$

(9)

and $\hat{a} = \bar{y} - \hat{b}\bar{x}$, where $c = p_y^2/p_x^2$

Similarly, the uncertainties in b and a, taken from York (1966), can be written as

$$\sigma_b^2 = \left(\frac{1}{n-2}\right)(\hat{b}^2 + bb' - 2b\hat{b})$$

(10)

$$\sigma_a^2 = \sigma_b^2 \Sigma_i x_i^2$$

If $p_y \gg p_x$, that is, the probable error in the values of x are negligible, then $c \to \infty$ and b, the best slope, approaches b, the slope of the simple regression of y on x, which presumes exact values of x, the independent variable. If $p_y \ll p_x$, $c \to 0$ and $\hat{b}$ approaches b', the slope of the regression of x on y.

DISCUSSION

It is clear that when the scatter in correlated data is ascribed to measurement uncertainties, rather than to inherently low correlation, it must be apportioned between the measured variables in some appropriate manner. The elemental concentrations in the Ikiztepe samples were determined by instrumental neutron activation analysis; it is reasonable here to assign a constant expected uncertainty in the measurement of the concentration of each element, while noting that the attainable precision varies widely among the elements. The estimated uncertainties were taken from the painstaking error assessment of Attas (1982) in analyzing similar samples with the same technique, and much the same equipment.

Figure 4 is a scatter plot of the hafnium and iron concentrations in the clay samples of pit II. An experienced analyst would suggest that all the scatter could be assigned to the much less precise hafnium values; with a value of c = 25 in expression 7 or 9, the best line does indeed coincide with the regression line of the hafnium or the iron concentrations. In Figure 3, the scatter plot of scandium and iron in the Ikiztepe pottery, the matter is not so clear cut; the greater precision of the iron determinations pulls the best line towards the regression of scandium on iron, but the two are not collinear.

In other analyses, other weighting regimes may be more appropriate (it may even be necessary to return to the general case), but the question of uncertainty in both variables must always be addressed.

REFERENCES

Attas, M., Regional ceramic trade in Early Bronze Age Greece: evidence from neutron activation analysis of Early Helladic pottery from Argolis and Korinthia, Ph.D. thesis, McGill University, Montreal, Canada (1982).

Deming, W.E., Statistical adjustment of data, John Wiley and Sons, New York (1943), as quoted by York (1966).

York, D., Least-Squares fitting of a straight line, Can. J. Phys. 44 (1966) 1079-1086.

Worthing, A.G. and J. Geffner, Treatment of experimental data, John Wiley and Sons, New York (1943), as quoted by York (1966).

119

22. The Mechanism of Iron Production in the Bloomery Furnace

D. J. KILLICK
Department of Anthropology, Yale University, New Haven, Conn., U.S.A.

R. B. GORDON
Department of Geology and Geophysics, Yale University, New Haven, Conn., U.S.A.

ABSTRACT: *Metallographic and petrographic analysis of iron smelting residues show that two basic mechanisms of iron formation are common to all bloomery furnaces.*

INTRODUCTION

Bloomery furnaces used for smelting iron in Europe, Asia, Africa and North America vary greatly in form and operation. They range from small bowl hearths through low shafts (that may or may not have provision for tapping slag), to tall shaft furnaces blown either by forced or natural draft. Some use a preheated air blast. All accounts of the bloomery process stress that a large element of skill is required for successful bloom smelting. The kind of skill required is the ability to carry on a complex process with incomplete technological understanding and limited information on the progress of events within the furnace. Interpretation of the different forms of the bloomery process in terms of social style and ritual, and evaluation of the smelter's skills should begin with an analysis of the technology of the process itself.

The accepted theoretical basis of the bloomery process is that the ore is reduced by carbon monoxide in the sequence, hydrated iron oxides - haematite - magnetite - wustite - iron. The equilibrium conditions for complete reduction are attained when the temperatures are greater than 800°C and the CO/CO_2 ratio greater than 75%. To effect separation of the iron from the gangue in the ore, some of the iron oxide in the ore is sacrificed to form a fluid slag with a composition near that of fayalite so as to have a solidus temperature of about 1200°C. If all of the gangue is to be removed this way, and if slag-forming reactions approach equilibrium, the ore must contain at least 49% iron for there to be any yield of metal. Because reduction of iron oxide to iron can be carried out in a bloomery at temperatures too low for elements such as manganese, silicon, and titanium that may be present in the ore to be reduced, relatively pure iron can be produced. Since the fuel used is always charcoal, bloomery iron is usually free of sulfur but phosphorus in either the ore or the fuel ash may be reduced and enter the iron. Either steel or iron can be made by adjusting the ore/fuel ratio and the temperature.

To this accepted account of bloom smelting, we would add that two mechanical processes must be successfully completed. First the particles of iron formed by reduction of the ore must be sufficiently aggregated to form a bloom with enough coherence to hold together when forged, and, second, the bloom must be successfully forged into metal reasonably free of included slag. The bloomery process, can fail in either the chemical or the mechanical steps.

Bloom smelting uses processes that are no longer practised in modern ferrous metallurgy and descriptions of the bloomery mechanism cannot be found in metallurgical textbooks. A further complication is that, as we will show, equilibrium is rarely, if ever, attained in bloomery furnaces, which means that the use of phase diagrams to reconstruct bloomery furnace parameters is of limited value. We report here the results of a metallographic and petrographic study of material remains from bloomeries operated in Africa and North America that illuminate the mechanism of the process.

OBSERVATIONS

Kasungu Bloomery, Malawi.

The furnace wastes studied from historic smelting sites in Malawi were produced in the early 20th century in induced-draft, slag-tapping furnaces 1.5 - 3 m tall. These furnaces typically produce a bloom of 20 - 30 kg in a smelting campaign lasting 5 - 7 days. The laterite ores used consist of pisoliths of almost pure, hydrated iron oxide in a groundmass of quartz, kaolin, and iron oxide. They contain only 20 - 30% Fe, and would not, therefore, yield any free iron in a bloomery furnace if equilibrium conditions were attained.

Dehydration of the ore in the upper shaft opens wide fissures that allow furnace gases to penetrate through the ore lumps. The pisoliths are reduced successively to magnetite, wustite, and iron by CO and form concentric shell structures of metallic iron before the slag forms in the groundmass. Consequently, the slags are exceptionally lean; they consist only of fayalite, glass, and unreacted quartz (Figure 1). These slags are very fluid (viscosity about 1 poise) and drain readily from the iron shells, which collapse and agglomerate under surface tension into a structure similar to that observed by Tholander (1987) in his experimental bloomery. Subsequent consolidation under the weight of the overburden in the stack produces a coherent bloom with little entrapped slag and variable carbon content.

The Kasungu bloomery illustrates the simplest form of the bloomery process because the iron and slag form directly from the ore without any necessity for secondary recovery of metal by reduction of iron from the liquid slag. The process was a skillful adaptation of bloom smelting to local geological and economic conditions in which the only ores available are very lean and must be carefully selected. As is shown by the assertions of former iron workers in Malawi, that which we call pisolitic laterites are more suitable than structureless (massive) laterites for smelting. Our microstructural evidence shows that it would probably have been impossible to smelt the massive ores. Our American bloomery process, which we describe next, operated by a quite different mechanism and was an adaptation to smelting rich ore for a market that required iron of high purity.

American Bloomery Process

The bloom smelting practised in the Adirondack region of New York State until the early years of the 20th century was the industrial acme of the process. A low, water-cooled hearth made of iron plates fitted with holes for tapping slag was used to smelt magnetite ore that was beneficiated by stamping, screening and washing. The air blast was preheated to about 400°C with waste heat from the bloomery. When hot blast was introduced, starting about 1840, the time required to make a 150 kg bloom was reduced from six to three hours but the character of the iron made was unchanged (Chahoon 1875; Egleston 1879).

Descriptions of the American bloomery process state that it is essential to get the bloom nucleus shaped and placed so that slag flows continuously over it, always protecting it from oxidation, and that slag must be drawn off at the proper rate. We have investigated the mechanism of the process by study of samples collected at seven forge sites in the Adirondack region by Richard S. Allen and by Morris F. Glenn. Two different mechanisms of iron formation have been observed in these samples. In one, magnetite ore fragments are reduced by CO to wustite which is pseudomorphic after the magnetite. This is then reduced to metallic iron in the form of ribbons. The marked contraction of volume inherent in this reaction pulls the iron ribbons away from the wustite-iron interface and exposes fresh wustite to the reducing gases. The structure produced is a labyrinth of iron ribbons that preserve the cubic or triangular outline of the original magnetite grains. This mechanism is, therefore, similar to that described for Kasungu, but the reaction rate is much slower because the magnetite grains are much less permeable to gases than the Kasungu laterites. Consequently, relict cores of magnetite or wustite are often seen within the iron labyrinths in slag samples from Adirondack bloomeries.

In the second and dominant mechanism, wustite pseudomorphic after magnetite is first dissolved in the slag (Figure 2), from which it must then be recovered. This is accomplished by nucleating metallic iron on the charcoal in the lower part of the hearth. This is made to grow by two mechanisms, reduction of iron directly from the downward flowing slag and capture of drops of solid or liquid iron in the slag. Many of these drops are formed by reduction of wustite dendrites precipitated in the slag during cooling. Growth of fayalite crystals may push the iron drops into clusters, which aggregate into larger particles. These will contribute to the growth of the bloom if trapped on the bloom surface.

The hearth of the American bloomery is similar to that of the Catalan forge, from which it is supposed to have been derived. In the Catalan process, slag is formed early in the smelt from ore dust that is charged into the hearth; this slag is tapped from the bottom of the hearth from time to time. Percy (1864), quoting Francois (1843), reports that either soft or hard (steely) iron could be produced in the Catalan process; to obtain steel, slag was tapped more frequently so as to suppress the powerful decarburizing effect of the slag on the bloom. Similar control of the carbon content was exercised in the Adirondack bloomery (Egleston 1879).

The American bloomery process operated on a mechanism completely different from that of the Kasungu shaft furnace because an iron-rich slag was formed first and the iron metal was then reduced from this slag. The process was an adaptation to local geological and economic conditions in which rich ore was abundant, charcoal relatively dear, and the market was for high purity iron to be used in making crucible steel. In the interest of saving fuel and avoiding reduction of unwanted elements, much wastage of iron in the discarded slag was tolerated.

Experimental Bloomery

Specimens taken from an experimental bloomery built by David Harvey at Colonial Williamsburg, Virginia, further illuminate the mechanism of smelting. The bog ore used consists of finely divided, hydrated iron oxides and clay minerals and is without visible structure. The ore is roasted in an open fire before smelting. This dehydrates the ore and opens fissures through the ore lumps, allowing gases to penetrate throughout. Because of the even dispersion and intimate contact of iron oxide and gangue, no metallic iron is formed in the early stages. Instead, the ore is reduced to micron-size particles of magnetite that subsequently form and dissolve in the surrounding slag, from which the metallic iron must then be recovered. The secondary reduction process is nucleated by the formation of thin layers of metallic iron at charcoal-slag interfaces as the iron-rich slag flows over the charcoal near the lower part of the hearth. The interface between the iron and slag is characterized by fine whiskers, such as those shown in Figure 3, which appear to be filaments of iron metal growing into the slag while the iron is being decarburized. These filaments are subsequently converted into solid metal by surface tension forces.

The second mechanism of iron formation found in the samples from the experimental bloomery is reduction of wustite dendrites formed as the iron-rich slag cools (Figure 4). The resultant drops of metallic iron then settle through the dendritic structure. Since the free fall speed of these drops is at a Reynold's number well below unity, the flow of the slag around the drops is laminar and little agglomeration is accomplished by turbulent mixing unless the slag itself is flowing rapidly. However, these drops of iron agglomerate as they are pushed together by the fayalite crystals that also form as the slag cools. Drops of iron that settle, or are driven, onto rims of iron formed on charcoal particles adhere and are incorporated into the rim, which can then continue to grow after it becomes too thick for effective transport of carbon by diffusion from the charcoal to the slag-metal interface.

In many of David Harvey's experimental smelts, a bloom that could be forged was not obtained. The principal difficulty encountered appears to have been the recovery of metallic iron from the iron-rich slag. When a forgeable bloom was formed, the resultant metal had a very variable composition, reflecting the highly heterogeneous conditions within the furnace.

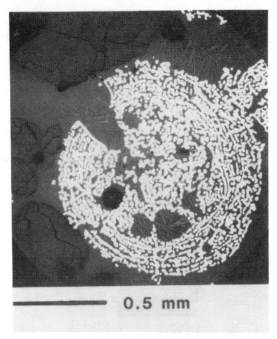

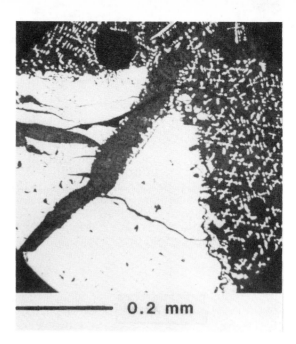

Figure 1. Kasungu, Malawi. Concentric shells of ferrite, pseudomorphous after a laterite pisolith, in slag of fayalite, glass and undissolved quartz.

Figure 2. Dedwater Ironworks, New York. Wustite grain pseudomorphous after magnetite, dissolving in a slag containing wustite, fayalite and glass.

DISCUSSION

Reduction

The microstructure and grain size of the ore, the heating rate, and the time spent in the low-temperature zone of the bloomery shaft are the main factors that determine whether metallic iron is formed directly from the ore or must be reduced from the slag. If only enough slag forms to protect the already-reduced iron from subsequent oxidation, and the solid iron particles can be successfully agglomerated, a bloom can be formed without reduction of iron from the slag, as at Kasungu. But, if all of the iron oxide is initially dissolved in the slag, a second stage of reduction is needed to form a bloom. This secondary reduction takes place by several mechanisms including reduction of wustite particles precipitated within the slag and the nucleation and growth of iron from the silicate melt on charcoal particles. (This process is similar to growth of iron from fayalitic slag in contact with graphite described by von Bogdandy and Engell (1971).) Most bloomeries appear to operate between the end points described above. We observe that the alternative paths by which metal can be formed in the bloomery produce iron in different physical forms, which can be recognized in the microstructure.

The opportunities for the application of the smelter's operating skills to the primary reduction stage of the bloomery process are largely in the selection of the ore and its roasting, which, by increasing its permeability, influences the rate at which the initial reduction reaction occurs. A high level of operating skill is crucial in the secondary reduction of iron because both fluidity of the slag and a strongly reducing gas flow must be maintained simultaneously while iron particles are nucleated and then grow.

Bloom Nucleation and Consolidation

The second and third steps in the bloomery process - the formation of the bloom and its subsequent working into wrought iron - are primarily physical processes. They have received little attention, in part because they are not part of any modern metallurgical technology.

The second essential step in the bloomery process is the agglomeration of the iron particles formed by primary or secondary reduction into the nucleus of a bloom. If primary reduction occurs while the iron is held in place within ore lumps and the ore is rich enough for the resultant iron particles to be in contact with each other, agglomeration of the iron under surface tension forces will begin and continue as long as the entrapped slag can escape. The "labyrinth iron" described by Tholander (1987) is formed this way. Since labyrinth iron surrounded by dense metal is often found in blooms, we believe that it can act as a nucleus for the accretion of iron particles formed by secondary reduction. Alternative processes by which a bloom can be nucleated are the growth of the iron rims that form where slag is in contact with charcoal or the agglomeration of iron drops in the slag as a result of gravitational settling or flow of the slag past obstacles that can trap the drops.

Bloom Forging

A bloom is useful only if it can be forged into wrought iron and a necessary condition for this appears to be that the iron in the bloom be the continuous constituent of the microstructure. If this is true, slag can be forced out of it by gentle forging or by squeezing while the bloom is at a temperature above the solidus of the slag. The skills required are similar to those of the shingler in the puddling process and have been described, for example, by Gale (1976: 74-76).

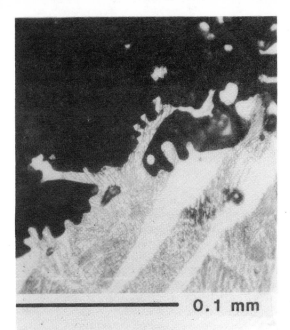

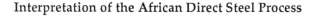

Figure 3. Experimental bloomery, smelt 5. Steel whiskers growing into slag from a steel rim around a charcoal particle.

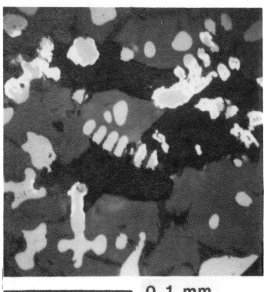

Figure 4. Experimental bloomery, smelt 4. Reduction of wustite dendrites to ferrite. Other phases are fayalite (dark grey) and glass (black).

Interpretation of the African Direct Steel Process

Because some of the Adirondack bloomeries operated with a preheated air blast, evidence from them is useful in evaluating claims that have been made for the metallurgical effects of using preheated air in prehistoric African bloomeries (Avery and Schmidt 1979; Rehder 1986). The hot blast in the former speeds the process and reduces fuel consumption but does not alter the nature of the product. It has recently been argued that prehistoric ironworkers in Africa developed a technology (the African direct steel process) that is quite different from the bloomery technology of Europe and Asia (Avery and van der Merwe 1982; Schmidt and Avery 1979). The evidence advanced for this interpretation is: (1) that African smelters consistently produced high-carbon blooms; and (2) microstructural evidence that the iron forms in these furnaces by precipitation from liquid slag. The data presented above show that both of these characteristics are integral parts of the bloomery process and are commonly found in non-African furnaces.

ACKNOWLEDGEMENTS

We thank Messrs Richard Allen and Morris Glenn for samples from New York State bloomeries and Dr. Erik Tholander for an advance copy of his doctoral dissertation.

REFERENCES

Avery, D.H., and P. Schmidt. A metallurgical study of the bloomery, particularly as practiced in Buhaya, Jour. Met. 31-10 (1979): 14-20.

Chahoon, G. The making of iron in Northern New York Catalan forges, The Iron Age, 16 - 7 (1875): 7.

Egleston, T. The American-bloomery process for making iron direct from the ore. Trans A.I.M.E. 8. (1879 - 80): 515-550

Francois, J. Recherches sur le Gisement et le Traitment Direct des Minerais de Fer dans les Pyrenees, et Particulairement dans l'Ariege, Paris, 1843.

Gale, W.K.V. The British Iron and Steel Industry, a Technical History, Newton Abbott: David and Charles, 1876.
Percy, J. Iron and Steel, London: John Murray, 1864

Rehder, J.E. Use of preheated air in primitive furnaces: Comment on the views of Avery and Schmidt, Jour. Field Archaeol. 13 (1986): 351-353.

Schmidt, P. and D.H. Avery. Complex iron smelting and prehistoric culture in Tanzania, Science 201 (1978): 1085-1089.

Tholander, E. Experimental Studies on Early Iron Making, Ph.D. dissertation, Royal Institute of Technology, Stockholm, 1987.

van der Merwe, N.J., and D.H. Avery. Pathways to steel, American Scientist 70 (1982): 146-155.

Von Bogdandy, L., and H.J. Engell. The Reduction of Iron Ores, New York: Springer 1971.

23. Surface Studies of Roman Bronze Mirrors, Comparative High-Tin Bronze Dark Age Material and Black Chinese Mirrors

N.D. MEEKS
British Museum Research Laboratory, Great Russell Street, London WC1B3DG, U.K.

ABSTRACT: *Tinned Roman mirrors were heat treated to produce a durable surface. Corrosion of high-tin bronze Roman mirrors and Dark Age buckles give structures similar to black Chinese mirrors.*

INTRODUCTION

Low-tin bronze Roman mirrors were examined for their tinning technology and compared with the surfaces of contemporary high-tin bronze mirrors in order to characterise their structures and to provide guidelines for the recognition of their technological type, because of uncertainty that has been noted in catalogued mirrors (Lloyd-Morgan 1981) and in conservation workshops. The group of over 25 mirrors had a range of colouration from silvery through grey to black, sometimes on the same mirror. Some also had extensive surface corrosion, but areas of original surface were always found. Similar colour surfaces were examined on naturally patinated Dark Age material. The surfaces and sections of black Chinese mirrors were examined to characterise their morphologies, and their structures and elemental distributions were compared with the other material to try to establish the type of process involved in blackening the surfaces.

METHODS OF EXAMINATION

Optical microscopy was used for the observation of surface colour, lustre and corrosion, but was often inconclusive by itself in determining the technological type of the Roman mirrors. Therefore scanning electron microscopy with quantitative EDX analysis was used to characterise the metallurgical structures on both unprepared surfaces and polished sections. Digital X-ray mapping was used to display the distribution of major and minor element concentrations in polished sections through the corroded surfaces. F.T. infrared spectrometry was used to directly examine the polished surface of a Chinese mirror because samples of black surfaces had not responded to X-ray powder diffraction analysis, giving only Delta compound and amorphous type scatter on the film. Objects were examined in their as-received state for observation and analysis in the SEM. Backscattered electron imaging using a large area scintillator detector in the off-axis reflected mode allowed topographical observation with no problems of specimen charging from surface dirt and corrosion. Areas of mirror surfaces free from corrosion were found for metallography and analysis. Polished sections of typical objects were prepared from already fractured pieces.

THE STRUCTURE OF TINNED SURFACES AND HIGH-TIN BRONZE

A freshly tinned surface consists of three well bonded layers (Meeks 1986; Tylecote 1985). The top layer is excess tin metal; below this are two intermetallic compound layers, Eta, Cu_6Sn_5, containing 61% tin on top of Epsilon,

Cu_3Sn, containing 38.2% tin. This underlying layer bonds to the bronze body metal. These layers form at the instant of tinning by diffusion (Kay and MacKay 1976). Subsequent heat treatment after tinning encourages further diffusion of the tin into the bronze with the growth of the compounds at the expense of excess tin metal, and when this is consumed Epsilon will grow at the expense of Eta, so that in a few minutes at 350 °C only the single Epsilon layer remains as the tin diffuses into the bronze beneath. Overheating to 450 °C will produce a solid layer of Delta compound, $Cu_{31}Sn_8$, containing 32.6% tin. Solid state thermal diffusion thus drives the system to lower tin content compounds in steps according to temperatures determined by the phase diagram. Heating to above the eutectoid isothermal of 520°C and then cooling allows the (hyper)eutectoid microstructure to form. The surface of a heat treated bronze shows angular crystals of the compounds in the surface which require fine grinding and polishing to obtain a mirror finish. The thermal history of a tinned mirror can be determined by the identification of the tin compounds on the mirror surface.

EXAMINATION OF THE ROMAN MIRRORS

Tinned Low-Tin Bronze Mirrors

The most common type of mirror in the surveyed group was that showing clear evidence of tinning on cast, low-tin bronze. However, a pair of small boxed mirrors was unusual in being made from 0.3 mm hammered sheet bronze (7% Sn) which was tinned. In general, the evidence of tinning is clearly seen as the optically shiny silvery coloured, corrosion resistant surfaces which show in the SEM as solid layers of the intermetallic compounds on top of the bronze core metal. Often the brittle surface layers were cracked with regions missing due to lifting by underlying corrosion. The intermetallic compounds on the surface were identified by quantitative EDX analysis in the SEM, although X-ray diffraction can be successfully used (Oddy and Bimson 1985).

All three compounds, Eta, Epsilon and solid Delta were found on the various tinned mirrors. One showed the layers of both Eta and Epsilon indicating low temperature heat treatment at about 250 °C, not much above the tinning temperature. All of the other tinned mirrors showed the effect of substantial heat treatment. The majority of these mirrors (8) showed the single Epsilon compound indicating heating to about 350 °C, some mirrors (2) had solid Delta compound indicating heating to about 450 °C. Several mirrors (5) had areas of Epsilon compound on top of hypereutectoid microstructures indicating that these mirrors must have been heated to above 520 °C to allow the underlying eutectoid to form on cooling, but were heated for insufficient time to allow all the Epsilon to change to Delta. Clearly all of the tinned mirrors, except perhaps one, had been heated far in excess of the temperature necessary for simple tinning. It appears that heat treatment was routinely carried out after tinning to allow the growth of the compounds at the expense of tin metal. The craftsmen would have recognised the hard, durable surface produced on heating and sought this on the finished product. This is a more economical use of tin than casting high-tin bronze mirrors for a similar reflecting surface.

High-Tin Bronze Mirrors

The high-tin bronze mirrors clearly showed the (cast) eutectoid microstructure when the surfaces were viewed in the SEM at about 1000X magnification by backscattered electron imaging. Roman high-tin mirrors invariably contain lead (Craddock 1975; Panseri 1957; Barnard 1961) and the round holes left in the original surface by the now corroded lead inclusions are clearly seen. The alpha bronze has also corroded as one would expect but the Delta of the eutectoid is generally uncorroded. No other intermetallic compound structures were seen, showing that tinning was not carried out on the high-tin bronzes, indeed there was no reason to do so. Some areas of internal corrosion in the high-tin mirrors has caused gross eruption and lifting of the uncorroded surface eutectoid, giving the optically misleading impression of a tinned surface on a corroding low tin bronze. However the SEM clearly shows the eutectoid structure of the high-tin bronze of these areas. A taper section through a typical high-tin bronze mirror confirmed the homogeneous eutectoid microstructure throughout and the fine lead globule distribution. Surface corrosion of the alpha phase and lead inclusions penetrated only some tens of μm. A section through an area of erupting core corrosion would have been interesting to identify the cause of the eruption, but a suitable sample for sectioning is still awaited.

Two of the high-tin bronze mirrors were extensively dark grey/black in colour and in the SEM were clearly different in surface morphology to the normal eutectoid bronzes (Figure 1). The mirrors showed three main characteristics, that coincidentally appeared very similar to the black Chinese mirrors: a) degradation of the surface Delta compound (as well as the expected alpha corrosion) leaving ghost mineralised structures; b) fine micro-crazing of the mineralised surface; c) by analysis, tin enrichment, copper depletion and the presence of various elements in the mineralised zone, particularly silicon and phosphorus which were uniformly distributed. Digital X-ray mapping and quantitative analysis of the sectioned mirrors clearly shows that in the mineralised zone tin is enriched in real terms, for example in one of the mirrors to about 46%, copper is depleted to 24% and there were additions of silicon 1.3%, phosphorus 0.3%, chlorine 0.1%, iron 0.4%, totaling 74%.

One of the black mirrors had areas missing from the original surface exposing, at some time in its history, the underlying core metal. This exposed metal has corroded in exactly the same way, and to the same depth as the original surface. It is therefore uncertain whether the whole mirror has patinated naturally or was originally treated to give the black surface or both. However, there is no historically recorded blackening treatment for Roman mirrors, only for tinning (Pliny), therefore it has to be suspected that corrosion is responsible for these blackened Roman mirrors.

DARK AGE HIGH-TIN BRONZE BUCKLES

The buckles are of similar composition to the Roman mirrors although the bronze is cast onto an iron core to give strength to the brittle metal. The buckles were of all colours from silvery to black, and the patination is thought to be natural corrosion. Indeed, some buckles have adjacent areas of silver and black that are clearly not decorative. Such adjacent areas, when observed in the SEM, often showed very similar eutectoid microstructures to each other, with little evidence of degraded Delta compound in the black areas. Clearly the naturally corroded black oxide surface can be extremely thin, but tenacious and can discolour the essentially unaltered eutectoid microstructure. However, some other buckles did show evidence of degraded Delta compound from natural corrosion, i.e., more advanced corrosion had occurred. Digital X-ray mapping and quantitative analysis of a sectioned silvery-grey surfaced buckle shows severe copper depletion and tin enrichment in the alpha bronze corrosion zone and also an increase in silicon with chlorine at the metal/corrosion boundary. Again the distribution is similar to the black Roman and Chinese high-tin bronze mirrors showing that the process involved in blackening the mirror surfaces is essentially one of advanced corrosion.

BLACK SURFACE CHINESE MIRRORS

The surfaces of eight black mirrors were examined in the SEM. Two of these mirrors were already broken and were therefore mounted to give polished sections for detailed metallography and analysis. In the SEM the black surfaces of all the mirrors clearly show degraded Delta compound of the eutectoid which has left ghost structures in the mineralised surfaces. The surfaces were also finely crazed (Figure 2), and this is not a characteristic of an original cast high-tin bronze surface. The section of the higher tin mirror (25.8% tin, 4.8% lead) had a microstructure of eutectoid with very little excess alpha bronze. The surface shows a thin 1-2 μm mineralised layer showing a ghost eutectoid structure which is continuous with the deeper alpha corrosion of the eutectoid below (Figure 3). The section of the lower tin mirror (22.6% tin, no lead) shows the deeper penetration of corrosion along the alpha dendrites, with degraded Delta compound at the surface (Figure 4). Digital X-ray maps of this mirror section clearly illustrate the elemental distributions that have occurred, and which appear to be typical of those found in all of the blackened mirrors. This section shows severe alteration in the concentrations of tin and copper compared with the original bronze, with associated ingress of particularly silicon and phosphorus. In the corroded zone of this mirror copper is reduced to 13% while tin is enriched to 58%, silicon is 2.8% and phosphorus is 0.2% all totalling 74%. It appears that silicon and phosphorus are constituents common to all the black mirror surfaces and are found throughout the corroded zone. Chlorine is sometimes only found at the interface between the body metal and the surface corrosion zone. Iron has a variable distribution and is not always present, and when it is, it often appears associated with the outermost surface of the corroded zone. This may represent part of the polishing compound for finishing the mirror which has become ingrained in the surface of the mirror rather than an active ingredient in the patination process.

F.T. infrared analysis of the surface of this Chinese mirror fragment showed the presence of tin oxide (SnO). This is a stable corrosion product that has previously been found on other high-tin bronzes (Rubin 1983). X-ray diffraction analysis of several powder samples taken from black mirror surfaces failed to show any crystalline oxides, only the presence of Delta compound scraped with the black samples, and diffused areas on the films indicating the presence of amorphous material.

An experiment to oxidise high-tin bronze in an electric furnace at both 300 °C and 550 °C resulted in black oxide layers of copper and tin, but their microstructure and composition were quite unlike the mirrors. The copper/tin ratio remained essentially the same as the original bronze and there are changes in the microstructure of the eutectoid due to thermal diffusion of tin and copper, and the surface becomes porous due to oxidation. From this simple experiment it is concluded that 'dry' oxidation heat treatment of Chinese mirrors was not the process involved with the black patination.

Although the sectioned Chinese mirrors have clearly revealed their microstructures and elemental distributions, and to some extent their mineral constitution, it is also clear that the structures do not appear to be significantly different from naturally corroded high-tin bronze. However it is always assumed, for good reasons, that the Chinese mirrors have been blackened deliberately, for example, from the few historical references (Needham 1962), and because of the uniform extent of the black colour and the specifically black patterned areas on other mirrors (Chase and Franklin 1979).

Therefore assuming that the mirrors were deliberately blackened, one can propose a process as follows. The black surfaces on the mirrors appear to be derived from accelerated corrosion, possibly from a hot solution patination treatment (Hughes and Rowe 1982) which mineralises both the alpha bronze and the intermetallic tin compound. The treatment involves severe loss of copper, real enrichment of tin, which requires the provision of extra tin ions from solution, the formation of tin oxide (SnO) and involves the introduction of silicon and phosphorus with the resulting formation of insoluble stable mineralised surfaces (Britton 1975; Soto 1983; Tylecote 1979). The mineralisation reaction occurs within the original polished surface of the mirror and is not an applied layer on top. Final polishing of a treated mirror would create the lustrous surface that we still have on the mirrors today.

CONCLUSIONS

Roman mirror technology has two branches. The first is the tinning and heat treatment of low-tin bronzes to produce hard intermetallic compound surfaces. The second is casting high-tin bronze to produce naturally silver coloured mirrors which do not require tinning to produce a highly reflective surface. An unusual finding appears to be the two black surfaced Roman mirrors that have surface

morphologies and mineralised compositions very similar to that of the black Chinese mirrors. The black Chinese mirrors and the comparable black Roman mirrors have three significant characteristics of their mineralised surfaces in common: a) degradation of the Delta eutectoid intermetallic compound leaving ghost structures; b) fine microcrazing through the mineralised surface; c) compositional changes showing extreme loss of copper and real enrichment of tin. Silicon and phosphorus appear to be common elements within the mineralised zone, and chlorine and iron can be of more variable distribution.

Natural corrosion seen on Dark Age high-tin bronze buckles can lead to similar structures and element distributions within the corroded alpha phase, although degradation of the Delta compound is usually, but not always, less severe than on the blackened mirror surfaces, and crazing is not as common.

However, the basic similarity between the black Chinese mirrors and naturally corroded high-tin bronze Roman mirrors suggests that the process of blackening was one of advanced natural corrosion for the Roman mirrors and a deliberate accelerated corrosion or mineralisation process within the original surfaces of the Chinese mirrors. The ghost eutectoid structures and lead globule porosity on the surfaces of these eight Chinese mirrors suggests that it is unlikely that additional layers were added onto the surfaces, otherwise these features would have been obscured. The surfaces also do not appear to be the result of oxidation by direct heat treatment.

The results of the examination of these Chinese mirrors show some differences in microstructure between these and other previously examined mirrors (Chase and Franklin 1979; Franklin and Notis, pers. comm.). It is therefore possible that there is not just one characteristic black mirror surface, but a range to be considered.

REFERENCES

Barnard. N. (1961). Bronze casting and bronze alloys in ancient China. The Australian University and Monuments Serica, Tokyo, 1961.

Britton. S.C. (1975). Tin versus corrosion, International Tin Research Institute publication No. 510, 1975.

Chase. W.T., and Franklin. U.M. (1979). Early Chinese black mirrors and pattern etched weapons, Ars Orientalis, Vol. 11.

Craddock. P.T. (1975). The composition of copper alloys used in the Classical world, Thesis submitted to the Institute of Archaeology, London.

Hughes. R., and Rowe. M, (1982). The colouring and patination of metals, The Crafts Council, London.

Kay. P.J., and MacKay. C.A. (1976). The growth of intermetallic compounds on common basis materials coated with tin and tin-lead alloys, in Transactions of the Institute of Metal Finishing, 54:68-74, (also International Tin Research Institute publication No 517).

Lloyd-Morgan. G. (1981). Description of the collection in the Rijkmuseum, IX, The Mirrors, G.M. Kan, Nijmegen, Holland, Ministry of Culture and Social Services.

Meeks. N.D. (1986). Tin-rich surfaces on bronze-some experimental and archaeological considerations, Archaeometry, 28, (2), August 1986.

Needham. J. (1962). Science and Civilisation in China, Vol 4, Pt. l, Cambridge University Press.

Oddy. W.A., and Bimson. M. (1985). Tinned bronze in antiquity, United Kingdom Institute of Conservation, Occasional paper No. 3: 33-39.

Panseri. C., and Leoni. M. (1957). The manufacturing technique of Etruscan mirrors, Studies in Conservation, 3: 49-62.

Pliny, Historia Naturalis Book XXXIV, Ch. XLVIII, (Translation by Racham.H, 1952), Vol. IX: 243-245,

William Heineman London.

Rubin.H., et. al, (1983). Studies of the black passive oxide film on bronze arrowheads unearthed with the terra-cotta warriors at Lintong Xiam, Studies in the History of Natural Sciences, 2, 4: 295-302.

Soto.L, et. al, (1983). On the corrosion resistance of certain ancient Chinese bronze artefacts, Corrosion science, vol 23, 3: 241-250.

Tylecote. R.F. (1979). The effect of soil conditions on the long term corrosion of tin-bronze and copper, Journal of Archaeological Science, 6: 345-368.

Tylecote. R.F. (1985). The apparent tinning of bronze axes and other artefacts, Journal of the Historical Metallurgy Society, 19, (2).

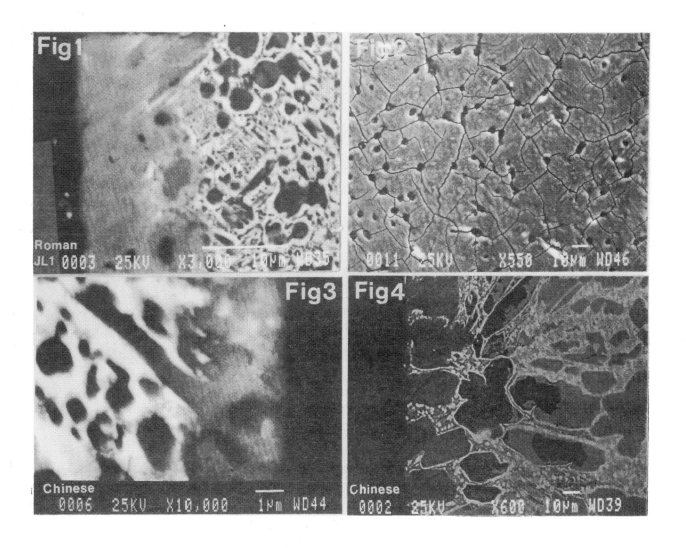

24. Bronze Metallurgy at Roccagloriosa

M.L. WAYMAN
Department of Mining, Metallurgy and Petroleum Engineering, University of Alberta, Edmonton, Alberta, Canada, T6G 2G6.

M. GUALTIERI
Department of Classics, University of Alberta, Edmonton, Alberta, Canada T6G 2E5.

R.A. KONZUK
Department of Mining, Metallurgy and Petroleum Engineering, University of Alberta, Edmonton, Alberta, T6G 2G6.

ABSTRACT: *Archaeological finds have been analysed metallurgically, demonstrating the occurrence of bronze-making at this Iron Age site. Simulations of several bronze-making techniques have also been carried out.*

INTRODUCTION

Roccagloriosa, about 200 km south of Naples, is a pre-Roman Iron Age site which was occupied during the 5th, 4th and early 3rd centuries B.C. by the Lucanians, an Oscan population which was one of the many Italic groups inhabiting the hinterland behind the Greek colonies on the nearby coast.

The most striking feature of the site is a massive fortification wall about 1200 m long and 2.5 m thick with a preserved height of up to 1.5 m. This wall together with an abrupt drop of about 80 m along one side of the site enclose an area of about 15 ha. Evidence of occupation has been uncovered both inside and outside this "fortified circuit." Outside, a major cemetery has been found with a wealth of undisturbed grave goods including many of gold, silver and bronze. Within the fortified circuit are at least three areas where excavation has revealed evidence of habitation activity, including aristocratic residences.

Although it is clear that much of the large enclosed area remained empty, at one location just inside the North Gate of the fortification wall, soundings trenches excavated in 1976-78 produced evidence of metalworking activity. This evidence includes both iron-stained and green-stained slag, as well as scraps of bronze, iron and lead, some of which are clearly fragments of objects. While pieces of slag and metal are found sporadically elsewhere on the site, here were found the remains of casting and groups of fragmented bronze objects, fairly densely concentrated, some of them in burnt layers, in total about 4.5 kg. The simultaneous presence of slag and this possible founder's hoard in a location near the wall on the down wind side of the site collectively suggest that excavation here might uncover furnace structures and associated ancillary material. Unfortunately, to date it has not been possible to carry out this excavation and hence it is necessary to rely on analysis of the recovered archaeological material and of the products of metallurgical process simulations in an attempt at understanding the nature of the metallurgical processes which are believed to have taken place at Roccagloriosa. A preliminary report on the results of both types of analysis is presented here.

THE BRONZE FINDS

This investigation is concerned with the three types of excavated bronze-related metallurgical find, namely metallic copper/bronze artifact fragments, shapeless metallic copper/bronze rounded droplets which are likely

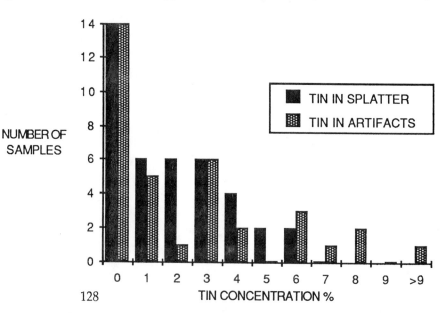

casting splatter, and pieces of slag. No complete artifacts are represented, all being in some way damaged or fragmentary - possibly discards and/or stock for a remelting operation. Along with the slag and splatter these are strongly indicative of bronze-making activities. However, the exact nature of the bronze-making activity is not apparent from a superficial examination of these finds. The three most likely possibilities are:

(1) that bronze objects were produced by the remelting of scrap bronze which was originally produced elsewhere; for example, during the period of interest, copper was being smelted in Calabria, Tuscany and likely Sardinia, and there was bronze-making in Capua (Campagnia);

(2) that bronze was produced from imported copper ingots and metallic tin ingots, both of which were traded widely in the Mediterranean area at the time;

(3) that bronze was produced from imported copper ingots and cassiterite, the oxide mineral which is the common ore of tin. Although there is no conclusive evidence for trade in cassiterite at this time, the economics of shipping the ore rather than the metal are quite favourable compared to other ores, as cassiterite contains nearly 80 % tin by weight.

All three of these processes could have been carried out in crucibles, or directly in furnace hearths.

It is of course possible that more than one of the three techniques was employed. For example, it is entirely likely that bronze-making from copper ingots using either tin or cassiterite would have been supplemented by scrap remelting. No casting operations today are free of recycled scrap because of the nature of the casting process which causes waste in the form of mold channels full of solidified metal, splash from metal pouring, defective castings, etc.

In an attempt to gain more information on the nature of the bronze-making technologies carried out at Roccagloriosa, detailed analyses of the metal and slag finds from the excavations were carried out at the University of Alberta.

DETAILED ANALYSIS OF THE FINDS

Conventional techniques for metallurgical analysis were employed in this investigation. Microstructures were studied by preparing polished and etched specimens which were examined using incident light optical metallography as well as scanning electron microscopy. Semi-quantitative chemical analysis was carried out using energy dispersive X-ray analysis in the scanning electron microscope. When necessary, these techniques were supplemented by electron probe microanalysis and X-ray diffraction.

The microstructures of the artifacts and the splatter particles were as expected for tin bronzes, both leaded and unleaded examples being present. The splatter and some of the artifacts were castings, while some of the artifacts had been mechanically worked. In the castings, lead was found to be interdendritic, and coring of the tin was frequently observed. Copper sulphide inclusions were frequently present in the bronze, often associated with interdendritic lead.

Energy-dispersive X-ray analysis showed that the artifacts and the splatter were all copper-based materials with a range of tin and lead contents as shown in the two histograms (Pages 128 and 129). Note that the lead contents can only be considered as estimates, since results obtained by this technique are sensitive to sample surface preparation methods.

These are in reasonable accord with the findings of previous workers (e.g., Craddock[1]), notably the tin contents and the enormous range of the lead contents. However, the information shown in these histograms does not provide information on the bronze-making technology since compositions such as these can be the result of any of the three suggested processes.

The other major source of information on the metallurgical activities is the slag finds. Analyses of these were carried out using the same techniques as for the metal finds, i.e., optical and scanning electron metallography with energy dispersive X-ray analysis. The slags were found to be heterogeneous in their microstructures, with free quartz often present in a background of glassy silicate which contained metal in the form of shapeless masses and spheroidal prills, tin oxide crystals which were lathlike and rhomboidal, cuprite and occasionally delafossite (CuO.FeO). Porosity was always present. A typical slag microstructure is shown in Figure 1. Microstructures similar to this have been reported by other workers,

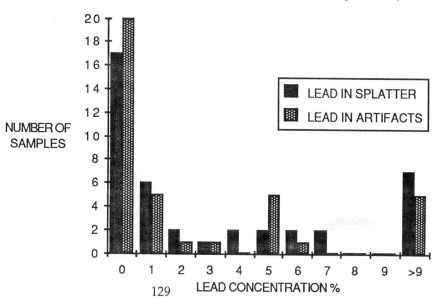

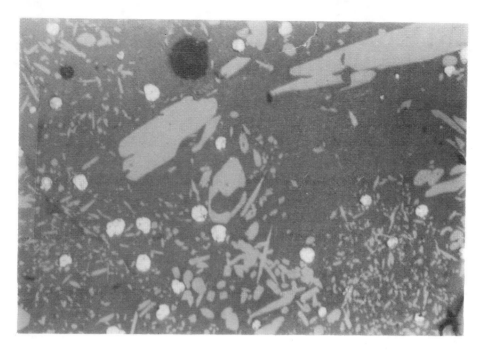

Figure 1. Microstructure of excavated slag. The bright phase is metallic bronze, the black discs are porosity and the light grey phase is tin oxide in a dark grey silicate matrix. Optical micrograph, magnification 375X.

Thirty-six analyses of the background silicate matrix gave an average composition of:

SiO_2	54.4 ± 7.6%	K_2O	2.2 ± 0.9%	Cu_2O	10.3 ± 8.9%
Al_2O_3	18.1 ± 4.0%	CaO	2.0 ± 2.2%	SnO_2	2.6 ± 3.8%
FeO	4.8 ± 3.3%	MnO	2.2 ± 2.6%	PbO	3.3 ± 0.6%

including Cooke and Nielsen[2], Zwicker[3] and Unglik[4] in what are believed to be residues from bronze-making activity at Nichoria (2100-1850 B.C.), Kition (Archaic Period) and Carthage (5th-7th centuries A.D.), respectively. Tin oxide crystals with the same morphology but embedded in a matrix of copper oxide dross have been reported by Rostoker et al.[5] in bronze-making residue from Isthmia (7th-5th centuries B.C.).

It is necessary to note that the Chart (this page) does not show bulk slag analyses - they are analyses of the glassy silicate phase in which particles of tin oxide, copper oxide, etc. are embedded. Further, they have been calculated assuming that the copper is present in the form of Cu_2O whereas in some cases, submicroscopic metallic copper grains are likely to have been included. The tin content was highly variable, partly because of submicroscopic tin oxide particles. The lead contents depend on the lead content of the metal associated with the slag, and as shown above, the lead contents of the artifacts and splatter particles were highly variable. The overall heterogeneity of the slags should also be borne in mind - there were normally significant amounts of free quartz, not included in this analysis.

The question of the origin of this slag is important. Why is there a slag? Bronze can be readily produced using any of the three technologies mentioned previously without the necessity of a slag being present. Slags (fluxes) are used in modern bronze-making for several purposes - to protect the molten metal from the loss of constituents by volatization and oxidation, to prevent the absorption of gases and to remove deleterious impurities and gases from the melt[6]. However it is not difficult to produce respectable small castings without a slag layer being present. It is likely that in the present case the slag resulted from attack on the walls of the furnace or crucible. This is suggested by the significant presence of aluminum oxide in the slag and is supported by simulation experiments as described below.

LABORATORY SIMULATIONS

One approach which has the potential for enhancing the understanding of these finds is the laboratory simulation of the three bronze-making techniques in an attempt to replicate the metal and slag finds. Such simulations have therefore been carried out in the laboratories of the University of Alberta (and previously elsewhere, for example by Charles[7] and Zwicker[3]). All three bronze-making methods were employed, using modern fire-assaying crucibles fired in air without lids in an electrically heated furnace. The parameters which were varied included charcoal, slag, temperature and time.

Charcoal

In some cases charcoal was added to the crucible charge, in other cases the experiments were carried out without charcoal, i.e., in the air atmosphere of the furnace.

Slag

In some cases a slag was used. In order to produce a slag consistent with that formed by the attack of the melt on the crucible or furnace lining, a crushed powder of baked clay ceramic was added to the charge, this being either a ceramic from Roccagloriosa or (for lack of material) an Alberta product of a similar composition. The use of crushed clay, with its large surface area, was intended to enhance the amount of slag formed, thereby providing more material for analysis. In some but not all cases charcoal was used with the slag.

Temperature and Time

Temperatures between 1100°C and 1300°C were used. Typically the crucibles spent 40 to 90 minutes total time in the furnace with removal at 10-15 minute intervals for examination and in some cases stirring with a graphite rod. At the conclusion of the process the crucibles with their contents were removed from the furnace and allowed to cool in air.

About 60 experimental simulations were carried out. Following each run, the product bronze ingots and, where applicable, the slags were sectioned, polished, etched and examined using optical and scanning electron metallography, supplemented by X-ray diffraction.

RESULT OF BRONZE-MAKING SIMULATIONS

Scrap Remelting

Bronzes containing tin and lead in the 3-10% range were produced by melting previously prepared leaded bronze in a crucible under either charcoal or a slag or both. Melting under charcoal readily produced high quality bronze ingots, however under these conditions slags did not form. Both slag and bronze could be formed, however, by the addition of a crushed powder of baked clay ceramic. When this was used *with* charcoal, the bronze ingots produced contained small amounts of oxidized tin, i.e., crystals of tin oxide. This was not the case for the archaeological metals, or for the metals produced by melting under charcoal alone without a slag. Furthermore, the microstructures of the slags produced did not resemble those of the archaeological slags.

If charcoal was *not* used, however, slag microstructures very similar to those of the archaeological slags (Figure 1) were observed; at the same time the compositions of the silicate matrices were also close to those of the archaeological slags except for their lead contents. The bronze ingots produced under these conditions contained some tin in solution but also again some tin in the form of tin oxide crystals, a situation never observed in the metal artifact fragments or the splatter particles.

Co-fusion of Metallic Tin, Lead and Copper

Bronzes were also prepared by the melting of the metallic constituents together in a crucible, either all together or by first melting the lead and tin and then adding the copper. Charcoal, slag or both were used. It was found that good quality bronze ingots could be easily made by scrap remelting under charcoal, however, as in the previous case no slag was produced by this operation. When slag formation was stimulated by the addition of crushed clay ceramic, the bronze ingot formed was again high in quality, with all tin present in solution in the bronze. The microstructures of the resultant slags, however, did not resemble the archaeological slags.

When co-fusion was carried out in a crucible with the powdered ceramic and heated *without* charcoal, slags formed with microstructures similar to those of the remelt slag, i.e., virtually indistinguishable from those of the archaeological slags. Furthermore, the composition of the matrix silicate was found to be comparable to that of the archaeological slags, except that the lead was much higher, reflecting the ability of the slag to remove lead from the alloy.

Reduction of Cassiterite into Molten Copper

Bronze-making was also attempted starting with cassiterite and metallic copper, using charcoal, slag or both. In most cases, the copper was melted first under a layer of charcoal and/or slag, then the cassiterite was added through this surface layer. By this method, at 1200°C, sound ingots containing up to 10% tin were produced, as predicted by the thermodynamic analyses of Charles[7] and Rostoker et al.[5], however, no slag was formed. The addition of ceramic powder, simulating attack on the crucible, along with the charcoal, resulted in a slag being formed, but this also seriously inhibited the reduction process, so that the bronze produced was low (generally <1%) in dissolved tin, and tin oxide crystals were present in the ingot. The microstructures of the slags which formed in this case were unlike those of the archaeological slags.

When bronze-making was attempted from cassiterite and copper using the slag cover *without* charcoal, the copper did not take tin into solution. The slag in this case contained particles of unreacted cassiterite, as well as large amounts of delafossite, giving a microstructure much different than those of the archaeological slags. Furthermore the copper oxide (and lead oxide) contents of the silicate were much higher than in the archaeological slags.

These results suggest that the oxidizing nature of the slag inhibited the reduction of tin from the cassiterite into solution in the ingot, so that medium or high tin bronzes could not readily be obtained under a slag layer, with or without charcoal. However, although it was not possible in these experiments to replicate the microstructures of the archaeological slags or metals, the possibility cannot be ruled out that this technique was used to make bronze at Roccagloriosa. This will be discussed further below.

DISCUSSION

With all three of the bronze-making techniques, conditions were readily found for the production of good quality bronze ingots having compositions and microstructures comparable to those of the archaeological metal finds. With all three techniques, however, some conditions different than these resulted in poorer quality ingots, in particular with regard to the form of the tin in the bronze. The use of charcoal in the process clearly was a critical factor necessary for the production of quality ingots.

Many different slag microstructures were produced in these bronze-making simulations, with such constituents as copper oxides, tin oxides, copper/bronze metal prills, delafossite, fayalite, magnetite and glassy silicate phases frequently observed. Again, with some but not all sets of conditions, slag microstructures and compositions strikingly similar to the archaeological slags were obtained. This was the case for the co-fusion of metallic copper, tin and lead as well as for the remelting of bronze scrap under a layer of slag, with the provision that charcoal was not used.

However the conditions for production of quality bronze and those for successful replication of the archaeological slag were seen to be mutually exclusive. For good bronze, charcoal was necessary - without charcoal the ingots contained tin oxide crystals, a situation never observed in the archaeological metals examined in the study (although their presence has never been reported in a bronze artifact from Nichoria)[2]. On the other hand the use of charcoal prevented the formation of a replicate of the archaeological slag. This is because the use of charcoal creates reducing conditions which allow a high dissolved tin content in the bronze, whereas the slag provides oxidizing conditions. The production of high tin bronzes in antiquity would certainly have involved the use of charcoal as well as conditions under which the attack on the crucible material was minimized, e.g., the use of temperatures and times as low and short as possible. As Rostoker et al.[5] state "any intelligent foundryman would keep a charcoal cover over the metal during melting."

If the slag and metal found archaeologically could not have been produced under the same metallurgical conditions, why then are they found together in the archaeological record? One possible explanation is that the slags were not formed on top of liquid bronze inside a crucible but rather when copper oxide reacted with either crucible or furnace lining material at another place or time either during the bronze production process or afterwards. The simultaneous presence of a high temperature (higher than those necessary or desireable for bronze-making) and an oxidizing atmosphere is required, conditions which would not be expected during operation of a crucible furnace, but could conceivably exist at a later stage after the removal of the crucible. A similar scenario was suggested by Rostoker et al.[5] to account for the Isthmia dross in what may have been a shaft furnace. Alternatively, the slag could reflect the conditions late in the last campaign of the furnace, perhaps a result of a mishap such as crucible failure or spill.

It must be noted that if, as suggested, the slag is not formed with the molten bronze during bronze-making, then the fact that the cassiterite reduction simulations were unable to replicate the archaeological slags does nothing to rule out the possibility of the use of cassiterite at Roccagloriosa. Any or a combination of the three bronze-making techniques may have been employed. It is hoped that further work can help to resolve this uncertainty.

CONCLUSIONS

Analyses have been carried out on excavated metal and slag finds from Roccagloriosa. The results show that the metal finds have compositions and microstructures consistent with the alloys of the period and that slags are clearly related to bronze-making.

Laboratory simulations were able to readily produce bronze metal of the appropriate composition and microstructure by three different bronze-making techniques: remelting of bronze scrap; co-fusion of metallic tin, copper and lead; and reduction of cassiterite into molten copper. However, the slags as excavated at Roccagloriosa could be replicated only by the first two techniques and only under operating conditions incompatible with the production of quality bronze ingots. On the basis of composition and microstructure it is believed that the slags formed when a component of the bronze-making process reacted with clay, likely from the crucible or furnace lining. It is suggested that this slag formed not above the molten bronze during bronze-making, but rather in the furnace either during or after the process. The analyses show clearly that bronze-making was being carried out at Roccagloriosa, however, the exact nature of the processes involved remains unresolved.

ACKNOWLEDGEMENTS

The Roccagloriosa excavations have been supported by grants from the Social Sciences and Humanities Research Council of Canada, and the Central Research Fund of the University of Alberta. The co-operation of the Italian Department of Antiquities is also gratefully acknowledged.

REFERENCES

[1]Craddock, P.T. (1986). The Metallurgy and Composition of Etruscan Bronze, Studi Etruschi 52: 211-271.
[2]Cooke, S.R.B. and Nielsen, B.V. (1978). Slag and Other Metallurgical Products, in Excavations at Nichoria in Southwestern Greece, G.Rapp Jr. and S.E. Aschenbrenner, eds., Minneapolis, University of Minnesota Press: 182-224.
[3]Zwicker, U., Greiner, H., Hofmann, K.-H. and Reithinger, M. (1985). Smelting, Refining and Alloying of Copper and Copper Alloys in Crucible Furnaces during Prehistoric up to Roman Times, in Furnaces and Smelting Technology in Antiquity, P.T. Craddock and M.J. Hughes, eds., British Museum Occasional Paper No. 48, London: 103-115.
[4]Unglik, H., Copper Alloy Objects, Iron Objects and Slag from Carthage, Fifth to Seventh Centuries A.D.: A Metallurgical Study, report of National Historic Parks and Sites Branch, Parks Canada, Ottawa.
[5]Rostoker, W., McNallan, M. and Gebhard, E.R. (1983). Melting/Smelting of Bronze at Isthmia, J. Hist. Met. Soc. 17: 23-27.
[6]Hanson, D., and Pell-Walpole, W.T. (1951). Chill-Cast Tin Bronzes, London, Arnold
[7]Charles, J.A. (1980). The Coming of Copper and Copper-Base Alloys and Iron: A Metallurgical Sequence, in The Coming of Age of Iron, T.A. Wertime and J.D. Muhly, eds., New Haven, Yale University Press: 151-181.

25. Prospecting of a Roman Castrum in Sarmatia from Discovery to Excavation

B. ERDÉLYI
Latinka Sándor u. 13. Budapest, H-1116, HUNGARY.

M. PATTANTYUS-Á
Eötvös Loránd Geophysical Institute of Hungary, P.O.B. 35, Budapest, H-1440, HUNGARY.

ABSTRACT: *A rectangular object similar in dimensions to a Roman castrum was discovered on an airphoto and investigated by geophysical methods. Computer image processing was carried out on the aerial photo. Geophysical anomalies were checked by shallow drillings prior to digging trial trenches which uncovered surprising results.*

BACKGROUND

During the interpretation of an aerial photograph taken for melioration purposes, a rectangular object similar in dimensions to a Roman camp was discovered on the outskirts of Turkeve (Erdélyi 1981), in the Great Hungarian Plain, at a considerable distance from the Pannonian limes, in the middle of Sarmatian land (Figure 1).

Literature sources provide wide possibilities for determining the age of the fortress: from the age of Marcus Aurelius (the sixties of the 2nd century) to the time of the alliance after the wars during the era of Constantinus, i.e., to the mid-4th century (Erdélyi 1984, in press). The time of building can be defined and made more exact only by means of archaeological excavation. In 1984, an attempt was made to localize the camp under the direction of Sándor Soproni, but the excavation was unsuccessful.

Since we could not achieve a greater accuracy using the original airphoto, application of digital image correction and mapping became necessary. This was realized in March 1985 at the laboratory of the Bayerische Landesamt für Denkmalpflege in Munich, with the help of Helmut Becker, to whom we express our thanks.

DIGITAL IMAGE CORRECTION

The digital processing of aerial photographs and geophysical measurements was introduced to archaeology by Irwin Scollar in 1976, at the laboratory of the Rheinisches Landesmuseum, Bonn. This complex equipment was developed for handling satellite images (Scollar 1977). Three computers simultaneously examine a photograph, handle the measuring results of the previous picture and, at the same time, apply the results of the last calculation

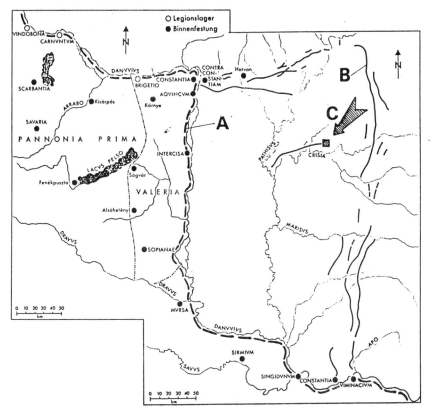

Figure 1. Great Hungarian Plain in the 3rd - 4th centuries A.D. A: limes Pannoniae; B: "limes Sarmatiae" (Soproni, 1985); C: Roman camp in question.

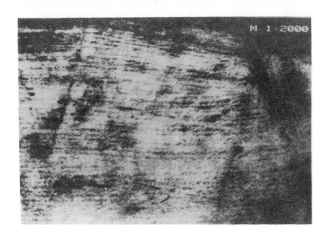

Figure 2. Picture of the rectangular object similar to a Roman castrum. This is the best picture-cut of the airphoto after enlargement and image correction made by the digital processing system of the Rheinisches Landesmuseum, for handling satellite images.

series onto a film and map it. The resolution of the system is more than 16 times as great as that of a normal television screen (Scollar 1978).

The lower performance equipment which we used in our tests, was put into operation in Munich in 1983 (Becker 1984).

In the first stage, the picture (which may be a photograph, a slide, or a negative, etc.) and the relevant sketch map were digitized by means of a video-camera and fed into the memory of the computer. Then the transformation of the digitized photograph was performed by means of some topographical fitting points after which the photo was superposed on the digitized map.

Since only a small part of the aerial photograph contains archaeological information, an appropriate picture-cut was taken (Figure 2). This activity requires enlargement and image-correction, simultaneously. The picture-cut can be selected on a monitor. During the tests the negatives were also examined.

As a final step, the fitted photo-map and the corrected positive and negative of the best picture-cut were copied onto 15 x 24 cm Polaroid photopaper by means of a video printer.

The next stage was the interpretation of the pictures. Our knowledge about the discovered object was further extended by this interpretation (Figure 3).

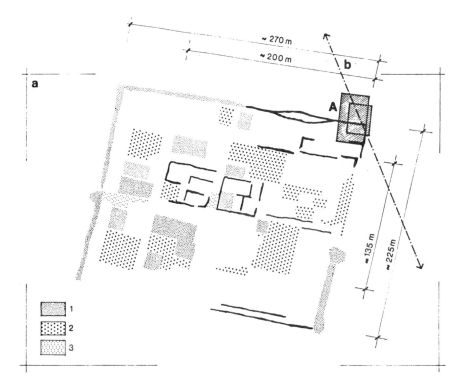

Figure 3. Archaeological interpretation of Figure 2. A: the geophysical test site; a: boundary of the Polaroid picture; b: a former road which can be seen on the photo; 1: calcareous stains appearing sharply, presumably houses and fortress walls; 2: more dimly visible stains suggesting the presence of a building; 3: possible traces of roads of the camp.

The magnification and fitting procedure described above ensures an accuracy of 15-20 m in the field, as was shown by the unsuccessful excavation performed in 1984. Thus, geophysical measurements were needed to localize the rectangle discovered on the airphoto.

RESISTIVITY MEASUREMENTS

On the basis of the aerial photograph fitted onto the topographic map, an area of 50 x 30 m was selected in the NE corner of the rectangular object for geophysical measurements (Figure 4). Shallow depth DC resistivity measurements were chosen as the measuring method in the hope that the disturbances caused by an assumed earthwork and by the possible debris would result in a suitably interpretable anomaly. Since geoelectric measurements are direction dependent as far as the electrode array is concerned, bidirectional measurement was performed with certain overlapping, using the dipole-dipole array, for the better detection of the objects meeting almost orthogonally at the corner.

Figure 5 A shows the anomaly map of the measurement in N-S direction. The isolines of the average values typical of the area are not drawn in, in order that the anomalous features can be emphasized. The higher resistivity zones can be distinguished easily at first sight, although they seem to reflect not only the effect of the linear object. Since

the effect looked for must also be included in this data system, processing by the appropriate filter, which is suitable for emphasizing this effect, is necessary.

FILTERING PROCEDURE

Many types of filters were applied to the map of Figure 5 A, and the application of a residual filter sensitive to a double edge was found to provide the best result (Figure 5 B). The filter was rotated until the feature took shape (i.e., in the case of filtering in the wrong direction, the anomalies fall apart), and it was the residual filter of NW-SE direction which provided an acceptable result.

Interestingly, it is not from the zones of higher or lower resistivity that the linearity can be seen well, but the effect looked for appears in a characteristic manner in the values of the horizontal gradient. This is why the residual filter of Ø sum had to be applied which, in the case of the edge filter, provides a picture about the increasing density of changes in a given direction.

On the raw anomaly map of the electrode array with a direction perpendicular to that of the previous one, at most, the effects described so far can be observed. Moreover, on the similarly filtered anomaly map, only the conclusions already drawn can be stated. No reliable information on the N-S direction of the earthwork could be obtained.

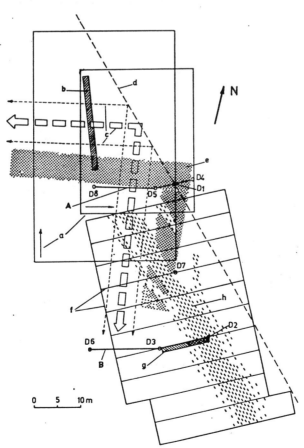

Figure 4. Location map of the geophysical measurements. a: boundary of DC resistivity measurements and the layout directions; b: archaeological trench located in 1984 on the basis of the airphoto; c: magnified picture of the NE corner of the rectangle which can be seen on the airphoto; d: one time road; e: line of the earthwork interpreted from the resistivity measurements made with the purpose of tracing the prehistoric trench; g: archaeological trench interpreted from geophysics; D1-D8: shallow drillings; A.B: profiles constructed from drillings (see Figure 6).

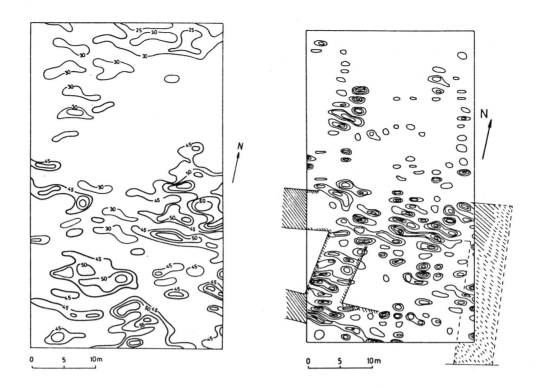

Figure 5. Resistivity maps. A: apparent resistivity map constructed from measurements of dipole-dipole array with a dipole distance of 3 m; B: filtered map of A, applying a symmetrical edge filter in NW-SE direction and of Ø sum. The interpreted linear feature is hatched.

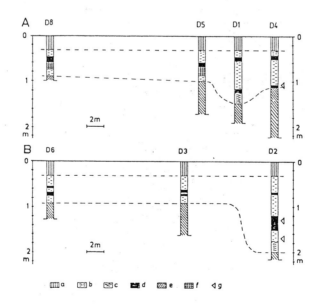

Figure 6. Geological profiles constructed from drillings. A: profile tracing the supposed Roman earthwork. Drilling D8 and D5 seem to cross the mound, while D1 goes through the ditch; B: profile tracing the prehistoric trench. Drilling D2 is almost in the middle of it; a: ploughed humus; b: black, mixed humus with some daub, pottery and bones; c: black humus filled with water; d: cultural layer; e: light yellow, clayey subsoil; f: very hard, mixed soil; g: pottery.

SHALLOW DRILLINGS

Figure 4 shows the sites of boreholes (D1 to D8) which were drilled to check the geophysical interpretation. Figure 6 illustrates two geological profiles constructed from the drilling digs. Profile A seems to prove the existence of a mound-like structure with a trench. Layers from several cultures can be found in the drillings because beginning from the prehistoric age, this area was inhabited in the Bronze Age, in the Roman Period, in the Arpadian Age and in the Middle Ages, as has been well demonstrated by findings on the surface. This is the reason why it is difficult to find a structure left untouched by later periods. Thus interpretation of the geophysical measurements is by no means a simple task. In profile B of Figure 6 a very deep prehistoric ditch can be seen although we looked here for the "fossa" belonging to the Roman castrum. Instead of this the resistivity mapping and excavation suggest a ditch of different orientation, filled with material originating from different ages and probably made in the Bronze Age.

Some resistivity profiles were also measured using the dipole-dipole array with 2 to 7 m dipole distance to trace the surprisingly deep ditch discovered by the previous drillings. Figure 7 shows the resistivity map of this area for the depths of 1.5 m and some depth pseudosections. This map and the sections also suggest that the ditch is intact and well interpretable in the SE part but it is disturbed and can be traced with difficulty in the NW part of the area as a result of the assumed disturbances made in the Roman and subsequent ages.

TRIAL TRENCHES

As was mentioned, trial excavation made in 1984 was unsuccessful (Figure 4b). Not a single characteristic feature was discovered at this site. The trial trench in 1987 - made after geophysics - crossed, with absolute certainty, the previously indicated ditch which unfortunately did not originate from the Roman Age. Figure 8 shows the archaeological section of this trial trench. Regardless of what has been said so far further excavation is necessary to prove conclusively the existence of the Roman camp sought on the basis of the airphoto and its interpretation.

CONCLUSIONS

Integrated research was carried out to locate a presumed Roman castrum discovered on an airphoto and located in a surprisingly strange site: far east from the Pannonian limes, in Sarmatia (Hungary). Geophysical interpretation, drillings and archaeological trial trenches made up to now have not conclusively demonstrated its existence. Detailed and more dense drilling profiles would be necessary prior to more extensive excavation. It is important to decide whether there is a Roman castrum here or not because this might change the history of this area in the Roman Age. It is planned that the prospecting will be continued this year.

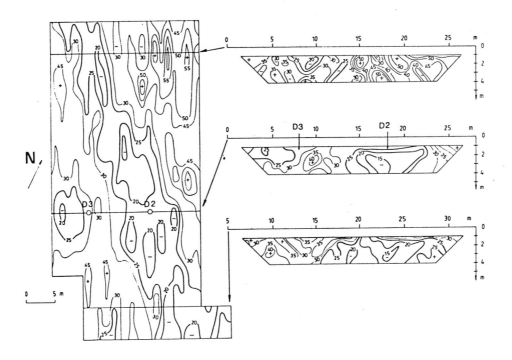

Figure 7. Resistivity map and some pseudosections measured above the prehistoric trench. The trench can be traced excellently in the SE part of the map but it is destroyed in the NW part by a subsequent age disturbance. This is visible on the depth sections too.

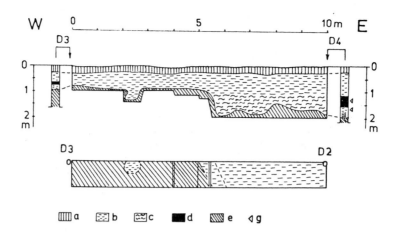

Figure 8. Archaeological section located on the basis of resistivity map and drillings through the prehistoric trench. Symbols are the same as in Figure 6.

REFERENCES

Becker, H. (1984). Aufbau einer Anlage zur digitalen Verarbeitung von archäologischen Luftbildern und Prospektionsmessungen: Das archäologische Jahr in Bayern 1983, Konrad Theiss Verlag: 201-203.

Erdélyi, B. (1981). A Roman military camp in the Great Hungarian Plain (in Hungarian): Geodézia és Kartográfia, Vol. 33, 2: 131-134.

Erdélyi, B. (1984). Castra in Sarmatia. A Roman military camp in the Great Hungarian Plain?: Archeologia Classica, Vol. XXXIII, 345-350.

Erdélyi, B., History and current aerial reconnaissance for archaeology in Hungary: Aerial Archaeology (in press).

Scollar, I. (1977). L'informatique appliquée á la photographie aérienne: Dossiers de l'Archéologie, 22: 78-87.

Scollar, I. (1978). Methoden den modernen Luftarchäologie: Methoden der Archäologie)Eine einführung in ihre naturwissenschaftliche Techniken, Barthel Hrouda: 40-47.

Soproni, S. (1985). Die letzten Jahrezehnte des Pannonischen Limes: C.H. Besk'she Verlagsbuch handlung, München.

26. Prospecting with the EM-31 on Archaeological Sites

B. CSATHÓ and M. PATTANTYUS-Á
Eötvös Loránd Geophysical Institute of Hungary, P.O.B. 35, Budapest, H-1440, HUNGARY.

ABSTRACT: *It was necessary to modify the EM-31 conductivity meter (product of Geonics) in order to make it suitable for archaeological purposes. Application of horizontal dipoles, interfacing a pocket computer to the receiver, and calculating and displaying apparent resistivity values in addition to conductivity allow successful use of this meter in solving archaeological tasks.*

INTRODUCTION

Apart from measuring the natural magnetic field and the earth's DC resistivity, electromagnetic field measurements have also become widespread in archaeological prospecting. By means of suitable EM equipment information can simultaneously be obtained on the magnetic and electric properties (conductivity and susceptibility) of the upper layers of soil. The development of equipment suitable for specific archaeological investigations and theoretical studies in methodology is currently in progress (Tabbagh 1984). At the same time, EM instruments developed for ore prospecting, can also be used for archaeological purposes (Frohlich and Lancaster 1986). Such equipment is, for example the EM-31 conductivity meter (product of Geonics). Since 1986 experimental measurements have been performed with this instrument on archaeological sites in Hungary, too.

INSTRUMENT

The principles of measurement and a description of the instrument can be found in the manufacturer's manual (McNeill 1980) and in several papers and reports, so it is not necessary to describe them here. Thus our attention might be focussed on the problems which arose during the use of the equipment and which we tried to eliminate. Similar attempts have been reported by other users, too (Frohlich and Lancaster 1986).

One of the problems is the instrument's analog meter which may cause subjective and parallax error, especially in vertical coil mode. The digital read-out has been solved by interfacing a pocket computer Sharp PC-1500 (Figure 1).

The use of the computer has other advantages as well, e.g., the possibility for data storage. Data are fed through an A/D converter from the analog output of the instrument to the memory of the pocket computer extended to 28 k bytes (Figure 2). The data collecting program can store 2,000 measurements (two parameters for each of them) simultaneously. The field report is replaced by the list of data printed out by the computer. After completion, the measurement data can be stored on a cassette tape recorder, but data transfer to an HP-9845 computer and plotter is also feasible. Automatic data storage has several advantages: besides speeding up the data processing it eliminates the subjective errors of measurements as well as enabling the simultaneous measurement of both channels.

Figure 1. Measurement with the EM-31 conductivity meter coupled with a microcomputer Sharp PC-1500.

The other problem is the difficulty in changing the position of the coils. In archaeological explorations, shallow depths should be investigated. In several cases, this can be realized only by 90° rotation of the whole instrument (horizontal dipoles). This, however, is a simple matter since after loosening the two sets of four screws, the two coil ends of the instrument can be rotated by 90° and can be re-fastened. Thus, measurement of a profile or a map can be performed with vertical coils but the equipment itself remains in the normal position.

Rotation of the instrument itself does not cause too great an inconvenience in multi-position measurement because the preprogrammed computer can be controlled by a push button located on a flexible cable. One should, however, check the correctness of the measured value before storage.

The necessity of measurement at different heights is closely connected with the problem of the investigation depth. Figure 3 shows the distribution of the induced secondary current. The relative contribution of different depth intervals to the electromagnetic field in the two positions and three heights can be determined from the curves. Because the measured apparent conductivity depends on the height of the instrument above the surface and its position, it is advantageous to transform the conductivity into apparent resistivity which is independent of the mentioned factors. Use of the pocket computer

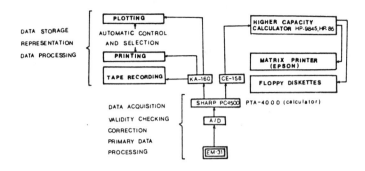

Figure 2. Block-diagram of the data storage and processing system of the EM-31.

facilitates this task: symbol of the geometric position, the values of the measured real and imaginary components and the apparent resistivity, appear simultaneously on the display of the calculator. If one calculates the difference in apparent resistivities obtained from measurements made at different heights and positions, the effect of different depth ranges can be determined.

APPLICATIONS

Medieval Settlement

This settlement consists of semisubterranean houses, outhouses, pits and holes. Hearths or stone remains can mostly be found in these houses. The settlement extends to several kilometres so the archaeological exploration of the area can be eased by geophysical prospecting. Several parts of the site were explored by DC resistivity profiling using the dipole-dipole electrode array with a dipole distance of 3 m. The resistivity map of one of these sites is shown in Figure 4. Zones of higher resistivity seem to give information concerning the structure of the settlement. One of these zones was explored by means of a trial trench. The deviation was really caused by the burnt-out hearth of a house.

We performed experiments to detect this DC resistivity anomaly utilizing the electromagnetic equipment as well. Measurements were performed on a smaller area in both positions (with horizontal and vertical coils), at a height of one metre and on the surface, respectively. The results of these comparative measurements are shown in Figure 5. The measurements carried out in the normal position at one metre height or even on the surface do not show features similar to the DC measurements.

Measurements made with vertical coils resulted in an acceptable similarity, but only on the surface. These results are supported by the current penetration curves shown in Figure 3, too. An experimental gradient calculation was also made, the result of which is shown on the map of Figure 5C. The object in question can be better identified on the gradient map despite the many disturbing anomalies that appear at the same time.

Unfortunately, there was no opportunity to carry out comparative magnetic measurements on this area.

Roman Homestead

Geophysical measurements were performed in order to locate the position of the buildings in the area of a Roman homestead existing between the 1st and the 4th centuries A.D. On the several hectares of the farm, the assumed building complexes were mapped solely on the basis of surface traces. Buildings Nos. I and II shown in Figure 6 are being explored.

The task was the more exact location of buildings Nos. III and IV. The main method applied in this area was DC profiling; the measurement of electromagnetic conductivity was used only as an experimental tool.

A larger area was surveyed by DC profiling. As a result, the location of the "mismapped" building No. IV could be corrected (Figure 6). Not only were the zones of higher resistivity plotted in this figure, but also the zones where resistivity increases with depth, in contrast to the general trend in the given area, i.e., the resistivity decreases with depth. Mathematical filtering was applied to these profiles, by means of which the effect of the remains of walls could be detected within the high resistivity detrital zones. Based on this, the most likely location of the building was plotted (Pattantyus-Á. 1986).

Results of the experimental EM conductivity measurements are shown on the map of Figure 6B which correlates well with the DC resistivity map. It can be concluded that this method has a much higher horizontal resolution, as shown in the previous example. EM measurements were made in two coil positions and at two heights of the instrument.

In shallow prospecting, mainly in the detection of resistive bodies, this method can give results which are suitable for replacing the resistivity measurements only if the coils are in the vertical position and the measurement is made on the surface.

Disturbed Site Manifesting Different Ages

Integrated research was carried out on an archaeological site where remains from different ages can be found by means of magnetometry, electromagnetics, DC profiling sounding, and shallow drilling. The interpretation was extremely difficult because the whole research area is located on the floodplain of the Danube River; in addition to the archaeological objects many disturbing geological effects could also be detected. In many cases, even archaeological excavations could not clear up every problem. As it later became evident, no interpretable archaeological object was found within the geophysical test area of 30 x 70 m. The only structure which could be identified with certainty was an accreted creek bed which could be detected by each method and thus allowed for comparison of the results.

Figure 7 shows the high-pass filtered magnetic map (A) and the EM resistivity map (B) of the area. The traversing creek bed can easily be identified on the NW part of the area. This is filled up with andesite gravels from the surrounding volcanic mountain. This is known from the excavation carried out nearby and was verified by drilling

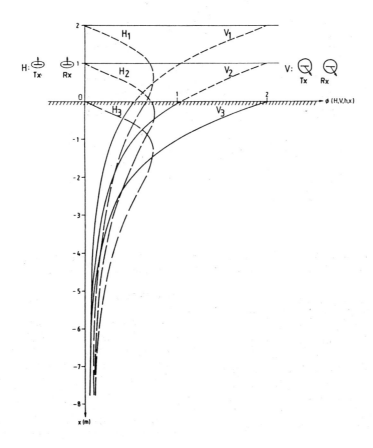

Figure 3. Function flow versus depth which describes the relative contribution of various depths to the developing secondary field. V1, V2, V3: vertical coils, the instrument heights are, respectively, 2 m, 1 m, 0 m; H1, H2, H3: horizontal coils, the instrument heights are, respectively, 2 m, 1 m, 0 m.

Figure 4. Apparent resistivity map measured by DC resistivity profiling in dipole-dipole array with a dipole distance of 3 m. The maxima provide information on the structure of the settlement. The strikingly high resistivity zone of the NW part indicates the place of a 14th century semisubterranean house with fireplace, judging from the excavation having been performed since then (place of the excavation site is marked). (From a medieval settlement in Jászdózsa, Hungary.)

141

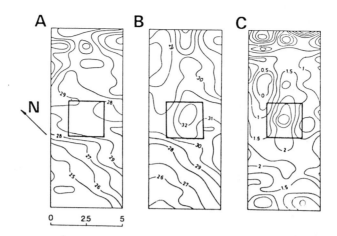

Figure 5. Maps of the EM apparent resistivity measurement performed at the NW part of the map of Figure 4. A: vertical coils at height of 1 m; B: vertical coils at height of 0 m; C: vertical gradient of maps A & B (the excavation site is marked).

here. No other characteristic anomaly can be seen on the magnetic map and structures could not be identified by drilling either. The electromagnetic map probably reflects the geological changes connected with stream deposits and filling up. This map, because of the higher horizontal resolution, is somewhat distorted. Some of these anomalies were checked by hand-drilling, but no interpretable archaeological object could be identified. The linear, transversal anomaly on the SE part of the map is probably the continuation of a trench which was uncovered on areas

out of this zone. It is of unknown origin and filled up with sand.

Very interesting comparative results can be seen in Figure 8. The magnetic and electromagnetic profiles, and the DC depth-section, as well as the drilling sections along the line crossing the filled-up creek bed offer a good possibility to compare the different methods above the same object. These EM profiles seem to verify the mathematical results obtained by vertical and horizontal magnetic dipoles (Tabbagh 1986). It is well worth comparing the EM apparent depth-section constructed

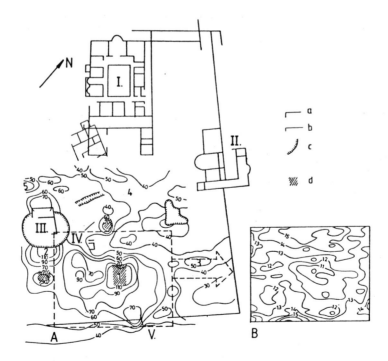

Figure 6. Maps of DC and EM measurements. A: DC resistivity map measured by resistivity profiling in a dipole-dipole array with a dipole distance of 3 m; B: EM conductivity map measured by EM-31 with vertical coils at a height of 0 m; a: excavated walls from the 1st century A.D.; b: excavated walls from the 3rd century A.D.; c: bushes, cairns, etc.; d: area characterized by resistivity increase with depth. (From a Roman homestead in Balácapuszta, Hungary.)

142

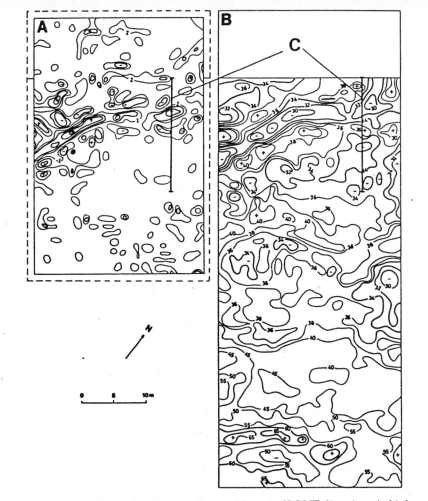

Figure 7. Maps of an archaeological site showing two linear objects in SW-NE direction. A: high-pass filtered magnetic map; B: EM apparent resistivity map measured by EM-31 with horizontal coils at a height of 0 m; C: comparative profiles (see Figure 8). Data are from the flood area of the Danube at Visegrád, Hungary.

from measurements made at different heights with the DC resistivity depth section.

CONCLUSIONS

It is obvious that EM conductivity measurement is an important tool in archaeological prospecting. The EM-31 equipment is also suitable for archaeological purposes, if the measurements are performed at an appropriate height and position and the theoretical characteristics of the method are taken into account during the interpretation. Judging from our experience, the measurement of EM conductivity cannot replace the magnetic and resistivity methods which are widespread in archaeological prospecting, but in special cases additional information can be obtained. If the modifications mentioned in the second section are realized, the EM-31 instrument is of considerable benefit to archaeology since it is economic in use and provides rapid results.

REFERENCES

Frohlich, A. and Lancaster, W.J. (1986). Electromagnetic surveying in current Middle Eastern archaeology: Application and evaluation: Geophysics 51, 7: 1414-1425.

McNeill, J.D. (1980). Electromagnetic terrain conductivity measurement at low induction number: Technical Notes, TN-6, Geonics Limited.

Pattantyus-Á, M. (1986). Geophysical results in archaeology in Hungary: Geophysics 51, 3: 561-567.

Tabbagh, A. (1984). On the comparison between magnetic and electromagnetic prospection methods for magnetic features detection: Archaeometry 26, 2: 171-182.

Tabbagh, A. (1986). What is the best coil orientation in the Slingarm electromagnetic prospecting method?: Archaeometry 28, 2: 185-196.

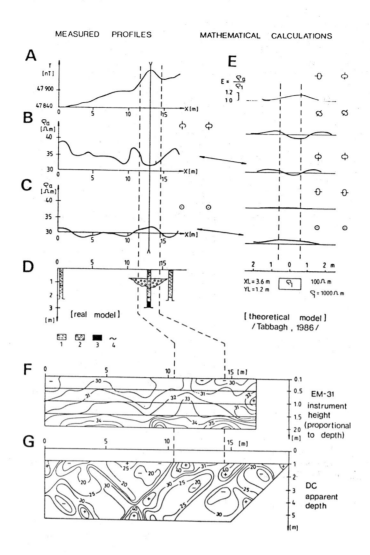

Figure 8. Magnetic, EM and DC comparative profiles and sections. A: total magnetic intensity at a height of 1.2 m; B: EM apparent resistivity at a height of 1 m with horizontal coils; C: EM apparent resistivity at a height of 1 m with vertical coils; D: interpreted geological profile controlled by drillings, 1: sandy clay, 2: andesite gravels, 3: river ballast, 4: cultural layer; E: EM quadrature results for a resistive body (mathematical calculations) from Tabbagh 1986; F: EM depth-section; G: DC resistivity section.

27. Surveying of a Prehistoric Settlement using Magnetic Gradientometry

A. PETKOV and M. GEORGIEV

Institute of Thracology, Bulgarian Academy of Sciences, Sofia, Bulgaria.

ABSTRACT: *The conditions and results obtained from the magnetic gradientometric measurements for surveying of a prehistoric settlement are described. The archaeological excavations carried out over a part of the prospected area have confirmed the geophysical anomalies.*

INTRODUCTION

Prehistoric settlements are archaeological sites which evoke a particular interest among specialists. For historians and archaeologists their prospecting and studying provide valuable information about the way of life of people who had lived thousands of years ago, at the time when human culture and civilization were born. Unfortunately, the centuries that have elapsed since have obliterated and destroyed slowly but inexorably a large part of the fragile products of the ancient human activities. Under these conditions the discovery of such sites is very difficult and raises definite problems before geophysicists as well, thus stimulating their interest to seek effective further methods of prospecting.

In 1978 Professor H. Todorova discovered, by means of archaeological drilling, a prehistoric settlement near the village Rebarkovo, northwestern Bulgaria. The settlement is characterized by two building horizons: the lower one dated to the Late Aeneolithic Age, and the upper one to the transitional periods from the Aeneolithic to Bronze Age.

Geophysical prospecting was carried out in 1986 in order to provide an orientation for the archaeological excavations, covering an area of about 800 m² localized to the west of the archaeological investigations performed until that moment.

The magnetic method was preferred among the various geophysical methods, in view of the character of the discovered remains of the settlement - predominantly fragments of ceramic vessels and tools, burnt plaster and traces of walls. The prospecting involved measuring of the vertical gradient of the magnetic field with the aim of experimenting with the possibilities offered by this variety of the magnetic method for surveying of archaeological sites of this type.

The area of the site offers good conditions for measurements, with its flat terrain with low vegetation, being relatively free from contemporary metal litter. The humus layer is 0.25 - 0.30 m thick, followed in depth by yellowish-brown undisturbed soil.

MEASUREMENT PROCEDURES

The measurements were performed along parallel profiles, 35 m long, with N-S orientation. The distance between two adjacent profiles was 2 m, while the distance between two adjacent measurement points was 1 m. Measurements at a distance of 0.5 m between the points were carried out in anomalous areas.

The values of the gradient of the magnetic field were measured using proton magnetometer MP-3 and equipment for gradient measurements manufactured by the firm Scintrex (Canada). The first sensor was at a height of 0.65 m above the terrain, the second one at 1.65 m, the distance between them being 1.0 m.

Before undertaking the magnetic measurements, the prospected area was surveyed with metal-detectors and metal litter was removed. Metal-detector ADS-7 of the firm Garrett (USA) was used. After magnetic measurements, the anomalous areas were checked again with the metal-detector.

RESULTS AND DISCUSSION

The results obtained from the measurements of the gradient of the magnetic field are presented on Figure 1 in the form of a contour map. Several interesting anomalous zones appear on this map, above all the two characteristic intensive oval zones localized in squares B 12 and G 11, respectively. Most probably they outline the contours of destroyed dwellings, rich in ceramic material.

The intensive anomalous zone in the eastern parts of squares E 14 and F 14 is caused by a destroyed wall with N-S orientation, part of which is revealed in squares E 15 and F 15.

It is also interesting to note the linear anomalous zone in the southern part of the area investigated - squares H 11, H 12, H 13, H 14 and G 14 - which is probably due to a destroyed wall.

Several other anomalous zones are outlined on the area investigated, and they should be verified through archaeological excavations. These are the zones localized in squares B 11, C 11, D 11 and E 12.

Immediately after the completion of the geophysical prospecting, archaeological excavations began, starting with square G 11, continuing in the adjacent squares F 11, F 12 and G 12, and ending in square E 12. The results of the archaeological excavations (Figure 2) are as follows:

Square G 11. An oval pit, probably from a dwelling, was found in the central and northern part of the square. Its northern part penetrates by 0.15 m into square F 11. The pit was dug into the yellowish-brown soil to a depth of 0.45-0.50 m. It is filled with large flat stones, broken burnt plaster, ash, cinders and ceramics. Some of the stones and

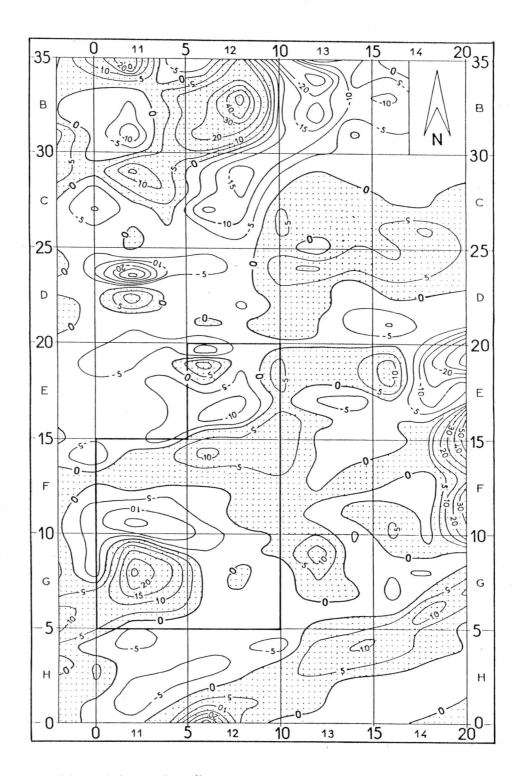

Figure 1. Contour map of the vertical magnetic gradient.

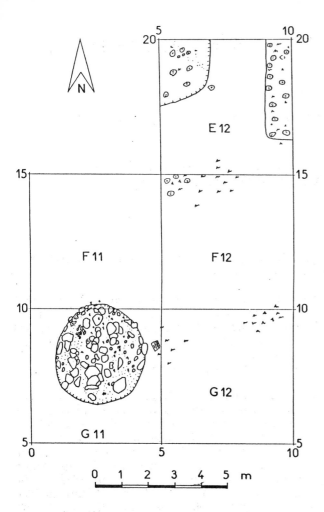

Figure 2. Plan of archaeological excavations.

covered shallow pits, 0.15 - 0.20 m deep, at the bottom of which there were broken clay vessels and ceramic tools. The pits were probably parts of dwellings. The localization of the finds coincided with the magnetic anomalies.

The archaeological excavations show that the settlement was with one building horizon in the area studied. The ceramic material discovered permits its dating to the first phase of the transitional period from the Aeneolithic to the Bronze Age. For the time being this is the only site in which this earliest stage of the Galatin culture has been attested.

CONCLUSIONS

The comparison between the localization and the intensity of the magnetic anomalies measured show good coincidence. The method used for measuring the vertical gradient of the magnetic field can be applied successfully for the surveying of prehistoric settlements and for suggesting the most promising sites for archaeological excavations.

the pieces of plaster cover the edges of the pit. The position of the remaining stones and fragments of plaster inside the pit suggest that this was a destroyed semi-underground dwelling, the overground walls of which were built of flat stones and clay. The state and the localization of the finds - fragments of clay vessels and ceramic tools - indicates that the dwelling was abandoned before the walls finally collapsed. Fragments of burnt plaster, lying at the level from which the pit was dug, were discovered in the northeastern part of the square, probably remnants of the walls of the dwelling. The pit's position coincides with the recorded anomaly of the vertical gradient of the magnetic field.

Square F 11. No archaeological finds were made. No intensive anomalies were registered.

Square G 12. Spots from strongly fragmented burnt plaster were discovered in the western and northeastern part of the square, at a depth of 0.25 - 0.30 m, below the humus layer.

Square F 12. Spots from burnt plaster covering fragments of ceramic vessels were found in the northwestern part of the square, at a depth of 0.25 - 0.30 m.

Square E 12. Spots of burnt plaster, ash and cinders were found in the northwestern and eastern part of the square, at a depth of 0.25 - 0.30 m. The plaster fragments

28. The Knife River Indian Villages National Historic Site: Recent Analysis of Magnetic Prospection Data

J.W. WEYMOUTH

Department of Physics and Astronomy and Department of Anthropology, University of Nebraska, Lincoln, NE 68588-0111 U.S.A.

ABSTRACT: *Some examples from six seasons of magnetic surveying at the Knife River Indian Villages National Historic Site, North Dakota are presented to show relations between prospection and archaeology.*

INTRODUCTION

The Knife River Indian Villages National Historic Site (KNRI) was created by an act of Congress in 1974 to preserve and interpret a group of pre-historic and proto-historic native American sites in North Dakota. It is located at the confluence of the Knife River with the Missouri River valley in the Dakotas. Within the boundaries of the KNRI are at least 55 identifiable sites including the locations of three major earthlodge villages. The entire property of the KNRI is on the National Register of Historic Places.

In 1976 the National Park Service commenced a program to determine the location and content of cultural resources lying within the boundaries of the KNRI. As part of this program, magnetic surveys were conducted on a selection of sites within the Park. These were designed to provide information on subsurface features in order to complement surface collection studies and test excavations. The surveys commenced in 1976 and continued through 1981. The field work was done by the Midwest Archaeological Center (MWAC) and the data were analyzed by my group at UNL. Table 1 is a list of the sites surveyed and the areas.

It can be appreciated from Table 1 that a large amount of data were obtained. In this short paper it is impossible to discuss all of the results or even a sizable fraction. This paper will deal with results from only three of the sites, chosen to exemplify relations between the prospection results and archaeology problems.

The surveys were done with two proton magnetometers in the difference mode using a 1 m grid interval. Until 1978 1 nT magnetometers were used and all data were hand recorded. During the 1977 season, a data logging system was developed by the University of Nebraska and the MWAC, using direct input from two 1 nT, base station magnetometers to a microcomputer. From 1978 on, the data logger was used on most of the sites. Before the 1980 season, the magnetometers were modified for 1/4 nT sensitivity.

Site Number	Site Name	Blocks 20m x 20m
32ME11	Sakakawea Village	76
32ME496	Ramble	1
32ME493	Sakakawea Cemetery	3
32ME8	Amahami Village	1
32ME9	Buchfink	4
32ME407	Poly	4
32ME12	Big Hidatsa	138
32ME10	Lower Hidatsa	104
32ME401	Elbee, Construction site	9
	Visitor's Center 1978, D	7
32ME499	Visitor's Center 1979, B	14
	" " 1979, C	27
32ME411	Lobodi	4
32ME412	Hotrok	1
Total		393
Area (block=400 m^2)		15.7 ha
		38.8 acres

Table 1. Knife River Indian Villages NHS magnetic surveys.

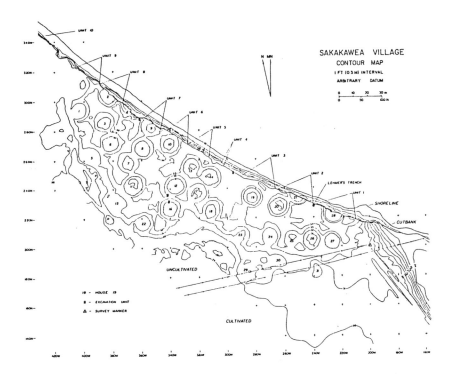

Figure 1. Topographic contour map of Sakakawea Village showing numbered house depressions, cutbank profile units, and location of excavations. Contour interval is 0.3 m (from Ahler, Weston and McMiller 1980: Figure 2).

SAKAKAWEA VILLAGE

Historical and archaeological evidence indicates that this village was occupied by an Hidatsa tribe from ca. 1795 to 1835 or 1837 and was occupied when Lewis and Clark wintered over nearby in 1804-1805. The present village area is about 2.2 ha. There are 31 observable house depressions on the surface which are sites of large earthlodges characteristic of the major villages in the KNRI. A map of the site from 1911 shows at least 46 house depressions. The Knife River has been eroding the village site and as a consequence a group from the University of North Dakota profiled the cutbank. Their study suggested that there were two episodes of occupation, the earlier houses being destroyed by fire (Ahler, Weston and McMiller 1980:44).

The magnetic surveys took place over four seasons and covered 76 blocks (Weymouth and Nickel 1977; Weymouth 1988). Figure 1 is a topographic map of the village with a 6 inch contour interval and Figure 2 is a magnetic map of the same area with no interpolation between the data points. The house sites produce a characteristic magnetic anomaly pattern. The central fire hearth produces a strong anomaly, the house floor is low and the surrounding midden is more magnetic. In addition to the 31 visible house depressions, the magnetic data can be used to identify at least 11 and possibly 18 more house sites. The archaeological evidence indicates that some of these houses belong to the earlier occupation period.

Figure 3 is a schematic map of the area surveyed. The "topographic" houses are those sites that produced

anomalies and are visible on the surface, while the "magnetic" houses produced anomalies but are not visible. These latter were given "priority" numbers, 1 being the most certain, 3 being the least certain.

As an interesting example of the interplay between the magnetic results and archaeology, we examine the northwest corner of the Village in Figure 4. This is a magnetic map with no interpolation. House 2 is visible on the surface but Houses A, B, and C are not. The cutbank profiling (Ahler, Weston and McMiller 1980) suggested a fortification ditch and some palisade posts where Houses A and C meet. If this interpretation of the profile is correct then the houses and the ditch did not occur at the same time. Thus the magnetic data provide information on the archaeological time sequence.

Another example can be seen at the boundary between cutbank units 1 and 2, on the edge of magnetic House H. According to Ahler, Weston and McMiller (1980:32) in this area there is burned roof fall present at the base of the midden deposits lying directly upon sterile sediments, suggesting that it represents an early house which was built then burned almost immediately. The significance of this is that an early, short-lived house is still visible in the magnetic record.

BIG HIDATSA VILLAGE

Big Hidatsa is the largest of the sites preserved in the KNRI. Occupied during historic times by the Hidatsa Indian tribe, it was abandoned in 1845. The beginning of the occupation is uncertain. Ahler and Swenson (1985:102) analyzed the archaeological data and concluded that the site was at least occupied from post-contact time (ca. 1600

149

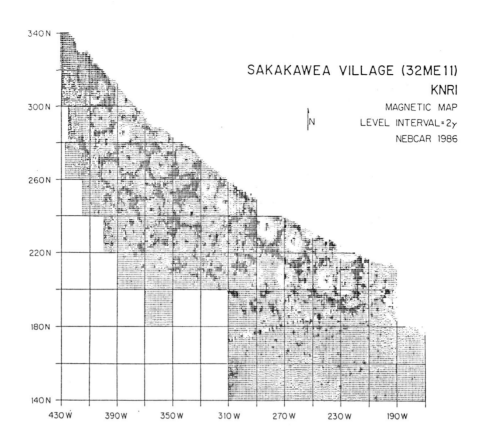

Figure 2. Grey-scale (line printer) magnetic map of Sakakawea Village, no interpolation, 2 nT intervals.

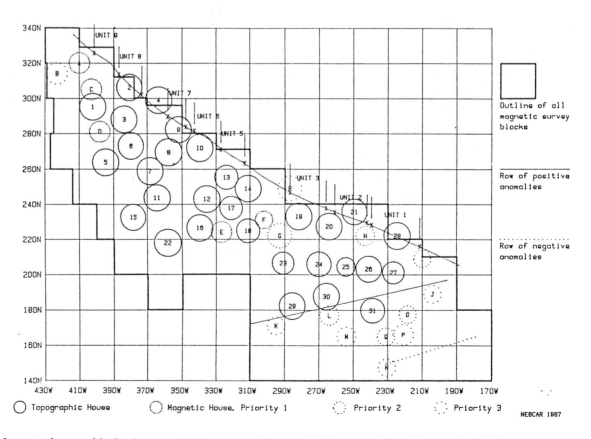

Figure 3. Layout of survey blocks, "topographic" houses, and "magnetic" houses, with priority levels, Sakakawea Village.

A.D.) and that there was some evidence for earlier occupation. The central occupation zone contains evidence of ca. 112 house depressions in an area covering about 6.6 ha. The total area of the village is about 24 ha.

The magnetic surveys took place over four seasons and covered 138 blocks (Weymouth 1986b, 1988). The results are shown in Figure 5. In 1985 thirteen excavation units and two trenches were placed in the Big Hidatsa Village. Ten of these were located in areas which had been magnetically surveyed. As an example, the house centred at about 235NE221, produced a magnetic anomaly pattern with a double ring suggesting more than one superimposed house. Also, the central hearth anomaly is elongated, suggesting either a large hearth or more than one closely adjacent hearth. Excavation in this house identified three separate burned roofs verifying the superposition of more than one dwelling.

As a check on the repeatability of the data from one season to another, one block was surveyed in 1978 and resurveyed in 1980. The magnetic maps of the two sets of data were almost identical. A numerical indication of the repeatability was calculated by subtracting the 1978 data from the 1980 data, each set corrected for diurnal variations and the offsets shifted so that the averages of the two sets were equal. The standard deviation of the differences of the two sets, taken point by point, was 4.4 nT. This figure is comparable with the variation obtained in repeated measurements of a single point.

VISITOR'S CENTER C

Area C, one of four areas identified as possible sites for a Visitor and Administration Center was evaluated for archaeological content. Area C had been under cultivation for many years. There was a light to moderate scatter of aboriginal and some Euroamerican artifacts. The magnetic survey in Area C covered 25 20 m x 20 m blocks (Weymouth 1986a). Immediately following the magnetic surveys, hand coring was carried out by a group from the University of North Dakota to identify sources of some anomalies. Two of the cultural features identified by the coring were a pit on the eastern edge (listed as "Probe" in Table 2) and a storage pit, Feature 6.

After these initial probes, a systematic program of test excavations was carried out. One metre wide strip-trenches were excavated in east-west rows spaced 20 m apart north-south. These went through the plow zone to about 20 cm surface depth and were used to look for features beneath the plow zone. Feature units were dug at various places to remove contents of cultural features. The systematic excavations provided good estimates of the volumes of the features. This in turn allowed a quantitative comparison between anomaly size and feature volume.

The test excavations in this area revealed several cultural features. Ten out of 18 features fell within the surveyed blocks. Some were in regions of missing or

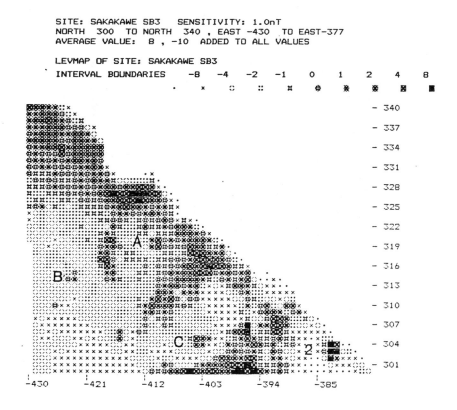

Figure 4. Grey-scale (dot-matrix) magnetic map of Sakakawea Village, north part of Northwest Sector, no interpolation, 1 nT intervals in the mid region.

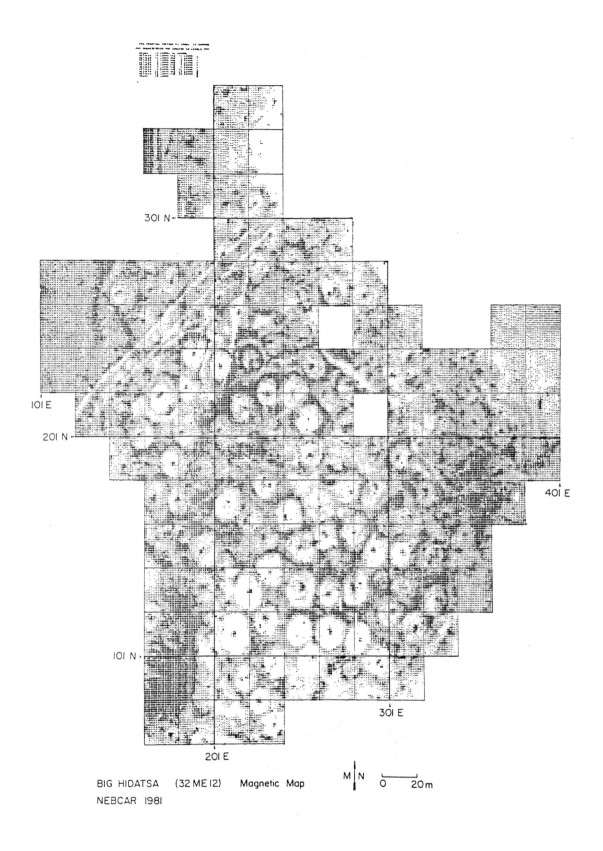

301 N

101 E

201 N

401 E

101 N

301 E

201 E

BIG HIDATSA   (32 ME 12)   Magnetic Map

NEBCAR 1981

M N

0   20 m

Figure 5. Grey-scale (line printer) magnetic map of Big Hidatsa Village, no interpolation, 2 nT intervals.

Table 2. Estimated feature volumes and related magnetic anomalies, Visitor's Center 1979, Area C (excavation data from Toom, Ahler and Falk, 1985, Table 6, P. 46)

Feature No.	Feature Type	Estimated Volume, m^3	Magnetic anomaly in nT
2	Small pit	.007	No observable anom*
3	Small pit	.002	NOA
4	Stain & debris	.022	NOA
6	Storage pit	.427	4 to 5
7	Storage pit	.154	2 to 3
8	Trench	.644	NOA
10	Burned earth	.006	NOA
Probe	Pit	No data	3 to 5 nT

*above background noise on this site of 1 to 2 nT.

incomplete data, in which case no conclusions can be drawn. Table 2 lists all of the excavated features for which there are magnetic data and the related magnetic signals. Of these only two, F6 and F7, produced anomalies above background noise on two or more points. In addition, the unexcavated probe had an associated anomaly. It is of value to consider the estimated volume of these features in relation to the anomalies. Table 2 lists those features for which there are magnetic data and the estimated volumes.

It can be seen that under the conditions of this survey on this site, pits with volumes greater than about 0.1 m^3 should produce observable anomalies. Feature 8 does not fit into this prediction because the volume is extended rather than concentrated. A 40 cm length of the trench contains only about 0.06 m^3. These considerations suggest that the pit found by probing should have a volume of about 0.5 m^3.

One further calculation which is consistent with the above discussion is an estimate of the soil magnetic susceptibility contrast (pit fill minus exterior subsoil) in Area C. Using the values from Feature 6 (volume=.43 m3, sensor to feature centre=1.03 m, field=47000 nT) a rough calculation gives a susceptibility contrast of 110 micro emu/cm³. This is similar to values measured on soil from Sakakawea Village.

CONCLUSIONS

Six seasons of magnetic surveys on the Knife River Indian Villages National Historic Site have produced a large amount of data that have provided useful information on the subsurface content of the site. The data are still available for further studies. Not only have a large number of earthlodge house sites been identified but the data contain information on interior features such as hearths, pits and entry ways. Where there has been excavation data that can be correlated with the magnetic data, conclusions can be drawn about expected minimum sizes of features that can be detected.

REFERENCES

Ahler, S.A. and A.A. Swenson (1985). Test excavations at Big Hidatsa Village (32ME12), Knife River Indian Villages National Historic Site, Report submitted to the Midwest Archaeological Center, National Park Service.

Ahler, S.A., T. Weston, and K.D. McMiller (1980). Cutbank profiling and test excavations at Sakakawea Village (32ME11), Knife River Indian Villages National Historic Site, Report submitted to the Midwest Archaeological Center, National Park Service.

Toom, D.L., S.A. Ahler, and C.R. Falk (1985). Test excavations at the Lower Hidatsa West Site (32ME499), Knife River Indian Villages National Historic Site. Report submitted to the Midwest Archaeological Center, National Park Service.

Weymouth, J.W. (1986a). Magnetic surveys of archaeological sites in the Knife River Indian Villages National Historic Site: small and non-village sites, Report submitted to the Midwest Archaeological Center, National Park Service.

Weymouth, J.W. (1986b). Archaeological site surveying program at the University of Nebraska. Geophysics, 51: 538-552.

Weymouth, J.W. (1988). Magnetic survey of archaeological sites in the Knife River Indian Villages National Historic Site: major village sites, Report submitted to the Midwest Archaeological Center, National Park Service.

Weymouth, J.W. and R. Nickel (1977). A magnetometer survey of the Knife River Indian Villages. Plains Anthropologist, 22, 2, Memoir #13.

29. Underwater Magnetic Archaeological Prospecting in Bulgaria

A. PETKOV, M. GEORGIEV and N. NENOV
Institute of Thracology, Bulgarian Academy of Sciences, Sofia, Bulgaria.

ABSTRACT: *The paper presents the results of the experimental underwater magnetic surveying of two regions of the southern Bulgarian Black Sea coast, carried out in the summer of 1987.*

INTRODUCTION

The need for substantial updating of the methods and equipment used, the means, the organization, the scientific and financial effectiveness, is being felt with an increasing urgency in Bulgarian underwater archaeology. The greatest hopes in this respect are in the field of underwater archaeometry, i.e., the complex of remote geophysical, geodetic, navigational and other technical methods and means for seeking, investigating and documenting underwater archaeological sites. Unfortunately, underwater archaeometry has two very hard requirements: very expensive equipment and highly trained technical staff. Not every institution can afford to invest such funds and to qualify such specialists. Therefore, underwater archaeometry offers an interesting opportunity for fruitful and mutually profitable international cooperation. The Institute of Thracology of the Bulgarian Academy of Sciences and the Laboratory of Archaeometry formed at the Institute in 1984 with the aim of developing underwater archaeometry in Bulgaria, would welcome with great interest any initiative in this respect.

In 1986 the Laboratory carried out successful experiments for applying the Bulgarian underwater towed vehicle Relief 0.5 for seeking underwater archaeological sites (Doukov 1987). The Relief 0.5 complex comprises: side scan sonar with 1200 m maximum coverage per channel; profiler; camera with flash; TV system. It operated in two basic modes: a large-scale surveying (acoustic mode), and a visual observation and photodocumentation mode. Relief 0.5 was used to discover an unknown ship and ancient harbour (according to the opinion of archaeologists*) in the sea water near the present-day Bulgarian town of Sozopol on the Black Sea.

In 1987 two marine archaeometric expeditions - Ropotamo '87 and Kiten '87 - were carried out with the aim of applying for the first time systems for underwater magnetometry and metal detecting, as well as for creating the respective methodologies.

Underwater archaeological sites and finds create different magnetic anomalies - of a point, linear or planar nature, ranging from very slight to very intense anomalies (of the order of thousands nT). The dimensions and the magnetic intensities of the archaeological sites require that they should be sought through detailed (1:5000 to 1:500) and very detailed (up to 1:50) surveys. However, the

investigation can also start with preliminary, tentative profile measurements. The detailed surveys and profile measurements are usually performed by more dynamic and more productive methods, most often when the sensor of the magnetometer is towed by some navigation vessel. Highly detailed surveying is achieved by static measurements.

Underwater magnetic measurements involve not only measuring the magnetic field and its variations, but also various other measurements and activities, e.g., precise navigation along the profiles with continuous determination of the coordinates of the navigation vessel and of the magnetic sensor, the course deviation and the respective deviation corrections, interpolation of the data measured in time and in the inter-profile spaces, etc.

The equipment used for the measurements was as follows:

- proton magnetometers MP-3 of the Canadian firm Scintrex, one of which has an underwater sensor with 50m cable length, and the other one is with a normal sensor for measuring geomagnetic variations. The devices can operate both in automatic and manual mode, and they can store the information measured;
- two theodolites for measuring the coordinates of the measurements;
- device for depth measurement below the boat;
- five stop-watches for determining the time of the measurements;
- five radiotelephones for contact between the groups;
- IBM PC/XT computer for storage and processing of the measured data;
- underwater metal detector of the XL-500 type of the firm Garrett, USA;
- non-metallic boat, diving equipment, transport, etc.

When we performed detailed magnetic surveying, in order to attain the values of the magnetic anomalies ΔT created by local magnetic disturbance, including disturbances caused by archaeological sites and objects, we measured:

T - the module of the Earth 's magnetic field at a distance of 0.5 m above the sea bottom, in nT;

T_{SB} - variations of the Earth 's magnetic field, in nT;

α_1 and α_2 - angles at which the boat is seen from two geodetic points at a distance L from one another, in grad;

H - depth of the water below the boat, in m;

t_T, t_{SB}, $t\alpha_1$, $t\alpha_2$ and t_H - times for measuring the respective values, in s.

From the measured values we calculated:

---

*The materials for this expedition have not been published yet.

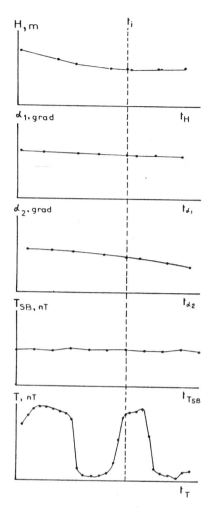

Figure 1. Curves of T, T_{SB}, a_1, a_2 and H as a function of the time of their measurement.

$\Delta T = T - T_{SB}$ - value of the magnetic anomalous field at a distance of 0.5 m above the bottom, in nT;

X, Y -coordinates of the boat, in m;

A = H - 0.5 - depth of the sensor below the boat, in m;

x, y, z - coordinates of the sensor under the water surface, in m.

The ΔT values calculated should be connected with the position of the underwater sensor (x, y, z) at the moment of the measurement, t_T. Unfortunately, the equations are valid only if all primary values (T, T_{SB}, $\alpha 1$, $\alpha 2$ and H) are measured simultaneously, which could not be done with the available equipment. The values measured could be linked only be introducing a common parameter, i.e., the time of measurement.

Depending on the way of measurement and on the experience of the operators, the different parameters were measured and recorded at a different frequency: T - at 3 s, TS_B - at 10 s, $(\alpha)_1$, $(\alpha)_2$ and H- at 20 ± 10 s. Consequently, each measured parameter appeared with its value and time of measurement, whereby in the general case, the times measurement do not coincide.

Figure 1 shows example curves of T, T_{SB}, α_1, α_2 and H, depending on the times when they were measured - t_T, t_{SB},

$t_{\alpha 1}$, $t_{\alpha 2}$ and t_H. On the basis of these synchronous curves it is possible to determine the value of each parameter at any random moment t_j which is of interest to us, including at the moment t_T, which makes it possible to calculate the relevant ΔT value and the coordinates of the sensor (x, z, z).

UNDERWATER EXPEDITION ROPOTAMO '87

The expedition was of an experimental-methodological nature. Methods of detailed and highly detailed underwater magnetic surveying were tested. The measurements were performed in September 1987 in the bay facing the mouth of the Ropotamo river, in a region with unusually beautiful and preserved nature, which has been declared a national reservation since 1940.

Underwater archaeological excavations were carried out in the 1982 - 1986 period (Karajotov 1987). The earliest finds are dated to the end of the Bronze Age - one stone anchor and ceramic fragments. Finds belonging to the Thracian period (5th century B.C. to 5th century A.D.) are also abundant, albeit with a certain hiatus around the 1st-2nd A.D. The finds dated to the Middle Ages and to the period of the Ottoman domination in Bulgaria are also numerous. No underwater excavations were performed in the region in 1987, this is why we selected this quiet and very suitable bay for performing our experiments.

Figure 2 presents a schematic plan of the region surveyed and the profiles measured. The experiments were carried out over an area of about 5 000 m², with dimensions of about 350 m in a N-S direction and 150 m in an E-W direction. The depths were about 1 m at the ends of the profiles and up to about 7 m in the middle part. The bottom in the northeastern part of the bay is rather rocky and overgrown with seaweed, while in the central and western part it is sandy. We do not possess exact information about the geology of the sea bottom in the scale needed for our experiments. Judging by the varied composition of the coastal rocks, it may be assumed that the bottom is not homogeneous and that one can find there both limestones and massive rocks with higher magnetic properties.

Detailed Underwater Magnetic Survey

The magnetic fields of the navigation vessel, of the engine, the load, the supply cable, etc., are known to cause deviations of variable values when they move along profiles with different directions. The recording and correcting of these deviations is difficult and it depends on the parameters of the navigational vessel, on the measuring methods used and on the value and sign of the slope of the earth's magnetic field in the concrete aquatoria (Milne 1984). With a view to eliminating these influences and corrections, we performed the measurements from a non-magnetic plastic boat with oars, moving at a speed of 0.4 ± 0.1 m/s.

The variations in the magnetic field were measured automatically at 10 s intervals at a base station on the shore, very close to the site. The boat's position was determined at every 20 ± 10 s by means of two theodolites placed at a distance of 276.4 m from one another. The position of the theodolites is shown on Figure 2 - one of them was located at the promontory in the northern part of the bay (GP 1), the other one - at the end of the pier (GP 2). The data on the

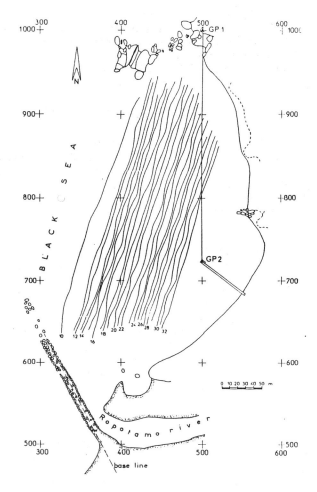

Figure 2. Plan of the prospected sea area in the mouth of the Ropotamo river.

angles α1 and α2, as well as the respective times of measurements $t_{\alpha 1}$ and $t_{\alpha 2}$, were recorded manually and were then introduced into the computer storage. The depth below the boat H was measured at 20 ± 10 s intervals from the boat's bow, then it was recorded, together with the time of measurement, and according to these factors the depth Z to which the sensor was submerged was corrected.

The distance between the profiles measured was about 5 m, i.e., the detailed underwater surveying was performed on a 1: 500 scale. The distance between the points of measurement along the profile was 1.2 ± 0.3 m.

Navigation was performed by means of five rows of buoys, suitably positioned in the aquatoria studied, and by means of radiotelephone communication between the boat, the geodetic points and a man standing on the shore, along the base line, following and correcting the boat's course.

In the course of elaborating and experimenting the methodology, we measured 30 regular profiles, each with a length of about 350 ± 50 m and with orientation almost N - S. Repeated measurements for control were performed along five of these profiles. The five profiles outlined by the buoys were also measured as cross-profiles with orientation almost E - W for control of the regular and repeated measurements.

The accuracy of the underwater magnetic survey (5.4 nT) was calculated on the basis of the measurements along the regular, repeated and cross-profiles, using standard mathematical procedures (Guidebook 1984). This accuracy was fully satisfactory for obtaining good geological surveying (mapping), for outlining vast culture layers containing abundant ceramic fragments, and for detecting strong magnetic disturbances on the bottom, including such that would be of archaeological interest. However, it was not sufficient for discovering low-magnetic and small-sized archaeological finds, because their detecting required a highly detailed surveying.

Figure 3 presents a contour map of the magnetic field in the investigated aquatoria near the mouth of the Ropotamo river. The contours are traced at 25 nT intervals up to $\pm$ 200 nT. The map permits an orientation in the general magnetic environment of the archaeological site:

- The extensive positive magnetic zones in the northern and southern parts of the map are due to geological factors: sea bottom with massive rocks, covered only partially with sand or totally exposed. Metal objects causing characteristic local anomalies accumulate along the uneven surface of the rocks. A small part of them were checked and proved to be metal litter, but it cannot be ruled out that some of these local anomalies may be caused by archaeological finds, therefore all magnetic anomalies should be checked with a metal detector by divers.

- The negative magnetic zone in the central part of the researched area coincides with the relatively sharp sinking of the sea bottom, forming something like a large oblong sand-filled hole, with a rather steep northern slope, marked by the high gradient of the magnetic field. It would be natural to expect to find accumulation and preservation of material brought by the river, remains of a nearby settlement, remnants from shipwrecks, etc., in this negative shape of the relief. And it is precisely in a small area of this zone that archaeological excavations were undertaken in the 1982 - 1986 period. The zone indicated by our measurements makes it possible to outline and expand an area which is promising for archaeological excavations, as well as to determine the most likely places for preliminary highly detailed magnetic surveying.

Highly Detailed Underwater Magnetic Survey.

As already mentioned, the search for low-magnetic and single archaeological sites requires magnetic surveying of a considerably higher accuracy, performed on highly detailed scale, e.g., 1: 50. Experiments in this respect were also carried out. A profile (No. 12) was chosen in the same area (Figure 2), which was traced along the sea bottom with a clearly visible white rope, marked at 1 m intervals. Then the profile was fixed geodetically with high precision. An accuracy exceeding ± 0.5 m was achieved in determining the coordinates of the measurement point.

The measurements started with preliminary metal detecting along the profile and in the area around it. All metal objects and litter (unfortunately in great amounts) were eliminated.

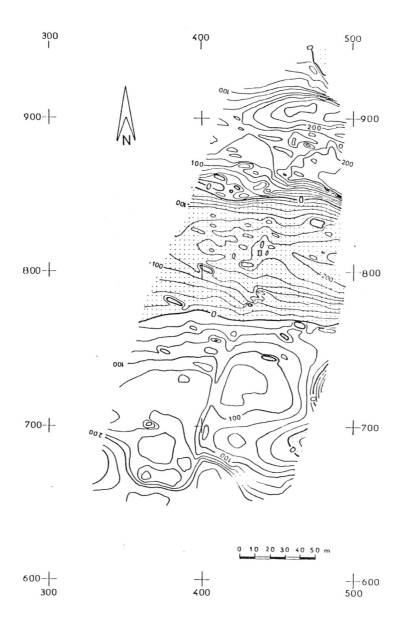

Figure 3. Contour map of the magnetic field in the prospected sea region near the mouth of Ropotamo river.

The sensor of the magnetometer was lowered from a non-magnetic boat positioned along the profile, at a distance of 30 - 40 m from the point of measurement. A diver took and moved the sensor to the point of measurement, then placed it on the sea bottom, retreated to a distance of more than 5 m and sent a signal for the start of the measurement. After receiving the signal that the measurement was performed, the diver returned to the sensor, moved it to the next point, and so on.

Profile No 12 was measured by means of these methods many times and under different conditions: at 0.5 m, 1.0 m and 2.0 m intervals, at different distances to the diver, at different positioning of the sensor on the sea bottom - erect, lying in different directions, etc. Unfortunately, we have not experimented placing the sensor at a certain distance above the bottom, e.g., 0.3 of 0.5 m. When the sensor is placed on the bottom, the maximum possible information

from the terrain and from the possible archaeological finds can be obtained. Perhaps it might be useful to achieve a certain filtering of the information for the surveying, which would result from measurements at a certain height.

The accuracy of the highly detailed magnetic measurements depending on the measurement conditions proved to be within the limits of 3 ± 2 nT, which makes it suitable for seeking archaeological objects. The principal shortcoming of the highly detailed measurements is their extremely low productivity.

UNDERWATER EXPEDITION KITEN '87

This expedition was a continuation of the experiments started in the Ropotamo Bay, however under considerably more difficult geophysical conditions: close to harbours, near ships lying at berth, with moving motorboats, etc.

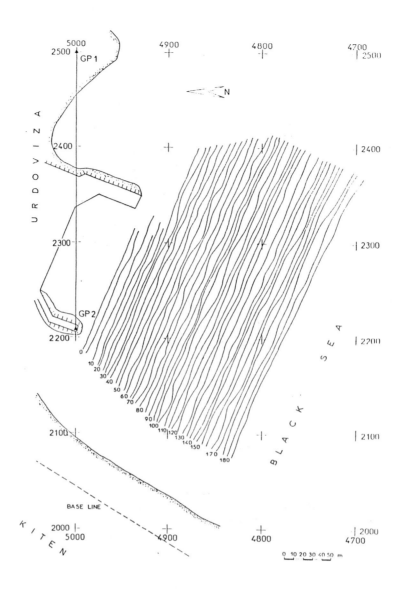

Figure 4. Plan of the prospected sea area in the southern part of the Urdoviza Peninsula, near the village of Kiten, Burgas district.

The expedition was organized at the end of September 1987 in the southern bay of the Urdoviza Peninsula, very close to the village of Kiten, Burgas district. Our choice of Urdoviza was guided by historical considerations as well: the name *Urdoviza* is of ancient Thracian origin - names in *-viza*, *byza* and *-diza* belong to the oldest layer of the Thracian toponymy in the present-day Bulgarian lands (the middle of the 2nd millennium B.C.). The underwater archaeological excavations carried out since 1967 suggest not only the existence of an ancient Thracian settlement which was contemporary to Troy, but also bear evidence of active life in these places from the remotest antiquity to our times. The geomorphology of the region, confirmed by underwater investigations, indicates that the greater part of the ancient Urdoviza Peninsula (more than 1 km²) had sunk into the sea, therefore detailed underwater archaeometric prospecting of the region is both promising and justified.

Figure 4 gives the plan of the investigated region and the positions of the profiles. The sea bottom is sandy and even. The depth increases evenly, by about 3 m for every 100 m (about 1.7°). In the northern part of the region in question there is a harbour with numerous boats, which create strong magnetic disturbances. Measurements were made along 38 regular profiles, with orientation almost E - W and with average length 400 ± 50 m, the distance between them being 5 m, i.e., we prospected an area about 80 000 m² in a 1: 500 scale, using the method described. Repeated measurements for control were performed along four of these profiles, as well as five cross-profiles with orientation almost N - S.

Figure 5 shows the magnetic contour map of the sea region studies. In the range of ± 100 nT the isolines pass at 25 nT intervals, in the ± 500 nT range - at 100 nT, while above 500 nT no isolines have been traced in order to keep the map relatively simple, although many points and anomalies with intensities even exceeding 2000 nT were registered. It can be seen from this Figure (5) that:
- The magnetic field in the northern part of the map shows strong disturbances, due both to the nearby harbour and to the abundant metal litter on the sea bottom;
- The absence of profiles in the upper northeastern part

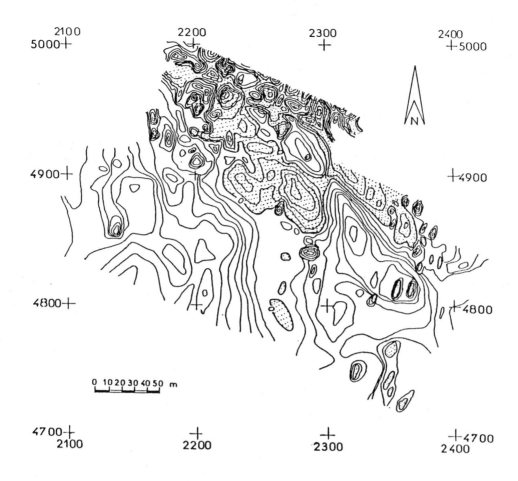

Figure 5. Contour map of the magnetic field in the prospected sea region in the southern bay of the Urdoviza Peninsula, near the village of Kiten, Burgas district.

of the map is due to the presence of a metal pontoon bridge there, used for the underwater archaeological excavations in progress at the moment. In spite of our great interest in the character and intensity of the magnetic field above the archaeological excavations, it was impossible to perform measurements, due to the strong disturbances;

- A considerable variety is observed in the magnetic field in the middle part of the map, where two elongated negative zones are outlined, being relatively homogeneous, similar in intensity and configuration to the negative zones in the mouth of the Ropotamo river. By analogy it may be assumed that these zones outline the culture layers abounding in ceramic fragments, which are of interest to us. In one of these zones - the northeastern one - excavations are in progress, confirming this assumption. In 1988 divers, archaeologists and geophysicists will investigate the outlined zones and will give their opinion on the hypothesis launched.

- It is certain that the map reflects the geological structure of the region, i.e., the area distribution of the andesite tuffes and dykes lying at a small depth below the sand;

- The magnetic field in the southern part of the map is much calmer and with positive values. This part, as well as the entire region investigated, clearly reveals local anomalies, small in area, but with high intensities, which mark metal objects on the bottom. These anomalies should be tested by divers with metal detectors, because some of

them may prove to be of archaeological value.

REFERENCES

Doukov, N. (1987). The Bulgarian Relief-0.5. Journal Morski Svjat, March 1987, pp. 23-25 (in Bulgarian).

Karajotov, I. (1987). The Sunken Harbour. Journal Morski Svjat, Febr. 1987, p.41 (in Bulgarian).

Magnetic Prospecting. A Guidebook for Geophysicists (1980). Nedra, Moscow. (in Russian).

Milne, P. (1984). Underwater Engineering Prospecting. Sudostroenie, Leningrad. (in Russian).

159

30. Thermo-Humidity Measurements of the Near Surface Air for the Prospecting of Stone Tombs

K. KIRCHEV and I. IVANOV
ENERGOPROEKT Research Technological Institute, Sofia, Bulgaria.

A. PETKOV and M. GEORGIEV
Institute of Thracology, Bulgarian Academy of Sciences, Sofia, Bulgaria.

ABSTRACT: *The paper presents the results of the experiments for determining applicability of thermo-humidity methods for the prospecting of stone tombs, the equipment designed and examples of field measurements.*

INTRODUCTION

The thermo-humidity method is a physical method based on measurement of the humidity and temperature of the air layer immediately over the earth's surface. At first glance, such a measurement offers no prospects, bearing in mind the lack of constancy of atmospheric factors in time. However, if the effect of the free air circulation is screened and if suitable optimum conditions for the measurement are provided, then the temperature and the amount of the humidity released from the earth's surface will contain measurable information about some characteristics of the ground to a depth of up to 1-2 m. This method and respective equipment are designed in principle for detecting fissures and ground water at a small depth, as well as discovering leakages from the hydrotechnical equipment. The principle on which this method is based and the equipment designed especially for it permitted its use in archaeological prospecting for finding stone tombs.

The thermo-humidity method was applied experimentally in 1982 and 1983 as part of the complex geophysical methods used for prospecting two necropolises of stone tombs along the northern Black Sea coast of Bulgaria, more specifically near the village of Kamen Brjag and in the "Jajlata" Archaeological Reservation. The areas prospected were characterized by the following features: smooth terrain, thin soil layer not exceeding 0.3 m in thickness, covering Karst and fissured limestone, numerous limestone fragments of various sizes and poor semi-desert vegetation. The most typical atmospheric factors are the strong solar radiation and the constant wind which facilitates the rapid drying of the terrain after rainfall.

The objects of the prospecting , i.e., the stone tombs, consist of an antechamber and a burial chamber hewn into the limestone rock. The antechambers are approximately 1.0 x 2.5 m in their upper part being rectangular in cross section. Their depth is 1.5-2.0 m. The burial chambers are approximately 0.8 x 2.0 m in their upper part with trapezoid cross-section and longitudinal section, sometimes reaching 3.5-4.0 m in depth. Some of the burial chambers are covered with thick limestone slabs. The antechamber and the burial chamber are separated by a rock barrier, 0.6-0.7 m thick in which a passage approximately 0.6 x 0.6 m in size is seen. The stone tombs are entirely filled with stones and earth, and they are invisible on the surface of the terrain. The characteristic types of tomb are shown in Figure 1.

PRINCIPLE METHOD

After abundant rainfall, the rainwater drains through the karst limestone to a great depth. Minimal humidity of the near-surface air is established very quickly over the denuded rock and over the areas with a thin soil cover. However, this is not the case over areas with a thicker soil cover, e.g., earth-filled fissures, karst forms, the chambers and the antechambers of the earth-covered stone tombs. They accumulate the soil moisture well and then release it into the atmosphere for a long time, thus forming anomalies in the humidity of the near-surface air. The evaporating process involves the absorption of heat, so that the increased humidity in the air will be accompanied by a certain drop in temperature. If this temperature drop is measured sufficiently accurately and without inertia, the temperature anomalies obtained will bear additional information similar to the anomalies in the humidity. The amplitude of the anomalies are proportional to the amount of water retained which corresponds to the thickness of the earth embankment. Since no natural earth-filled negative shapes more than 1.0 m thick were observed on the terrain, and since the tombs sought were at a depth of about 2.0 m and were about 3-10 m^2 in volume, with clearly typified shape, size and orientation, there are real prerequisites for their successful discovery by means of the thermo-humidity method.

EQUIPMENT

The relatively small changes in the relative humidity and especially in the temperature of the near surface air pose high requirements to the resolution of the measuring equipment. An experimental measuring system, shown schematically in Figure 2, was designed for investigating the possibilities offered by this method. The humidity released from the soil surfaces together with the near surface air, is directed through the collector to the body of the system, thus passing by the sensors for humidity and temperature. A ventilator creates forced circulation of the air in the body of the system.

The designed equipment measures the humidity with a precision of ± 0.1%, while the amplitude of the anomalies over the stone tombs exceeds the background values by more than 10-12% relative humidity. The temperature measurements were with an accuracy of ± 0.1°C which proved insufficient for obtaining sufficiently expressive

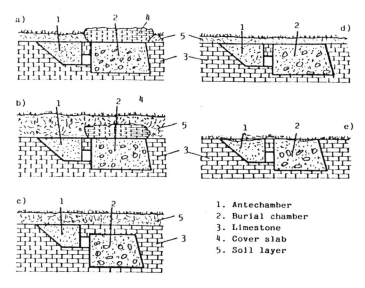

Figure 1. Longitudinal sections of the characteristic types of stone tombs.

1. Antechamber
2. Burial chamber
3. Limestone
4. Cover slab
5. Soil layer

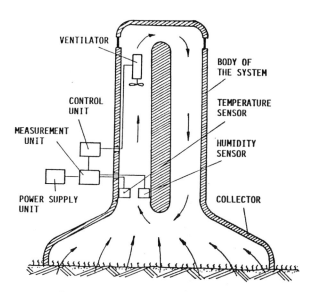

Figure 2. Diagram of an experimental measurement system for determining the humidity and temperature of the near-surface air.

results, therefore we are not reporting the data of the temperature measurements in the present paper.

The time needed for one measurement ranges between 10 and 20 s, depending on the values measured. The productivity is about 180-200 measurements per hour which is acceptable when compared with other geophysical methods.

EXPERIMENTAL METHODOLOGICAL INVESTIGATIONS

The applicability of the method for seeking stone tombs and for establishing the influence of various terrain and atmospheric factors on the accuracy of measurements was tested through numerous prolonged experimental methodological investigations. They were carried out under different atmospheric conditions over the sections of the necropolises characterized by different depth embankment and different vegetation, as well as over one stone tomb only. In the course of the measurements, only contours of the burial chamber, the partitioning wall and part of the antechamber were barely perceptible. These features were used for orienting the measurement profiles (Figure 3), over the tomb which was classified as belonging to the type shown in Figure 1e.

Part of the results obtained when the measurements were performed along the profiles over the tomb are shown in Figure 4 and Figure 5. The two curves in Figure 4 are obtained for two successive days at different atmospheric conditions and during different hours of the day. A better contrast is observed for the results shown on the curve L1-19, obtained under better conditions for measurement: early afternoon, low general air humidity and high temperature. The measurements presented in curve L1-20 were made in the later afternoon during a period of high general humidity and strong wind. The total background of the humidity and the fluctuations were considerably higher, while the anomaly was less representative.

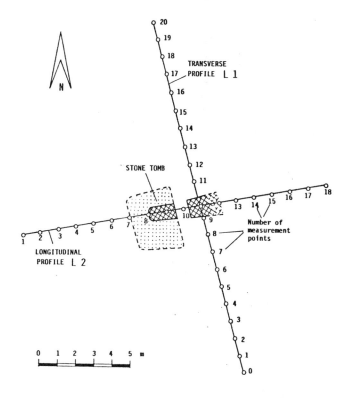

Figure 3. Plan of the measurement profiles over the stone tomb.

161

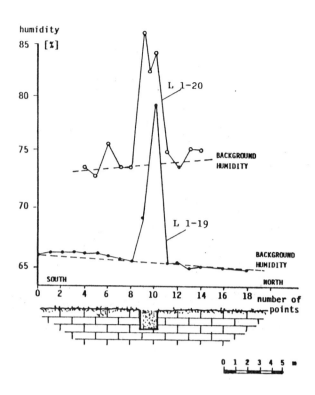

Figure 4. Curves reflecting the change in the humidity of the near-surface air along a profile which is transverse to the antechamber of the stone tomb.

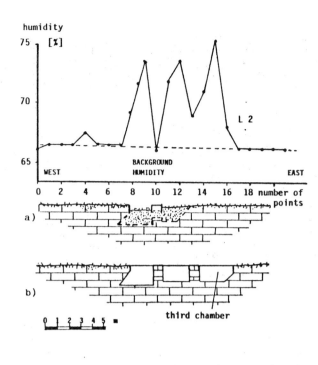

Figure 5. Curve reflecting the change in the humidity of the near-surface air along a profile coinciding with the axis of a stone tomb: a-hypothetical section; b-section after archaeological excavation.

The results obtained from the measurements along the profile coinciding with the axis of the tomb (Figure 5) outline well the chambers and the rock partitioning walls between them. Of particular interest was the third humidity maximum (on the east). Its amplitude, shape and dimensions suggest a negative form, relatively regular and with a thick embankment. Until the tomb was excavated, no one assumed that the anomaly resulted from the existence of a third chamber, because all the stone tombs known until then were with two chambers. After this, greater reliability was attributed to the thermo-humidity method.

The experimental and methodological work with the thermo-humidity method for measuring the near-surface air showed that in addition to its indisputable advantages, its application should necessarily take into account the negative effect of some factors. Measurements over characteristic anomalous areas, repeated several days later, were characterized by reduced intensity of the anomalies, although their general form and localization remained the same. This fact can be explained easily with the limited volume of the cause of the anomaly and with the depletion of the moisture in it. The sharp anomalies observed over the tombs in the first days after rainfall become smooth and unrepresentative. The attenuation of the anomalies with time is a factor which limits the applicability of the method. The measurements carried out for 40 days over the characteristic area of the necropolises and over the described tomb showed the existence of a sufficiently long period of time in which the results of the thermo-humidity measurements are sufficiently representative. For the

conditions of the necropolises under consideration this period lasts 18 days- from the 12th until the 30th day after rainfall (Figure 6).

Another important factor limiting the universality of the thermo-humidity method is the existence of vegetation over the areas of interest. The evaporation from the leaves of the plants additionally increases humidity of the near-surface air, whereby the background values increase by about 10-20 %, depending on the total biomass. The problem of the necessary correction has not been solved. In the concrete case, the necropolises prospected are covered with a poor semi-desert type of vegetation, which creates no problems for the interpretation of the well expressed humidity anomalies caused by the existence of the earth-covered stone tombs.

The optimum dimensions of the prospecting network are of considerable importance when the thermo-humidity method is applied for discovering stone tombs. The experiments carried out have shown that a square prospecting network, 1.3 x 1.3 m, is needed so that at least one of the measurements could be above the opening of one of the chambers, even with the least favourable orientation of the profiles and dimensions of the collector. Since the tracing of such a network on the terrain is not expedient, the measurements can be performed using a 1.0 x 1.0 network, with a probability for coincidence for a minimum of 3-4 measurements over one tomb, or using a 1.5 x 1.5 m network, with a negligible probability for missing a tomb. If the orientation of the tomb is known in advance, a rectangular prospecting network with a 2.0 m distance between profiles and a 1.5 m distance between the

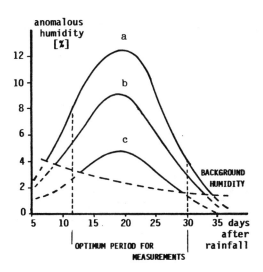

Figure 6. Changes in the humidity anomalies depending on the time of the measurement - days.

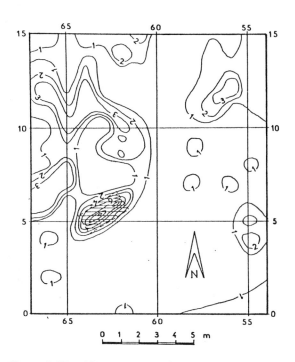

Figure 8. Humidity contour with an anomalous zone caused by the antechamber of the tomb.

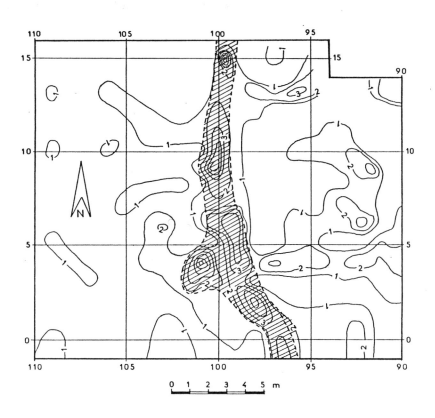

Figure 7. Humidity contour map with an anomalous zone caused by a natural geological form filled with bulk material.

measurement points can be used. In principle, whenever an anomaly with an amplitude exceeding 10% is registered, detailed measurements should be made in order to outline the cause of the anomaly.

The interpretation of the result of the thermo-humidity method does not differ substantially from the interpretation of most field geophysical methods. However, there exist specific problems as well, one of which is the constant drift of the zero line as a result of the constant changes in humidity, temperature and wind velocity. The minimum values for each profile are linked by means of a solid line on the graph, taking into account all atmospheric changes during the measurement. This line is referred to as "zero line" and above it one can perceive fluctuations of a background type (0.5-2.5 %), of an intermediate type (5.0-7.0 %), connected with the changes in the thickness of the soil cover and the vegetation, and finally the serious anomalies above 10%, suggesting the possible existence of a stone tomb. With a sufficiently dense prospecting network, maps in isolines of the relative humidity of the near-surface air are plotted. There are obligatory corrections for the time which has elapsed since the last rainfall.

The most probable localizations of the earth-covered stone tombs are determined after careful comparison of all data collected: intensity of the anomaly, dimensions, azimuth. Usually the absence of intensive humidity anomalies is considered as an indication of an absence of a tomb. It is compulsory to compare the thermo-humidity data with the results obtained using other geophysical methods.

FIELD MEASUREMENTS

The thermo-humidity method was used to prospect 1000 m² of the necropolis near the village of Kamen Brjag. The measurements were performed using a 1.0 x 1.0 m network during an optimum period, i.e., 20-30 days after rainfall (Figure 6) and in favourable atmospheric conditions. Detailed prospecting with a 0.5 x 0.5 m network were performed over certain areas of interest. The isolines on the map presented in Figure 7 clearly show a series of anomalies with intensity between 4.0 and 7.0 % above the background humidity. These anomalies form a linear anomalous zone with N-S orientation, probably caused by natural fissures in the limestone, filled with bulk material. The excavations confirmed the assumption. The thickness of the earth layer in this zone varies from 0.4 to 0.7 m.

In the southwestern part of the map shown on Figure 8 one can see an intensive anomaly with amplitude exceeding by 13% the background humidity, and with shape and dimensions characteristic of a stone tomb. Archaeological excavations of this area revealed the antechamber of a stone tomb.

CONCLUSION

The thermo-humidity method proved suitable for prospecting earth-covered stone tombs, in spite of the dependence of this method on atmospheric changes. There exist real possibilities for this method to be applied successfully for the prospecting of other types of archaeological sites: walls and monolithic buildings at a small depth, ditches, canals, etc. This method can also be applied for the prospecting of burial mounds.

31. Neutron Activation Analysis of Mycenaean Pottery from the Argolid: The Search for Reference Groups

H. MOMMSEN, E. LEWANDOWSKI and J. WEBER
Institut für Strahlen- und Kernphysik, Universität Bonn, F.R.G.

CH. PODZUWEIT
Institut für Vor-und Frühgeschichte, Universität Bonn, F.R.G.

ABSTRACT: *Late Bronze Age Mycenaean pottery from Mycenae-Berbati and from Tiryns-Asine is discernible by NAA. Reference groups are given.*

INTRODUCTION

Although there is a large variation in vessel shapes and decors of Mycenaean pottery from the Argolid during the late Helladic III (LHIII) period, archaeologists have not been able to discern different manufacturing places by visual examination. Only chemical analyses with methods capable of discerning fine distinctions in elemental compositions like Neutron Activation Analysis (NAA) have brought to light different clay sources and possibly different pottery workshops. French et al. (1984), without giving concentration values, report of at least three different clay sources used for the Argolid fineware during LHIIIB. Vessels of these different groups are found at all sites sampled (Mycenae, Berbati, Tiryns, Zygouries). So, no definite composition reference groups for these places could be assigned. Bieber et al. (1976), analyzing among others Late Bronze Age (LBA) pottery from Berbati, discerns three subgroups too. Two sherds from Mycenae show the same composition as one of the Berbati groups found. Ceramic vessels with different clay composition seem to have been distributed to many places in the Argolid in the LBA. To establish reference groups for distinct sites and to determine the provenance of Mycenaean pottery inside the Argolid, material of doubtless origin has to be chosen.

SAMPLE DESCRIPTION

We present here NAA results of 20 Mycenaean kiln wasters found at different locations and levels in the Unterburg of Tiryns and sampled there.

Kiln wasters - although not connected to a kiln in Tiryns - have high probability of having been sorted out directly after production and therefore will give a reference group for a pottery workshop in or near Tiryns. Additionally, data of LHIIIA, B and C fineware sherds found in Tiryns (14 pieces), Mycenae (18 pieces) and Berbati (15 pieces) from the sherd collection of the University of Marburg are reported. Included too are results of sherds found in Asine (14 pieces) of the later geometric period from the same collection. All the sherds are listed in Table 1.

METHOD OF ANALYSIS AND GROUPING

The NAA procedure employed here is a modified version of that described by Perlman and Asaro (1969) and outlined in Mommsen et al. (1987). Irradiations have been done at the FRG-1 reactor, Geesthacht, and at the FRM reactor, Munich, with neutron fluxes of about 2.5×10^{13} n/ (cm²s) during 3h. As standard a ceramic is used calibrated against the Berkeley pottery standard of Perlman and Asaro (1969).

The first step of our search for groups of sherds of similar composition is the construction of a dendrogram using the unweighted pair-group method. The resulting groups are then verified in a second step by comparing the individual elemental compositions with the group mean values and its rms deviations (spreads). During this step, a correction for small neutron flux inhomogeneities and weighing errors and for an always present "production variation" of the ancient potters due to a variable amount of added diluents like sand is done : a best relative fit of the individual concentration data to the mean group values, a so-called dilution factor is calculated. The error (standard deviation) of this dilution factor or derived from it, a "reduced x^2" is calculated describing the goodness of fit, which serves as a dilution independent similarity measure between two samples or groups of samples in the multivariate statistical data analysis of the first step (Mommsen et al. 1988). The 12 elements considered for grouping are marked in Table 3.

RESULTS

A dendrogram constructed as described from the data of all the 81 Mycenaean sherds from the Argolid is shown in Figure 1. The vertical spacing gives the between group distance and is introduced only to help the eye in locating the groups. The middle group represents 10 samples of coal fly ash (CFA 1633a, National Bureau Standards, Washington D.C., reference material) with well known homogeneous element concentrations. These 10 samples are included in the statistical analysis to obtain a measure of the dissimilarity value for the homogeneous, identical samples due to the experimental errors. Since in pottery always a natural inhomogeneity of elemental concentrations of a few percent occurs, dissimilarity values of a group of sherds of the same origin are expected to be somewhat larger. Several sherds marked by dots in the dendrogram have been measured repeatedly in different runs and in some cases using different reactors and again allow an estimation of the experimental precision.

The dendrogram predicts two main groups of sherds

Table 1. List of fineware sherds found in Mycenae, Berbati, Tiryns and Asine.

Lab. No	Reg. No	description[+]	possible date[++]	group[§]
Mycenae				
1	1837	unpainted body sherd	–	s
2	1836	unpainted body sherd, coarse ware	–	s
3	3223	unpainted body sherd from shoulder of a c. v.	IIIA/B	M
4	1840	unpainted body sherd, c. v.	IIIA/B	M
5	1842	unpainted foot of a kylix	IIIB	T
6	2984	big handle with wavy line, two lip bands inside, jug, amphora or hydria	IIIB/C	M
7	2954(110)	body sherd of krater with whorl shell(?) and triglyph(?)	IIIB	M
8	2959	c. v., from shoulder, three horiz. bands	IIIA/B	M
9	2954(112)	body sherd of krater with triglyph, deep band inside	IIIB	M
10	2954(113)	body sherd of krater with tricurved arch	IIIB	M
11	2965(132u)	body sherd, most probably of a skyphos, monochrom inside, outside 3 horiz. bands, double wavy line	IIIC Adv. or Late	T
12	2965(132k)	body sherd of uncertain shape (rolled), unidentified pattern	IIIC	T
13	2965(132l)	c. v., body sherd, tassel pattern	IIIC Late	s
14	3224	c. v., from shoulder, 3 horiz. bands	IIIA/B	M
15	2965	o. v., body sherd, 2 horiz. bands outside	–	M
16	3042e	small c. v.(jug?), from shoulder, stemmed spiral(?)	IIIB	M
17	3042l	c. v., body sherd, foliate band	IIIA/B	M
18	3042t	body sherd of krater, deep band or monochrome inside, spiral outside	IIIC	T
Berbati				
1 –	no Reg.	different sherds, No's 1, 3, 7, 12	IIIA	M
15	No's	rest all	IIIA/B	M
Tiryns				
8	4721	rim sherd of unpainted, carinated kylix	IIIB/C	T
9	1823	stem of goblet or kylix, unpainted	IIIa	T
10	4722	rim sherd of goblet, monochrome in- and outside	IIIA–C	M
11	3226	body sherd of kylix, linear decoration in- and outside	IIIB/C	M
12	3227	unpainted stem of kylix	IIIB/C	T
13	4724a	small c. v., rim sherd, lip band	IIIB/C	s
14	2996	foot of skyphos A, linear decoration in- and outside	IIIB	M
15	2960(1301)	o. v., body sherd, lin. decor. outside	IIIB	M

Lab. No	Reg. No	description[+]	possible date[++]	group[§]
16	2960(130b)	o. v.(skyphos), body sherd, deep band outside	IIIB	M
17	4727a	body sherd of skyphos A, burned, deep band outside, rest of triglyph(144-2)	IIIB/C	T
18	4727b	o. v., body sherd(skyphos B?), monochrome interior, linear decoration outside	IIIC	T
19	2960	c. v., body sherd, burned, linear decoration outside	IIIB/C	T
20(Kas42)	–	body sherd of krater, fish design	IIIB	T
21(Thes4)	–	body sherd, leave pattern	IIIC	T

Tiryns, kiln wasters (date corresponds to date of find stratum)

			description	possible date	group
1	Ti LXII 42/43	IX	body sherd	undated	s
2	Ti LXIII 59		body sherd	undated	T
3	Ti LXI 40/27	XVa, R120	body sherd	IIIB/C	T
4	Ti LXII 44/21	IXb, R127	body sherd	IIIC Adv.1	T
5	Ti LXI 41/7.17	IX,632	part of handle	IIIC Early	T
6	Ti LXII 36/17		sherd with rim	Early Iron	T
7	Ti LXII 43/83-93	Lx, Nr.9	body sherd	IIIC Adv.1	T
8	Ti LX 40/16	XVIIa,R120	body sherd	(intrusion)	T
9	Ti LXII 35/65	IIa	body sherd	Early Iron	T
10	Ti LXII 44/35	V	sherd with base	undated	T
11	Ti LXI 35/64	Va, KW14	sherd with rim	IIIC Adv.1	T
12	Ti LXI 35/85	VI	body sherd	IIIC Adv.2	T
13	Ti LXIII 44/1	IVc	sherd with rim	undated(IIIC)	s
14	Ti LXII 36/1	III9	sherd with base	Early Iron	s
15	Ti LXI 38/92	VIIId	body sherd	IIIC Early	T
16	Ti LXII 44/37	XIIa	body sherd	IIIC Adv.1	T
17	Ti LXII 44/81	VIII	sherd with rim	undated	T
18	Ti LXII 44/19	XI, R127a	body sherd	IIIC Adv.1	T
19	Ti LXI 40/96	Vd, 632	body sherd	IIIB/C	T
20	Ti LXIII 43/41	VIa	sherd with part of handle, painted	undated	T

Asine

				group
1 – 15	no Reg. No	all body sherds with linear decoration or monochrome, badly perserved, if notable all from geometric period (except Lab. No 13, possibly from Early Bronze Age vessel)		all T (except No's 3, 6, 15:s)
(not included here:13)				

[+] o. v. , c. v.: open, closed vessel
[++] sequence of periods in Tiryns: IIIA, IIIB, IIIB/C, IIIC Early, IIIC Developed, IIIC Advanced 1, IIIC Advanced 2, IIIC Late, Early Iron
[§] M: group Mycenae - Berbati, T: group Tiryns - Asine, s: singles

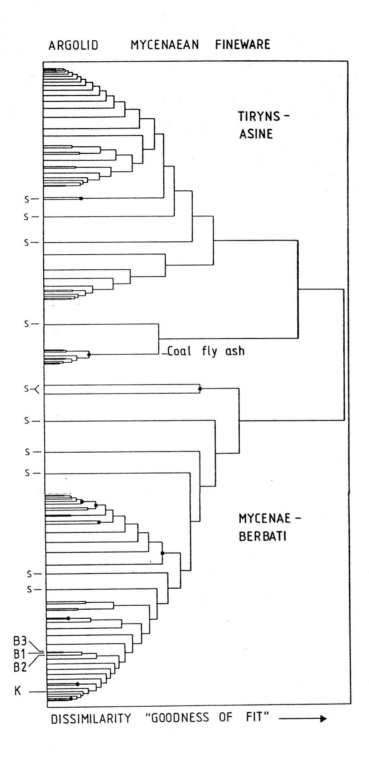

ARGOLID   MYCENAEAN   FINEWARE

TIRYNS -
ASINE

Coal fly ash

MYCENAE -
BERBATI

DISSIMILARITY   "GOODNESS OF FIT"   ⟶

Figure 1. Dendrogram resulting from a cluster analysis of Mycenaean fineware from the Argolid (explanation of lettering and dots in text).

find place	No of samples	Group Tiryns-Asine	Group Mycenae-Berbati	not grouped (singles)
Tiryns				
kiln wasters	20	17	–	3
other	14	8	5	1
Asine	14	11	–	3
Mycene	18	4	11	3
Berbati	15	–	15	–
totals	81	40	31	10

Table 2. Overview of grouping results of LHIII Argolid fineware.

and a number of sherds of unique composition. Closer inspection of the data itself proves that the cluster criterion used in constructing the dendrogram tends to aggregate sherds of similar composition in two closely packed subgroups, an upper and lower one, around several sherds which have less similar composition. Sometimes these "centre" sherds have to be taken out of the group, since their inclusion results in much higher, wrong elemental spreads of the group values. Such sherds are labelled s (singles) in the dendrogram.

Table 2 gives an overview of the final grouping. Since all the kiln wasters (except three single sherds) are found in the upper group and none in the lower, we assign this group to one or several workshops using the same claybed probably located in the southern part of the Argolid.

In the lower, we assign this group to one or several workshops using the same claybed probably located in the southern part of the Argolid. According to the find strata of the kiln wasters (late LHIIIB to first period of Early Iron Age) and to the archaeological classification of the other sherds in this group, one of these pottery workshops produced vessels at least from the LHIIIA period until the geometric period and distributed them throughout the Argolid. The second, lower group contains the most sherds from Mycenae and all the samples from Berbati, although some sherds found in Tiryns belong to this group too. Karageorghis et al. (1972) published data of a group of 16 sherds from the LLIIIB period collected in Mycenae which are very close in composition to this second group. The position of the group values of Karageorghis et al., if treated as a single sample in the cluster calculation, is indicated in the dendrogram by the letter K. The letters B mark the positions of the three subgroups of Berbati given by Bieber et al. (1976) which are not resolved in our cluster analysis probably because we do not include the element Na, which discerns these groups most clearly. The reason Na is not considered as a cluster forming element is that it very often varies strongly due to pottery making practices as indicated by the large spread values of Na in Table 3.

In this table the mean concentration values and spreads of the two Argolid groups are given. The last column in Table 3 lists the difference of the mean concentration values of each element normalized to the average error of the two group values. The largest differences of the composition values are found for the elements Cs, Rb and

Co. As an example, the concentration distribution for Co is shown in Figure 2 together with the group values of Karageorghis et al. (1972) and of Bieber et al. (1976). Both our Argolid groups are well separated.

The exact origin of the Mycenae-Berbati group is not yet proven. It seems to represent the composition of a claybed somewhere in the northern Argolid. NAA on kiln wasters or other material which can be safely assigned to this part of the Argolid would strengthen our finding of two well separated groups for the Argolid fineware of the LBA and their apparently different production places.

We acknowledge with gratitude the help and support of Professor Perlman in setting up the NAA system in Bonn. The material analyzed was made available to us by Dr. Weißhaar, University of Marburg, and by the Ephor of the Argolid and Dr. Schöfeld, DAI Athens, to whom we are very thankful.

REFERENCES

Bieber A.M., Brooks, D. W., Harbottle, G. and Sayre, E.V. (1976). Application of multivariate techniques to analytical data on Aegean ceramics, Archaeometry 18:59-74.

French, E., Newton, G.W.A., Robinson, V.J. and Scourtelli, A. (1984). Provenance of Late Helladic IIIB pottery from the Argolid, in Ancient Greek and Related Pottery, Proceedings of the Int. Vase Symposium, H.A.C. Brijder (ed.), Allerd Pierson Series, Amsterdam, 5: 13-15.

Karageorghis, V., Asaro, F. and Perlman, I. (1972). Concerning two Mycenaean sherds from Kouklia, Cyprus, Archäologischer Anzeiger 87: 188-197.

Mommsen, H., Kreuser, A., Weber, J. and Büsch, H. (1987). Neutron Activation Analysis of ceramics in the X-ray energy region, Nucl. Intr. Meth. Phys. Res. A257: 451-461.

Mommsen, H., Kreuser, A. and Weber, J. (1988). A method for grouping pottery by chemical composition, Archaeometry 30: 47-57.

Perlman, I. and Asaro, F. (1969). Pottery analysis by neutron activation, Archaeometry 1:21-52.

Table 3. Mean elemental concentration values M and standard deviation σ(spread) of the two Argolid reference groups of the northern (Mycenae-Berbati) and southern (Tiryns-Asine) parts, adjusted for dilution. All numbers are in parts per million (ppm) except Ca, Fe, K and Na in %. Elements marked with * are taken for the cluster analysis. The letter D describes the difference in the composition of groups T and M normalized to the average error of the group mean values.

| | | Group M Mycenae – Berbati (39 samples)[#] | | | | Group T Tiryns – Asine (40 samples) | | | | D difference number (T-M) |
		M	+/-	σ	σ(%)	M	+/-	σ	σ(%)	
Ca(%)		10.34	+/-	2.04	19.7	9.04	+/-	1.52	16.8	− 3.2
Ce	*	63.49	+/-	1.32	2.1	66.72	+/-	1.72	2.5	9.4
Co	*	29.32	+/-	2.64	9.0	22.83	+/-	0.93	4.1	−14.5
Cr	*	243.90	+/-	25.8	10.6	211.3	+/-	24.7	11.7	− 5.7
Cs	*	8.95	+/-	0.75	8.4	4.59	+/-	0.49	10.7	−30.5
Eu		1.22	+/-	0.18	14.3	1.32	+/-	0.05	4.1	3.4
Fe(%)*		5.20	+/-	0.17	3.2	4.97	+/-	0.10	2.0	− 7.3
Hf	*	3.64	+/-	0.46	12.7	4.59	+/-	0.34	7.5	1.0
K(%)		2.59	+/-	0.38	14.7	2.06	+/-	0.24	11.5	− 7.3
La	*	31.88	+/-	1.31	4.1	30.92	+/-	0.78	2.5	− 3.9
Lu		0.44	+/-	0.03	6.2	0.43	+/-	0.02	5.0	− 1.7
Na(%)		0.58	+/-	0.23	40.3	1.35	+/-	0.24	17.7	14.3
Nd		27.0	+/-	1.56	5.8	28.88	+/-	1.39	4.8	5.7
Ni		210.9	+/-	36.7	17.4	189.4	+/-	30.3	16.0	− 2.8
Rb	*	156.6	+/-	13.1	8.4	108.1	+/-	13.2	12.2	−16.4
Sc	*	21.46	+/-	0.81	3.8	19.65	+/-	0.60	3.0	−11.3
Sm		5.07	+/-	0.21	4.2	5.58	+/-	0.20	3.6	11.1
Ta		0.92	+/-	0.10	10.4	0.94	+/-	0.07	7.6	1.7
Tb		0.73	+/-	0.07	9.6	0.78	+/-	0.20	25.5	1.6
Th	*	11.25	+/-	0.73	6.5	11.20	+/-	0.27	2.4	− 0.3
U	*	2.32	+/-	0.12	5.3	2.10	+/-	0.15	7.3	− 7.1
Yb	*	2.66	+/-	0.10	3.9	2.73	+/-	0.13	4.8	2.5

average dilution factor

1.002 +/- 0.063   0.996 +/- 0.046

including 8 repeated measurements

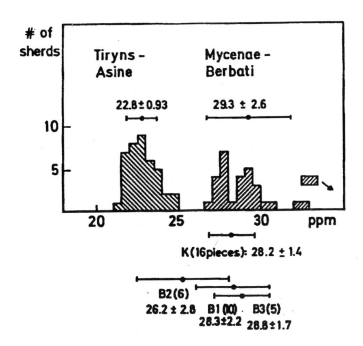

Figure 2. Concentration distribution of element cobalt in Argolid fineware of the LBA compared to average concentrations from the literature. Two sherds one from Mycenae and one from Berbati show unusually high Co values of 36.5 ppm. K: group value of Karageorghis et al. (1972) for Mycenae; B 1, 2, 3: group values of Bieber et al. (1976) for Berbati.

32. Chemical and Mineralogical Characterization of Pre-Beaker and Beaker Pottery from Ferreira do Alentejo (Beja, Portugal)

J.M.P. CABRAL, M.I. PRUDENCIO and M.A. GOUVEIA
Departmento de Quimica, ICEN, LNETI, 2865 Sacavem, PORTUGAL.

J. MORAIS ARNAUD
Inst. de Arqueologia, Fac. de Letras, Univ. de Lisboa, 1600 Lisboa, PORTUGAL.

ABSTRACT: *INAA and XRD methods were used to determine some elemental concentrations and the mineralogy in sherds from the Pre-Beaker and Beaker levels of a Chalcolithic settlement located at Ferreira do Alentejo. Clays from the area were also analysed. The results show that the Pre-Beaker and Beaker sherds have similar compositional patterns. They also reveal that the ceramics from both levels were very probably made locally.*

INTRODUCTION

The aim of this research project is to establish whether the Bell Beaker potteries found at the large Chalcolithic settlement of Ferreira do Alentejo were imported or produced locally.

Until the discovery of this settlement the main concentration of Bell Beaker pottery in Portugal was in Estremadura, where a large number of sherds of this pottery complex have been found in a wide range of types of settlements and burials. The abundance of sherds attributed to the earliest style of Beaker pottery (the so-called "Maritime" or "International" style) at the well known fortified site of Vila Nova de São Pedro (Azambuja) and the existence in the pre-Beaker Chalcolithic levels of that site of a rich tradition of channelled, impressed and incised potteries, lead several authors, namely Harrison (1977), to defend a local origin for the Bell Beaker potteries, as a result of gradual evolution of the pre-Beaker decorative traditions.

With the discovery and beginning of the excavation of the vast settlement of Ferreira do Alentejo (Arnaud 1982), the situation is becoming much more complex. As a matter of fact, in spite of the reduced area so far excavated (about 30 m²), in comparison with sites of Vila Nova de São Pedro and Zambujal, which are much smaller but were almost completely excavated, the number of sherds and the variety of the decorative patterns found in the site, located 100 km to the southeast of Vila Nova de São Pedro, are very striking indeed, and outnumber those found at any other settlement in Portugal.

On the other hand, in contrast with what has been observed at most of the Chalcolithic settlements in Estremadura, at Ferreira do Alentejo very few decorated sherds of any style were found in the pre-Beaker levels. This indicates that the introduction of the characteristic Bell Beaker potteries shows a complete rupture in relation to the local traditions of shaping and decorating pottery. This rupture is reinforced by the occurrence at the Beaker levels of at least one copy of each of the items which have been traditionally associated with the "Beaker Culture" or the "Beaker Folk" (Childe 1925, 1957): gold and copper objects; V-perforated bone buttons and stone "wristguards".

It was thus expected that the analysis of this first series of samples would give a contribution to the solution of the classical controversy about the geographical origin, socio-economic context of production and distribution, and the ideologic meaning of the most sophisticated prehistoric pottery produced in temperate and Mediterranean Europe.

COLLECTION OF POTTERY AND CLAYS

Fifty-five sherds were taken for analysis from two different archaeological contexts of the Ferreira do Alentejo Chalcolithic settlement: the pre-Beaker levels and the Beaker levels. The identification of these is presented in Table 1. Eleven samples of clays collected from the ground at a depth of about 15 cm in loci used by actual potters or close to abandoned potteries in the vicinity of the settlement, as well as five samples of modern ceramics either from local potters or collected from the ground in the immediate vicinity of abandoned potteries, were also taken for study. Their identification and provenance are indicated in Table 1. Sampling loci are shown in Figure 1.

It is worth noting that in the area adjacent to the settlement one may distinguish the following geological units: gabbros and diorites, quartz, porphyries, Silurian and Devonian schists and graywackes and Palaeogene-Miocene and Pliocene sediments.

This diversity of geological and environmental factors has certainly affected the chemical composition of soils and clays in that area. As seen in Figure 1, the Chalcolithic settlement is situated on Palaeogene-Miocene sediments and so are the now working potteries at Beringel which is the most important pottery centre in the area. Interviews with local potters at Beringel revealed, however, that the raw material preferred for pottery making is the soil derived by weathering from gabbros and diorites, the so-called "barro de Beja". It was decided therefore, to collect a larger number of samples from this type of soil than from other types.

METHODS

Ceramic and clay samples were prepared for analysis by using the procedures employed in earlier works (Cabral et al. 1983; Prudencio et al. 1987).

Reference	Type of material	Provenance
PB1-PB14	Non-decorated pottery	Pre-Beaker levels
PBD	Decorated pottery	" " "
PBW1-PBW5	"Loomweights"	" " "
BND1-BND15	Non-decorated pottery	Beaker levels
BW1-BW5	"Loomweights"	" "
BD1-BD15	Decorated pottery	" "
S1-S6	Soils derived by weathering from gabbros and diorites	From loci shown in Fig.1
S7;S9-S11	Palaeogene-Miocene-Pliocene sediments	" " " " "
S8	Soil derived by weathering from schists and grauwackes	" " " " "
MC1	Modern tile, dried in air	From the same locus as S8
MC2	" " , heated	" " " " " "
MC3,MC4	" bricks	From a local potter
MC5	" vase	" " " "

Table 1. Identification and provenance of materials studied.

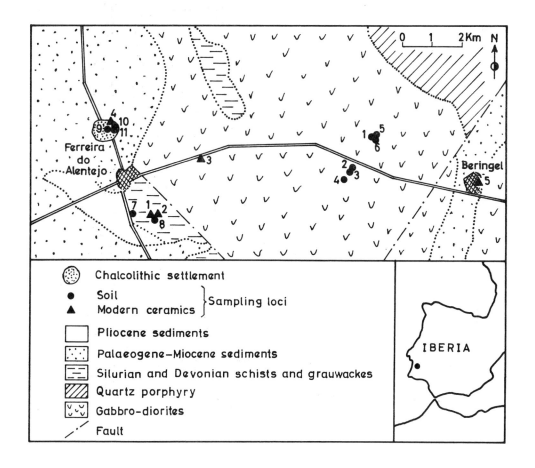

Figure 1. Map showing the Chalcolithic site of Ferreira do Alentejo and sampling loci.

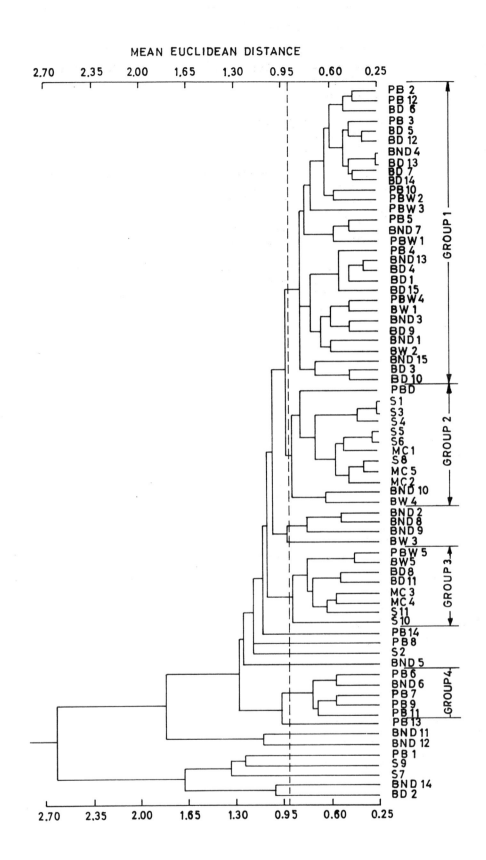

Figure 2. The dendrogram of the 71 ceramics and clay samples in study, based on UPGMA cluster analysis of mean Euclidean distances. The cophenetic correlation coefficient was 0.89.

Table 2. Concentration means for compositional groups of ceramic and clay samples.

Element[+]	GROUP 1 (30)[*]			GROUP 2 (12)			GROUP 3 (8)			GROUP 4 (5)		
	Mean	± s	% s	Mean	± s	% s	Mean	± s	% s	Mean	± s	% s
Na_2O %	2.49	± 0.36	14.6	2.33	± 0.38	16.4	2.15	± 0.41	19.2	2.21	± 0.19	8.8
K_2O %	0.471	± 0.127	27.0	0.461	± 0.133	28.9	0.983	± 0.440	44.8	0.413	± 0.089	21.4
CaO %	5.38	± 1.48	27.6	5.37	± 1.61	29.9	4.79	± 1.17	24.5	8.39	± 0.96	11.4
Sc	34.1	± 10.5	30.8	39.5	± 8.8	22.3	24.9	± 4.7	18.7	57.7	± 9.4	16.3
Cr	96.7	± 33.4	34.6	178	± 32	18.1	147	± 25	17.2	132	± 70	53.0
Fe_2O_3%	8.86	± 1.70	19.2	8.47	± 0.94	11.1	5.65	± 0.98	17.3	13.3	± 1.2	9.0
Co	39.0	± 5.9	15.0	39.0	± 3.0	7.7	26.8	± 4.4	16.3	52.9	± 2.4	4.5
Cs	0.88	± 0.21	23.5	0.68	± 0.25	37.2	1.24	± 0.34	27.4	0.94	± 0.11	11.7
Ba	725	± 172	23.8	275	± 189	68.7	395	± 246	62.3	722	± 218	30.2
La	5.01	± 1.70	34.0	4.65	± 2.27	48.8	8.71	± 1.40	16.1	4.74	± 1.01	21.3
Ce	9.47	± 3.53	37.3	9.60	± 4.32	45.0	18.3	± 3.3	17.9	8.71	± 2.06	23.6
Sm	1.31	± 0.32	24.2	1.31	± 0.39	29.8	1.97	± 0.28	14.0	1.71	± 0.28	16.6
Eu	0.80	± 0.07	9.0	0.72	± 0.15	20.1	0.72	± 0.09	13.2	0.94	± 0.07	7.8
Lu	0.24	± 0.06	27.2	0.24	± 0.06	27.2	0.26	± 0.05	19.0	0.38	± 0.06	15.8
Hf	0.92	± 0.303	33.0	0.92	± 0.30	33.0	2.20	± 0.46	21.0	0.99	± 0.20	20.6
Th	1.47	± 0.62	42.1	1.47	± 0.62	42.0	2.88	± 0.48	16.7	1.28	± 0.37	28.7

[*] Number of samples in the group
[+] Concentrations in PPM except where noted

The chemical analysis was carried out by INAA. Six US Geological Survey standard rocks, namely G-2, BCR-1, GSP-1, AGV-1, PCC-1 and DTS-1 were used as standards. Samples and standards were irradiated together for 70 h (14 h periods on 5 successive days) at a flux of about 10^{12} n. $cm^{-2}.s^{-1}$ in the RPI reactor (Sacavem). Details on measurement and processing of the gamma spectra are given by Prudêntio et al. (1986). These analyses provided the concentrations of 18 elements: sodium, potassium, calcium, scandium, chromium, iron, cobalt, cesium, barium, lanthanum, samarium, serium, europium, terbium, ytterbium, lutetium, hafnium and thorium. However, terbium and ytterbium concentrations could only be obtained for some of the analyzed samples. The mineralogical analysis was done by XRD using a Debye-Scherrer powder camera.

The data analysis was carried out by methods of numerical taxonomy which have been fully described elsewhere (Cabral et al. 1983). Computations were performed employing the numerical taxonomy system of multivariate statistical programs devised by Rholf et al. (1982).

RESULTS AND DISCUSSION

Figure 2 shows the dendrogram of the materials studied, based on the UPGMA cluster analysis of mean Euclidian distances obtained operating upon the chemical analysis data excluding terbium and ytterbium concentrations. These data are not presented in the paper but can be made available on request. The cophenetic correlation coefficient was 0.89 indicating a good agreement on the dendrogram with the original distance matrix. A good agreement was also found between this dendrogram and the result of the complete linkage clustering.

As seen in Figure 2, at a dissimilarity value of 0.90, four main compositional groups were formed. These together accounted for 42 of the 55 sherds analyzed, for eight of the 11 samples of clays collected and for all samples of modern ceramics. The larger of the four groups, called Group 1, contains 30 operational taxonomic units (OTU's) consisting of six pre-Beaker non-decorated sherds, four pre-Beaker "loomweights", six non-decorated sherds and two "loomweights" of the Beaker level, and 12 Beaker decorated sherds. Another compositional group, Group 2, has 12 OTU's representing the only analyzed pre-Beaker decorated sherd, one non-decorated sherd and one "loomweight" of the Beaker level, six clay samples and three samples of modern ceramics. The third compositional group, Group 3, contains eight OTU's consisting of one pre-Beaker "loomweight", one "loomweight" of the Beaker level, two Beaker decorated sherds, two clay samples and two samples of modern ceramics. The smaller of the four groups, Group 4, has five OTU's representing four pre-Beaker non-decorated sherds and one non-decorated sherd of the Beaker level. For each of these compositional groups, the mean concentration value for each element and the corresponding standard deviation are listed in Table 2.

A common feature of the four main compositional groups is the presence of both pre-Beaker and Beaker ceramics. This characteristic suggests that whatever may be the clays employed for manufacturing the ceramics of those groups, their use in pottery-making lasted a long period of time.

On the other hand, Table 2 shows a very high similarity between the concentration means of Group 1 (except for chromium and barium) and those of Group 2 which is composed mainly of soil and modern ceramic samples. Most of these soil samples (S1, S3-S6) represent soils derived

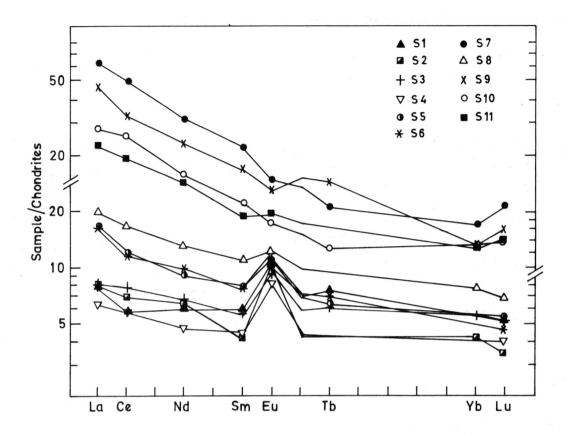

Figure 3. Chondrite-normalized REE distribution in samples of clays collected in the vicinity of the settlement.

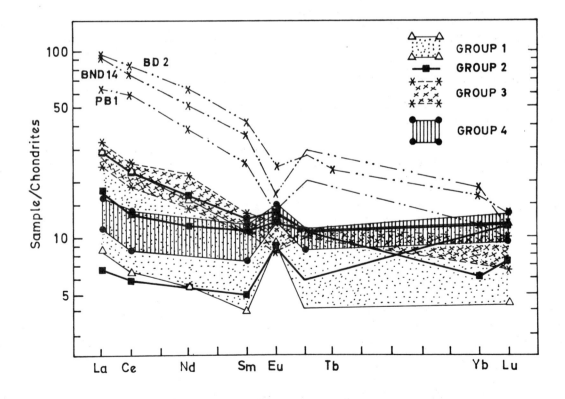

Figure 4. Range of chondrite-normalized REE abundances in pre-Beaker and Beaker ceramics grouped according to the results of cluster analysis.

modern ceramic samples (MC5) is the vase collected from a potter at Beringel who is using these types of soils according to the traditions of that pottery centre. The remaining soil sample in Group 2 (S8) corresponds to a soil derived by weathering from schists and graywackes, and the other two modern ceramic samples (MC1, MC2) are those collected from the ground in the immediate vicinity of an abandoned pottery centre at the same locus as S8. The results of Table 2 indicate therefore that the pre-Beaker and Beaker ceramics of Groups 1 and 2, which account for 60% of the sherds analyzed, were probably made locally using clays from around the site, of the same nature as the so-called "barros de Beja" or the soils derived by weathering from schists and graywackes. The fact that the barium concentration mean of Group 1 is much higher than that of Group 2 may be due to a barium pollution effect of the type already detected by Picon (1985). The difference between the chromium concentration means of these two groups may arise from the leaching of this element during the burial of pottery as a result, for example, of chemical interaction with groundwater.

Table 2 also shows that the concentration means of Group 3 differ significantly from those of Groups 1 and 2. However, as in the case of Group 2, Group 3 contains samples of modern locally produced ceramics (MC3, MC4) as well as clays collected in the immediate vicinity of the settlement (S10, S11). Thus, the results of Table 2 also indicate that the pre-Beaker and Beaker ceramics of Group 3 were very probably made locally, although in this case using clays of a different nature, namely Palaeogene-Miocene sediments.

It is interesting to point out that the distinct geochemical nature of the clay sources which have been utilized by the potters is well reflected on the rare elements (REE) distribution in the entities forming the four compositional groups, as Figures 3 and 4 show. In fact, while the clays of Group 3 (S10, S11) present no Eu anomaly, they have higher values of total REE concentrations (taking into account only the elements determined) and higher (light REE)/(heavy REE) ratios than the clays of Group 2 (S1, S3-S6, S8) which reveal a positive Eu anomaly. A similar behaviour is observed in Figure 4 for the corresponding ceramics.

The concentration means of Group 4, which accounts for about 10% of the sherds analyzed, also differ appreciably from those of the other three compositional groups but in this case neither modern ceramics nor clay samples are included in the group. Nevertheless, Figure 4 shows that the REE patterns of the sherds of Group 4 are similar to those of the ceramics and clays of Groups 1 and 2, suggesting that the pre-Beaker and Beaker potteries of Group 4 might also have been made locally using clays similar in nature to the soils derived by weathering from the gabbros and diorites or from schists and graywackes.

As the dendrogram of Figure 2 indicates, at a dissimilarity value of about 2.00, two compositional groups were formed. The larger group arose mainly as a consequence of the clustering of the four groups referred to above. The smaller one resulted from the clustering of five OTU's, consisting of one pre-Beaker non-decorated sherd (PB1), one non-decorated sherd of the Beaker level (BND14), one Beaker decorated sherd (BD2) and two samples of clays collected (S7, S9). It is important to note

(see Figure 4) that the REE patterns of these three sherds are quite different from those of the other sherds, particularly as the Eu anomaly is concerned. And so are the REE patterns of clays S7 and S9 (see Figure 3), though in this case the Eu anomaly is not so negative as it is for the sherds. It seems likely therefore that the pre-Beaker and Beaker potteries of this smaller group, notwithstanding the fact that they have the most dissimilar chemical composition in comparison with the ceramics of Groups 1 and 2, might also have been made locally using clays from the Pliocene-Palaeogene-Miocene sediments.

No significant differences were observed in the mineralogical composition of the ceramics and clays studied which always contained quartz, feldspars (mainly plagioclase) and amphiboles (hornblende).

Calcite, dolomite, micas (illite) and iron hydroxides (goethite) were also found in some samples. It is very probable, however, that the goethite detected in sherds has been formed during the burial of pottery. Although the results of the mineralogical analysis alone have not succeeded in distinguishing different types of ceramics and clays, they have contributed to support the idea of local pottery making inferred from the results of the chemical analysis. As a matter of fact, the constant presence of plagioclase and hornblende in the Ferreira do Alentejo ceramics is characteristic of the soils around the site.

CONCLUSIONS

This study has demonstrated that the pre-Beaker and Beaker potteries at the Chalcolithic settlement of Ferreira do Alentejo were made locally from at least three chemically distinct clays available in the immediate vicinity of the settlement. It has also shown that these chemically distinct clays are probably due to geochemical differences in the clay sources utilized by the potters: one of these sources, namely the soils derived by the weathering from gabbros and diorites, the so-called "barros de Beja", is still being used today by local potters at Beringel.

The present paper is only a first contribution to the study of the conditions of production and distribution of the Beaker pottery in SW Iberia, and has to be completed with the analysis of material from sites like Zambujal and Vila Nova de São Pedro, in which large numbers of sherds have been found, as well as with the analysis of material from dispersed settlement and burial sites in Alentejo, which have provided only a few sherds of this type of pottery. It seems however already possible to suggest that Beaker pottery was not introduced in this area as a result of some trade or "prestige goods" distribution network, but was massively produced locally reflecting a substantial ideological change. Whether this new ideology was introduced "culturally" or "physically" is not entirely clear.

REFERENCES

Arnaud, J.M. (1982). O povoado calcolitico de Ferreira do Alentejo no contexto da bacia do Sado e do sudoeste peninsular. Arqueologia 6: 48-64.

Cabral, J. M. P., Gouveia, M.A., Alarcão, A.M. and Alarcão,

J. (1983). Neutron activation analysis of fine grey pottery from Conimbriga, Santa Olaia and Tavarede, Portugal. Journal of Archaeological Science 10: 61-70.

Childe, V. G. (1925). When Did the Beaker Folk Arrive? Archaeologia 64: 159-178.

Childe, V.G. (1957). The Dawn of European Civilization. London: Routledge Kegan Paul.

Harrison, R.J. (1977). The Bell Beaker Cultures of Spain and Portugal. Cambridge, Harvard University.

Picon, M. (1985). Une example de pollution aux dimensions kilometriques: la fixation du barium par les ceramiques. Revue d' Archeometrie 9: 27-29.

Prudêncio M.I., Gouveia M.A. and Cabral, J.M.P. (1986). Instrumental neutron activation analysis of two French geochemical reference samples-basalt BR and biotite Mica-Fe. Geostandards Newsletter 10: 29-31.

Prudêncio M.I., Cabral, J.M.P., and Tavares A. (1987). Identification of clay sources used for Conimbriga and Santa Olaia pottery-making. Proceedings of the International Symposium on Archaeometry, May, 19-24, Athens. In press.

Rholf F.J., Kishpaug J. and Kirk, D. (1982). NTSYS user manual. New York: Dept. of Ecology and Evolution, State University of New York, Stoney Brook.

33. A Re-examination of the Provenance of Eastern Sigillata A

J.M. ELAM and M.D. GLASCOCK
Research Reactor Facility, University of Missouri, Columbia, MO, 65211 U.S.A.

K.W. SLANE
Department of Art History and Archaeology, University of Missouri, Columbia, MO, 65211 U.S.A.

ABSTRACT: *The results of a comprehensive neutron activation analysis of eastern Sigillata A pottery are reported. Statistical analyses suggest a Syrian origin rather that the previously postulated Cypriote provenance.*

INTRODUCTION

Of the many ceramic types identified in archaeological deposits of the eastern Mediterranean datable to late Hellenistic and early Roman phases, few have proven as interesting and difficult to interpret as the fine red slipped ware together referred to as Eastern Terra Sigillata. Indeed, little if any consensus has been reached among researchers concerning their chronology or original provenance. Eastern Sigillata A (ESA), a sub-type of Eastern Terra Sigillata, is of widespread occurrence and has been recovered from sites in Greece, the Aegean, Turkey, Syria, Jordan, Israel and Egypt (See Figure 1). The extensive distribution of this pottery is a reflection of its popularity during its heyday in the second and first centuries B.C.E. Because the ware is so widely dispersed, it is highly useful as a marker of the exchange patterns and practices of the late Hellenistic and early Roman world. The goal of this study is two fold. First, it is to serve as a comparison to an earlier investigation of ESA by Gunneweg et al. (1983). Second, it is to attempt to link chemically a sample set of ESA to a group of wares thought to be precursors ("Maroon ware") and thereby clarify the questions of chronology and provenance.

THEORETICAL BACKGROUND

A complete review of the history of research on ESA is beyond the scope of this report so only a summary will be presented here (Gunneweg et al. 1983; Cornell 1980). Briefly, the pottery was first identified by Zahn in 1904 (Cornell 1980) who attributed its origin to Pergamon and hence named it "Pergamene ware". Later excavations and reports by Waage (1948) at Antioch and Goldman (1950) at Tarsus suggested a Syrian provenance and temporal origin of 150 B.C.E. Waage also renamed the ware "Late Hellenistic Red". This interpretation stood unchallenged until a report by Crowfoot et al. (1957) in which Kathleen Kenyon concluded that the ware should date no earlier than 50 B.C.E. and was in fact a Roman rather than a Hellenistic product. Kenyon also renamed the ware "Eastern Sigillata A". A later study by Lapp (1961) concurred with Kenyon's analysis and there the matter rested until 1983 with the comprehensive analysis reported by Gunneweg et al. (1983). This group of researchers employed a program of neutron activation analysis (NAA) on a large sample of ESA collected from a number of sites in Israel. Unlike Waage, Gunneweg and his compatriots concluded that the ware was of Cypriote rather than a Syrian provenance basing this affirmation on the strong chemical similarities noted between ESA and wares found in Cyprus. The also renamed the pottery "Eastern Terra Sigillata I".

As mentioned above, the objectives of this study are to re-examine the results of Gunneweg's (1987; et al. 1983) analyses in an effort to test those results in terms of the correct provenance of ESA. Like Gunneweg, a NAA protocol was employed, but a smaller sample of ESA was analyzed and it came only from the site of Tel Anafa located in extreme northern Israel.

Tel Anafa was chosen for three reasons: first, a sample of Anafa ESA was also analyzed by Gunneweg and thus provides a useful comparison and control for the results obtained in the present study; second, it is the only known site where the hypothesized "proto-ESA" Maroon wares occur in any appreciable quantity; third, the site lies in northern Galilee on a shatter zone between the ancient Seleucid, Phoenician and Ptolemaic polities. Hence, its location may aid in determining if ESA is of Syrian or Cypriote origin.

ANALYTICAL METHODS

A sample of 62 pottery sherds from the Hellenistic and early Roman levels at Tel Anafa were selected for analysis utilizing comprehensive NAA protocol. Within this sample were 25 examples of ESA and 9 other examples of Maroon ware thought to be ESA precursors. Also included in the sample as the control were several examples of Attic-black ware, Cypriote glaze Sigillata Campana A (a Roman trade ware), Knidian ware and several types thought to be local including a little Pinkware which imitates the forms of the ESA.

To prepare the sherds for analysis they were first carefully cleaned by a rinse in deionized water (DI H2O). Any surface treatment, such as sintering in the case of ESA, or strongly adhered dirt or line scale were removed by scraping the sherd's surface with a sapphire scaper. The scraped sherds were again rinsed and dried 24 hours in a Transite oven stabilized at 100°C. The cleaned and dried sherds were then ground into powder with grain size of roughly 200 microns in an agate mortar and pestle. The powdered sherd materials are then placed in clean glass vials and stored in an airtight desiccator vessel. For each example, two aliquots of the prepared material weighing about 75 mg and 200 mg were sealed in polyethylene vials

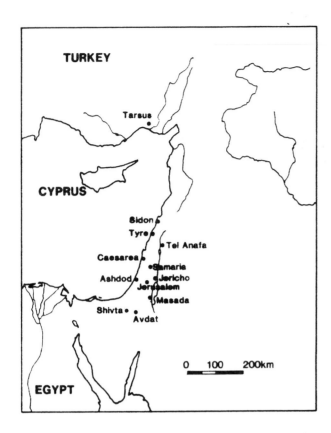

Figure 1. Map of sites with ESA pottery in the Syro-Levantine region.

and quartz vials, respectively.

The aliquots sealed in polyvials were irradiated in the University of Missouri Research Reactor (MURR) via a pneumatic tube system for five seconds in a thermal flux of 8.0×10^{13} neutrons/cm²/sec. The samples were allowed a 25-minute decay and counted on a Ge(Li) Gamma Ray Spectroscopy system for 12 minutes. Elements with short half-lives such as Al, Ca, Na, Ti, and V were measured in this fashion. The 200 mg aliquots in the quartz vials were sealed in an aluminum can and placed in an in-pool irradiation position at the MURR for 24 hours in a thermal flux of 5.0×10^{13} neutrons/cm²/sec. After a seven-day decay the samples were counted for 30 minutes on a Ge(Li) gamma ray spectroscopy system. The samples were allowed to decay an addional 14 days and were recounted. Elements with half-lives greater than seven days were measured in this manner. Standard reference materials in both experiments were NBS SRM-679 Brick Clay and USGS AGV-1 Andesite. Analysis of the resulting gamma-ray spectra was done on a MicroVAX II Computer. A total of 32 elements were measured and include: Ba, La, Lu, Nd, Sm, U, Yb, Ce, Co, Cr, Cs, Eu, Fe, Hf, Rb, Sb, Sc, Ta, Tb, Th, Zn, Zr, Al, Ca, Dy, K, Mg, Mn, Na, Sr, Ti, and V.

The measured element values were tabulated into a LOTUS 123 spreadsheet. Simple descriptive statistics were calculated for the 25 samples of ESA. Table 1 illustrates the comparison of the mean element values for the Anafa ESA reported by Gunneweg et al. (1983) versus those measured in this investigation. While the MURR values do not exactly equal those reported by Gunneweg, they are quite close. In

most instances, the range of variation expressed by the standard deviations create an overlap between the respective means and thus meet the criterion for the inter-lab comparison purposed by Harbottle (1982).

Next, the data set was uploaded to a MicroVAX II computer for detailed statistical treatment. Histograms of the element distributions were graphed to determine which elements exhibited deviation from a normal distribution and were in need of transformation. Elements that were visibly skewed or kurtotic were transformed into their base 10 logarithms. A correlation matrix of the element variables was then calculated using the CORR procedure in the SAS codes. The resultant matrix was then analyzed using principal components, common factor and alpha factor analysis with the FACTOR procedure in SAS. The results of the factor analysis were used to identify redundant variables allowing the selection of the best set of variables for the discriminating differences in the sample set. The variables identified as good discriminators included: Al, K, Mg, Mn, Ce, Cr, Eu, Fe, Ta, Ti, V, and Ba.

These variables were then used to cluster the samples into groups. Clustering was performed with the SAS procedure CLUSTER and the Brookhaven codes (Bishop 1985). The last statistical analysis of the data was to use the same variable subset just described to scale the samples via an alternating least squares algorithm. This was done on an IBM 4381 Mainframe using ALSCAL program.

The factor analysis described above revealed a number of highly correlated and hence redundant variables. Variables that loaded high (>.40) on more than one of the six significant factors identified by the analysis were thus excluded. This left a pool of roughly 18 or 19 elements for clustering the data. This set was further reduced by first plotting the variables against one another to see if distinctive, recognizable clusters were formed. The potential usefulness of the remaining variables in a cluster analysis was in this way assessed. An example of one of the more definitive plots is found in Figure 2. The ESA and associated Maroon wares may be seen to tightly clump together in the upper left portion of the graph. Using bivariate plots of the remaining elements and the correlation matrix produced by the factor analysis, the set of variables was again reduced to about 12 to 14. These variables were then used to obtain interpretable linkages amongst the samples. The best clustering solution was the one produced utilizing the elements listed above. A schematic representation of this cluster solution (average linkage, mean Euclidian distance) is rendered in the dendrogram in Figure 3.

The large cluster of samples at the top is the ESA and the Maroon wares. Sample numbers 1-25 are ESA and the Maroon is represented by the numbers 39, 40, 43, 44, 48, 49, 50, 55 and 56. Note that only numbers 43 and 48 do not link with the ESA, but rather with the clusters of Pinkware and Cypriote pottery (it is possible that these were incorrectly typed). Also, number 51 which links at the lower end of the ESA cluster was originally thought to be of Knidian signature, but the typological identity of the sherd was insecure due to its badly eroded condition. It now seems that it is more likely a piece of Maroon ware or ESA. Numbers 58, 62, 52 and 59 which link in the middle of the dendrogram are the Attic-black ware examples. Three

Element	Units	QEDEM Values (mean ± s.d.)		MURR Values (mean ± s.d.)	
Calcium	(%)	10.5 ±	1.6	10.4 ±	1.1
Cerium	(ppm)	42.9 ±	2.6	41.6 ±	1.3
Cesium	(ppm)	5.46 ±	0.32	5.15 ±	0.35
Cobalt	(ppm)	32.4 ±	2.4	32.6 ±	1.6
Chromium	(ppm)	356. ±	26.	357. ±	40.
Europium	(ppm)	1.02 ±	0.05	1.09 ±	0.04
Iron	(%)	5.75 ±	0.14	5.56 ±	0.18
Hafnium	(ppm)	3.12 ±	0.10	3.11 ±	0.10
Lanthanum	(ppm)	20.9 ±	0.8	23.9 ±	0.7
Lutetium	(ppm)	0.33 ±	0.01	0.36 ±	0.02
Rubidium	(ppm)	92. ±	11.	85.1 ±	20.5
Samarium	(ppm)	3.89 ±	0.13	4.14 ±	0.12
Scandium	(ppm)	23.3 ±	0.7	20.9 ±	0.7
Sodium	(%)	0.76 ±	0.07	0.78 ±	0.07
Tantalum	(ppm)	0.69 ±	0.03	0.75 ±	0.03
Thorium	(ppm)	7.23 ±	0.20	6.75 ±	0.21
Titanium	(%)	0.43 ±	0.01	0.44 ±	0.05
Uranium	(ppm)	1.80 ±	0.10	1.92 ±	0.54
Ytterbium	(ppm)	2.18 ±	0.10	2.40 ±	0.11

Table 1. Comparison between QEDEM and MURR results by NAA for ESA.

Campana A sherds may be found linked in the lower left corner. As can be seen, the clustering procedure produced a number of typologically meaningful groups and demonstrated a strong connection between the ESA and Maroon wares.

As a final confirmation on the results of the cluster analysis, the data were then scaled using the multi-dimensional scaling (MDS) algorithm described above. The same variable subset was used as in the cluster analysis. The best solution was three dimensional with a stress coefficient of 0.01 and an R² value of 1.0. This solution is graphically depicted in Figure 4. Again the ESA/Maroon ware cluster may have been seen in the upper left corner. The roughly C-shaped cluster is the Cypriote/Pinkware group and the Attic-Black ware is the four points closely aligned below the Cypriote/Pinkware.

INTERPRETATION AND DISCUSSION

This small study has produced several interesting results. First, the ESA trace element signature for the Anafa ESA defined by Gunneweg et al. (1983) has been confirmed. Additionally, this demonstrates the achievement of inter-laboratory compatibility as defined by Harbottle (1982). Second, the statistical analysis discriminated the Pinkware into several distinct groups one of which links to the Cypriote pieces. This result will require further analysis before any further statement about the nature of these wares can be made. Third, the tight linkages between ESA and the Maroon ware confirms the typological hypothesis that the Maroon ware was but a precursor form of ESA. Since the Maroon ware is a precursor to ESA, this strongly suggests a Syrian provenance for ESA as opposed to the Cypriote origin suggested by Gunneweg. Indeed, Gunneweg's evidence of a Cypriote origin for the ESA is quite weak and may be seen in the fashion in which the connection was established. The ESA was linked to Cyprus on the basis of a simple comparison of the elemental signatures between ESA and a Bronze Age ware produced in Cyprus called Enkomi. However, the elements used to define the link are largely those identified by the factor analysis in this study as non-discriminatory. In fact, six of the elements found to be highly discriminatory, Al, K, Ba, Mn, Mg and V, were not even reported by Gunneweg. Also, those elements identified as the discriminators here and included by Gunneweg in his comparison (Ce, Cr, Eu, Fe, Ta and Ti) are generally the weakest links between the two wares. Thus, the failure to identify the most discriminating elements in order to test the proposed linkage of ESA to Enkomi is the most striking flaw in Gunneweg's analysis. Add to this the lack of Maroon ware at sites in Cyprus and a Syrian provenance for the ESA seems even more probable. Fourth, the breakdown of the ESA/Maroon cluster into several subgroups possibly indicates a number of different manufacturing centres in the Syro-Levantine region.

CONCLUSIONS

The elemental signatures defined by ESA by Gunneweg et al. (1983) have been confirmed. However, the evidence presented by Gunneweg as demonstrating a Cypriote origin for ESA has been shown to be exceedingly weak

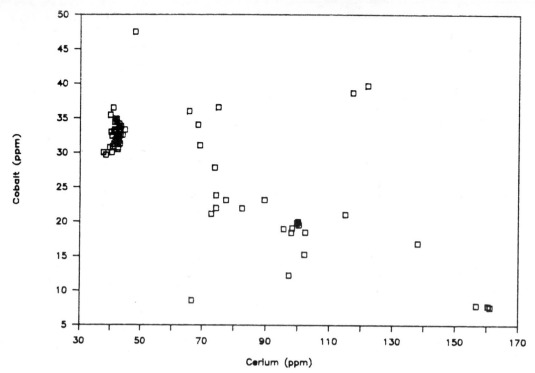

Figure 2. Bivariate plot of cobalt versus cerium for Anafa pottery.

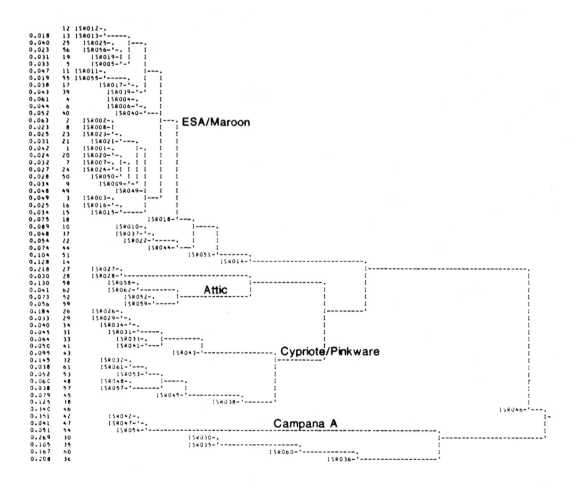

Figure 3. Average linkage/mean Euclidian distance dendrogram of Anafa pottery.

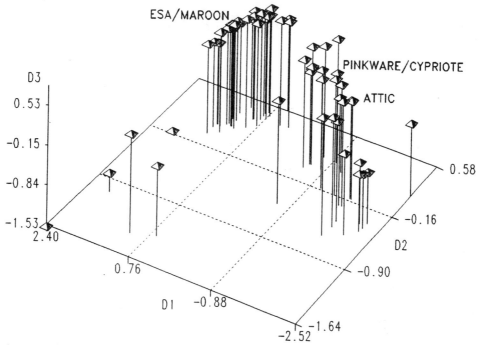

Figure 4. Multi-dimensional scaling plot of Anafa pottery.

and strong evidence indicating a Syrian provenance is presented. Clearly, more work is required in order to resolve the question of provenance of the ESA and Maroon wares. This would include further laboratory analyses as well as fieldwork oriented towards locating evidence of ESA production (kilns, wasters, etc.). Only in this manner will the problem of ESA provenance be completely resolved.

ACKNOWLEDGEMENTS

The authors acknowledge the assistance of Dr. S. Herbert, Department of Classics, University of Michigan for supplying a portion of the ceramics analyzed in this study. One of the authors (J.M.E.) acknowledges financial support from the MURR during his graduate program.

REFERENCES

Bishop, R.L. (1985). Introduction to Data Analysis with the Smithsonian Archaeometric Research Collections and Records (SARCAR) Facility. Version 1.1, Conservation Analytical Laboratory, Smithsonian Inst., Washington.

Cornell, L.A. (1980). Late Hellenistic and Early Roman Red-Slipped Pottery from Tel Anafa 1968-1973. PhD Dissertation, University of Missouri-Columbia.

Crowfoot, J.W., Kenyon, K.M. and Crowfoot, G.M. (1957). Samaria-Sebaste. Vol III: The Objects, London.

Goldman, H. (1950). Excavations of Gozlu Kule, Tarsus. Vol. I: The Hellenistic and Roman Periods, edited by H. Goldman, Princeton.

Gunneweg, J. (1987). Roman Pottery Trade in the Eastern Meditterannean. Rei Cretariae Romanae Fautorum Acta XXV/XXVI: 119-129.

Gunneweg, J., Perlman, I. and Yellin, J. (1983). The Provenience, Typology and Chronology of Eastern Sigillata. QEDEM 17, Hebrew University, Jerusalem.

Harbottle, G. (1982). Provenience Studies Using Neutron Activation Analysis: The Role of Standardization. Archaeological Ceramics, edited by J.S. Olin and A.D. Franklin, Smithsonian Inst., Washington: 67-77.

Lapp, P. (1961). Palestinian Ceramic Chronology: 200 B.C. - A.D. 70, New Haven.

SAS Inst. (1985). SAS User's Guide: Statistics., Cary, North Carolina.

Waage, F.O. (1948). Antioch-on-the Orontes. Vol IV Part One: Ceramics and Islamic Coins, edited by F.O. Waage, Princeton.

34. Islamic Ceramics: Petrography and Provenance

R.B. MASON and E.J. KEALL
West Asian Department, Royal Ontario Museum, 100 Queen's Park, Toronto, Ontario, Canada, M5S 2C6.

ABSTRACT: *Petrographic analysis is used to distinguish between main types of Islamic lustre-wares, and assign each type to production sites or areas.*

INTRODUCTION

The production of glazed ceramics with an overglaze metallic lustre pigment can be attributed, in successive periods, to Iraq, Egypt, Syria and Iran (Watson 1985: 24-36). Traditional attribution of production to a particular site has relied on the amount of pottery found at the site, on medieval manuscripts, and more reliably on inscriptions on the vessels. Physical evidence of ceramic production, such as the presence of wasters and kiln furniture, exists for coarser or undecorated wares, but not for lustre-wares. One reason for this is that lustre-pigment is applied after the main firing of the vessel, which is when it is exposed to the stress that creates a waster.

Pottery assemblages of sites in the Near East, although dominated by local wares, often contain lustre-painted and other fine wares. If identified they aid site dating and indicate culture and trade contacts. However the imports are often represented by small abraded sherds rather than recognizable vessels.

This material poses two main archaeological questions: (1) Is it possible to provenance this pottery? (2) Can the physical characteristics of each type be used to identify sherds from excavation, regardless of external decoration or state of preservation?

Petrographic analysis of wasters and sherds from various sites in the Near East was undertaken to answer these questions. Each lustre-ware type and associated wares will be considered in turn.

IRAQI GROUP

A group of ceramics with a buff fabric, opaque white glaze, and lustre- or other painted decoration, is associated

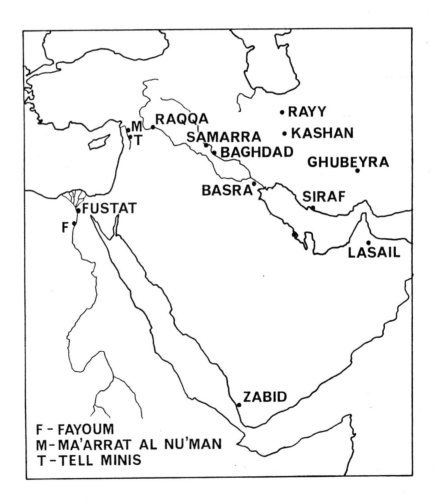

Figure 1. Map showing sites mentioned in text.

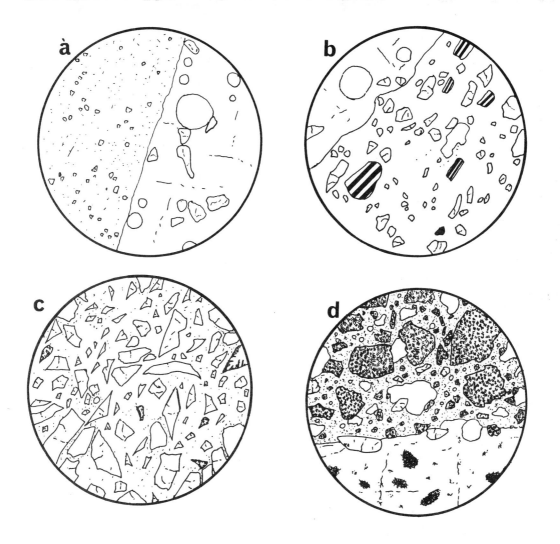

Figure 2. Micrographs of lustre-ware fabrics: a, Abbasid; b, Fatimid A; c, Syrian "Raqqa" ware; d, Persian. See text for description.

with the Abbasid Caliphate, with capitals at Samarra and Baghdad (Figure 1). As a group this material began in the ninth century. Samples are from Samarra (Royal Ontario Museum collection, purchased from the British Museum in 1923), Siraf (R.O.M. collection, B.M. excavations, 1966/73), and Lasail (R.O.M. survey, 1974). Of possible production centres, only Basra has evidence of manufacture (Metropolitan Museum of Art collection). Unfortunately this material was not available for analysis before this paper's submission.

All of these wares are of a single uniform fabric, Abbasid fabric A, consisting of 1 to 2 % of fine quartz, with trace amounts of amphibole and feldspar (Figure 2a).

EGYPTIAN GROUP

Egypt is attributed with production of lustre-wares under the Fatimid dynasty, in the 11th and 12th centuries. The body of the pottery can be seen to be represented by a buff and a red-coloured fabric. Samples are from Fustat (R.O.M. collections, American Research Centre in Egypt excavations, 1964/81; purchase from Cairo dealer, 1909). The buff-coloured, Fatimid fabric A, consists of 10 to 15% quartz, 3 to 4% plagioclase feldspar, 1% amphibole, and minor amounts of clinopyroxene and biotite (Figure 2b).

The red-coloured, Fatimid fabric B, consists of about 4% quartz and 3% carbonate.

Analysis of contemporaneous wares with a coarser, more rustic appearance, identified two petro-fabrics. One is identical to Fatimid fabric A. Wares of this type are known as wasters at Fustat, and are to be analyzed as a continuation of this study.

SYRIAN GROUP

Production of lustre-painted and associated wares in Syria is considered to have started shortly before the end of the Fatimid Dynasty in Egypt, in 1171, and to have largely ended with the Mongol invasions of the mid 13th century. Art historians divide this material into two main groups: "Tell Minis" ware is finer, earlier and largely confined to western Syria, while "Raqqa" ware is supposedly more robust, later, and more widespread. Production of "Tell Minis" is attributed to Ma'arrat al-Nu'man, where wasters have been recovered (Porter and Watson 1987). Production of "Raqqa" ware has been attributed to a number of sites, but evidence is only known from Raqqa itself (Porter 1981:11). Wasters from Ma'arrat al-Nu'man were sampled (Ashmolean Museum collection). No samples were available from Raqqa. "Raqqa" wares

185

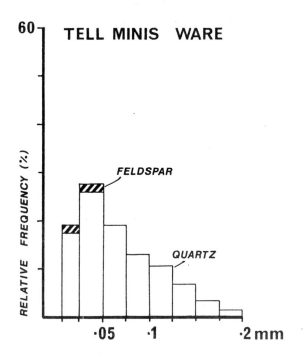 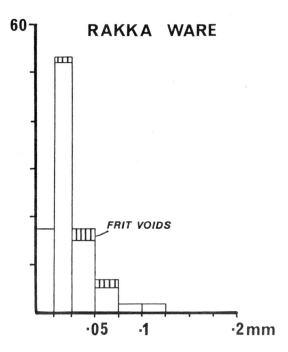

Figure 3. Grain-size histograms for Syrian fabrics.

are from Abu Sudairah in Iraq (Ashmolean Museum collection) and Fustat in Egypt (R.O.M. collection, purchase from Cairo dealer, 1909).

Both of these types are of stonepaste fabrics, also often termed "faience", "artificial paste", "quartz-frit ware" or "frit-ware", amongst others. Stonepaste is nearer to the terminology of present-day potters in the Near East (Wulff 1966:165), and will be the term used here. Recipes for stonepaste exist from medieval sources (Allan 1973) and recent artisans (Wulff 1966; Centlivres-Demont 1971). It consists of about 10 parts powdered quartz (or other silica), one part of an alkaline frit, and one part of white clay.

Essentially both Syrian types can be described as angular quartz in a vesicular glass matrix (Figure 2c). On the basis of the samples so far analyzed, it is possible to distinguish between these types, with the "Raqqa" wares being composed of finer grains, with more voids due to frit-additives, while the coarser grain-size of the "Tell Minis" wares is accompanied by greater amounts of other minerals, such as feldspars (Figure 3).

PERSIAN GROUP

The finest Iranian lustre-wares were produced from the late twelfth century to the mid-thirteenth century, and are of three types. The "Monumental" and "Miniature" styles are traditionally attributed to Rayy, while the "Kashan" style is attributed to Kashan. Other sites are suggested as sites of production, but only Kashan has evidence, as inscriptions on a number of "Kashan" style vessels attribute manufacture to this site (Watson 1985). These lustre-wares are also of stonepaste fabrics. Samples are from Siraf (R.O.M. collection, B.M. excavations, 1966/73), Ghubeyra (R.O.M. collection, U. of London excavations,

1971/76), and Rayy (University of Pennsylvania collection, Joint Expedition excavations, 1934/36). The Rayy samples include enameled "Minai" wares, and monochrome wares, including a waster. All of the lustre-wares and "Minai" pieces, together with some monochrome wares, are of the same petrographic fabric, consisting of chert and some quartz in a vesicular glass matrix (Figure 2d). The remaining monochrome wares, including the waster, were of other fabrics, some superficially resembling the Syrian fabrics, being mostly composed of angular quartz. This would indicate that lustre-painted and "Minai" wares were not produced in Rayy, and as this petrographic group includes the type associated with Kashan, this site is considered to be the manufacturing centre.

SHERD IDENTIFICATION

As the above ceramics were traded across the Islamic sphere during their period of production, they form a small but important component of many ceramic assemblages throughout this region. An example of this is on the Red Sea coast of North Yemen. Here a project of the Royal Ontario Museum has spent three seasons in surface reconnaissance and one season excavation, in a field area centred on the town of Zabid. Petrographic analysis has shown that the bulk of the ceramic assemblage was produced within the study area (Mason et al. 1986; Mason and Keall 1988). The imports should, if identified, help in dating the assemblage, and indicate trade contacts of the region. Amongst these imports are lustre-wares, usually represented by small abraded specimens with traces of lustre-paint. Petrographic characterization of the principal lustre-ware types has allowed identification of all sherds, mostly Abbasid Iraqi, but including one Fatimid Egyptian, and one Syrian piece, petrographically identical to the "Rakka" types.

CONCLUSION

Each lustre-ware type is shown to have a distinct petrographic fabric, which can be easily used in the identification of otherwise non-diagnostic sherds. There remain problems in attributing a precise provenance for this material. Work will continue on this question. The Ábbasid wasters from Basra are to be analyzed, and even if they are of the Ábbasid lustre-ware fabric, further work on other Iraqi kiln sites will still be necessary. Wasters from Fustat are to be analyzed. Work will continue on defining Ma'arrat al-Nu'man products, and enquiries made into the location of any wasters from Raqqa. Final attribution of Persian lustre-wares to Kashan will require sampling either a waster actually from Kashan, or a vessel with epigraphic attribution to Kashan, together with further negative evidence from other Iranian kiln sites. The distinctive fabrics of this material suggest that the answer to the first archaeological question is yes, but further work is required to achieve it.

REFERENCES

Allan, J.W. (1973). Abu'l-Qasim's treatise on ceramics. Iran 11:111-120.

Centlivres-Demont, M. (1971). Une communaute de potiers en Iran. Verlag, Wiesbaden.

Mason, R.B., Hallett, J.R. and Keall, E.J. (1986). Provenance studies of Islamic pottery from Yemen: INAA and petrographic analysis. Proceedings of the 25th International Symposium on Archaeometry.

Mason, R.B., and Keall, E.J. (1988). Provenance of local industry and the characterization of imports: petrography of pottery from medieval Yemen. Antiquity, 62:452-463.

Porter, V. (1981). Medieval Syrian Pottery. Ashmolean Museum, Oxford.

Porter, V., and Watson, O. (1987). "Tell Minis" Wares. Oxford Studies in Islamic Art, IV. Oxford.

Watson, O. (1985). Persian Lustre Ware. Faber & Faber, London.

Wulff, H.E. (1966). The Traditional Crafts of Persia. M.I.T., Cambridge.

35. Lead Isotope Studies of Spanish, Spanish-Colonial and Mexican Majolica

E.C. JOEL, J.S. OLIN and M.J. BLACKMAN
Conservation Analytical Laboratory, Smithsonian Institution, Washington, D.C. 20560 U.S.A.

I.L. BARNES
Inorganic Analytical Division, National Bureau of Standards, Gaithersburg, MD 20899 U.S.A.

ABSTRACT: *Lead isotope data demonstrate new world procurement of raw materials for majolica glaze production by Spanish colonists in the sixteenth century.*

INTRODUCTION

Throughout the Spanish Colonial period majolica ceramics were used as basins, bowls, pitchers and other types of containers and serving pieces. They represent a sophisticated ceramic technology. The body of the ceramics is made of a calcareous clay or a mixture of calcareous and non-calcareous clays to produce a porous fabric. The glaze applied to the body is a tin opacified lead glaze to which a variety of pigments may be added. Procurement of the raw materials for the body and the glaze is also complex. Evidence for sixteenth century majolica production in the New World comes from both the historical record and studies of the chemical and mineralogical composition of the ceramic paste (1,2). Although the historical records do not document in detail when this production began, artifacts from the excavations of the Metropolitan Cathedral in Mexico City which predate 1573 have been analyzed by neutron activation analysis and petrography (3,4). When the composition of the majolica sherds from these excavations was recalculated for dilution by calcium carbonate, the paste composition of some of the majolica ceramics was found to match closely the composition of Aztec ceramics. Although it was assumed earlier that the source of the calcium carbonate was a secondary calcareous deposit during burial in the wet soil of Mexico City, it is now known that its source was the calcareous clays which were used in majolica production. In addition to the chemical data, the petrographic evidence is that the volcanic ash temper present in the sherds attributed to Mexican production is characteristic of local clay sources. Other majolica ceramics present in the excavated material from the Metropolitan Cathedral have a chemical and mineralogical compostion characteristic of Spanish production (3,4).

The evidence for sixteenth century majolica manufacture in the New World by the Spanish, documents a transfer of the technology of production but not the local procurement of glazing materials. The manufacture of the glazing compounds could have been more conservative, with production remaining in Spain, or the transfer could have been total, with lead and other materials for the glaze procured from Mexican sources at an early date. Although there is some historical evidence for the early use of New World lead sources by the Spanish, the documentation is not extensive (5). Lead isotope analyses of the glazes from majolica ceramics having chemical and mineralogical paste compositions characteristic of Mexico, would provide evidence for the source of lead. The comparison of our results with lead isotope data on Mexican ore sources would provide additional evidence for a local source.

Recently, Olin and Blackman have refined the classification of Mexican majolica using neutron activation analysis (6). Sherds from excavations at the Metropolitan Cathedral in Mexico City and from excavations on St. Catherines Island, Georgia extended the analyses of majolica ceramics to include seventeenth century types. The chemical classification of sixteenth-seventeenth century Mexican majolica produced two very distinct groups based on the differences in the measured concentrations for chromium, iron and scandium. One of the groups closely matched the composition of modern Puebla ceramics and was assigned as being of Puebla manufacture. The other compositional group was assigned to Mexico City. This was based on the fact that there is historical evidence for majolica production in Mexico City during the sixteenth century. The types which were chemically classified in this group have been assigned to Mexico City based on archaeological evidence. They include a plain white ware similar to the widely distributed Spanish white ware which is called Mexico City White. In our investigation of the lead composition in the glazes, samples of both Puebla and Mexico City production were included in order to determine whether separate sources of the lead used could be identified.

In addition to samples of Mexican production, sherds manufactured in Spain were included in this study. This data is important for confirming that lead from Spanish sources was not used in majolica production in the New World. Further work with the lead isotope data from these glazes is planned for the future in conjunction with work we are carrying out on recently excavated majolica from Spanish sources. Earlier published lead isotope data for other Spanish colonial artifacts will then serve as an important reference (7).

The seventy-four sherds analyzed for their lead isotopic compositions were excavated from fifteenth and sixteenth century Spanish sites in the Caribbean, Venezuela, Mexico and Spain. Descriptions and excavation sites are listed in Table 2. Additional sherds obtained from the Pureza street kiln-site in Seville, Spain (8), and Le Calle Juan Baron and Parque Colon in the Dominican Republic were also sampled. The major majolica types represented are Colombia Plain, Yayal Blue on White, Mexico City White and San Juan Polychrome.

EXPERIMENTAL PROCEDURES

Lead isotope ratios were determined using a National Bureau of Standards' thermal ionization mass spectrometer designed for high precision measurements. The isotopic ratios for the glaze samples were calibrated and corrected for the effects of fractionation using NBS Standard Reference Material 981 for lead and are generally accurate to within 0.1% (95% limit of error) (9). The type of precision that can be obtained is shown in Table 1. The seven analyses of SRM 981 were run over a period of three days and show a relative standard deviation of 0.015% for the 208/206 ratios and 0.007% for the 207/206 ratios. The chemical separation of microgram quantities of lead by acid dissolution and electrodeposition techniques is well documented (10). The method's efficiency for lead recovery is 95% and is applicable to a wide variety of matrices. The analytical blank for this method, determined by isotope dilution mass spectrometry, is generally at the 2-3 nanogram/gram level.

The amount of lead extracted from the tin oxide glaze samples was 800 to 1000 μg in size. Approximately 0.5 μg of the extracted lead was loaded into the mass spectrometer and run at a temperature of 1200 C using the silica gel-phosphoric acid technique (10). Two of the samples, SC 37 and SC 38, were run in duplicate to test for sample homogeneity and reproducibility of the method (Table 2). The average standard deviation was less than 0.1% for multiple measurements of lead isotope ratios on a given sample.

RESULTS AND DISCUSSION

The results of these analyses are listed in Table 2. As shown in Figure 1, three groups were readily defined using the corrected 208/206 versus 207/206 ratios. The two groups in the upper right hand corner of the graph consist entirely of samples from Spain and early Spanish colonial sites (open and closed triangles). The closed squares are samples excavated from the Metropolitan Cathedral with few exceptions and based on previous elemental analyses, assigned to a Mexican production.

The upper Spanish majolica group (closed triangles) consists of sherds attributed to a Spanish production and excavated from sites in the Caribbean, Venezuela, the Metropolitan Cathedral in Mexico City and from Jerez and the Pureza street kiln-site in Seville, Spain. The lower Spanish group, (open triangles), consists of majolica samples excavated from Spanish settlements in the Dominican Republic, with one exception, a Colombia Plain sherd from Cuzco, Peru. Although this group does not include any majolica from Spain, the samples can be assigned to a Spanish origin based on typology and the chemical composition of the paste. All samples in the Mexican group (Figure 1) can be assigned to Mexican production based on chemical composition (6). The lead isotope ratios for this Mexican group are very homogeneous. Based on the assumption of multivariate normality, the lead values fall within the 95% probability limits of belonging to the same group with the exception of two samples. The major types of majolica represented in the group consist of Mexico City White and San Juan Polychrome. The two exceptions are a Puebla Polychrome from the Dominican Republic and an unidentified type from Cubagua, Venezuela.

The results of our analyses were compared to a lead isotope study on thirty-four mineral deposits from northern Mexico by Cumming et al. (11). These deposits were divided into categories of massive sulfide deposits, sedimentary deposits, vein deposits and limestone replacement deposits. The deposits from this area contain almost all of the important lead mineralization in the country and exhibit a systematic distribution throughout northern Mexico. The massive sulfide deposits are confined to the west coast; the vein deposits extend from the west coast to central Mexico; and the limestone replacement deposits extend from central to eastern Mexico.

The analytical procedure used by Cumming et al. for lead isotope determination was similar to that of our study. Using NBS Standard Reference Material 981, the reproducibility of the mass discrimination measurement was 0.03%. To analyze for internal reproducibility, nine duplicate sets of samples were run. The standard deviation for these nine sets was 0.07%, well within the acceptable limits for 0.1% accuracy, and is comparable to the type of precision obtained by our laboratory. The geological ore samples were compared to the Mexican majolica glaze group for the purpose of determining possible lead sources. Using Mahalanobis distance and Hotelling's T2 statistics, samples from seven of the thirty-four deposits fell within the 95% confidence interval for the Mexican glazes and are potential ore sources (Table 2). Three of the deposits were from the same area. Figure 2 is a graph of the lead isotopic ratios for both the Mexican group and the ore data to illustrate the distribution of the ore data in relation to the Mexican glaze samples. A map of the geological region associated with the ore data and majolica production sites is shown in Figure 3.

In view of the geographical distribution of the ores and their possible use in majolica glazes, we are inclined to limit the list of sources even further. It is interesting to note that high probabilities given for the two massive sulfide deposits, Cuale and Campo Morado, are widely separated geographically. Cumming et al. state that the Cuale and Campo Morado are part of a group of similar deposits found within the Mesozoic submarine volcanic complex of western Mexico and that similar rocks, possibly moved eastward by tectonic activity, have been recognized in isolated outcrops between Camp Morado and El Pavo. Therefore, the most probable source or sources of lead used in Mexican majolica is thought to be similar to that found in the sulfide deposits of central Mexico.

CONCLUSIONS

Spanish and Mexican majolica can be distinguished on the basis of their lead isotopes. Furthermore, the lead isotope data provide evidence which documents an indigenous Mexican procurement and production system for majolica before 1573. Based on a previously published study by Cumming et al. on lead depositions in Mexico, we have been able to identify five sources of lead which are isotopically similar to the lead used in the glaze of Mexican ceramics.

The lead used in Spanish majolica would appear to have come from two sources. Additional analyses on newly excavated ceramics from Spain will provide more information on the number of lead sources available.

189

ACKNOWLEDGEMENTS

We acknowledge the continuing interest of Florence and Robert Lister (University of Arizona) who provided the sherds from the excavations at the Metropolitan Cathedral, and the late Charles Fairbanks (University of Florida) who provided sherds from the Dominican Republic and Venezuela. The additional sherds from the Dominican Republic were supplied by Dr. Molban Lacucer, Director of the Museo del Hombre Dominicano in Santo Domingo for which we are very grateful. We also wish to thank Emlen Myers (SI) for providing us with sherds excavated at the Pureza street kiln-site in Seville, Spain. We are thankful for the assistance of Edward Sayre (SI) for his sound advice; to Hector Neff (SI) for the computer generated plots; and to Jack Fassett (NBS) for his excellent comments. Finally, we wish to acknowledge Drs. Joaquin Ruiz and Peter Coney, Department of Geological Sciences, University of Arizona, for providing the ore data which became a very important part of this paper. This research is supported jointly by the Conservation Analytical Laboratory and the National Bureau of Standards, and is part of an ongoing research project utilizing lead isotope data in archaeological and art historical studies.

REFERENCES

1. Goggin, J.S., Spanish Majolica in the New World, Types of the Sixteenth to Eighteenth Centuries; Yale University Publications in Anthropology No. 72; Yale University Press, New Haven, CT.

2. Lister, F.C.; Lister R.H., Sixteenth Century Majolica Pottery in the Valley of Mexico; Anthropological Papers of the University of Arizona No. 39; University of Arizona Press, Tucson, AZ.

3. Olin, J.S.; Harbottle, G.; Sayre, E.V., "Elemental Compositions of Spanish and Spanish-Colonial Majolica Ceramics in the Identification of Provenience"; Archaeological Chemistry II; Carter, G.F., ed.; ADVANCES IN CHEMISTRY SERIES No. 171; American Chemical Society; Washington, D.C., (1978) : 200-229.

4. Maggetti, M.; Westley, H.; Olin, J.S., "Provenance and Technical Studies of Mexican Majolica Using Elemental and Phase Analysis"; Archaeological Chemistry III; Lambert, J.B., Ed.; ADVANCES IN CHEMISTRY SERIES No. 205; American Chemical Society; Washington, D.C. (1984): 151-191.

5. Lister, F.C.; Lister, R.H., Andalusian Ceramics in Spain and New Spain; The University of Arizona Press, Tucson, AZ, (1987).

6. Olin, J.S.; Blackman, M.J., "Compositional Classification of Mexican Majolica Ceramics of the Spanish Colonial Period"; Archaeological Chemistry IV; ADVANCES IN CHEMISTRY SERIES; American Chemical Society; in press.

7. Brill, R.H.; Barnes, I.L.; Tong, S.S.C.; Joel, E.C.; Murtagh, M.J., "Laboratory Studies of Some European Artifacts Excavated on San Salvador Island"; 1st San Salvador Conference-Columbus and His World; compiled by Gerace, D.T.; published by CCFL, Bahamian Field Station, (1987).

8. Morilla, J.L.; Reina, M.V., "Informe-Memoria de las Actividades Arqueologicas Realizadas en C/Pureza no. 44 Y C/Pelay Correa no. 15-17-19 de Sevilla".

9. Catanzaro, E.J.; Murphy, T.J.; Shields, W.R.; Garner, E.L., "Absolute Isotopic Abundance Ratios of Common, Equal-Atom, and Radiogenic Lead Isotopic Standards" Journal of Research of the National Bureau of Standards-A. Physics and Chemistry (1968). 72, 32.

10. Barnes, I.L.; Murphy, T.J.; Gramlich, J.W.; Shields, W.R., "Lead Separation by Anodic Deposition and Isotope Ratio Mass Spectrometry of Microgram and Smaller Samples"; Analytical Chemistry (1973). 45, 11: 1381-85.

11. Cumming, G.L.; Kesler, S.E.; Krstic, D., "Isotopic Composition of Lead in Mexican Mineral Deposits"; Economic Geology (1979). 74: 1395-1407.

TYPICAL PRECISION FOR
LEAD ISOTOPIC STANDARD[a]

Run No.	$^{208}Pb/^{206}Pb$	$^{207}Pb/^{206}Pb$
1.	2.16300	0.91376
2.	2.16276	0.91388
3.	2.16288	0.91383
4.	2.16342	0.91374
5.	2.16362	0.91370
6.	2.16335	0.91383
7.	2.16344	0.91377
Average	2.16321	0.91379
SD	0.00033 (0.015%)	0.00006 (0.007%)

[a] SRM 981, National Bureau of Standards

Table 1. Type of precision obtained in thermal ionization mass spectrometry.

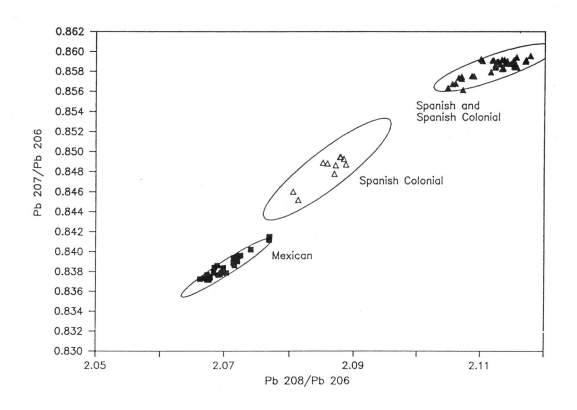

Figure 1. Plot of 208/206 versus 207/206 for all Majolica samples. Ellipses represent 95% confidence intervals.

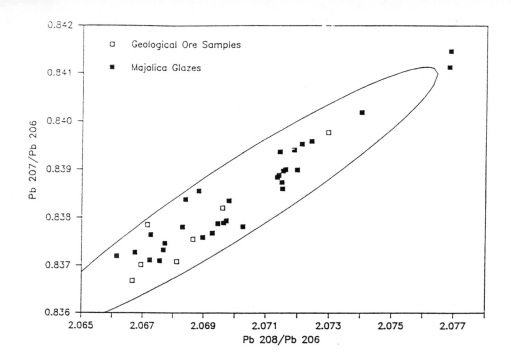

Figure 2. Plot of 208/206 versus 207/206 isotope ratios for Mexican glaze group and geological ore samples. 95% confidence ellipse based on glaze samples only.

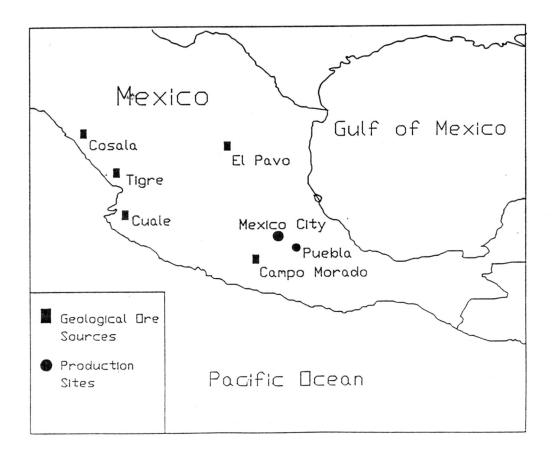

Figure 3. Map of some of the geological ore sources in Mexico.

Table 2. Lead isotope ratios of Majolica pottery.

SPANISH AND SPANISH COLONIAL

CAL#	NBS#	208/206	207/206	204/206

COLUMBIA PLAIN, CONVENTO DE SAN FRANCISCO, DOMINICAN REPUBLIC

CAL#	NBS#	208/206	207/206	204/206
SA 11	1750	2.112336	0.858419	0.054957
SB 86	1837	2.113174	0.858735	0.055050
SB 87	1838	2.115698	0.858451	0.055087
SB 88	1839	2.107130	0.856170	0.054798
SB 89	1840	2.115070	0.859023	0.055094
SB 90	1841	2.114698	0.858790	0.055141
SB 93	1842	2.106919	0.857294	0.054781

YAYAL BLUE ON WHITE, CONVENTO DE SAN FRANCISCO, DOMINICAN REPUBLIC

CAL#	NBS#	208/206	207/206	204/206
SB 70	1830	2.113347	0.859190	0.055053
SB 73	1831	2.112311	0.858659	0.055022
SB 78	1832	2.111841	0.859143	0.054909
SB 79	1833	2.117080	0.859174	0.055098
SB 80	1834	2.109962	0.859276	0.054963
SB 81	1835	2.108861	0.857539	0.054918
SB 82	1836	2.112046	0.859137	0.054928

COLUMBIA PLAIN, LA VEGA VIEJA, DOMINICAN REPUBLIC

CAL#	NBS#	208/206	207/206	204/206
SD 55	1855	2.113743	0.859202	0.055048

"ALAFIAS ARABES", LA VEGA VIEJA, DOMINICAN REPUBLIC

CAL#	NBS#	208/206	207/206	204/206
SD 58	1851	2.113314	0.858269	0.054930
SD 59	1852	2.113552	0.858324	0.054989

COLUMBIA PLAIN, NUEVA CADIZ, VENEZUELA

CAL#	NBS#	208/206	207/206	204/206
SA 18	1751	2.117006	0.859025	0.055105
SB 60	1826	2.114176	0.859044	0.055088
SB 61	1827	2.115363	0.858432	0.055074
SB 62	1828	2.113838	0.858803	0.055081
SB 66	1829	2.112382	0.858435	0.054983

YAYAL BLUE ON WHITE, NUEVA CADIZ, VENEZUELA

CAL#	NBS#	208/206	207/206	204/206
SB 52	1823	2.111618	0.857951	0.054917
SB 55	1824	2.115111	0.859160	0.055021
SB 56	1825	2.108525	0.857585	0.054885

YAYAL BLUE ON WHITE, CUBAGUA, VENEZUELA

CAL#	NBS#	208/206	207/206	204/206
SB 29	1755	2.112542	0.858973	0.055062

SEVILLA WHITE, METROPOLITAN CATHEDRAL, MEXICO CITY

CAL#	NBS#	208/206	207/206	204/206
SC 26	1762	2.112789	0.859003	0.055014
SC 27	1763	2.110239	0.859099	0.055007

YAYAL BLUE ON WHITE, SURFACE FINDS, JEREZ, SPAIN

CAL#	NBS#	208/206	207/206	204/206
SD 08	1769	2.104848	0.856368	0.054795
SD 11	1770	2.105975	0.856831	0.054820
SD 17	1771	2.105507	0.856760	0.054820

```
          COLUMBIA PLAIN, PUREZA KILN SITE, SEVILLE, SPAIN
     PU1712    1987      2.115606    0.859472       0.055009
     PU1825    1988      2.106449    0.857397       0.054806
     PU1869    1989      2.106919    0.857514       0.054783
     PU1874    1990      2.117771    0.859583       0.055121
     PU2049    1991      2.115260    0.858534       0.055057


                        SPANISH COLONIAL

   COLUMBIA PLAIN, CONVENTO DE SAN FRANCISCO, DOMINICAN REPUBLIC
     SA 01     1750      2.087931    0.848492       0.054285
     SA 03     1820      2.088737    0.848724       0.054327


         COLUMBIA PLAIN, LA VEGA VIEJA, DOMINICAN REPUBLIC
     SA 51     1752      2.087697    0.849124       0.054220
     SA 58     1822      2.087812    0.849476       0.054290
     SD 54     1847      2.088379    0.849297       0.054252


                   COLUMBIA PLAIN, CUZCO, PERU
     SB 43     1759      2.081293    0.845212       0.054092

   UNIDENTIFIED TYPE, LA CALLE JUAN BARON, DOMINICAN REPUBLIC
     SD 51     1844      2.086951    0.847822       0.054208

   BLUE OVER WHITE, PLAZA OF THE PRIESTS, DOMINICAN REPUBLIC
     SD 52     1845      2.087128    0.848658       0.054274


      BLUE ON BLUE, PARQUE COLON, DOMINICAN REPUBLIC
     SD 56     1849      2.085122    0.848907       0.054365


    BLUE ON BLUE, LA CALLE JUAN BARON, DOMINICAN REPUBLIC
     SD 57     1850      2.080506    0.846043       0.054157



                          MEXICAN

       UNIDENTIFIED TYPE, METRO EXCAVATIONS, MEXICO CITY
     SB 27     1754      2.069443    0.837875       0.053448


          UNIDENTIFIED TYPE, CUBAGUA, VENEZUELA
     SB 36     1756      2.076822    0.841122       0.053785


   MEXICO CITY WHITE, METROPOLITAN CATHEDRAL, MEXICO CITY
     SC 12     1765      2.069270    0.837677       0.053466
     SC 13     1966      2.067559    0.837094       0.053495
     SC 16     1760      2.069708    0.837934       0.053431
     SC 17     1967      2.066139    0.837192       0.053549
     SC 20     1968      2.071414    0.839357       0.053635
     SC 21     1969      2.068963    0.837586       0.053554
     SC 22     1970      2.069632    0.837890       0.053451
     SC 24     1971      2.074012    0.840180       0.053574
     SC 25     1761      2.067230    0.837109       0.053505
     SC 28     1764      2.067727    0.837460       0.053476
```

```
SC 29      1972      2.067677      0.837321      0.053488
SC 30      1973      2.069795      0.838348      0.053538
SC 57      1974      2.072108      0.839518      0.053628
```

SAN JUAN POLYCHROME, METROPOLITAN CATHEDRAL, MEXICO CITY
```
SC 37      1765      2.071384      0.838875      0.053514
SC 37      1975      2.071342      0.838835      0.053482
SC 38      1766      2.071865      0.839395      0.053585
SC 38      1976      2.072414      0.839580      0.053595
SC 40      1977      2.071592      0.838993      0.053493
SC 42      1978      2.071969      0.838986      0.053496
SC 43      1979      2.068824      0.838551      0.053583
SC 46      1981      2.066729      0.837268      0.053557
SC 47      1982      2.067261      0.837639      0.053556
SC 48      1983      2.071479      0.838731      0.053500
SC 50      1984      2.071503      0.838598      0.053436
SC 52      1986      2.070254      0.837813      0.053461
```

VALLE WARE, METROPOLITAN CATHEDRAL, MEXICO CITY
```
SC 62      1768      2.067753      0.837340      0.053501
```

SAN LUIS POLYCHROME, PARQUE COLON, DOMINICAN REPUBLIC
```
SD 50      1843      2.068385      0.838376      0.053555
```

PUEBLA POLYCHROME, PARQUE COLON, DOMINICAN REPUBLIC
```
SD 53      1846      2.076862      0.841461      0.053749
```


MEXICAN ORE DEPOSITS, (CUMMING ET AL.)

CAL#	OTHER #	208/206	207/206	204/206
		CUALE		
CUM005	CL-CS	2.069605	0.838213	0.053625
		CAMPO MORADO		
CUM007	CM	2.072959	0.839779	0.053568
		TIGRE		
CUM012	TIG	2.066663	0.836689	0.053545
		COSALA		
CUM020	CSL-LA	2.066949	0.837036	0.053645
CUM021	"	2.068132	0.837095	0.053605
CUM022	"	2.068656	0.837565	0.053680
		EL PAVO		
CUM057	M-EP-LY	2.067160	0.837862	0.053599

36. Mössbauer and Neutron Activation Analysis Study of Ceramic Finds from Canapote, Colombia

R. GEBHARD, W. IHRA, F.E. WAGNER and U. WAGNER
Physik-Department, Technische Universität München, D-8046 Garching, FRG.

H. BISCHOF
Völkerkundliche Sammlungen der Stadt Mannheim im Reiss-Museum, D-6800 Mannheim, FRG.

J. RIEDERER
Rathgen-Forschungslabor, Staatliche Museen Preussischer Kulturbesitz, D-1000 Berlin, FRG.

A.M. WIPPERN
Institüt für Ur -und Frühgeschichte, Universität Heidelberg, D-6900 Heidelberg, FRG.

ABSTRACT: *Neutron activation analysis, thin section microscopy and Mössbauer spectroscopy were used to describe early ceramic finds from Canapote, Colombia. The study yields three major groups. Although the material is severely weathered, original firing conditions can be assessed. The results are discussed together with the excavation stratigraphy and stylistic arguments.*

INTRODUCTION

During a rescue excavation in 1962, a large amount of early ceramic ware was found in a shellmound in Canapote, near Cartagena, Colombia. Nine sections (A to K) with up to 18 layers were excavated. For some of the sections the sequence of stratigraphic levels is shown in Figure 1. The material, pertaining to the Canapote, Tesca and Barlovento periods, is believed to be amongst the earliest ceramics found in South America (Bischof 1966, 1973; Wippern 1988). The sequence was established by stylistic analysis based on the decoration of the pottery and the succession of the refuse deposits found in situ. Two ^{14}C dates (Y-1317 and Y-1318) bring the finds roughly into the second half of the 3rd millennium B.C. The finds are of special interest in connection with material from several other sites in the lower Magdalena Valley at Malambo, Barvolento, Puerto Hormiga and Monsú. We report on a neutron activation analysis (NAA), thin section microscopy (TSM) and Mössbauer spectroscopy (MS) study, undertaken in an attempt to correlate the material properties of the finds with the archaeological description. Eighty-three sherds representing the different types of material and stemming mostly from sections A and J were studied.

Throughout all periods the globular round-bottomed vessel is the common pottery shape. Decorations made by incised lines are characteristic of the different styles. The Canapote pottery is an unpolished, hard ware with an orange or dark grey outer layer and a dull orange or dark brownish grey inner part. It is normally sand tempered. In the lowest excavation level, however, occasionally some sherds with additions of shell temper were found. There is a rather continuous transition between Canapote and Tesca material. Tesca pottery is unpolished, soft, and frequently has a dull yellow orange outside, while the core is brownish grey. Mollusc shells are the predominant temper. Intermediate excavation layers imply a coexistence of Late Tesca and Early Barlovento ceramics. The Barlovento material is soft, tempered with sherds and sand and generally has an orange outside and a brownish grey inner part. The colours were determined according to the standard soil colour charts for material from the different layers after separation.

NEUTRON ACTIVATION ANALYSIS AND THIN SECTION MICROSCOPY

Seventeen trace and four major element concentrations were determined by NAA of two independent samples from each sherd. Prior to irradiation the powdered samples were heated to 850°C for 24 h (Kilikoglou et al. 1988). The logarithms of the mean values of each pair of samples were used in the cluster analysis. The dendrogram obtained by the weighted average linkage method is shown in Figure 2, together with the results of TSM. The dendrogram stays unaltered after application of the hillclimbing procedure. Sherds in clusters 1 and 2 have low Ca contents, ranging between 1.2 and 2.5%, with an average value of (1.6 ± 0.3) %. Almost all of the samples in group 1 stem from sections B and J and pertain to the Barlovento period. TSM shows that they contain little temper and have a fine matrix. The material in cluster 2 comes from section A and is more heterogeneous with coarse quartz inclusions. According to stratigraphic arguments and stylistic appearance, the sherds in cluster 2 are the earliest encountered in the shellmound and belong to the Canapote period, while cluster 4 is from the following Tesca period. Ca contents in the sherds in cluster 4 range between 2.8 and 14% with an average value of (6.5 ± 2.4)%. TSM shows coarse shell temper with differing amounts of quartz of varying particle sizes. Sand, clay and soil from the excavation site are found at the end of the dendrogram. They are uncharacteristic for the ceramic material and could therefore not be used for model experiments. Three sherds from level 15, the earliest in the shellmound, do not fall into any of the other groups. They are extremely heterogeneous as far as the trace element concentrations are concerned, but seem interesting because they represent only a small part of the material in the lowest levels. Running the cluster analysis without the Ca contents blurs the difference between finds from the Tesca and the Canapote periods, while both remain separated from the Barlovento material. Ca has been introduced in the fabrics by the use of shell temper. Any analytical errors by eventual reformation of calcite during burial was excluded by heating the material prior to analysis.

196

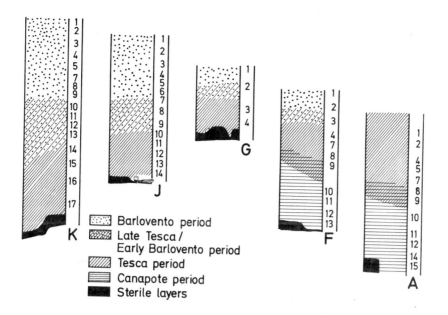

Figure 1. Scheme of stratigraphic sequence for part of the sections. The layers are not continuous.

Legend:
- Barlovento period
- Late Tesca / Early Barlovento period
- Tesca period
- Canapote period
- Sterile layers

MÖSSBAUER SPECTROSCOPY

Mössbauer spectroscopy provides information on the chemical and physical state of the iron present in the ceramics. The most relevant parameters are the quadrupole splitting and the isomer shift. They fall into characteristic regions and give information on the local symmetry around the iron atoms and on their valence state. Additionally oxidic phases can be observed on account of magnetic ordering phenomena (see Wagner et al. 1986a and references therein).

Mössbauer transmission spectra were measured at RT for the separated outer layer and inner core of all sherds. The spectra were fitted with a superposition of Lorentzian lines. It was attempted to use the smallest necessary number of lines. Since the line widths are often quite large, the fitted components have to be regarded as representing maxima of distributions of magnetic fields or quadrupole splittings.

Ten different types of Mössbauer spectra were distinguished (Figure 3). For each type the mean values of the fitted parameters are compiled in Table 1. Type 1 spectra are a superposition of a high amount of paramagnetic and superparamagnetic Fe^{3+} components with some Fe^{2+} species. In type 2 spectra some additional magnetically split Fe^{3+}, most probably haematite, is already present at RT. Type 3 spectra consist of a well ordered six line pattern of haematite together with a distribution of magnetic fields, caused by the presence of oxidic fractions of small particle sizes and/or ferrihydroxides (Wagner et al. 1988). Types 4, 5 and 6 correspond to types 1, 2 and 3, but without Fe^{2+} species. Type 7 spectra can only be fitted with two Fe^{3+} quadrupole doublets, one of them with a rather high quadrupole splitting. Such species are observed in fired clay minerals after dehydroxylation of the octahedral layers of the clay lattice around 500°C (Wagner et al. 1986a) and also after oxidation of clays which have previously

been fired in a reducing atmosphere (Wagner et al. 1986b). Type 8 corresponds to type 7 with additional magnetic oxides present, while types 9 and 10 represent ceramics fired in a strongly reducing environment, with two or three Fe^{2+} components in addition to an Fe^{3+} doublet of varying intensity and no magnetic oxides visible at RT.

In Table 2 all studied sherds are classified according to their type of Mössbauer spectra and the NAA cluster to which they belong. Despite a number of exceptions, one observes characteristically different Mössbauer patterns for the material from the Barlovento, Tesca and Canapote periods. Generally the cores of the Barlovento sherds in cluster 1 exhibit Mössbauer spectra of types 1 and 2. Ten percent of the total iron are in Fe^{2+} state, in addition to paramagnetic and superparamagnetic Fe^{3+}.

Magnetically ordered Fe^{3+} may or may not be observable in the core of the Barlovento sherds; it is, however, always present in the outer layers of these samples, either as well crystallized haematite or giving rise to a distribution of magnetic hyperfine fields. Fe^{2+} is always present in the cores, but may be lacking in the outer layers. This supports the idea that the sherds were fired in a covered pit in an oxygen deficient environment and exposed to an oxidizing atmosphere at the end of the firing, before the temperature decreased below the reaction level. Most of the Canapote ceramics in cluster 2 stem from the lowest excavation levels; they are rich in Fe^{2+} and generally contain haematite only in their outer layers. These sherds appear to have been predominantly fired under reducing conditions throughout the whole heating period. The oxidized outer layers are usually very thin and could well be formed by weathering. The three sherds from the lowest level of the Canapote period, which exhibit heterogeneous trace element contents, however, have been fired in the same manner as the majority of the Canapote ceramics. The material from the Tesca period in cluster 4 has experienced oxidizing as well as reducing firing

197

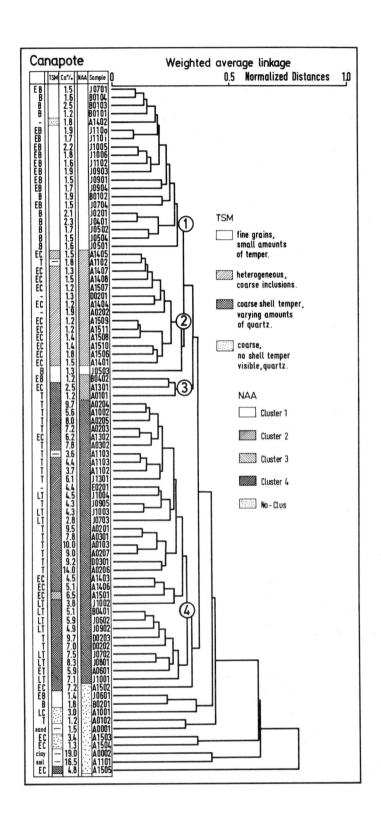

Figure 2. Dendrogram obtained by the cluster analysis of the NAA data. The characters in the sample names refer to the excavation sections, the first two digits to the number of the layer. The last two digits are consecutive numbers of the samples studied in the respective layers. The Ca contents and the results of the TSM are noted on the left. The following abbreviations are used: EC = Early Canapote, LC = Canapote, ET = Early Tesca, T = Tesca, LT = Late Tesca, EB = Early Barlovento and B = Barlovento.

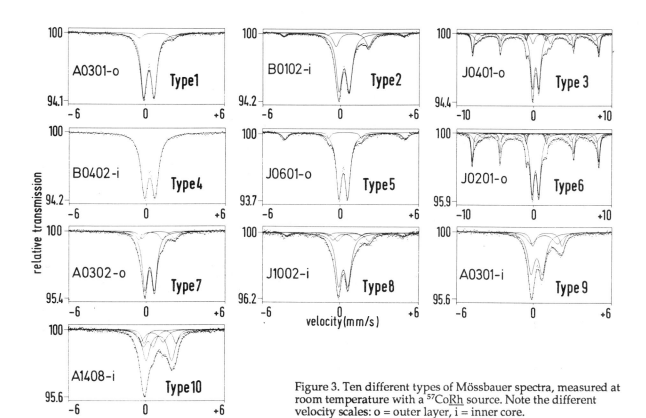

Figure 3. Ten different types of Mössbauer spectra, measured at room temperature with a ^{57}CoRh source. Note the different velocity scales: o = outer layer, i = inner core.

Type	No.		H (T)	A_{Mag} (%)	QS (mm/s)	SQ (mm/s)	WQ (mm/s)	AQ (%)
1	25	Fe^{3+}			0.78(6)	0.26(1)	0.61(8)	89.2(5.1)
		Fe^{2+}			2.50(16)	0.85(9)	0.63(7)	10.8(5.1)
2	30	Fe^{3+}	49.0(1.0)	16.6(8.3)	0.81(5)	0.26(1)	0.68(11)	71.2(9.1)
		Fe^{2+}			2.42(17)	0.93(8)	0.71(12)	12.2(4.9)
3	14	Fe^{3+}	14.4–50.8	45.4(7.8)	0.87(11)	0.27(1)	0.76(13)	46.0(10.9)
		Fe^{2+}			2.46(15)	0.94(8)	0.76(11)	8.6(4.0)
4	5	Fe^{3+}			0.87(8)	0.25(1)	0.69(9)	100
5	14	Fe^{3+}	49.4(1.2)	17.7(9.2)	0.81(6)	0.25(1)	0.64(6)	82.3(9.2)
6	16	Fe^{3+}	12.7–50.0	46.5(13.1)	0.86(11)	0.26(1)	0.73(12)	53.5(12.6)
7	9	Fe^{3+}			0.71(3)	0.27(1)	0.59(5)	74.6(9.2)
					1.73(19)	0.38(8)	0.62(8)	14.9(6.5)
		Fe^{2+}			2.71(19)	0.84(11)	0.63(8)	10.5(3.5)
8	9	Fe^{3+}	48.5(1.1)	11.0(3.2)	0.70(6)	0.26(1)	0.55(5)	67.6(5.3)
					1.70(13)	0.36(6)	0.61(8)	10.8(3.1)
		Fe^{2+}			2.35(24)	1.01(8)	0.57(11)	10.6(4.4)
9	4	Fe^{3+}			0.85(8)	0.23(3)	0.68(3)	57.0(15.7)
		Fe^{2+}			1.99(6)	0.89(5)	0.71(3)	24.3(9.2)
					2.37(29)	1.05(9)	0.53(9)	18.7(6.5)
10	18	Fe^{3+}			0.79(5)	0.21(2)	0.58(4)	37.9(11.1)
					1.75(12)	0.38(9)	0.68(8)	13.0(4.6)
		Fe^{2+}			1.90(11)	0.97(5)	0.72(9)	32.4(7.7)
					2.29(7)	1.12(3)	0.51(7)	16.7(4.1)

Table 1. Group averages and standard deviations (in parentheses) of the Mössbauer parameters observed for the different types of Mössbauer spectra measured at RT. No. is the number of samples. The parameters are given as measured against a source of ^{57}CoRh. H is the magnetic hyperline field, A_{Mag} is the fractional area of the magnetically ordered part of the spectrum. The maximum and minimum magnetic fields are listed in cases where a distribution of 5 to 9 magnetic fields was fitted to the spectra. QS, SQ and WQ are the quadrupole splittings, isomer shifts and experimental full line widths at half maximum. The AQ are the fractional areas of the Fe^{3+} and Fe^{2+} doublets.

Type	Cluster 1		Cluster 2		Cluster 4		No-Clus.+Clus.3	
	outer layer	inner core	outer layer	inner core	outer layer	inner core	outer layer	inner core
1		EB J0904 - A1402 EB J0701 EB J0903	EC A1401		T A0201 T A0203 T A0204 T D0301 T A1002 ET A0601 T A0301 T A0207	T A0201 T A0203 T A0204 T D0301 T A1002 - E0201 T A0205 LT J0801 T J1301	EC A1503	T A0102 T A0101 EB J0601
2	EB J1006 EB J1102 EB J0904 - A1402	EB J1006 EB J1102 B J0401 B J0504 B B0102 B B0104 B J0201 B J0501 B J0502 EB J0704 EB J1005 EB J1101 B B0101	EC A1404 EC A1511	- A0202 - D0201	EC A1406 LT J1001 T A0103 EC A1501 EC A1403	EC A1406 LT J1001 LT B0401 LT J0703 LT J0905	EC A1301 EC A1504	- A0001 B J0503
3	B J0401 B J0504 B B0102 B B0104 B B0103		EC A1508 EC A1506 EC A1510 EC A1407 EC A1507	EC A1508 EC A1509	E0201	LT J1004	B J0503	
4	EB J0701				T A0205	T A0103	T A0102	EB B0402
5	EB J0903			- A0202 - D0201	T A0206 T D0202 T D0203 LT B0401 LT J0902	T A0206 T D0202 T D0203	T A0101 EB J0601 EB B0402	
6	B J0201 B J0501 B J0502 EB J0704 EB J1005 EB J1101 B B0101 EB J0901				LT J0801 T J1301 LT J0703 LT J0905 LT J0702 LT J1002 LT J1003	LT J0602 T A1102	B B0201	
7				EC A1506 EC A1510	T A0302 EC A1302 LT J0602	T A0302 EC A1302 ET A0601		Soil A1101
8		EB J0901	EC A1405	EC A1401		LT J1004 LT J0902 LT J0702 LT J1002 LT J1003	EC A1502	Clay A0002
9						T A0301 EC A1501	LC A1001	LC A1001
10		B B0103	EC A1408 EC A1509	EC A1408 EC A1404 EC A1511 EC A1407 EC A1507 EC A1405		T A0207 A1403 T A1103	EC A1505 EC	EC A1505 EC A1503 EC A1301 EC A1504 B B0201 EC A1502

Table 2. Classification of the studied sherds according to the types of Mössbauer pattern of their outer layers and cores and the NAA cluster to which they belong.

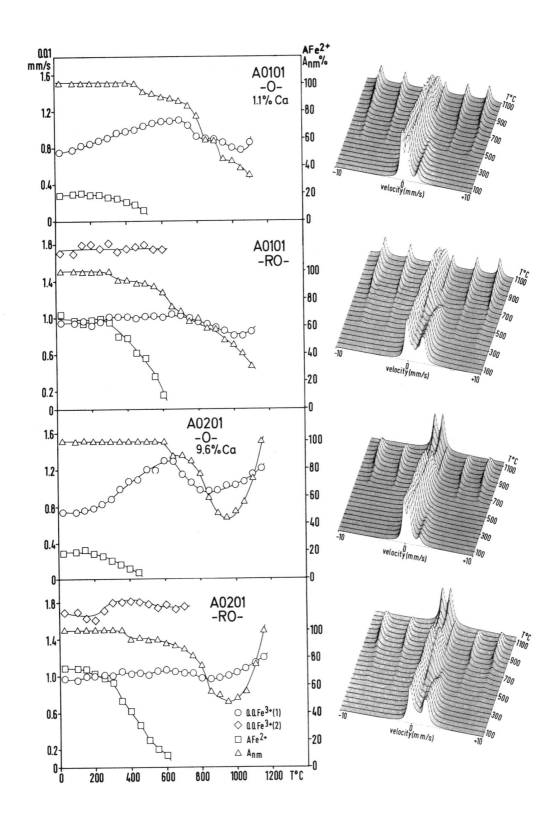

Figure 4. Dependence of Mössbauer spectra (right) and some relevant Mössbauer parameters on refiring temperature, measured at RT for the inner part of two sherds with 1.1 and 9.5% Ca, with (-RO-) and without (-O-) previous laboratory reduction. QQ1 is the quadrupole splitting of the Fe^{3+} doublet; A_{nm} and A_{Fe}^{2+} are the content of nonmagnetic iron (Fe^{2+} plus Fe^{3+}) and of nonmagnetic Fe^{2+} alone. Two Fe^{3+} species (QQ_{Fe}^{3+} (1) and (2)), both of low concentration, appear up to about 600°C in the spectra of samples treated by a preceding reduction step.

conditions. One exception should be mentioned here. Sherd J0602 contains ceramic temper in the inner part, which therefore appears more oxidized than the outer layer.

REFIRING EXPERIMENTS

Since no relevant clay was available for model firing experiments, the main layers of 5 sherds were chosen for 12 laboratory refiring series. The samples were refired in air for 48 h with and without previous reduction with charcoal at 800°C for 3 h. Mössbauer spectra were taken at RT. For sherds A0101 and A0201 with 1.1 and 9.6% of Ca respectively, the fitted curves are shown in Figure 4, which also gives the temperature dependence of some relevant parameters.

In a naive picture, no changes in the Mössbauer parameters are to be expected during laboratory refiring, until the refiring temperature surpasses the original firing temperature. This is clearly not the case for refiring in air of the samples represented in Figure 4. An increase of QQ1 on refiring in air at temperatures below 600°C was, in fact, observed in all studied cases, except for the highly reduced sherd A1408 (not shown). This increase is typical for the distortion of the octahedral layers in the clay lattice during dehydroxylation. Although it is less steep than during the first firings of clays, its observation indicates a reformation of clay minerals in the ceramics by weathering, perhaps because the original firing temperatures were sufficiently low for the clay lattice structure to remain in a stable state able to respond to rehydroxylation. In the high-calcareous sherd A0201 spinel formation (Maniatis et al. 1978) is indicated above 900°C by an increase of the quadrupole splitting and the relative $A_{Fe}{}^{3+}$ fraction. Such spectra were not observed in any of the studied sherds, due to the rather low original firing temperatures. The low-temperature region of the refiring curves for laboratory-reduced material is dominated by the oxidation of the Fe^{2+} species. The quadrupole splitting of the weak Fe^{3+} component starts at the high value of 1.1 mm/s. Dehydroxylation must already have taken place during the preceding reduction. In the low-temperature region a second Fe^{3+} species with a high quadrupole splitting is observed. Above 500°C it can no longer be distinguished from the main Fe^{3+} component. Spectra like those observed in this temperature region are frequently observed in archaeological material. This suggests a reducing original firing with some oxidation at the end.

STUDY OF WEATHERING

Weathering effects were studied in detail for 14 sherds pertaining to the different stratigraphic levels. For three of them Figure 5 shows the spectra, while Table 3 gives the relative fractional areas for all iron species. A detailed description of all data will be presented elsewhere. A comparison of RT and liquid He measurements of the outer layer and the inner part of sherd A0101 reveals a high content of superparamagnetic oxides present in form of haematite as well as small particle oxides or oxyhydroxides giving rise to a distribution of magnetic fields at 4.2 K. In sherd J0201, originally fired in oxidizing conditions, well crystallized haematite, which undergoes the Morin transition, coexists with small-particle oxidic phases. Iron bearing silicates were formed in sherd A1001 by reduction during the original firing. They are much less sensitive to formation of oxyhydroxides by weathering.

CONCLUSIONS

The three major groups observed by cluster analysis of NAA data and by Mössbauer and thin section microscopy studies are in general agreement with the main stratigraphic and a stylistic sequence of the Barlovento, Tesca and Canapote periods. Further archaeological subdivisions of these periods are not reflected in the material properties. In the earliest phase strongly reducing firing conditions were common. This also applies to a number of sherds in the same level which are otherwise very heterogeneous. During the Tesca period different raw materials and reducing as well as oxidizing firing cycles were used. Late Tesca and Early Barlovento material stemming from the same strata exhibits different material properties. Oxidizing firing conditions are predominant in the Barlovento phase. The whole material is severely weathered, but the ceramics in the lowest levels are less affected. This might be due to both the stratigraphic situation and the fact that material fired in a strongly reducing environment is less sensitive to modification by weathering.

ACKNOWLEDGEMENTS

We wish to thank Mrs. M. Bartel and Mr. J.E. Punsch for their enthusiastic help in preparing the samples and conducting the experiments. Support by the Deutsche Forschungsgemeinschaft is gratefully acknowledged.

REFERENCES

Bischof, H. (1966). "Canapote - An Early Ceramic Site in North Colombia". Proc. of the 36th International Congress of the Americanists. 1: 483-491.

Bischof, H. (1973). "The Origins of Pottery in South America". Proc. of the 40th International Congress of the Americanists. 1: 269-281.

Kilikoglou, V., Y. Maniatis and S.P. Grimanis (1988). "The Effect of Purification and Firing of Clays on Trace Element Provenance Studies", Archaeometry, 30: 37-46.

Maniatis, Y., A. Simopolous, A. Kostikas (1981). "Mössbauer Study of the Effect of Calcium Content on Iron Oxide Transformations in Fired Clays". J. Am. Ceram. Soc., 64(5): 263-269.

Wagner, U., F.E. Wagner, J. Riederer (1986a). "The Use of Mössbauer Spectroscopy in Archaeometric Studies". In Olin, J.S. and M.J. Blackman, eds., Proc. of the 1984 Symposium on Archaeometry, Washington D.C., Smithsonian Institution Press: 129-142.

Wagner, U., F.E. Wagner, A. Stockklauser, R. Slazar, J. Riederer, F. Kauffmann-Doig (1986b). "Mössbauer Analysis of Recent Finds from Chavin". Hyperfine Interactions, 29: 1113-1116.

Wagner, U., W. Knorr, A. Forster, E. Murad, R. Salazar, F.E. Wagner (1988). "Mössbauer Study of Illite Associated with Iron Oxi-Hydroxides". Hyperfine Interactions, 41: 855-858.

Wippern, A.M. (1988). "Evidencia Estratigráfica en el Desarrollo del la Cerámica Temprana de la Costa Caribe de Colombia". Presented during the 46th International Congress of Americanists, 4-8 July 1988, Amsterdam.

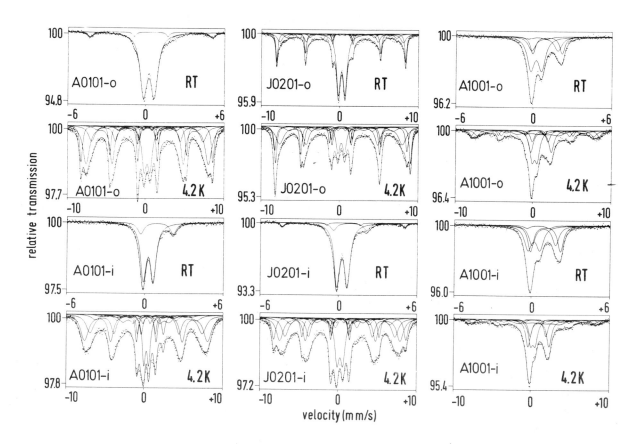

Figure 5. The left column shows Mössbauer spectra of the outer layer (o) and core (i) of sherd A0101 measured at RT and 4.2 K. The second and third column pertain to sherds J0201 and A1001. The source of ^{57}CoRh was always at the same temperature as the absorber. Note the different velocity scales.

Sherd	Type	Layer		A_{Mag}	$A_{Mag,dis}$	A_{Fe3+}	A_{Fe2+}	$A_{Fe2+,mag}$
A0101	5	outer	RT	17.6	—	82.4	—	—
			4.2 K	15.8	70.1	14.1	—	—
	1	inner	RT	—	—	81.2	18.8	—
			4.2 K	—	83.0	11.9	5.1	—
J0201	6	outer	RT	21.1	38.3	40.6	—	—
			4.2 K	17.1 + 20.9*	51.0	11.0	—	—
	2	inner	RT	11.5	—	77.9	10.6	—
			4.2 K	13.5	67.7	15.2	3.6	—
A1001	9	outer	RT	—	—	56.0	44.0	—
			4.2 K	—	32.5	24.4	28.9	14.2
	9	inner	RT	—	—	40.5	59.5	—
			4.2 K	—	23.7	21.1	40.9	14.3

Table 3. Relative fractional areas (in %) of iron-bearing species in the spectra of sherds A0101, J0201 and A1001 measured for the outer layers and inner cores at RT and 4.2 K. A_{Mag} is the haematite fraction, * is the Morin-type haematite. A_{Fe}^{3+} and A_{Fe}^{2+} refer to the nonmagnetic Fe^{3+} and Fe^{2+} species, and $A_{Fe}^{2+}{}_{,mag}$ represents the area of a magnetically split Fe^{2+} species observed at 4.2 K.

37. A Pattern Recognition and Scanning Electron Microscope with X-Ray Fluorescence Analysis of Glaze-Paint Anasazi Pottery from the American Southwest

N. BOWER, D. RADAMACHER, T. SHIMOTAKE, and T. ANSELMI
Chemistry Department, Colorado College, Colorado Springs, CO 80903, U.S.A.

S. PECKHAM
Laboratory of Anthropology, Museum of New Mexico, Santa Fe, NM 87502-4463, U.S.A.

ABSTRACT: *SEM-XRF is used to provide a simple, nondestructive, surface elemental analysis of Anasazi pottery. After employing various clustering methods, conclusions about the provenance and materials of manufacture are made.*

INTRODUCTION

Pottery has long been of use in determining the geographic distribution of a given culture. A number of archaeometric methods have supplemented the traditional stylistic analyses, particularly when only small, unidentifiable sherds are available (Bower et al. 1974; Hall et al. 1973). The parametric data generated by a multielement technique such as X-ray fluorescence or neutron activation analysis are particularly amenable to computer-generated pattern recognition techniques (Ward 1974). However, it is becoming increasingly important that even seemingly worthless sherds be analyzed by nondestructive methods, as they represent a non-renewable cultural resource. Scanning electron microscopy coupled with an energy dispersive X-ray fluorescence detector (SEM-XRF) provides such a nondestructive method. In addition it allows the user to analyze areas from a few microns to a few centimetres in diameter, as needed, by changing the working distance and aperture in order to avoid sampling errors due to inclusions (Bromund et al. 1976). Finally, as its depth of penetration is limited to a few microns, depending upon the excitation energy used for the incident electron beam, analyses of surface decorations are possible without having to remove them from the main body of the sherd.

In this study, pottery sherds from northwest New Mexico, northeast Arizona, and southwest Colorado (Figure 1) were analyzed for their pigment and the surface next to the pigment. These wares date from about A.D. 700 to 1500 (Table 1), and they represent a wide range of cultural groups and decorating materials. The major impetus of this study was to see if there were discernable, typical elemental compositions for the black pigments used in this region. A secondary goal was to compare various clustering methodologies to see which would be most applicable. Prior experience (Bower et al. 1986) suggested that good results (>90% accuracy) could be obtained by using the unweighted pair-group method based on arithmetic averages (UPGMA) for clustering similarity coefficients calculated using a correlation coefficient matrix of z-score normalized elemental data. (Calculating z-scores removes undue weighting inherent in those elements which have higher concentrations.) Somewhat less satisfactory results were obtained in the previous study using Euclidean distances instead of the correlation coefficient similarities. However, Ward's method is also popular, and it was decided to compare a number of clustering methods using data normalized with

the analytical uncertainties instead of with the population standard deviations.

METHOD

Twenty-eight sherds from the Museum of New Mexico Laboratory of Anthropology, eight sherds from the University of Colorado Museum (all from the Yellow Jacket site in southwest Colorado), and four sherds from the Crow Canyon Archaeological Center (also in southwest Colorado) were selected for the analysis (Table 1). Sherds with a very thin pigment layer of known polychrome wares were excluded. An attempt was made to include both presumed vegetable and mineral pigments.

The elemental analysis was accomplished with an International Scientific Instruments model SS40 SEM equipped with a Princeton Gamma Tech System 4 XRF with a DEC-11 computer. Spectra of the K_α lines for all of the elements (except Pb, which was analyzed using its L_α line) were normally acquired using 18-20 keV excitation with a 1 mm^2 sampling area on the sherd. Both the background (often a slipped surface) and the pigment were analyzed on each sherd. (Cotton thread, which could be seen in the SEM, was tied around the sherds to delineate the areas.) Count times varied from 100 to 500 s and spot size was adjusted as needed in order to obtain total spectrum counts of 200,000 or more. This resulted in relative errors of less than 10% for elements whose compositions were at least 1%. Sampling errors were usually 1-5%, though some sherds exhibited significantly worse homogeneity. A standardless, semiquantitative analysis program (NOSTD) was used to calculate the percent elemental compositions from the spectra, and USGS microprobe rock standards AMP-1, FEL-1, and CPX-1 were run as a quality assurance. The X-ray diffractions were run with a Scintag XRD from 2° to 60° with steps of 0.03°. Peak intensities were typically about 200 cps (S/N = 10).

Before running the clustering programs, the data was normalized by subtracting the mean percent composition for each element. The result was then divided by the analytical uncertainty for each element. This effectively weights the data heaviest for those elements which are best known. The analytical errors used in these divisions were obtained from replicate analyses and they include instrumental sampling error. The errors obtained were as follows: Mg, 0.5; Al, 0.7; Si, 1.0; P, 0.5; K, 0.7; Ca, 1.0; Ti, 0.3; Mn, 0.2; Fe 1.0; Ni, 0.2; Cu, 0.4; Zn, 0.6; and Pb, 1.8 percent.

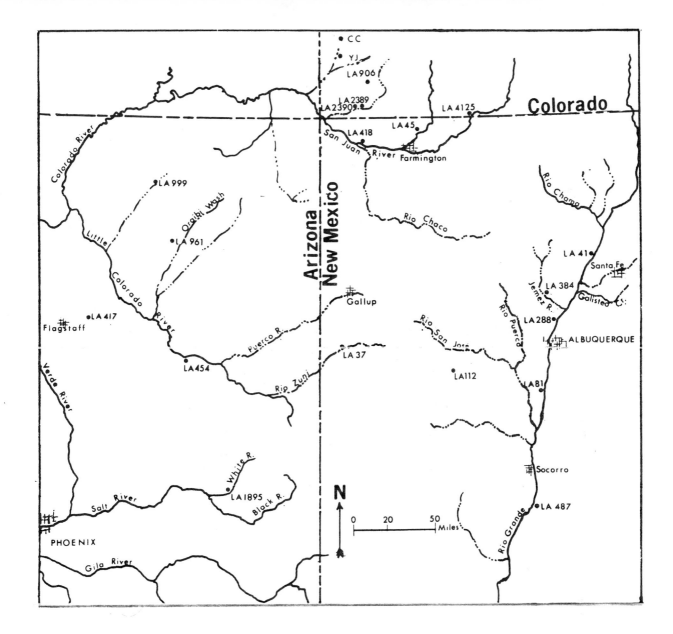

Figure 1. Location of sites from which samples were taken.

Ni and Zn were not used in the clustering step, as these elements did not have percent compositions significantly exceeding their analytical errors for any of these samples. S and Cl were also excluded, and though they are of value in identifying certain organic pigments, they were severely overlapped by the Pb M lines in the glazed wares, and therefore could not be measured for all of the sherds. Na, though observable in some samples, suffers from poor detector sensitivity, and it was not used in this study.

The clustering programs tested were average linkage between groups (UPGMA), average linkage within groups, single linkage (nearest neighbour), complete linkage (furthest neighbour), centroid clustering, median clustering, and Ward's method (in which clustering expansion is minimized by choosing the smallest "sum of squares" when combining clusters). The squared Euclidean distance measure should be used with the last three, while the first three clustering methods work with either the squared or simple Euclidean distance measures. They were all available in the Statistical Package for the Social Sciences (SPSS), which was run on a VAX 11/750 computer.

RESULTS AND DISCUSSION

Figure 2 presents the dendrogram obtained using Ward's method for clustering. The square roots of the agglomeration schedules have been taken in order to rescale the dendrogram more realistically. This method gave the best results, with only three sherds completely misplaced (93% accuracy). The other methods tended to show fairly severe chaining (in which each group is plotted as a subset of the next cluster, rather than the groups being separated), with single linkage and the centroid methods being worst, followed by the average linkage methods, and the complete and median methods being the best. Even Ward's method seemed to show some chaining for those locations represented by only one or two sherds. Having "seed" sherds that unknown sherds may cluster around seems to reduce this problem.

The other clustering methods also did not have as high an accuracy in clustering the known sherds, though the clustering of the organic pigments for the southwest Colorado region and for the Rio Grande organic and glaze pigments was apparent in all of the methods. None of the dendrograms was particularly meaningful in its grouping at higher levels. These results are in general agreement with those found by other workers (Romesburg 1984; Zupan 1982), suggesting that the more popular UPGMA may not be quite as applicable when used with distance measures for these kinds of problems as Ward's method. However, when the UPGMA was used with a similarity measure based on the correlation coefficients of z-scores, nearly the same accuracy of assignment was obtained (Bower et al. 1986). In fact, preliminary results on a subset of the data suggest that Ward's method applied directly to r^2 data obtained from data normalized using analytical uncertainties gives even better results than either of the other methods (98% versus 93% and 91%, respectively). However, more controlled studies on equivalent data sets are needed to compare the methods fully.

Although the dendrogram in Figure 2 is not particularly useful at showing large scale groupings, it does appear to do a very good job at separating the organic from the mineral pigments. Though this may seem a simple task, the pigments from the Four Corners region (southwestern corner of Colorado) can be very difficult to identify on small sherds. Both organic and mineral pigments were used. Since the carbon in the organic pigments is not itself analyzed, the surface underneath will confuse the clustering method if data from the background is not also included.

Table 1. Identification of sherd samples

No.	Loc.#	Pottery Type
1	LA37[1]	Tularosa B/W -- Tularosa Ware (c 1200?)
2	37	Hawikuh -- Zuni Glaze ware (c 1300)
3	41	San Ildefonso -- Biscuit Ware A (1400-1600)
4	41	San Ildefonso -- Biscuit Ware B (1400-1600)
5	41	Perage -- Biscuit Ware B (1400-1600)
6	45	Wingate Corrugated -- White Mountain Ware (1050-1200)
7	45	Puerco B/R -- White Mountain Red Ware (1000-1200)
8	45	Puerco B/R -- White Mountain Red Ware (1000-1200)
9	45	Tusayan B/R -- San Juan Red Ware (1050-1200)
10	45	Wingate B/R -- White Mountain Red Ware (1050-1200)
11	45	La Plata/Deadmans B/R -- San Juan Red ware (775-1066)
12	81	San Clemente -- Rio Grande Glaze A (1300-1400)
13	112	Acoma -- Glaze Ware (c 1300)
14	384	Ko-ha-sai-ya -- Rio Grande Glaze A (1300-1400)
15	417	Tusayan B/R -- San Juan Red Ware (1050-1200)
16	418	Wingate B/R -- White Mountain Red Ware (1050-1200)
17	454	Tuwiuca B/O -- Winslow Orange Ware (1250-1300)
18	454	Tuwiuca B/O -- Winslow Orange Ware (1250-1300)
19	454	Tuwiuca B/O -- Winslow Orange Ware (1250-1300)
20	487	San Pascual -- Rio Grande Glaze A (1300-1400)
21	906	La Plata B/R -- San Juan Red Ware (850-1000+)
22	999	Deadmans B/R -- San Juan Red Ware (775-1066)
23	999	Deadmans B/R -- San Juan Red Ware (775-1066)
24	1895	Wingate/St. Johns B/R -- White Mountain Red Ware (1050-1200)
25	2389	Abajo R/O -- San Juan Red Ware (700-875 or 900)
26	2389	La Plata B/R -- San Juan Red Ware (850-1000+)
27	2390	La Plata B/R -- San Juan Red Ware (850-1000+)
28	4125	Basketmaker III -- Preglaze ware (400-700)
29	CC[2]	McElmo/Mesa Verde B/W -- organic pigment (1100-1300)
30	CC	McElmo/Mesa Verde B/W -- organic pigment (1100-1300)
31	CC	Mancos B/W -- mineral pigment (c 1050)
32	CC	Mancos B/W -- mineral pigment (c 1050)
33	YJ[3]	Mancos Corrugated B/W -- (c 1050)
34	YJ	Mancos B/W -- (c 1050)
35	YJ	Mancos B/W -- (c 1050)
36	YJ	Mancos B/W -- (c 1050)
37	YJ	Mesa Verde B/W -- (1100-1300)
38	YJ	Mesa Verde (?) B/W -- (1100-1300)
39	YJ	Mesa Verde B/W -- (1100-1300)
40	YJ	Kayenta B/R -- San Juan Red Ware (800-1050)

1. Laboratory of Anthropology, Museum of New Mexico Site Number
2. Crow Canyon Archaeological Center, Cortez, Colorado
3. Yellow Jacket, near Cortez, Colorado; from the University of Colorado Museum

In addition, provenance information is often more dependent upon the clay body composition than it is on the surface paint. Apparently local clays were used to make the bodies, while glaze-paint pigments were manufactured from materials (or followed mixing traditions) that were transported over longer distances. However, certain pigments are characteristic of particular areas and cultures, making provenance identification possible in many cases just by using the glaze-paint composition.

Of particular interest to this study is the separation of the Mancos mineral pigment wares from the Mesa Verde organic pigment wares. These two are often found at the same sites. In many cases, there seems to have been some inclusion of mineral matter even in the organic pigments, as seen by the presence of additional iron and lead in the pigment layer (see Table 2, group 1 and 2). Whether this was intentional or simply the result of contamination from mixing pigments using the same tools is unclear. Some of the pigments appear to be powdered iron compounds applied simply as a slurry in water, producing a brown paint that does not adhere very well. Possibly organic pigments were used as a glue for the mineral pigments in some cases, as well as using the carbon in the vegetable matter as a reducing agent to favour the darker iron (II) oxide over the iron (III) oxide. Usually, the vegetable pigments leave a carbon residue, and variable amounts of elements like sulfur.

The presence of small amounts of lead in many "organic" pigments is also difficult to explain. The earliest "glaze wares" seem to have been made as much by accident as by design during the Basketmaker III period (A.D. 400-700) in southwestern Colorado. Lead compounds seem to have been used initially for the dark greenish colour (and glaze) they form, and potters may have continued using them in small amounts as a fluxing binder until they began to take complete advantage of their glazing properties at the end of the Pueblo III period (A.D. 1300) in the upper regions of the Little Colorado river. The idea spread from there to the east to the Zunis and then the Rio Grande valley, where it continued to be used in pottery designs until the arrival of the Spanish (A.D. 1600). The traditions for both the tempering materials and the use of organic versus mineral paints, started in the Basketmaker III period, seem to have continued through at least the Pueblo III period, with the organic pigments being favored in the west (and in places in the Rio Grande valley) and the

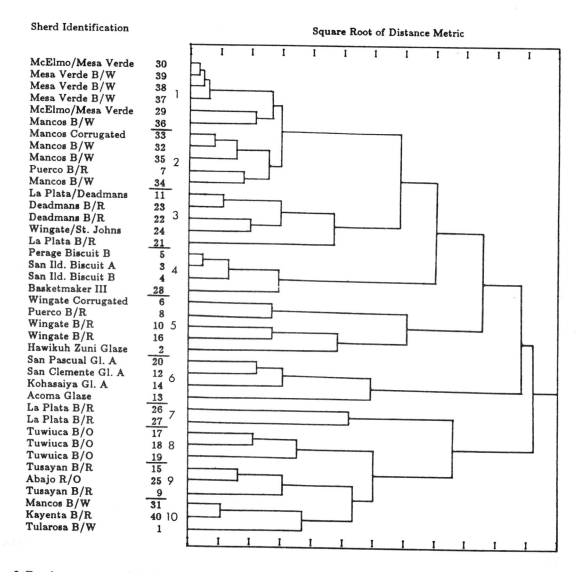

Figure 2. Dendrogram using Ward's method on normalized elemental data.

207

mineral pigments more to the east. Of all of the organic pigments analyzed here, the organic pigments used in the Espanola Basin of the northern Rio Grande Valley seem to be the "purest", and even they show some lead (group 4).

The clustering of the La-Plata Black-on-red and Deadman's Black-on-red in group 3 is as expected. In the early 1930's Deadman's was named by archaeologists in Arizona who found large numbers of the sherds near Flagstaff and thought that it originated near there. Researchers in northwest New Mexico and at Mesa Verde named a similar pottery La Plata Black-on-red, also back in the 1930's. They have more recently been found to have a common origin (called San Juan Red Ware) belonging to drainages of the San Juan in the vicinity of Shiprock, New Mexico (LA 418) down to the junction with the Colorado. Two other groups (7 and 9) should be grouped more closely with group 3, as they are from the same general region and they differ primarily in the level of the iron in the body of the sherd, indicative of a local variation in clay compositions. All three of these groups have significant levels of manganese as well as iron in their pigment layer. Increasing the analytical uncertainties for iron and manganese might bring these groups into closer proximity in the clustering, but that is not a desirable solution, since the analytical errors were determined before the clustering step. The presence of manganese in the northeastern Arizona types has been noted before, though some sherds from southeastern Utah have been determined to lack manganese (Dave Snow, personal communication), possibly relating more to our groups 1 and 2. This might be the origin of the misgrouped sherd #2 appearing in group 3 with the Mancos sherds. The manganese used in the

pigments in this group may have its origin in the stains observable on sandstones in the Four Corners region. Certainly, in the Zuni area and into east-central Arizona, prehistoric potters ground up sandstone to obtain white slips, some of which show minute fragments of sandstone. Even today, there is an Acoma Pueblo potter who grinds up red sandstone to make a red slip she uses on her pottery.

There is also a distinct grouping of sherds (group 5) known as the White Mountain Red Wares from a region whose source is roughly between El Morro, New Mexico (east of Zuni) and Springerville, Arizona. This group is distinctive for having significant levels of copper in its pigment layer. This makes some sense, as there are substantial copper deposits (malachite and azurite) in the Zuni mountains south of Bluewater Lake. Both minerals would have been mined or surface-gathered by the Indians, since the copper minerals are ceremonially important for decorating prayer-sticks and other altar pieces, as well as for body paint.

Group 6 consists of glaze wares primarily from the early Rio Grande Classic period (A.D. 1300 to 1700), which were treated in detail in an earlier study (Bower et al. 1986). The sherds in group 6 also have significant levels of copper, having been selected for this study for that reason. Their production was apparently influenced by traditions from the White Mountain area, as most of the other Rio Grand Glaze Wares lack copper. The clustering within this group is not exactly as expected, as sherd #20 should be the most different of the four, having the lowest copper and the highest manganese composition, and therefore being most

TABLE 2. ELEMENTAL COMPOSITION OF CLUSTERS, IN PERCENT

	Group 1	Group 2	Group 3	Group 4	Group 5	Group 6	Group 7	Group 8	Group 9	Group 10
Pigment										
Mg	0.9±0.4	0.6±0.4	0.5±0.7	2.8±1.2	3.2±3.4	1.3±0.8	0.1±0.2	0.4±0.5	0.1±0.2	1.2±1.2
Al	12.9±1.1	12.0±2.1	9.7±1.3	9.2±0.5	10.6±2.7	4.5±2.7	4.6±1.8	10.3±0.5	7.8±2.1	11.0±0.8
Si	26.3±1.9	24.9±0.3	24.8±1.6	32.1±2.1	19.5±4.1	12.1±2.7	14.2±6.1	19.7±2.8	21.8±0.6	22.5±2.4
P	0.4±0.4	0.9±0.6	0.8±1.0	0.3±0.0	0.8±0.9	0.5±0.5	0.0±0.0	0.2±0.1	0.0±0.0	0.1±0.1
K	3.9±0.9	2.2±0.6	2.1±0.6	7.6±2.3	2.0±1.9	1.5±0.3	1.8±0.4	1.5±0.2	2.5±0.1	2.6±0.6
Ca	3.1±1.6	4.1±3.1	4.3±1.6	2.2±0.8	1.6±1.7	2.6±1.5	2.8±0.4	2.3±1.9	2.9±1.0	1.5±0.5
Ti	0.5±0.3	0.5±0.3	0.3±0.2	0.2±0.1	0.2±0.2	0.2±0.1	0.6±0.0	0.6±0.1	0.5±0.1	0.4±0.2
Mn	0.1±0.1	0.1±0.1	1.9±1.4	0.0±0.0	0.0±0.0	1.3±1.4	4.8±2.4	3.6±0.7	1.1±1.4	0.1±0.1
Fe	3.1±1.3	6.5±2.3	6.8±4.2	2.1±0.4	10.7±5.5	4.5±2.5	31.4±10.	18.8±6.7	21.2±2.0	17.6±5.6
Ni	0.0±0.0	0.0±0.0	0.1±0.1	0.0±0.0	0.0±0.0	0.0±0.0	0.0±0.0	0.2±0.3	0.0±0.0	0.0±0.1
Cu	0.0±0.0	0.1±0.1	0.1±0.1	0.0±0.0	5.6±3.0	3.6±2.0	0.1±0.0	0.3±0.0	0.2±0.1	0.0±0.0
Zn	0.0±0.0	0.1±0.2	0.2±0.2	0.1±0.0	0.1±0.1	0.1±0.2	0.0±0.0	0.4±0.1	0.1±0.1	0.0±0.0
Pb	1.1±1.0	2.3±4.4	3.1±2.6	6.3±8.3	2.8±3.0	40.0±8.1	1.4±0.9	0.6±0.5	0.1±0.1	1.0±1.7
Background										
Mg	0.4±0.4	0.8±0.3	0.4±0.4	3.3±1.0	1.2±1.7	2.0±1.3	0.0±0.0	0.1±0.2	0.1±0.1	1.2±0.8
Al	14.0±1.9	13.2±0.7	11.8±1.1	10.4±1.0	11.1±3.2	9.0±0.9	7.0±0.7	14.6±1.6	9.0±1.0	14.4±3.5
Si	27.9±1.4	26.5±1.0	24.9±0.9	34.0±1.7	23.0±2.7	26.3±5.8	22.5±1.7	25.1±2.7	25.3±2.0	28.9±2.9
P	0.8±0.9	0.6±0.5	0.3±0.5	0.6±0.9	0.2±0.2	0.3±0.1	0.0±0.0	0.0±0.1	0.0±0.0	0.2±0.1
K	3.0±0.5	2.6±0.3	2.8±0.7	5.5±2.7	2.7±0.5	3.2±0.9	3.4±1.0	1.8±0.6	3.3±0.5	3.3±0.6
Ca	2.2±1.8	2.9±1.3	2.9±1.1	2.3±1.0	2.2±1.3	4.6±2.1	4.5±2.0	3.8±1.9	3.1±0.9	1.5±0.9
Ti	0.3±0.3	0.7±0.2	0.4±0.1	0.2±0.1	0.4±0.3	0.4±0.1	0.5±0.1	0.7±0.0	0.7±0.1	0.4±0.1
Mn	0.1±0.1	0.1±0.0	0.3±0.2	0.0±0.0	0.0±0.1	0.0±0.0	0.0±0.0	0.2±0.2	0.1±0.1	0.0±0.0
Fe	2.2±1.0	4.2±0.8	10.0±3.1	2.8±0.6	14.7±8.9	5.7±1.6	16.7±4.7	4.8±1.0	12.4±3.3	2.9±2.4
Ni	0.0±0.0	0.1±0.0	0.0±0.1	0.0±0.0	0.0±0.0	0.0±0.0	0.0±0.0	0.1±0.1	0.1±0.0	0.0±0.0
Cu	0.4±0.5	0.3±0.2	0.1±0.1	0.1±0.1	0.4±0.2	0.1±0.1	0.1±0.0	0.6±0.5	0.5±0.5	0.1±0.1
Zn	0.0±0.0	0.1±0.1	0.1±0.1	0.1±0.1	0.1±0.2	0.0±0.0	0.0±0.0	0.8±0.7	0.3±0.3	0.0±0.0
Pb	0.6±0.8	1.0±1.0	0.9±1.2	3.6±5.2	1.3±1.1	13.7±12.	0.4±0.5	1.3±2.2	0.6±0.3	0.7±0.9

representative of the typical composition of the other Rio Grande Glaze wares (not represented here). It might have been more accurately clustered if some of those sherds had been included as well, as this affects the "chaining".

Group 8 represents a distinct group known as the Tuwiuca Black-on-orange Ware, belonging to the Winslow Orange Wares, and originating near Winslow, Arizona. This group is characterized by having fairly low iron in its background surface compared to the pigment, as well as having fairly high levels of manganese in the pigment. This is not very different from the San Juan Red Wares, but is different enough to be separable into its own group, though on the larger scale it joins a collection of other wares appearing in groups 9 and 10. All of the sherds in groups 9 and 10 come from nearby areas except for the misplaced Mancos sherd.

A rough factor analysis was also done by rotating the data matrix (R-analysis) so that the elements could be clustered instead of the sherds. This demonstrated a significant degree of correlation between the pigment composition and the background surface, implying that the electron beam is penetrating through the pigment. This gives spectra for the pigments which are not "pure". Considering the number of carbon based pigments included in the data, this is not a surprising result, as carbon does not show up in the spectra. In addition, many of the sherds have very thin glaze-paint layers, even for the mineral pigments. A similar factor analysis of just the pigment layer gives 6 groups; one for Si, K, and Al (typical of clays), one for Mn, Fe and Ti (representing the black mineral pigments), one for Ca and P (possibly from apatite or from vegetable pigments), one for Ni and Zn (which were both negligible in this study), one for Pb, used to make the glazes, and one for Cu and Mg, whose clustering seems to be spurious, unless the Cu L_α is overlapping the Mg K_α

The X-ray diffraction analysis of some Rio Grande Glaze A sherds supports and supplements the elemental analysis, as it found quartz, feldspars, calcite, and MnO or $MnCO_3$ in the mineral pigments, while quartz and feldspars were found in the main body. These minerals are about what would be expected, and in the future we expect to explore the technique further to see what additional information we may gain about the manufacturing materials. In addition, we intend to investigate how resemblance measures such as the correlation or cosine coefficients affect the clustering as they are more sensitive to the shape of the data than the simple Euclidean or squared Euclidean distances. Since the SEM-XRF determines essentially all of the major elements (producing totals of 100% when oxygen is calculated from stoichiometry) except carbon, a shape sensitive measure should be the best. When a few "known" sherds from each suspected group are included in the analysis as "seeds" for the clustering algorithm, chaining is minimized with Ward's method, and accurate group assignments are possible. The use of analytical uncertainties instead of population standard deviations for normalizing parametric data also improves the diagnostic value of the data, and when known, they should probably be used.

CONCLUSIONS

Ward's method, when used with the parametric data

generated by the SEM-XRF, clearly provides information about provenance and manufacturing materials. The accuracy of the clustering using squared Euclidean distances with Ward's method was still not perfect, and preliminary results indicate Ward's method applied to correlation coefficients calculated from normalized data based on analytical uncertainties may provide the best results. We intend to pursue this line of research, as well as incorporating information from X-ray diffraction to see if even more accurate analyses can be made nondestructively.

ACKNOWLEDGEMENTS

We would like to thank Fred Lange (University of Colorado, Boulder) and Bruce Bradley (Crow Canyon Archaeological Center, Cortez, CO) for the loan of the sherds from their museums. We would also like to thank Larry Lockrem for measuring the X-ray diffraction patterns. This work was supported in part by a grant from the Pew Memorial Trust.

REFERENCES

Ambler, R., (1977). The Anasazi, Museum of Northern Arizona: 31-43.

Bower, N., Bromund, R., and Smith, R. (1974). Atomic absorption for the archaeologist: an application to pottery from Pella of the Decapolis, Field Archaeology, 2: 389-398.

Bower, N., Faciszewski, S., Renwick, S. and Peckham, S. (1986). A preliminary analysis of Rio Grande Glazes of the Classic period using scanning electron microscopy with X-ray fluorescence, Journal of Field Archaeology, 13: 307-315.

Bromund, R., Bower, N., and Smith, R. (1976). Inclusions in ancient ceramics: an approach to the problem of sampling for chemical analysis, Archaeometry, 18: 218-221.

Hall, E., Schweitzer, F., and Toller, P. (1973). X-ray fluorescence analysis of museum objects: a new instrument, Archaeometry, 15: 53-78.

Romesburg, H. (1984). Cluster Analysis for Researchers, Belmont, CA: Lifetime Learning Publications (Wadsworth), 135 pp.

Ward, G. (1974). Comparison of source and artifact characterization data using a generalized distance measure, American Antiquity, 39: 473-477.

Zupan, J. (1982). Clustering of Large Data Sets, Chichester: Research Studies Press (Wiley and Sons), 25 pp.

38. Site Variation in Provenance Studies: The Carrara Marble Example

T. GILL[1], B. KUSKO[1], C. HIGGINS[2], S. HOWARD[3] and T. CAHILL[1]
[1]Crocker Nuclear Laboratory and Departments of [2]Geology and [3]Art, University of California, Davis, CA 95616, U.S.A.

ABSTRACT: *Mineralogical and elemental content of marbles from Carrara, Italy, varies within and between quarries, with different analytical techniques, and with the physical state of the sample.*

INTRODUCTION

The accurate determination of the provenance of classical marble artifacts has been one of the aims of archaeometry since at least the previous century (Washington 1898). Identification of the stone used in an object (by district or ideally an individual quarry) could be used as a tool in the detection of fakes, reassembly of fragmented works, and assignment of origin to unattributed sculptures. Many scientific techniques (petrological, isotopic, elemental, etc.) have been used to attempt attribution of provenance of marble specimens, with varying results (Howard et al. 1984).

The Carrara (Luna) quarries were among the most active marble localities of the classical period in the Roman region. These quarries were opened during the first century A.D., and produced stone prevalent in Roman architecture for approximately a century (Dworakowska 1983). The Carrara marbles are of Jurassic age, massive in appearance, and vary in colour from nearly pure white to grey. Although much of the grey colour in Carrara marbles may owe to variations in carbon content, the wide range in their appearance may accompany a range in accessory elements. Elemental and petrological studies of marble from this area have been performed by Luck et al. (1973), Bratter et al. (1975), Conforto et al. (1975), and Lazzarini et al. (1980).

METHODS

Marble samples, approximately 10 cubic centimetres in size, were obtained from exposed surfaces on the first level of the Fantiscritti quarry. Samples 1 through 8 were obtained 70 cm apart along the near-horizontal bedding of the original sediment, while Samples A through H were taken 35 cm apart along a vertical transect perpendicular to the bedding located directly below Sample 7. Polished sections were prepared from each specimen. Additional samples were obtained from quarries in the Colonnata region, Carrara district, as follows: Samples 1,2,3 from Bedziano; Samples 4,5 from La Piana Quarry; Samples 6,7,8,17,18 from Lorenzi Quarry; Sample 9 from Centro Calagio Colonnata Quarry; and Samples 10,11,12, and 13 from Colonnata Quarry.

Each sample was scrutinized carefully with a hand lens, and polished sections were analyzed under a petrographic microscope. The properties investigated were patterned after those discerned by Lazzarini et al. (1980) for Italian, Greek and Turkish marbles. The polished sections were analyzed for mineralogy by X-ray diffraction (XRD). Two of the polished sections were analyzed by energy-dispersive X-ray analysis (EDAX) with an electron microprobe; seven (Specimen 2) or nine (Specimen 4) spots approximately 150 μm in size per sample were analyzed. Sixteen of the polished sections were analyzed by X-ray fluorescence (XRF). All samples (bulk specimens and polished sections, from Fantiscritti quarry and Colonnata quarries) were also analyzed by external beam proton-induced X-ray emission (PIXE proton milliprobe). A summary of the instruments and analytical conditions used in this study is given in Table 1.

RESULTS AND DISCUSSION

The petrology of the Carrara samples is summarized in Table 1 of the Appendix. The Fantiscritti samples show some variability in their characteristics across the quarry face. The groundmass colour varies from white to medium grey, with bands or streaks of buff, orange and salmon. Specks of dark minerals occur in varying quantities within the groundmass. These minerals include graphite and/or mafic species; tiny graphite crystals may be the cause of greyish colour in some marble. Lazzarini et al. (1980) describe both categories of minerals as present in samples from Fantiscritti.

The shape and texture of the $CaCO_3$ grains can be a characteristic of marbles from a particular metamorphic belt and often varies between marble districts, indicating the amount and extent of regional metamorphism.

Textural characteristics can be a useful adjunct to elemental and isotopic techniques in marble "fingerprinting". These samples show the pronounced polygonal grain shape which is characteristic of Carrara marbles (Lazzarini et al. 1980). The samples all show textures which are indicative of recrystallization, some being highly recrystallized during metamorphism. However, the grain size of the Fantiscritti samples is consistently smaller than Lazzarini et al. (1980) reported (generally 0.3 - 0.6 mm as opposed to 1.0 - 1.3 mm). Grain boundaries of the Carrara marbles are straight or curved, as opposed to sutured or embayed (characteristic of some marbles from other districts).

XRD was used to determine the presence of major mineral phases in the samples. Dolomite, $CaMg(CO_3)_2$, is a particularly common component of most carbonate rock deposits. Some marble is predominantly dolomite, while other deposits contain only trace quantities of this mineral. In the Fantiscritti examples, most of the specimens taken along the bedding plane (numbered samples) showed resolvable dolomite, while none of the samples taken perpendicular to the bedding plane showed its presence.

Table 1. Summary of analytical techniques and conditions.

TECHNIQUE	INSTRUMENT	SAMPLES ANALYZED	ANALYTICAL CONDITIONS & TIMES
XRD (X-ray diffraction)	Diano XRD-8000 diffractometer	16 polished sections, Fantiscritti	Cu K-alpha radiation filtered through graphite monochrometer, specimens rotated at 2°/ minute through angles of 4° to 65°
XRF (X-ray flourescence)	Kevex 7800 XRF spectrometer	16 polished sections, Fantiscritti	Ag secondary target at 20 eV/ch. to detect Rb,Sr,Y,Zr,Nb,Pb,Th Ge secondary target at 10 eV/ch. to detect K,Ca,Ti,Mn and Fe Cl secondary target at 10 eV/ch. (direct excitation) to detect Na,Mg,Al,Si and P: not on samples 5,6 and 7. Acquisition time 5 minutes/sample.
PIXE (Proton-induced X-ray emission)	UC Davis 76-inch isochronous cyclotron, external beam	16 polished sections and 16 bulk chips, Fantiscritti: 16 bulk samples, Colonnata region	4.5 MeV proton beam filtered with 147 mg/cm^2 polyethylene detector filter; Acquisition time 2 minutes/ sample.

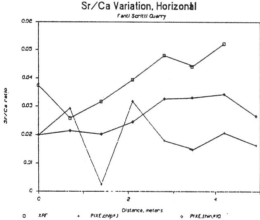

Figure 1.

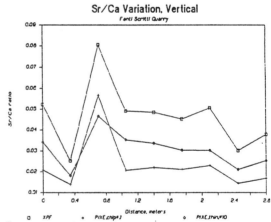

Figure 2.

Magnesium occurs in marble not only as dolomite, but also by substituting for calcium in the calcite lattice structure. This substitution changes the orientation of the crystal planes and causes a progressive shift in the XRD d-spacings. This phenomenon has been quantified by Chave (1952), Goldsmith and Graf (1958), and St. Arnaud and Herbillon (1973). The change in d-spacings was calculated for the Fantiscritti samples by calibrating them to a pure calcite standard. The results are summarized in Table 2 of the Appendix. Due to limitations in diffractometer accuracy, only approximate results were obtained; they imply that the Mg/Ca ratio in calcite varies by almost an order of magnitude, and that there is no direct relationship between the Mg content of the calcite and the presence of dolomite in a given sample.

The results of X-ray spectrometric analysis (by XRF and PIXE) of Carrara marble are summarized in Table 3 of the Appendix. The elements found most often in addition to Ca were Sr, Mn, and Fe. These elements all can substitute for Ca in the $CaCO_3$ crystal lattice; Mn and Fe also occur in accessory minerals. Sr was present in every sample analyzed by both methods; this element has often been used as a tool in the elemental attribution of marble provenance, taken as a ratio to Ca. The elemental ratios across the Fantiscritti transects are illustrated in Figures 1 and 2. The ratios to Ca of these elements obtained in the Colonatta samples are, however, consistently and significantly lower than those at Fantiscritti.

There appears to be a systematic relation between the values obtained for the three cases (XRF and PIXE of polished sections and PIXE of bulk samples); in general, the ratio of an element to calcium for polished sections is an order of magnitude greater for PIXE than XRF, and the elemental ratio for PIXE (bulk sample) is an order of magnitude higher than XRF (polished section). This variation appears to be caused by the differential response

Table 2. Elements found in Carrara marble samples.

FANTISCRITTI QUARRY

Sample #	Method	Elements Found, Ranking
1	XRF	Ca>Sr
	PIXE, bulk sample	Ca>Fe>Sr>Mn>Zn>Hg>Rb>Ti
	PIXE, polished section	Ca>Sr>Fe>Cr>Mn
2	XRF	Ca>Sr>Fe>Nb>Th
	PIXE, bulk sample	Ca>Sr>Fe>Mn>Cr>Pb>Zn
	PIXE, polished section	Ca>Sr>Fe>Mn>Cr
3	XRF	Ca>Sr>Fe>Nb>Th
	PIXE, bulk sample	Ca>Sr>Fe>Mn>Rb>Zn
	PIXE, polished section	Ca>Fe>Sr>Mn>Cr>Hg>Cu
4	XRF	Ca>Sr>Fe>Th
	PIXE, bulk sample	Ca>Sr>Fe>Mn>Zn>Pb>V
	PIXE, polished section	Ca>Sr>Fe>Pb>Mn>Cr>Zn
5	XRF	Ca>Sr>Fe
	PIXE, bulk sample	Ca>Sr>Fe>Mn>Cr>Zn
	PIXE, polished section	Ca>Sr>Fe>Cr
6	XRF	Ca>Sr>Fe
	PIXE, bulk sample	Ca>Sr>Fe>Mn
	PIXE, polished section	Ca>Sr>Fe>Cr>Mn>Zn
7	XRF	Ca>Sr
	PIXE, bulk sample	Ca>Sr>Fe>V
	PIXE, polished section	Ca>Sr>Fe>Cr>Mn>Zn
8	XRF	(N/A)
	PIXE, bulk sample	Ca>Sr>Fe>Cr>Mn>Zn
	PIXE, polished section	Ca>Sr>Fe>Cr>Mn
A	XRF	Ca>Sr>Y>Nb>Th
	PIXE, bulk sample	Ca>Sr>Cr>Mn>Fe
	PIXE, polished section	Ca>Sr>Cr>Mn>Fe>Ni
B	XRF	Ca>Sr>Nb>Mn>Th
	PIXE, bulk sample	Ca>Sr>Fe>Cr>Zn
	PIXE, polished section	Ca>Sr>Fe
C	XRF	Ca>Sr>Nb
	PIXE, bulk sample	Ca>Sr>Mn>Fe>Zn
	PIXE, polished section	Ca>Sr>Mn>Fe
D	XRF	Ca>Sr>Nb>Th
	PIXE, bulk sample	Ca>Sr>Fe>Mn>Cr>Zn
	PIXE, polished section	Ca>Sr>Fe>Mn>V>Cr

(Continued on next page)

212

```
FANTISCRITTI QUARRY
Sample #  Method                        Elements Found, Ranking

E         XRF                           Ca>Sr>Nb
          PIXE, bulk sample             Ca>Sr>Fe>Cr>Zn
          PIXE, polished section        Ca>Sr>Mn>Cr>Fe

F         XRF                           Ca>Sr>Nb>Mn>Th
          PIXE, bulk sample             Ca>Sr>Fe>Cr>Mn>Zn
          PIXE, polished section        Ca>Sr>Mn>Fe>Cr

G         XRF                           Ca>Sr>Fe
          PIXE, bulk sample             Ca>Sr>Fe>Cr>Zn
          PIXE, polished section        Ca>Sr>Fe>Cr>Mn


COLONNATA QUARRIES -
RESULTS FROM PIXE OF BULK SAMPLE.
Sample #            Elements Found, Ranking

1                  Ca>Sr>Fe>Pb>Mn>Zn
2                  Ca>Sr>Fe
3                  Ca>Sr>Fe>Pb>Mn
4                  Ca>Fe>Sr>Mn>Cr>Zn
5                  Ca>Sr>Fe>Mn>Zn
6                  Ca>Sr>Fe>Cr
7                  Ca>Fe>Sr>Mn
8                  Ca>Sr>Fe>Pb>Cr>Zn
9                  Ca>Fe>Sr>Cr>Zn
10                 Ca>Sr>Fe>Mn>Cr>Zn>V
11                 Ca>Fe>Sr>Pb>Mn>Cr>Zn
12                 Ca>Sr>Fe>Pb>Mn>Cr>Zn
13                 Ca>Fe>Sr>Mn>Cr>Zn
17,Whitish         Ca>Sr>Fe
17,Grayish         Ca>Fe>Sr>Zn>Mn>Cr>V>Ti
18                 Ca>Fe>Sr>Mn>Cr>V>Rb
```

Table 3. Sr/Ca ratios for Carrara marble specimens.

	XRF	FANTISCRITTI PIXE, polished	PIXE, bulk	COLONNATA PIXE, bulk
(Sr/Ca)	.043	.003	.193	.054
Standard Deviation	.013	.001	.113	.020

of the spectrometric methods to the dominant Ca X-rays. Most geochemical data indicate that the Sr/Ca ratio for calcite is on the order of 0.001 to 0.01; therefore, PIXE of the polished section, which provides a uniform unweathered surface to the proton beam, comes closest to the magnitude of the "true" value. The presence of accessory minerals distorts some trace-element concentrations in the sample; Mn and Fe ratios to Ca are poorly correlated because of the contamination effect of mafic minerals in the samples. The spectrometric method cannot separate the accessory grains from the $CaCO_3$ matrix, so it is not known how much of these elements occurs in the marble itself.

Somewhat surprisingly, the variation of elemental ratios across the quarry face perpendicular to the bedding is significantly more consistent than the ratio of the samples taken within the individual stratum. Though the transect perpendicular to the bedding plane is more consistent in terms of elemental ratios and extent of recrystallization, the transect along the bedding more consistently contains dolomite. This indicates the possibility of having located an aberrant overturned, folded stratum within a generally dolomite-bearing zone.

Table 2 summarizes the elements found in all samples by all techniques, as well as their rankings by relative abundance. While the PIXE method and RACE data reduction code (Harrison and Eldred 1973) allows the detection of all elements above atomic number 14 (Si), the XRF technique and data reduction code was only capable of detecting an incomplete set of elements. With this in mind, the same elements are generally observed in the same rankings for XRF, polished section PIXE, and bulk specimen PIXE. In general, limits of detection for most elements are higher with XRF, but some elements (Y, Nb, Th) were discerned only by XRF. There is only limited consistency in the detection and ranking of elements by PIXE between bulk samples and polished sections. There is no systematic variation for either sample type in terms of detection or relative ranking of any specific element.

The detection and concentration of Ti, Cr, Ni, Cu, Zn, Rb, Y, Nb, Pb and Th between the quarries and within the Fantiscritti quarry varied widely, even in adjacent samples in the same bedding plane. In general, the same elements in the same rankings were detected in samples from the Colonnata quarries and the Fantiscritti quarry. Zn was present in most samples from throughout the region; this could indicate that sphalerite is one of the accessory minerals present (Leoni and Orlandi 1975).

The only clearly useful and possibly determinative elemental ratio for the Carrara marble is Sr/Ca. This ratio (Table 3) is fairly consistent for the entire suite of samples for all analytical methods, most consistently by XRF. The other elemental ratios all have standard deviations of equal or greater magnitudes themselves. The Sr/Ca ratios from PIXE for the Colonnata samples are approximately 1/4 of the values obtained by PIXE at Fantiscritti quarry, and roughly equivalent to ratios from XRF at the latter site.

The results of the electron microprobe analyses of two of the Fantiscritti samples are given in Table 4 of the Appendix. Since the electron beam only analyzes a tiny fraction of the sample at a given time, it is not useful for the bulk characterization of an individual sample, much less an entire quarry or region. This technique is generally useful only for detecting elements lighter than Fe, so it is of limited use for detecting many of the important trace elements. This technique is useful for investigating the small-scale variation of light elements across the surface of a polished section, mapping Mg/Ca ratios, and indirectly mapping the distribution of accessory rock-forming minerals across the sample. For example, the data implies that Mg/Ca ratios occur as two distinct forms; on the order of several percent magnesium as low-Mg calcite, and as tens of percent magnesium in high-Mg calcite and/or dolomite.

CONCLUSIONS

We have shown that a suite of Carrara marble specimens shows wide variation with respect to the presence, concentrations, and ratios of elements in individual samples. The most consistent parameter is the Sr/Ca ratio. The petrological properties of the specimens also vary. These variabilities occur not only between quarries in the region, but also between adjacent specimens within an individual quarry. Similar analytical techniques (XRF, PIXE) may provide different results for the same samples, and different results may be obtained for a given specimen and method with different sample preparation techniques.

Elemental and petrological analysis is a demonstrably useful tool in provenance determination of classical marble. However, the researcher must be wary of attributing provenance based on these techniques alone. Differences in analytical techniques and variations in rock chemistry within and between individual sites must be carefully considered, or misleading results may be produced. The most reliable determinations of marble provenance will be made by combining both petrological and elemental analysis with other techniques (i.e., isotopic ratios), to find a unique set of parameters which describes the marble of a given region.

ACKNOWLEDGEMENTS

Some samples were obtained with the help of M. Franzini and L. Leoni, University of Pisa. We thank L. Whitting, Department of Land, Air and Water Resources, and P. Schiffman and S. Margolis, Department of Geology, all at the University of California, Davis, for access to their laboratory facilities and useful discussions. This project has been funded in part through a UC Davis Faculty Research Grant, a UC Davis Instructional Improvement Grant, and the MacArthur Foundation.

REFERENCES

Bratter, P., J. Lausch and U. Rosick, (1975). Neutronen aktivierungsanalytische Multielementbestimmung in Carrara-Marmor und Kalksteinstandard KH. Z. Anal Chem. 275: 359-363.

Chave, K.E. (1952). A solid solution between calcite and dolomite. J. Geol. 60: 190-192.

Conforto, L., M. Felici, D. Monna, L. Serva and A. Taddeucci, (1975). A preliminary evaluation of chemical data (trace element) from classical marble quarries in the Mediterranean. Archaeometry, 17: 201-213.

Dworakowska, A. (1983). Quarries in Roman provinces. Polska Akademika Nauk Bibliotheca Antiqua. 16: 205 pp.

Goldsmith, J.R., and D.L. Graf (1958). Relation between lattice constants and composition of the Ca-Mg carbonates. Amer. Mineral. 43: 84-101.

Harrison, J.F., and R.A. Eldred. (1973). Automatic data acquisition and reduction for elemental analysis of aerosol samples. Adv. in X-Ray Anal. 17: 560- 570.

Howard, S., T.A. Cahill, N. Herz, C. Higgins, E. Kinmonth and B.H. Kusko (1984). Computer-assisted accelerator-based methods of determining the provenance of ancient marbles. In: Corti, L., ed., Automatic Processing of Art History Data and Documents, Pisa, Italy, Regione Toscana: 258- 271.

Lazzarini, L., G. Moschini and B.M. Stievano (1980). A contribution to the identification of Italian, Greek and Anatolian marbles through a petrological study and the evaluation of Ca/Sr ratio. Archaeometry, 22: 173- 183.

Leoni, L., and P. Orlandi (1975). Sphalerite in marbles from Carrara (Apuan Alps). Rend. Soc. Ital. Mineral. Petrol. 31: 65- 71.

Luck, J., P. Moller and W. Szacki, (1973). Massenspektromische Multielementanalyse von Carrara-Marmor. Z. Anal Chem. 267: 279-298.

St. Arnaud, R.J., and A.J. Herbillon (1973). Occurrence and genesis of secondary magnesium-bearing carbonates in soils. Geoderma, 9: 279- 298.

Washington, H.S. (1898). The identification of the marble used in Greek sculpture. Amer. J. Archaeol. 2: 1- 18.

APPENDIX PETROLOGICAL DATA ON CARRARA MARBLE SAMPLES

Ho= Homeoblastic

He= Heteroblastic

Table 1.   FANTI SCRITTI QUARRY

Sample #	Groundmass Color (Munsell)	Major Accessory Minerals (seen on XRD)	Grain Size (mm)	Grain Boundary Shape	Texture	Grain Shape	Apparent Recrystallization
1	9	-----	.3-.4	Mostly Curved	Ho	Polygonal	High
2	11	Dolomite	.7-.8	Straight to Curved	He	Polygonal	Some
3	12	Dolomite	.4-.8	Straight to Curved	Ho	Polygonal	Some
4	10	Dolomite	.4-.5	Mostly Curved	He	Polygonal	Some
5	9	-----	.3-.4	Straight to Curved	Ho	Polygonal	Some
6	10	Dolomite	.2-.3	Straight to Curved	Ho	Polygonal	Some
7	11	Dolomite	.3-1.0	Straight to Curved	He	Polygonal	Some
8	11	-----	.2-.3	Straight to Curved	Ho	Polygonal	Some
A	7	-----	.5-.9	Straight to Curved	Ho	Polygonal	High
B	12	-----	.3-.4	Mostly Curved	Ho	Polygonal	High
C	9	-----	.4-.5	Straight to Curved	Ho	Polygonal	High
D	10	-----	.5-.8	Straight to Curved	He	Polygonal	High
E	7	-----	.4-1.2	Mostly Curved	He	Polygonal	High
F	8	-----	.3-.6	Straight to Curved	Ho	Polygonal	High
G	12	-----	.2-1.2	Straight to Curved	He	Polygonal	High
H	10	-----	.3-.4	Straight to Curved	Ho	Polygonal	High

COLONNATA QUARRY

Sample #	Groundmass Color (Munsell)	Color & Texture (Descriptive)	Average Grain Size (mm)	Texture	Grain Shape	Apparent Recrystallization	Grain Boundary Shape
1	5	White, massive	.5	Ho	Polygonal	Slight	Mostly Straight
2	6	Pale grayish white, massive	.4	Ho	Polygonal	Some	Straight to Curved
3	8	Pale whitish gray, massive	.4	Ho	Polygonal	Some	Mostly Straight
4	6	Creamy white, massive	.4	Ho	Polygonal	Some	Mostly Straight
5	6	Creamy white, massive	.4	Ho	Polygonal	Some	Straight to Curved
6	5	White, massive	.4	Ho	Polygonal	Some	Straight to Curved
7	7	Grayish white, granular	.6	Ho	Polygonal	Some	Mostly Curved
8	11	Light gray, massive	.3	Ho	Polygonal	Some	Straight to Curved
9	6	Chalky white, massive	.5	Ho	Polygonal	Some	Straight to Curved
10	4	Brilliant white, massive	.5- crypto.	He	Polygonal	High	Straight to Curved
11	5	White, massive	.5	Ho	Polygonal	Some	Mostly Straight
12	12	Gray, massive to granular	.7- crypto.	He	Polygonal	High	Straight to Curved
13	14	Dark gray, massive	.3	Ho	Polygonal	Some	Straight to Curved
17	6	Creamy white, granular	.6	Ho	Polygonal	Some	Straight to Curved
18	18	Black	NA	NA	NA	NA	NA

215

Table 2. X-ray diffraction results of Fantiscritti quarry samples, Carrara marble.

Sample #	Major Accessory Minerals (seen on XRD)	Position of Calcite Strongest Reflection (degrees, with Cu K-alpha radiation)	Corresponding D-Spacing (Angstroms)	Change in D-spacing from Pure Calcite (Angstroms)	Corresponding Inferred Mole % Mg Carbonate	Ratio of Dolomite to Calcite (on 104 reflection used at left)
1	----	29.7	3.005	0.03	10-12%	NA
2	Dolomite	29.6	3.015	0.02	6-8%	0.057692
3	Dolomite	29.6	3.015	0.02	6-8%	0.128571
4	Dolomite	29.7	3.005	0.03	10-12%	0.142857
5	----	29.7	3.005	0.03	10-12%	0.097222
6	Dolomite	29.7	3.005	0.03	10-12%	0.133333
7	Dolomite	29.6	3.015	0.02	6-8%	0.04
8	----	29.7	3.005	0.03	10-12%	NA
A	----	29.5	3.025	0.01	2-4%	NA
B	----	29.6	3.015	0.02	6-8%	NA
C	----	29.5	3.025	0.01	2-4%	NA
D	----	29.7	3.005	0.03	10-12%	NA
E	----	29.8	2.995	0.04	14-16%	NA
F	----	29.9	2.985	0.05	18-20%	NA
G	----	29.9	2.985	0.05	18-20%	NA
H	----	29.4	3.035	0	0%	NA
X1	Dolomite	29.7	3.005	0.03	10-12%	0.09375
X2	Dolomite	29.9	2.985	0.05	18-20%	0.206896
X3	Dolomite, Feldspar	29.7	3.005	0.03	10-12%	0.098591

Table 3. XRF and PIXE analyses for marble samples from the Fantiscritti and Colonnata Quarries.

Elemental Data for Marble Samples   Values in nanograms/cm^2

× = Not Detected
FANTISCRITTI

SAMPLE	Ca	Sr	Fe	Mn	Cr	Zn	Pb	Cu	V	Rb	Ti	Y	Nb	Th	Other
1, XRF	1478	55.93	×	×	×	×	×	×	×	×	×	×	×	×	×
PIXE, chip	39.1	7.78	13.45	0.611	×	0.395	×	×	×	0.269	0.088	×	×	×	×
PIXE, thin	20300	40.6	7.86	2.81	4.64	×	×	×	×	×	×	×	×	×	×
2, XRF	1353	35.01	11.14	0.85	×	×	×	×	×	×	×	×	0.1456	×	×
PIXE, chip	45.36	13.28	7.06	0.429	0.292	0.126	0.265	×	×	×	×	×	×	×	×
PIXE, thin	16100	34.6	24.3	2.91	1.81	×	×	×	×	×	×	×	×	×	×
3, XRF	1522	48.11	10.56	×	×	×	×	×	×	×	×	×	0.3333	0.0361	×
PIXE, chip	47.5	11.18	7.82	0.687	×	0.126	×	×	×	0.212	×	×	×	×	×
PIXE, thin	18500	37.5	38.6	2.92	0.98	×	×	0.09	×	×	×	×	×	×	×
4, XRF	1301	51.35	12.75	×	××	×	×	×	×	×	×	×	×	0.0123	×
PIXE, chip	42.06	13.37	1.84	0.575	×	0.341	0.28	×	0.041	×	×	×	×	×	×
PIXE, thin	18000	44.3	34.5	2.05	1.74	0.29	2.65	×	×	×	×	×	×	×	×
5, XRF	1681	80.88	2.08	×	×	×	×	×	×	×	×	×	×	×	×
PIXE, chip	56.1	10.1	3.71	4.64	×	×	×	×	×	×	×	×	×	×	×
PIXE, thin	17000	55.4	12.5	2.68	1.54	×	×	×	×	×	×	×	×	×	×
6, XRF	1952	86.1	7.097	×	×	×	×	×	×	×	×	×	×	×	×
PIXE, chip	44.2	6.52	3.71	0.464	×	×	×	×	×	×	×	×	×	×	×
PIXE, thin	17500	57.8	17.7	1.74	2.74	0.067	×	×	×	×	×	×	×	×	×
7, XRF	1921	100.21	×	×	×	×	×	×	×	×	×	×	×	×	×
PIXE, chip	58	12.05	1.21	×	×	×	×	×	0.233	×	×	×	×	×	×
PIXE, thin	21700	74.2	5.7	3.78	2.65	×	×	×	×	×	×	×	×	×	×
8, XRF	(N/A)	(N/A)	(N/A)	(N/A)	(N/A)	(N/A)	(N/A)	(N/A)	(N/A)	(N/A)	(N/A)	(N/A)	(N/A)	(N/A)	(N/A)
PIXE, chip	48.7	7.99	2.21	0.395	0.427	0.032	×	×	×	×	×	×	×	×	×
PIXE, thin	26400	70.2	20.5	2.97	8.07	×	×	×	×	×	×	×	×	×	×
A, XRF	1420	35.94	×	×	×	×	×	×	×	×	×	×	0.2666	0.1467	0.03	×
PIXE, chip	31.8	4.41	0.207	0.282	0.335	×	×	×	×	×	×	×	×	×	×
PIXE, thin	15500	28.2	1.92	1.96	4.8	×	×	×	×	×	×	×	×	×	× Ni .166
B, XRF	1634	131.55	×	0.0542	×	×	×	×	×	×	×	×	0.2833	0.0356	×
PIXE, chip	41.57	23.51	64.5	×	0.361	0.073	×	×	×	×	×	×	×	×	×
PIXE, thin	12400	57.8	2.45	×	×	×	×	×	×	×	×	×	×	×	×
C, XRF	1302	63.9	×	×	×	×	×	×	×	×	×	×	0.0267	×	×
PIXE, chip	50.1	10.4	0.321	0.528	×	0.098	×	×	×	×	×	×	×	×	×
PIXE, thin	5900	20.8	0.52	1.72	×	×	×	×	×	×	×	×	×	×	×
D, XRF	699	33.85	×	×	×	×	×	×	×	×	×	×	0.8033	0.66	×
PIXE, chip	34.8	7.67	0.523	0.325	0.208	0.016	×	×	×	×	×	×	×	×	×
PIXE, thin	602	2.03	0.33	0.32	0.18	×	×	×	0.23	×	×	×	×	×	×
E, XRF	1676	75.89	×	×	×	×	×	×	×	×	×	×	0.5433	×	×
PIXE, chip	22.8	4.82	0.155	×	0.119	0.027	×	×	×	×	×	×	×	×	×
PIXE, thin	10400	31.6	0.94	2.99	2.38	×	×	×	×	×	×	×	×	×	×
F, XRF	1368	69.14	×	0.0306	×	×	×	×	×	×	×	×	0.25	0.0538	×
PIXE, chip	49.6	11.4	0.521	0.37	0.343	0.281	×	×	×	×	×	×	×	×	×
PIXE, thin	14700	44.6	2.68	3.86	1	×	×	×	×	×	×	×	×	×	×
G, XRF	1012	30.65	1.616	×	×	×	×	×	×	×	×	×	×	×	×
PIXE, chip	48.2	6.95	3.05	×	0.277	0.04	×	×	×	×	×	×	×	×	×
PIXE, thin	15900	33.4	17.6	2.41	2.65	×	×	×	×	×	×	×	×	×	×
H, XRF	1223	46.33	×	×	×	×	×	×	×	×	×	×	0.7367	×	×
PIXE, chip	45.1	7.57	0.539	×	0.448	0.025	×	×	×	×	×	×	×	×	×
PIXE, thin	25200	64	5.57	6.86	4.01	0.072	×	×	×	×	×	×	×	×	×

———COLONNATA QUARRY SAMPLES, PIXE ANALYSIS OF CHIP ———

Sample	Ca	Sr	Fe	Mn	Cr	Zn	Hg	Pb	Cu	V	Rb	Ti
1	34.51	3.03	1.15	0.343	×	0.081	×	0.37	×	×	×	×
2	65	4.1	1.53	×	×	×	×	×	×	×	×	×
3	52.8	2.96	1.74	0.5	×	×	×	0.957	×	×	×	×
4	40.9	2.57	4.31	0.244	0.094	0.092	×	×	×	×	×	×
5	49.4	3.07	1.14	0.567	×	0.051	×	×	×	×	×	×
6	23.2	1.11	0.682	×	0.098	×	×	×	×	×	×	×
7	31.3	1.3	1.41	0.353	×	×	×	×	×	×	×	×
8	33.4	1.69	0.84	×	0.184	0.078	×	0.689	×	×	×	×
9	28.8	1.25	1.37	×	0.198	0.053	×	×	×	×	×	×
10	17.6	0.894	0.726	0.19	0.04	0.03	×	×	×	0.023	×	×
11	24	1.34	2.05	0.144	0.088	0.054	×	0.31	×	×	×	×
12	68.3	3.6	2.44	0.501	0.365	0.029	×	0.46	×	×	×	×
13	58.6	4.01	5.24	0.831	0.159	0.029	×	×	×	×	×	×
17N	73.5	3.48	0.67	×	×	×	×	×	×	×	×	×
17G	33.1	1.52	16.9	0.202	0.114	0.3	×	×	×	0.04	×	0.022
18B	56.5	6.32	8.83	0.375	0.188	×	×	×	×	×	0.037	Present	×

Table 3. contd. PIXE, bulk samples for Carrara marble, Fantiscritti and Colonnata quarries. Values in ppm.

Sample	Fe	Sr		Sample	Fe	Sr
Horizontal Transect				*Vertical Transect*		
1	39	50		A		47
2	131			B	5	224
3	51	83		C	5	69
4	366	65		D	7.1	63
5	31	89		E	4.4	64
6	119	61		F	26	80
7	24	81		G	59	65
8	103	68		H	7	70
Mean	108	71		Mean	16	85
Stnd Dev	112	14		Stnd Dev	20	57

Carrara Marble,   Colonnata

Location	Cr	Mn	Fe	Zn	Sr
Bedziano					
	4.9		11	0.5	16
		8	16		21
	3.9	6.4	18	0.8	18
La Piana					
	8.5	4.6	59	0.6	25
	3.4	4.6	24	0.5	23
Lorenzi					
	4.5		28	1	28
		8.5	53	1.1	22
	5.1		42		26
Centro Calagio, Colonnata					
	3.7	5.6	49	1.2	
Colonnata					
			16	0.5	14
		9.8	16	0.7	15
		12	68	1.4	22
	2.5	13	77	0.7	22
			12		14
	3.2		26		22
	4.1		20	2.2	19

Table 4. Electron microprobe analyses, counts/second (10 eV/ch, 100 sec acquisition time)

Spot	Mg	Al	Si	P	S	K	Ca	Ti	Fe
A	13.84	1.966	5.374	ND	ND	16.16	1065	ND	ND
B	12.82	ND	5.910	ND	ND	13.58	1072	.3000	ND
C	26.21	6.861	14.57	ND	ND	21.68	1040	ND	ND
D	27.47	1.348	9.632	.9400	ND	15.02	1053	ND	ND
E	174.2	15.61	33.71	ND	ND	10.51	793.5	ND	1.310
F	143.4	19.89	37.35	1.320	ND	17.09	680.5	ND	ND
G	180.3	46.70	93.40	ND	ND	35.05	725.2	ND	ND
H	106.2	30.50	62.81	ND	ND	29.28	869.6	ND	ND
I	14.14	1.320	9.455	ND	ND	19.66	1020	ND	ND
K	13.41	4.112	9.108	ND	ND	16.81	948.4	ND	ND
L	52.33	7.552	17.54	.4100	ND	19.55	999.0	ND	ND
M	208.3	141.15	36.32	ND	ND	13.06	662.5	ND	3.430
N	127.1	149.5	435.7	4.510	ND	134.0	528.7	1.210	ND
P	17.60	5.066	20.58	ND	ND	22.91	1035	ND	ND
Q	8.870	5.015	15.43	ND	ND	15.06	733.7	ND	ND
R	28.36	.8200	7.016	ND	.5800	16.27	1028	ND	ND

39. Chemical, Isotopic and Petrographic Characterization of Ancient White Marble Quarries

P. ROOS, L. MOENS and J. DE RUDDER
Institute for Nuclear Sciences, Rijksuniversiteit Gent
Proeftuinstraat 86, B-9000 Gent (Belgium).

P. DE PAEPE and J. VAN HENDE
Laboratory of Geology, Rijksuniversiteit Gent
Krijgslaan 281, B-9000 Gent (Belgium).

M. WAELKENS
Department of Archaeology, Katholieke University Leuven
Blijde Inkomststraat 21, B-3000 Leuven (Belgium).

ABSTRACT: *Petrographical and chemical analysis contribute substantially to the discrimination between white marbles from the major antique Mediterranean quarries. It is necessary to apply E.G. cluster analysis to the data in order to extract the discriminating information. The use of isotopic data further improves the discrimination.*

INTRODUCTION

In order to determine the provenance of marble artifacts, researchers have applied different types of techniques[1-8]. Each of these techniques turned out to be discriminative for some quarry districts but failed to separate each major district from all the others. This paper will try to demonstrate that a satisfactory solution can only be found when the results from the different techniques are combined. To realize this goal we have established an interdisciplinary project which enabled us to sample the major quarry sites in a systematic way and submit each sample to petrographic, chemical and isotopic analysis. The gathered information on the quarry samples forms a data base that will serve later as a reference for provenancing artifacts.

TECHNIQUES

Isotopic analysis yields information on the $^{13}C/^{12}C$ and the $^{18}O/^{16}O$ - ratios by analyzing gaseous CO_2 samples with mass spectrometry (MS). The gaseous samples can be obtained by dissolving 10 mg aliquots of $CaCO_3$ in 105% H_3PO_4.

As the other analytical techniques were already described in previous papers[9,10,11], we will confine ourselves to a short description here. Petrographic data were obtained by microscopic study of thin sections. Chemical analysis was mainly performed using neutron activation analysis (NAA). For a few elements for which NAA was unsuited, we used atomic absorption spectroscopy (AAS). Both flame (for Mg) and electrothermal (for Al and V) AAS were used. Si was determined by colorimetry.

SAMPLING

The sampling is dealt with in detail in previous papers[10-13]. Only a short review will be given. Sampling was carried out in 3 successive campaigns at the locations indicated on the map represented in Figure 1. In the first campaign in Italy, 91 samples for the quarry district of Carrara were obtained. The second one, in Turkey, yielded 166 samples originating from 8 quarry districts. The last campaign concerned 9 Greek quarry districts and overall 194 samples were taken. Since in the majority of the major antique quarry sites calcite marble is found, coloured and grey hand specimens as well as specimens bearing more than 10% dolomite were not included in this study. Moreover, altered samples, occasionally collected to study the effect of weathering, were discarded and especially for Carrara a further selection was made to obtain a set of samples equally representative for the different subregions within the district.

RESULTS

In the present paper the results are shown for 8 quarry districts: Carrara (27 samples), Afyon (27 samples), Marmara (24 samples), Usak (16 samples), Pentelikon (24 samples), Paros (22 samples), Naxos (12 samples) and Thasos (22 samples). It should also be mentioned that until now only petrographical and chemical analysis were applied to the quarry material. Additional information on the isotopic signatures of the marble from the studied regions is obtained from literature[14].

Petrography

Petrographical characteristics such as mineral inclusions and grain-texture proved to be of little use in separating the 8 quarry districts[9,11,12]. However, the maximum grain size (MGS) of the calcite-grains has real discriminative power. The ranges for MGS together with their median are shown for all districts in Figure 2. Obviously, the MGS enables the investigator to distinguish some quarry districts from one another: e.g., Carrara can be separated from Marmara, Paros, Naxos, and Thasos, Marmara from Afyon, Pentelikon and Thasos, Pentelicon from Paros, Naxos and Thasos.

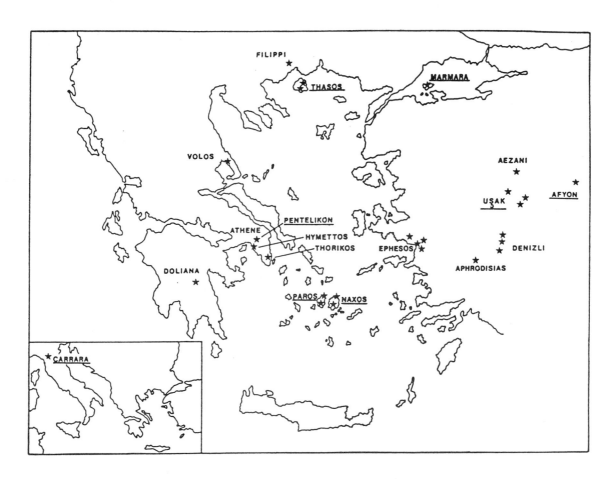

Figure 1. Map indicating the major ancient quarry districts sampled in this project. The underlined districts will be discussed here.

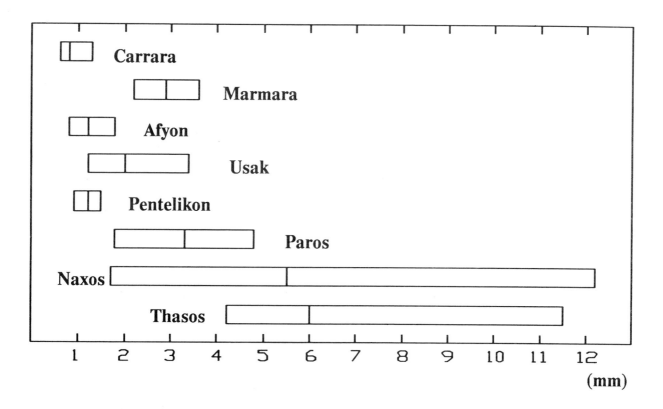

Figure 2. Range of the MGS for the 8 investigated quarry districts. Medians are indicated by vertical lines.

Chemical Data

Of the 30 elements that are currently determined by chemical analysis, 15 were found to be especially useful: Na, Mg, Al, K, Sc, Cr, V, Mn, Fe, Co, Sr, Zn, La, Th and U. For these elements, concentrations could be obtained in all samples and at no time were we forced to consider upper limits. An extra element, Hf, was included for the comparison of the Italian and Turkish quarry districts since in 15 Greek marble samples upper limits were found. It was found that elemental concentrations show a wide spread within each quarry and that their distribution can be described by a log-normal empiricism[11].

Inter-quarry Discrimination

The wide concentration ranges show a considerable overlap for the different districts. To extract the discriminating information hidden in the data set, mathematical techniques must be applied. In this work a pragmatic choice was made for cluster analysis, using the Euclidian distance as a dissimilarity measure and applying the Wards error sum clustering strategy. The applied program is part of the DPP[15] package. Because of their log-normal distribution, the logarithms of the concentrations were used to perform cluster analysis. As we want all samples of 1 district to group together after cluster analysis, we tried to compose, by trial and error, a set of attributes capable of doing so. As expected, no set of attributes was found to be discriminative for all districts. Therefore quarries were compared two-by-two, composing for each pair a set of attributes yielding the best possible separation. The results of cluster analysis can be represented as a dendrogram, a tree-like structure clearly showing the progressive grouping of the samples as well as the dissimilarity between samples and groups of samples. Since our investigation includes 8 districts, a set of attributes for each of the 28 two-by-two comparisons had to be found. Only a few comparisons will be shown in detail. The overall result is shown in Figure 3. In this figure each box contains the set of attributes that yields the best possible separation between the corresponding quarry pair. In addition it shows the total number of samples included in the cluster analysis (on the right hand side of the slash) and the number of samples that were misclassified (on the left). Three categories of comparisons can be distinguished.

In 15 out of 28 two-by-two comparisons the samples are correctly grouped in separated clusters. As an example for this group, a comparison between the districts of Carrara and Marmara is shown; K, Mn, Co, Hf and the MGS were used as attributes. From the dendrogram shown in Figure 4, it can be concluded that these parameters allow one to characterize both quarries. Moreover, the

	Carrara	Marmara	Afyon	Usak	Pentelikon	Paros	Naxos
Marmara	K, Mn, Co Hf, MGS. 0/51	**Marmara**					
Afyon	Na, Sc, Cr, Mn, Fe, Sr, U, MGS. 2/54	Cr, Mn, Co, Sr, U, MGS. 0/51	**Afyon**				
Usak	Na, K, Cr, Mn, U, MGS. 1/43	Co, U, MGS. 4/40	Cr, Mn, Sr, U, MGS. 1/43	**Usak**			
Pentelikon	Al, Cr, Mn, Fe, Co, MGS. 0/51	Mn, MGS. 0/48	Na, Al, Sc, V, Mn, Zn, Sr, La. 2/51	Mg, Al, Cr, Mn, Fe, Co, Zn, La, Th, U, MGS. 0/40	**Pentelikon**		
Paros	Mg, MGS. 0/49	Al, Mn. 6/46	Mn, MGS. 1/49		Mn, MGS. 0/46	**Paros**	
Naxos	K, MGS. 1/39	Al, Mn, MGS. 0/36	Sc, Cr, MGS. 1/39	Mn, MGS. 2/28	Mn, Fe, MGS. 0/36	Mn, Fe, MGS. 2/34	**Naxos**
Thasos	MGS. 0/49	MGS. 0/46	Mg, MGS. 0/49	Zn, MGS. 0/38	Mn, MGS. 0/46	Mn, MGS. 0/44	

Figure 3. Result of 28 two-by-two comparisons between the marble from 8 major quarry districts. The attributes selected for cluster analysis and the ratio of the number of misclassified samples to the total number of samples are indicated.

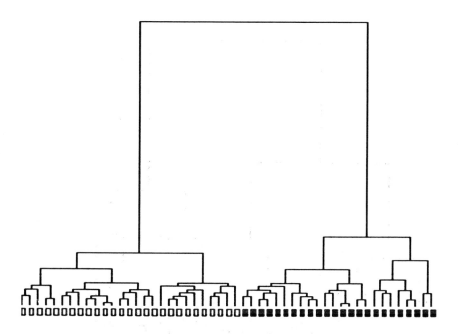

Figure 4. Classification-dendrogram (relative dissimilarity scale) obtained by hierarchical cluster analysis with K, Mn, Co, Hf and the MGS as attributes, including 27 samples from Carrara (open squares) and 24 samples from Marmara (black squares).

inter-quarry dissimilarity is very high compared to the within quarry dissimilarities.

In 9 two-by-two comparisons 1 (5 cases) or 2 (4 cases) samples are misclassified. As an example for this category Afyon is compared to Naxos using the elements Sc, Cr and the MGS as attributes. The dendrogram shown in Figure 5 is obtained. One group entirely consists of samples of the Afyon quarries. Any artifact classified by cluster analysis within this group is therefore very likely to originate from the Afyon district. Although no complete separation and an intra-quarry dissimilarity larger than in the first category is obtained, the separation is acceptable.

Finally, an unsatisfactory separation was found in 4 two-by-two comparisons. In Figure 6 the dendrogram of the Marmara - Paros comparison is presented. To separate the samples from these districts Al and Mn were used as attributes yielding a group that contains all samples from Marmara plus 6 samples from Paros and a pure Paros-group. Over 12% of the samples are misclassified. Comparison of Marmara and Usak based on the elements Co, U and MGS, results in a Marmara-group that contains 3 samples from Usak and a Usak-group that contains 1 sample from Marmara. For the 2 remaining comparisons, Usak with Paros and Naxos with Thasos, no discriminative set of attributes was found.

Isotopic Analysis

The previous results were obtained using only petrographical and chemical data. Recently, we started to do isotopic analysis on all our samples. These data will be available within a few months. For the time being we can rely on literature data (Herz[14]) to demonstrate the usefulness of this technique. The results of isotopic analysis are usually represented in a 2 dimensional scatterplot. To obtain these plots the $^{13}C/^{12}C$ and the $^{18}O/^{16}O$ - ratios for the sample are compared to those of a standard (PDB = Pee Dee Belemnite). The difference between the ratios of the standard and the sample, expressed in per mille, are plotted. In Figure 7 the literature data for the 8 investigated districts are shown. The fields are obtained by encircling all the data points from one quarry. In a manner similar to petrography and chemical analysis, widespread and numerous overlaps occur. So, isotopic analysis alone is not sufficient to separate all the quarry sites. Isotopic analysis however turned out to complement petrographical and chemical analysis. As mentioned above there are 4 comparisons yielding an unsatisfactory separation when only petrographical and chemical data are considered (see Figure 3). One of these cases concerns the marble from Usak and Paros. From Figure 8, showing the fields obtained by isotopic analysis for these 2 quarries, it is clear that isotopic analysis does separate both quarries. The same observation was made for 2 other comparisons: Usak with Paros and Naxos with Thasos. The complementarity also works the other way around. Figure 9 clearly shows that it is impossible to separate Pentelikon and Naxos using only isotopic data while petrographical and chemical data allow a complete separation (Figure 3). In only 1 of these 4 cases (comparison between Usak and Marmara) neither chemical plus petrographical analysis, nor isotopic signatures allow a complete separation (see Figures 3 and 7). It may not be likely that an archaeological question will ever be raised where an artifact has to be attributed to the quarries of either Marmara or Usak. However, from an analytical point of view separating Marmara from Usak is a problem which could be solved when isotopic, chemical and petrographical analysis are applied to the same samples and when the complete data base are subjected to cluster analysis.

CONCLUSIONS

It was shown that chemical plus petrographical analysis allows in many cases a clear separation to be made between the material from different major quarry sites of white marble used in antiquity. The discriminating power of this

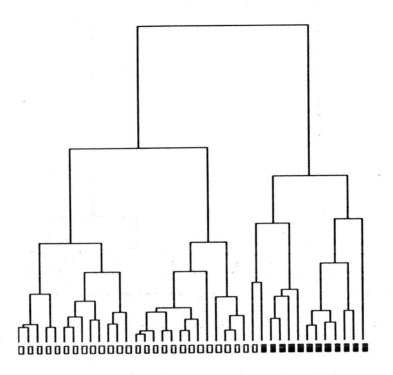

Figure 5. Classification-dendrogram (relative dissimilarity scale) obtained by hierarchical cluster analysis with Sc, Cr and the MGS as attributes, including 27 samples from Afyon (open squares) and 24 samples from Naxos (black squares).

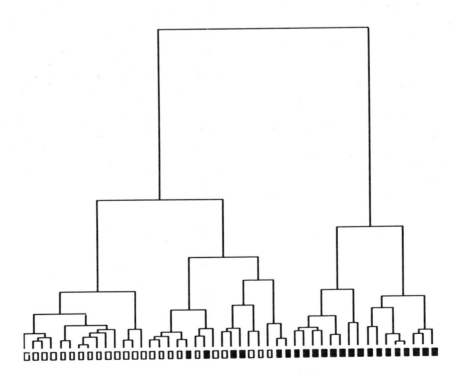

Figure 6. Classification-dendrogram (relative dissimilarity scale) obtained by hierarchical cluster analysis with Al and Mn as attributes, including 24 samples from Marmara (open squares) and 22 samples from Paros (black squares).

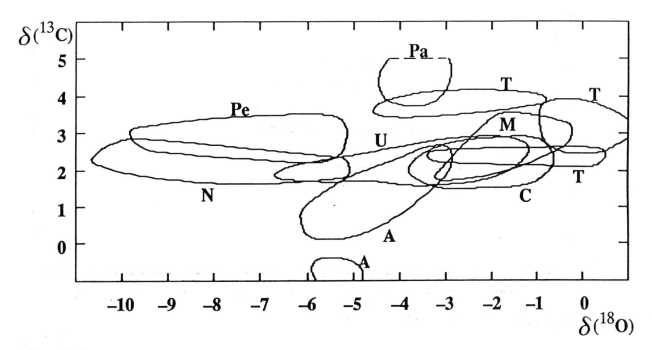

Figure 7. Isotopic signatures for the 8 investigated quarry districts: Carrara (C), Afyon (A), Marmara (M), Usak (U), Pentelikon (Pe), Paros (Pa), Naxos (N), Thasos (T) (Herz[14]).

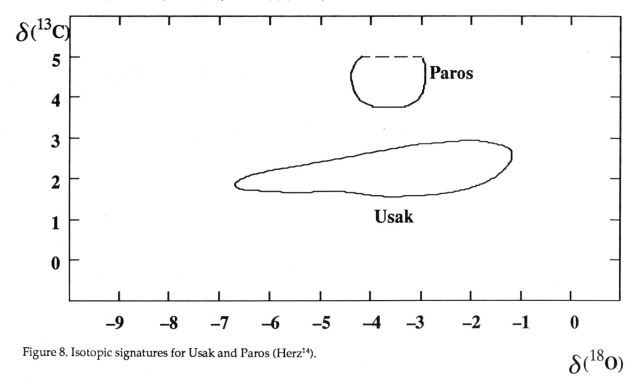

Figure 8. Isotopic signatures for Usak and Paros (Herz[14]).

approach only appears when applying appropriate mathematical procedures, such as cluster analysis, to the data base. Chemical and petrographic data are remarkably well complemented by isotopic signatures. Therefore, one can be reasonably confident that applying all three methods to the same samples and using e.g., cluster analysis to extract the discriminating information from the data base, will finally allow a successful inter-quarry separation and a clear provenance determination of artifacts.

To test the latter in practice, a few marble artifacts were analyzed using the three techniques. The results of this investigation are discussed in detail in a separate paper[16].

ACKNOWLEDGEMENTS

The authors are highly indebted to the National Fund for Scientific Research (NFWO), the Interuniversity Institute for Nuclear Science (IIKW) and the Fund for Collective Fundamental Research (FKFO) for their financial support that made this project possible. We also wish to thank authorities of Italy, Turkey and Greece for their cooperation during the sampling in the marble quarries.

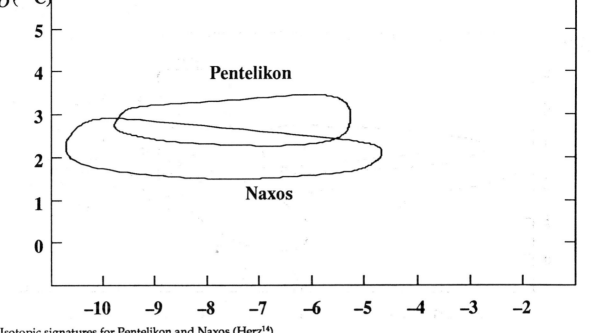

Figure 9. Isotopic signatures for Pentelikon and Naxos (Herz[14])

REFERENCES

1. Herz, N., Mose, D.G. and Wenner, D.B. (1982). $^{87}Sr/^{86}Sr$ - ratios: a possible discriminant for classical marble provenance. Geological Society of America, Abstracts with programs, 14: 514.
2. Conforto, L., Felici, M., Monna, D., Seva, L. and Taddeucci, A. (1975). A preliminary evaluation of chemical data (trace elements) from classical marble quarries in the Mediterranean. Archaeometry, 17 (2): 201-213.
3. Craig, H. and Craig, V. (1972). Greek marbles: determination of provenance by isotopic analysis, Science, 176: 401-403.
4. Renfrew, C. and Peacey, J.S. (1968). Aegean Marble: a petrological study. Annual of the British School at Athens, 63: 45-66.
5. Germann, K., Holzmann, G. and Winkler, F.J. (1980). Determination of marble provenance: limits of isotopic analysis. Archaeometry, 22: 99-106.
6. Cordischi, D., Monna, D. and Segre, A.L. (1983). ESR analysis of marble samples from Mediterranean quarries of archaeological interest. Archaeometry, 25: 33-41.
7. Lloyd, R.V., Smith, P.W. and Haskell, H.W. (1985). Evaluation of the manganese ESR method of marble characterization. Archaeometry, 27: 108-116.
8. Herz, N. (1985). Isotopic analysis of marble. In G. Rapp, Jr. and J.A. Gifford (Eds.), Archaeological geology, New Haven. Yale University Press.
9. Moens, L., Roos, P., De Rudder, J., Hoste, J., De Paepe, P., Van Hende, J., Maréchal, R. and Waelkens, M. (1986). White marble from Italy and Turkey: an archaeometric study based on minor- and trace element analysis and petrography. Journal of Radioanalytical and Nuclear Chemistry: 123, in press.
10. Moens, L., Roos, P., De Rudder, J., Hoste, J., De Paepe, P., Van Hende, J., Maréchal, R. and Waelkens, M. (1986). Chemical and petrographical identification of white marbles from the Mediterranean area I. Comparison between Carrara and Marmara marbles. Presented at the 25th symposium on Archaeometry, Athens (Greece), 19-23 May 1986. Archaeometry, in press.
11. Moens, L. Roos., P., De Rudder, J., De Paepe, P. and Waelkens, M. (1987). Identification of archaeologically interesting white marbles by instrumental neutron activation analysis (INAA) and petrography: comparison between samples from Afyon and Usak (Turkey). Journal of Trace and Microprobe Techniques. 5 (2&3): 101-114.
12. Roos, P., Moens, L., De Rudder, J., De Paepe P., Van Hende J. and Waelkens M. (1988). Chemical and petrographical characterization of Greek marble from Pentelikon, Naxos, Paros and Thasos. Presented at the NATO international scientific exchange programme: advanced research workshop: Marble in ancient Greece and Rome: geology, quarries, commerce, artifacts, Lucca (Italy), 9-13 May 1988, in press.
13. Moens L., De Rudder J., De Paepe P. and Waelkens J. (1986). Preparation of white marble samples for instrumental neutron activation analysis. Bulletin des Sociétés Chimiques Belges, 95: 399-406.
14. Herz, N., (1987). Carbon and oxygen isotopic ratios: a data base for classical Greek and Roman marble. Archaeometry, 29: 35-43.
15. Van Espen, P. (1984). A program for the processing of analytical data (DPP). Analytical Chimica Acta, 165: 31-49.
16. De Paepe, P., Moens, L., Roos, P. and Waelkens, M. (1988). Source analysis of the raw material of four classical marble sculptures using chemical, microscopic and isotopic criteria. Presented at the NATO international scientific exchange programme: advanced research workshop: Marble in ancient Greece and Rome: geology, quarries, commerce, artifacts, Lucca (Italy), 9-13 May 1988, in press.

40. Combined INAA, O, C, and Sr Isotopic Analyses in Determining the Provenance of Classical Marbles

M. J. M. DUKE

Department of Geology, University of Alberta, Edmonton, Alberta, Canada, T6G 2N8.

ABSTRACT: *Assigning a marble artifact a source solely on the basis of stable isotope data will often give erroneous results. The combined use of techniques (such as INAA, O, C, and Sr Isotopic analyses) will likely avoid such mistakes.*

INTRODUCTION

In 1981 the Department of Classics at the University of Alberta purchased a Roman sculpture of Antonia Minor for its collection. The history of the piece has not, however, been well established. Antonia Minor was a woman of historical importance being the daughter of Mark Antony and Octavia, niece of emperor Augustus, and mother, grandmother, and great grandmother of the emperors Claudius, Caligula, and Nero, respectively. The sculpture is made up of two main pieces - the head, a white but weathered marble, and the bust, a much yellower marble. The style of the bust dates it at about 165 - 175 A.D., while the head is tentatively dated at about 50 A.D. (A. Small, pers. comm.). Such reconstruction of broken or damaged classical works was common practice for the collections of the 18th and 17th century dilettanti.

A study to determine the provenance of the marbles used to fabricate the head and bust was initiated in part because of the similarity of the Albertan bust to one of Antonia Minor at the Fogg Museum, Harvard University (Herz and Wenner 1981). The similarity of the two interests classical scholars because of the implications it has on methods of production of such works, i.e., were they 'mass produced' from plans/casts, or are they unique, individual pieces?

Recent History of Marble Provenancing

Identifying the provenance of classical marbles utilized in buildings and artifacts has been of interest and proven problematical to the archaeologist for over a hundred years. The importance in being able to source marbles lies not only in the obvious ability to identify copies and forgeries of artifacts, but is of value in elucidating trade patterns between the various Greek states (and later the Roman Empire); and checking the reconstruction of stele. A number of techniques have been utilized for the purpose of identifying the source of marbles and have included, for example, thin-section petrography and elemental analysis (e.g., X-ray fluorescence (XRF), neutron activation analysis (NAA), and atomic absorption spectrometry (AAS), and X-ray diffraction (XRD)). Each of these approaches has proven successful, or at least helpful, in some cases. In many instances, however, the high purity of many of the marbles utilized by the ancient Greeks and Romans render marble colour, accessory mineral content, and XRD patterns virtually useless for the purpose of differentiating marble-types.

Trace element analysis of marbles and artifacts for provenancing purposes have been performed by a number of workers (e.g., Rybach and Nissen 1964; Conforto et al. 1975; Lazzarini et al. 1980), and has also met with mixed success. On occasion it has been possible to differentiate select sources satisfactorily on the basis of various elements (Conforto et al. 1975). However, to date, lack of trace element homogeneity has plagued efforts to uniquely assign a trace element 'fingerprint' to the various classical marble quarries, unlike numerous pottery clay sources. Intrasample element variations, as great as a factor of a hundred, have been found demonstrating the severity of the problem.

Throughout the 1950's and 60's marble provenancing remained a problem and misidentification was common when based solely on visual observations and elemental analyses. By about 1970 marble 'fingerprinting' was in disrepute. It was at about this time that Harmon and Valerie Craig (1972) applied the technique of stable isotope analysis to the study of marble provenancing. One of the attractive features of the technique as applied to the analysis of carbonates and marble artifacts, is that only 5 - 20 mg of sample is required for analysis. Consequently, this amount may be removed with minimal damage to an artifact. Craig and Craig (1972) collected and analyzed some 170 samples of marble from ancient Greek quarries. Graphical representation of approximately 35% of their data on a $\delta^{13}C$ - $\delta^{18}O$ diagram produced generally well-defined fields for each of the marble-types. They also isotopically analyzed ten marble artifacts and were able to assign a probable provenance to five of them. They concluded that C and O isotopic ratios were probably the most useful test to date for determining the origin of Greek marbles, especially when used in conjunction with other techniques. They cautioned, however, that the coincidence of a sample with one of the isotopic fields was not in itself a unique indication of provenance. Unfortunately, the early promise of sourcing marbles on the basis of their stable isotope signature faded somewhat as marbles from additional Greek, Turkish, Aegean, and Roman quarries were analyzed (e.g., Manfra et al. 1975; Germann et al. 1980; Herz and Dean 1986). The discrete fields published by Craig and Craig (1972) are now known to be overlain, either wholly or in part, by geographically distinct marble sources (Figure 1), thus limiting the usefulness of the method (Herz 1987). Consequently, most workers have concluded that stable isotope analysis when used in isolation will only rarely result in an unequivocal answer to marble sourcing and additional tests will likely be necessary.

Variations in the $^{87}Sr/^{86}Sr$ ratio, due to the radioactive decay of ^{87}Rb to ^{87}Sr, were used to determine the provenance of obsidian (Gale 1980). Following this work Herz et al. (1982) applied the technique to marble provenancing. Strontium, coprecipitated with $CaCO_3$ out of seawater, inherits the seawater Sr isotopic signature which, in carbonates, remains essentially unchanged to the present time because of the virtual absence of Rb in seawater. The $^{87}Sr/^{86}Sr$ ratio of seawater has varied with time as shown by Burke et al. (1982) due to a variety of factors and consequently many carbonates and their metamorphosed equivalents retain an $^{87}Sr/^{86}Sr$ isotopic signature. Although not necessarily unique the ratio can aid in differentiating certain marble sources (Herz et al. 1982).

METHODS

Sampling

For this study samples were unobtrusively taken from the back of the Albertan Antonia Minor statue with the aid of a dentist's tungsten carbide drill. The surface layer was first removed so as to avoid any weathered marble. One sample was taken from the head, and two from opposing ends (some 40 cm apart) of the bust. One of these samples was split and analyzed in duplicate as an 'unknown' for stable isotope analysis. Samples of Parian (2), Marmaran (2), Ephesian (2) and Carraran (5) marble were supplied by Norman Herz; Keith Matthews of the British Museum sent a number of Carraran marble samples the majority of which were selected for full analysis. Although necessary in only a few cases, suspected weathered surfaces were removed prior to sampling.

Trace Element Analysis

Instrumental neutron activation analysis (INAA) was chosen as the preferred method of elemental analysis because of its non-destructive and highly sensitive nature. The extremely small samples from the University statue dictated that only a short irradiation and analysis should be employed so that upon decay of the induced radioactivity the sample could be split and used for the subsequent isotopic analyses. Consequently, 10 to 30 mg of the various marbles were accurately weighed into HNO_3 washed polyethylene microtubes. Analysis of these vials have shown them to contain very low levels of contaminants.

Samples were batch irradiated in an inner site of the SLOWPOKE II nuclear reactor at the University of Alberta for 20 min at a nominal thermal neutron flux of 1×10^{12} n cm^{-2} s^{-1}. Following a decay period of 2 - 3 hrs, each sample was counted for 600 - 900 s live-time at a geometry of 1 cm. All counting was performed with a hyperpure-Ge detector coupled to Nuclear Data (ND) 660 multichannel analyzer

and associated electronics. The detector has a nominal relative efficiency of 20% and a measured FWHM of 1.9 keV for the 1332.5 keV photopeak of ^{60}Co. Spectra were assigned 4096 channels and stored on a floppy disc for off-line analysis. The concentrations of Sr, Mn and Na were determined by the semi-absolute NAA comparator method (Bergerioux et al. 1979) using ^{87m}Sr, ^{56}Mn, and ^{24}Na,

	Sr	Mn	Na
This work (n=4) *	185 ± 11	19.9 ± 0.7	51.4 ± 5.9
Freitas et al. (1988) **	196.3 ± 9.8	20.34 ± 0.88	46.9 ± 2.9

(uncertainties at the: * - 68%, and ** 95% confidence level; all values in parts per million, ppm)

Table 1. INAA results for Carrara marble standard.

respectively. United States Geological Survey BCR-1 (basalt) and W1 (diabase) together with NBS SRM 1633a (fly ash) were used to calculate the decay and pulse pile-up corrected sensitivities (cts/μg) of the above mentioned elements. Filby et al. (1985) have shown that BCR-1 and NBS 1633a are homogeneous for use in microanalysis at masses less than were used in this work. The accuracy and precision of measurements were assessed by analyzing 25 mg aliquots of a recently proposed reference sample of Carrara marble (Freitas et al. 1988). The agreement between listed (analysis of 500 mg aliquots) and measured Sr, Mn and Na concentrations is excellent (Table 1).

Stable Isotope Analysis

Samples of marble weighing 10 to 25 mg were reacted with phosphoric acid and the evolved CO_2 collected and the ratio of the O, and C isotopes analyzed by mass spectrometry. The samples analyzed were run on a VG Micromass 602-C isotope ratio mass spectrometer at the University of Alberta.

As is the practice in marble provenance studies, the results are reported relative to the PDB (Pee-Dee Belemnite) standard. The O and C values for the duplicates, and the second sample taken from the bust, agreed within 1%.

Radiogenic $^{87}Sr/^{86}Sr$ Analyses

Samples of marble weighing between 10 and 50 mg were dissolved in ultrapure HNO_3, and Sr separated and purified by repeated chemical precipitation, and cation exchange chromatography. Aliquots of the purified Sr were loaded on Re filaments and the Sr isotopic composition measured by mass spectrometry. To this end a VG Micromass-30 solid source mass spectrometer at the University of Alberta was used. Analysis of NBS 987 gave a $^{87}Sr/^{86}Sr$ value of 0.71028 ± 6 (1s). A value of 0.70769 ± 3 (1s, n=2) was obtained for the above mentioned Carraran standard (Freitas et al. 1988). However, to date there are no other $^{87}Sr/^{86}Sr$ data known for this material with which to compare this value.

RESULTS

The INAA, O, C, and Sr isotopic results of this study are either listed in Tables 2 - 4, or displayed graphically in Figures 2 - 4.

Comparison of Figures 1 and 2 show that one of the Parian marbles supplied by Norman Herz falls well outside the accepted Paros field. Although elevated, however, the Mn and Na content of the sample are not outside measured ranges for Parian marble (combined data from Ryback and Nissen (1964), and L. Moens, written communication).

The Albertan head and second Parian marble sample fall well within the Parian marble $\delta^{13}C$ - $\delta^{18}O$ field (and one of the two fields of Ephesos) and are indistinguishable on the basis of their Sr isotopic signature and measured trace element content. Unfortunately, the Ephesian marbles supplied by Herz are from the ^{13}C-poor Ephesian marble field and consequently their trace element and $^{87}Sr/^{86}Sr$ data cannot be used to differentiate between these two possible sources. Further analyses of ^{13}C-rich samples will be necessary. Note, however, that the $^{87}Sr/^{86}Sr$ values obtained for the two Ephesian marbles, the Albertan head, and the second Parian marble sample are indistinguishable (Table 2).

It is interesting that Herz and Wenner (1981) assigned a Parian source to the head and a fragment of the bust of the Harvard University statue on the basis of ^{13}C - ^{18}O data with apparently no consideration of an Ephesian source. Similarly, they assigned a Carrara source for the remaining fragments of the bust without considering the various Greek and Turkish marbles with which their data coincide (e.g., Hymettus, Tempi, Gonnos, and Marmara). The potential for misidentification of Italian Carraran marble with these Greek and Turkish marbles has previously been noted: "Additionally one of the Carrara marbles analyzed by Baertschi (1957) fits well into the centre of the Hymettus-Gonnos field" (Germann et al. 1980: 101). As will be shown, to assign a Carrara source to the Albertan bust, although supported by the stable isotope data, would be in error.

The $^{87}Sr/^{86}Sr$ analyses of fifteen Carrara marbles from Roman quarries gives a ratio of 0.70779 ± 8 (including the Renaissance quarry samples has an insignificant effect on the mean) which is significantly different from the $^{87}Sr/^{86}Sr$ bust value (> 3 sigma, see Tables 2 and 4). Figures 3 and 4, where the $^{87}Sr/^{86}Sr$ ratios for each sample are plotted against their $\delta^{13}C$ and $\delta^{18}O$ values respectively, demonstrate this difference effectively. Similarly, the high concentration of Sr and low level of Mn of the bust fall outside the measured ranges for Carrara marbles obtained in this (Table 3) and other studies (Conforto et al. 1975; Germann et al. 1980; L. Moens, written communication).

CONCLUSIONS

This study suggests that the head of the Albertan Antonia Minor statue is most likely made from Parian marble, although without further analyses, the ^{13}C-rich marbles of Ephesos cannot be ruled out as a possible alternative. Radiogenic Sr and trace element analyses show that the bust of the Albertan statue is not made from Carrara marble. However, the limited data available here, and lack of Sr isotopic data for Gonnos and Hymettus, make it currently impossible to identify the source of the marble used to fabricate the bust.

This study, although raising further questions, supports the claims of earlier workers that assigning a source to a marble or a marble artifact solely on the basis of its O and C signature is inviting disaster and demonstrates that additional data (e.g., $^{87}Sr/^{86}Sr$ ratios and trace element concentrations) will often alert the archaeologist to the possibility of misidentification and aid in determining the correct source.

Additional Greek and Anatolian marbles are currently being analyzed and with time the full extent of the main classical marble $\delta^{13}C$ - $^{87}Sr/^{86}Sr$ and $\delta^{18}O$ - $^{87}Sr/^{86}Sr$ fields will become known and may be used with increasing confidence to determine the provenance of marble. One of the advantages of the combined application of INAA, and stable and radiogenic isotope analysis of marble is that all three techniques may be carried out with as little as 40 mg of material.

ACKNOWLEDGEMENTS

Many thanks to Norman Herz and Keith Matthews for supplying samples; to Karlis Muehlenbachs, Cathy Connelly, and Pat Cavell for their help and expertise; and finally to Alastair Small for his interest and study.

REFERENCES

Bergerioux, C., Kennedy, G. and Zikovsky, L. (1979). Use of the semi-absolute method in neutron activation analysis. J. Radioanal. Chem., 50: 229-234.

Burke, W.H., Denison, R.E., Hetherington, E.A., Koepnick, R.B., Nelson, H.R. and Otto, J.B. (1982). Variation of seawater $^{87}Sr/^{86}Sr$ throughout Phanerozoic time. Geology, 10: 516-519.

Coleman, M. and Walker, S. (1979). Stable isotope identification of Greek and Turkish marbles. Archaeometry, 21: 107-112.

Conforto, L., Felici, M., Monna, D., Serva, L. and Taddeucci, A. (1975). A preliminary evaluation of chemical data (trace element) from classical marble quarries in the Mediterranean. Archaeometry, 17: 201-213.

Craig, H. and Craig, V. (1972). Greek marbles: Determination of provenance by isotopic analysis. Science, 176: 401-403.

Filby, R.H., Nguygen, S., Grimm, C.A., Markowski, G.R., Ekambaram, V., Tanaka, T. and Grossman, L. (1985). Evaluation of geochemical standard reference materials for microanalysis. Anal. Chem., 57: 551-555.

Freitas, M.C., Moens, L., De Paepe, P. and Seabra e Barros, J. (1988). Preparation and analysis of a marble reference material. J. Radioanal. Nucl. Chem., (in press).

Germann, K., Holzmann, G. and Winkler, F.J. (1980). Determination of marble provenance: limits of isotopic analysis. Archaeometry, 22: 99-106.

Herz, N. and Wenner, D.B. (1981). Tracing the origins of marble. Archaeology, 34: 14-21.

Herz, N., More, G. and Wenner, D.B. (1982). $^{87}Sr/^{86}Sr$ ratios: a possible discriminant for classical marble provenance. Geol. Soc. Amer. Abs. Prog., 14: 514.

Herz, N. and Dean, N.E. (1986). Stable isotopes and archaeological geology: the Carrara marble, northern Italy. Applied Geochem., 1: 139-151.

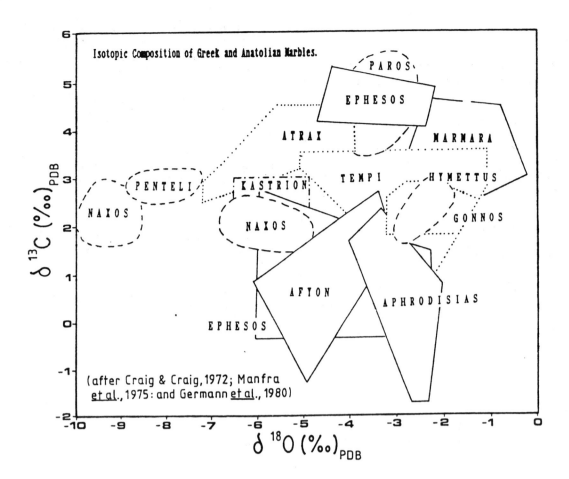

Figure 1. Stable isotope compositional fields for Greek and Anatolian marbles.

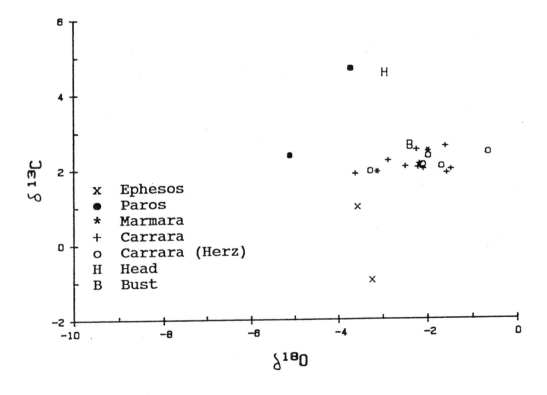

Figure 2. Stable isotope composition of marbles analyzed in this study.

230

Quarry/Piece	Sr	Mn	Na	$^{87}Sr/^{86}Sr$
Paros	155 ± 7	25.3 ± 0.5	38.3 ± 1.2	0.70763 ± 4
	195 ± 6	2.32 ± 0.11	19.8 ± 0.9	0.70747 ± 5
Marmara	186 ± 6	6.10 ± 0.19	63.8 ± 1.7	0.70764 ± 3
	224 ± 7	1.01 ± 0.13	105 ± 3	0.70792 ± 3
Ephesos	71.0 ± 4.2	9.42 ± 0.25	48.9 ± 1.4	0.70735 ± 2
	70.9 ± 4.2	11.7 ± 0.3	18.2 ± 0.8	0.70736 ± 4
Head	201 ± 9	3.36 ± 0.24	26.7 ± 1.3	0.70737 ± 9
Bust	604 ± 16	3.65 ± 0.22	47.9 ± 1.9	0.70732 ± 3

(trace elements in ppm ± 1 sigma; isotopic data ± 1 sigma in 5th place)

Table 2. INAA and $^{87}Sr/^{86}Sr$ isotopic ratio results for various classical marbles, and the head and bust of Antonia Minor.

(n=18)	Sr	Mn	Na
Mean	174	24.9	65.3
S.D*	37	11.9	53.8
Median	170	22.2	52.0
Range	113 - 292	8.76 - 47.6	22.1 - 251

(* - 1 sigma; all values in ppm)

Table 3. INAA results for Carrara marbles.

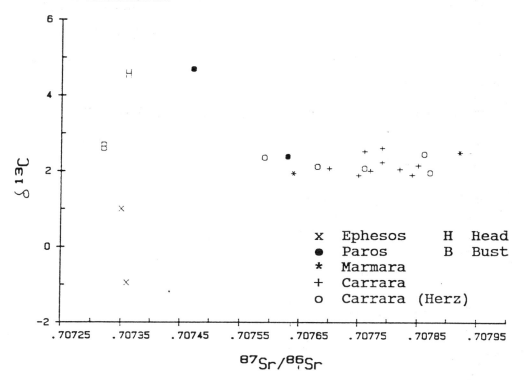

Figure 3. δ13C - $^{87}Sr/^{86}Sr$ diagram of marbles analyzed in this study.

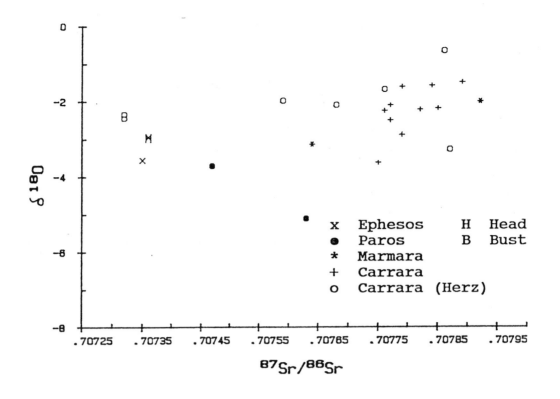

Figure 4. $\delta^{13}C$ diagram of marbles analyzed in this study.

Roman Quarries	Mean (± 1s)	Median	Range	n
Colonnata	0.70775 ± 9	0.70775	0.70759 – 0.70785	7
Miseglia	0.70784 ± 6	0.70784	0.70777 – 0.70789	3
Torano	0.70780 ± 4	0.70780	0.70776 – 0.70782	5
Total	0.70779 ± 8	0.70779	0.70759 – 0.70789	15
Renaissance Quarries				
Seravezza	0.70786 ± 14	0.70786	0.70776 – 0.70797	2

Table 4. $^{87}Sr/^{86}Sr$ isotopic ratios for Carrara marbles.

Herz, N. (1987). Carbon and Oxygen isotopic ratios: a data base for classical Greek and Roman marble. Archaeometry, 29: 35-43.

Lazzarini, L., Moschini, G. and Stievano, B.M. (1980). A contribution to the identification of Italian, Greek and Anatolian marbles through a petrological study and the evaluation of a Ca/Sr ratio. Archaeometry, 22: 173-183.

Manfra, L., Masi, U. and Turi, B. (1975). Carbon and oxygen isotope ratios of marbles from some ancient quarries of western Anatolia and their archaeological significance. Archaeometry, 17: 215-221.

Rybach, L. and Nissen, H.U. (1964). Neutron activation analysis of Mn and Na traces in marbles worked by the ancient Greeks. In: Radiochemical Methods of Analysis, 1: 105-117. Int. Atomic Energy Comm., Vienna.

41. INAA of Lithic Materials from the Western Lake Superior Region, North America: Determination of Raw Material Sources

P. J. JULIG
Department of Anthropology, University of Toronto, Canada, M5S 1A1.

L. A. PAVLISH
Department of Anthropology and Department of Physics, University of Toronto, Canada, M5S 1Al.

R. G. V. HANCOCK
SLOWPOKE Reactor Facility and Department of Chemical Engineering and Applied Chemistry, University of Toronto, Canada, M5S 1A4.

ABSTRACT: *Difficulties exist in the precise visual identification of lithic materials, particularly on Paleoindian sites, where samples from geologically remote sources may be represented. Often the presence of only complete tools and occasional small flakes preclude petrographic methods of identification. In this provenance study, chemical identification of archaeological lithics and prospective geological source materials was carried out using INAA.*

INTRODUCTION AND GENERAL ARCHAEOLOGICAL PROBLEM

Difficulties exist in the precise visual identification of many lithic materials, particularly on Paleoindian sites, where geologically remote sources may be represented. For almost a century, the problems associated with the visual identification of chert types and source areas have evoked comment in the archaeological literature (Fowke 1888:488; Holmes 1919:176; Moorehead 1892:38; Phillips 1900:38; Mills 1921:109; Shaeffer 1958:190; Losey 1971:151; Leudtke 1978). These problems can become particularly acute when analysts attempt to deal with widespread Paleoindian social interaction spheres (cf. Hayden 1982), and the concomitant movement of lithic materials over long distances between widely spaced source areas (Earle and Ericson 1977).

SPECIFIC PROBLEM AND RATIONALE FOR ANALYSIS

The nature of the Cummins exotic lithic archaeological specimens, small flakes and occasional complete tools, precluded the petrographic (thin section) method of identification. Therefore, instrumental neutron activation analysis (INAA) of short half-life radioisotope producing elements (major, minor, and trace) was conducted with four objectives:

1. characterizing archaeological samples with respect to a specific suite of short half-life radioisotope producing elements;
2. characterizing prospective geological sources;
3. comparing the results in attempting to determine sources; and
4. analyzing intact artifacts without damage or need for excessive 'cool-off' periods [low and medium neutron flux reactors create 'hot' artifacts that are permanently lost to the analyst].

ARCHAEOLOGICAL CHERTS AND AGATES

Although taconites predominate, small quantities (<1%) of exotic lithics are present at Cummins, as on other Thunder Bay Paleoindian sites (Figure 1). Included are small amounts of dark (7.5 YR 4/2) to light brown (10 YR 8/3) and reddish brown (7.5 YR 3/3) cherts, occurring as small flakes and particularly as end scrapers. A few biface thinning flakes of this material are present, but only a single biface fragment has been reported. Occasional lanceolate (Plano) points of high quality lithic material have been interpreted by Fox (1975) as Hudson Bay Lowland (HBL) chert. Visual characteristics of excavated materials recovered during three field seasons at Cummins suggested that Knife River Flint (KRF) (source region in North Dakota) and local Lake Superior agates (from the Osler Formation) should also be considered as possible sources (Figure 2). Certain of the Cummins site end scrapers showed internal parallel sedimentary structures that are not characteristic of Hudson Bay Lowland chert, but are common on both KRF (Clayton et al. 1970) and on agates.

KRF is reported (based on visual identification) in the Thunder Bay region Archaic sites and a sample of specimens from the Dog Lake area (Figure 1) was analyzed. KRF has also been reported in archaeological assemblages from Alberta (Wormington and Forbis 1965:150) to Ohio (Braun et al. 1982:85) over a considerable time span. It was a widely used lithic source among late Paleoindian Plano groups throughout the northern Plains (Loendorf et al. 1984: 13-14).

QUARTZITES AND RELATED ARCHAEOLOGICAL MATERIALS

Exotic quartzites present in very small quantities on Lakehead Complex sites include a sugary quartzite that varies from white to orange in colour. This lithic material compares favourably with Hixton silicified sandstone, a

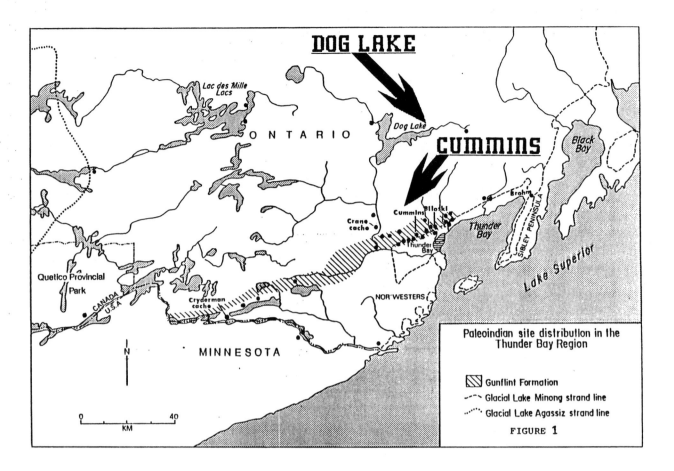

Figure 1. Site distribution in the Thunder Bay area showing site locations mentioned in text.

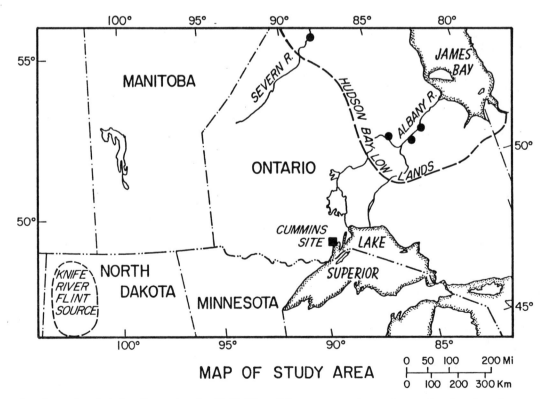

Figure 2. Map of study region showing Cummins site, Knife River Flint source region and sampling locations for Hudson Bay lowland chert.

type of quartzite from Silver Mound in Jackson County, west central Wisconsin (Porter 1961). Hixton lithic material was widely used by Paleoindians in Wisconsin (Mason 1963; Salzer 1974), and possible finds have been reported from northwestern Minnesota, Lake Agassiz beaches in northwest Ontario (including Quetico Park), and east to Thunder Bay (Fox 1975; Arthurs 1987). Clovis points of Hixton lithic material have been reported from Wisconsin and to the south of the Great Lakes, but the most common point type of this material is Scottsbluff and other stemmed lanceolates.

Another type of sugary (white to pink) quartzite utilized by upper Great Lakes Plano groups to the east is Lorraine quartzite, from northern Lake Huron. Large quarries are present at the Sheguiandah site on northern Manitoulin Island (Lee 1955).

GEOLOGICAL CONTROL SAMPLES (TESTED)

The source region for KRF is Dunn and Mercer Counties in western North Dakota, and a number of samples from various quarries were used as a control for this lithic type (Figure 2). The locations of samples of HBL from the Hudson Bay Lowlands that were analyzed as geological controls are also shown on Figure 2. Dark-brown, and reddish-brown translucent banded agates from Thunder Bay beaches were also analyzed.

For the quartzite sourcing, samples of geological material were used from the Hixton quarries in Wisconsin. Various colour varieties of geological Lorraine quartzite from the Sheguiandah area were obtained as well. These locations are shown in Figure 4.

INAA METHODOLOGY

The concentrations of 15 major, minor and trace elements, which produce short-lived radioisotopes upon neutron activation, were determined for a series of samples at the University of Toronto SLOWPOKE Reactor Facility. Individual lithic samples (200-300 mg) were neutron-irradiated for five minutes at a flux of 5×10^{11} n. cm^{-2} s^{-1}. After a delay time of 18 minutes to allow the ^{28}Al to decay to reasonable levels, each sample was assayed using a solid state gamma-ray spectrometer. All samples were assayed for a period of five minutes, and elemental concentrations were calculated from the net gamma-ray peak areas using the comparator method. For artifacts that could not be subsampled, a newly designed analytical approach using larger containers was utilized. Thus, a non-destructive analysis of whole artifacts was possible; and we were able to make chemical distinctions, without damage to the artifact.

RESULTS AND DISCUSSION

For the brown cherts and/or agates, of the fifteen elements measured, most proved to be "non-diagnostic". The five most consistent and "diagnostic" trace elements of the samples analyzed are U, Dy, Al, Si, and Cl. These five elements are paired, standardized, normalized, and graphed on a ternary diagram (Figure 3).

Although they are not a primary part of this study, for comparative purposes, examples of some other Great Lakes cherts (Fossil Hill [Collingwood], Ontario; Warsaw [Upper Mercer], Ohio; and Charity Island [Bayport], Michigan) were analyzed (Figure 3).

The KRF samples cluster consistently in the upper left portion of the ternary diagram (Figure 3). This is a result of higher standardized and normalized U and Dy values and generally lower Al/Si ratios.

Two samples from the Cummins site did not clearly separate from the Mercer County KRF and may be imports. These were recovered from a biface flaking area at Cummins site where several partly completed lanceolate points of Gunflint material were also recovered. These are the only archaeological samples analyzed that may be KRF. The remaining Cummins archaeological samples group in the lower left of Figure 3 along with the HBL and Lake Superior agates.

At present it is not possible to clearly separate HBL from agates with this suite of elements. Further research with longer lived isotopes may provide a solution.

KRF has been shown to be sparsely, if at all, represented at Cummins. This allows us to say confidently that some of the archaeological specimens are agates, since several of the end scrapers exhibit an internal banding not characteristic of the HBL cherts. The possibility remains that the non-banded archaeological specimens are HBL cherts, or some other source yet to be tested.

The fact that small end scrapers are the only tool type recovered at Cummins that has been made from these exotic brown cherts or agates suggests that the raw material may be imposing technical design constraints. Agates commonly occur in pebble form, whereas HBL (in the source region) is not uncommon as large cobbles. If the raw material was large enough, it seems probable that larger bifacial or unifacial tool types of this material should be present in the archaeological assemblage, since large bifaces of HBL are found on Archaic sites in the region. The INAA and archaeological evidence suggests that local agate pebbles collected along the cobble beaches were one source of these exotic lithic specimens from Cummins site, and KRF may be sparsely represented. The Archaic specimens analyzed from Dog Lake also fall outside of the KRF cluster, indicating these artifacts are likely HBL chert.

The results of the INAA analysis of the Cummins quartzite (C) and the geological sources (H, S) are shown on Figure 4 (cf. Julig et al. 1987). Of the 16 elements measured, Dy, Al and U were the most diagnostic. Sheguiandah quartzite clearly separates from the Cummins archaeological quartzite, with greater dysprosium (Dy). Local Thunder Bay Shield quartz was also tested, and it is singularly lacking in Dy. The archaeological samples tested match well with the geological Hixton material from the Wisconsin quarry (Figure 4), suggesting that Hixton silicified sandstone was transported to the Lakehead area by regional Paleoindians, probably as a result of social interaction with the southern bands, as previously suggested by Fox (1975). The INAA results support the previous visual identification of Hixton artifacts in the Thunder Bay region.

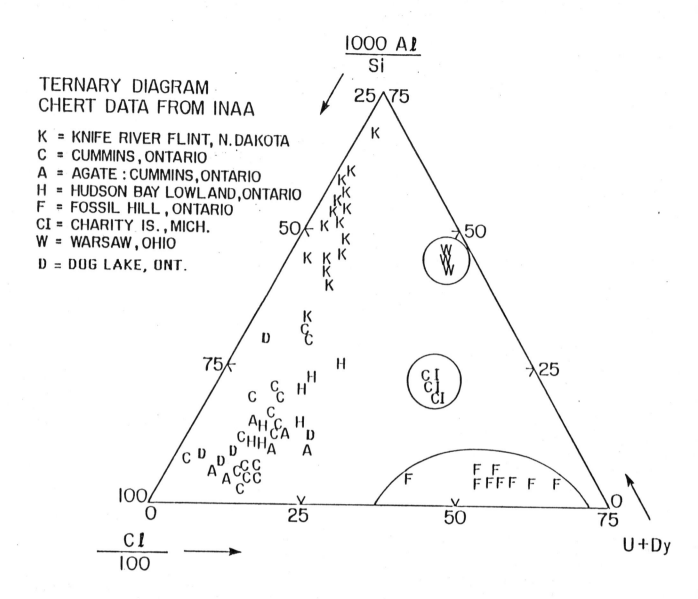

Figure 3. Ternary diagram showing the nearly complete separation of Knife River Flint (K) samples and those from Cummins (C). There is no separation between Cummins material and those from Hudson Bay Lowlands (H) and Thunder Bay agates (Osler Formation) (A). Fossil Hill chert (Collingwood) (F), Charity Island (Bayport) (CI), and Warsaw (Upper Mercer) (W) materials are included to show examples of the potential for clear chemical separation of samples from differing source areas. The Archaic material from Dog Lake (D) indicates chemical similarity with HBL chert and local Agates.

CONCLUSIONS

Although the collections are dominated by local Gunflint Formation lithic materials, small amounts of exotic lithics were discarded at Cummins and other Preceramic regional sites. Complete and broken siltstone points and biface flakes are present, but unifaces of this material are rare. The agate/chert assemblage is dominated by small end scrapers and small flakes, while western exotics (e.g., KRF) are sparsely represented. Hixton silicified sandstone recovered in the Thunder Bay region and along the Boundary Waters region to the west consists of lanceolate points, oval bifaces and fragments, and large and small flakes. The points are of both the Agate Basin

and Scottsbluff types.

The Paleoindian lithic industries in the Lakehead area are thus dominated by local materials, with only Hixton artifacts being confirmed as a distant exotic, likely obtained as a result of social interaction with the southern bands. The nature and extent of these southern contacts requires further investigation. The Archaic artifacts tested are likewise not KRF, as has been previously reported on the basis of visual identifications. HBL and local agates were used throughout the Preceramic period with minimal utilization of distant exotics.

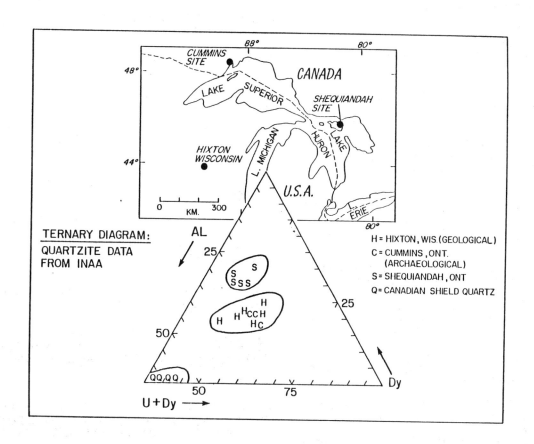

Figure 4. shows the source location of materials analyzed. The Ternary diagram indicates geological quartzites from Hixton Wisconsin (H) are chemically similar to Cummins archaeological quartzite (C) and clearly separated from Sheguiandah quartzite (S). Canadian Shield quartz from the Thunder Bay area is also chemically distinct. The data on the ternary diagram is derived from the formula:

$$(U + Dy) + Dy + Al = Total\ T$$

Thus: $\dfrac{(U + Dy)\%}{T} + \dfrac{Dy\%}{T} + \dfrac{Al\%}{T} = 100\%$

Included by permission of Current Research in the Pleistocene. From Julig et al. 1987.

ACKNOWLEDGEMENTS

We wish to thank William Ross, Stanley Ahler, Andrew Hinshelwood, and J. Luc Pilon for providing portions of the geological lithic samples for this study. The Ontario Heritage Foundation and Social Sciences and Humanities Research Council of Canada funded the Cummins Paleoindian site investigations. The INAA was made possible by an NSERC infrastructure grant to the SLOWPOKE Reactor Facility.

REFERENCES

Arthurs, David (1987). Hixton Silicified Sandstone Artifacts in Quetico. Wanikan, 87, 1: 8-15. Newsletter of the Thunder Bay Chapter, Ontario Archaeological Society, Thunder Bay, Ontario.

Braun, D.B., J.B. Griffith, and P.F. Titterington (1982). The Snyders Mounds and Five Other Mound Groups in Calhoun County, Illinois, Technical Reports No. 13, Research Reports in Archaeology, Contribution 8. University of Michigan, Museum of Anthropology, Ann Arbor.

Clayton, L., W.B. Bickley, Jr., and W.J. Stone (1970). Knife River Flint. Plains Anthropologist, 15(50):282-290.

Earle, T.K., and J.E. Erickson (1977). Exchange Systems in Archaeological Perspective. In Exchange Systems in Prehistory, edited by T.K. Earle and J.E. Erickson, Academic Press.

Fowke, G. (1888). The manufacture and use of aboriginal stone implements. Ohio Archaeological and Historical Quarterly, 9:485-502.

Fox, W.A. (1975). The Paleo-Indian Lakehead Complex. Canadian Archaeological Association, Collected Papers, edited by P.Nunn. Research Report No. 6, Historic Sites Branch, Ontario Ministry of Natural Resources.

Hancock, R.G.V. (1978). Some aspects of the analysis of ancient artifacts by neutron activation. Journal of International Institute of Conservation, Canadian Group, 3(2): 21-27.

Hayden, B. (1982). Interaction parameters and the demise of Paleo-Indian craftsmanship. Plains Anthropologist, 27(96):109-123.

Holmes, W.H. (1919). Handbook of aboriginal American antiquities Part I: lithic industries. Bulletin 60, Bureau of American Ethnology, Smithsonian Institution, Washington, D.C.

Julig, P.J., L.A. Pavlish, and R.G.V. Hancock (1987). INAA of archaeological quartzite from Cummins Site, Thunder Bay: determination of geological source. Current Research in the Pleistocene, 4: 59-61.

Lee, T.E. (1955). The Sheguiandah expedition, Manitoulin Island, Ontario. American Antiquity, 21 (1): 63-71.

Loendorf, L.L., S.A. Ahler, and D. Davidson (1984). The proposed national register district in the Knife River flint quarries in Dunn County, North Dakota. North Dakota History, 51(4):4-20.

Losey, T.C. (1971). The Stony Plain Quarry site. Plains Anthropologist, 16:138-154.

Luedtke, Barbara E. (1978). Chert sources and trace element analysis. American Antiquity, 43:413-423.

Luedtke, Barbara E. (1979). The identification of sources of chert artifacts. American Antiquity, 44:744-757.

Mason, R. (1963). Two Late Paleo-Indian complexes in Wisconsin. Wisconsin Archaeologist, 44(4):199-211.

Mills, W.C. (1921). Flint Ridge. Ohio Archaeological and Historical Quarterly, 30:90-161.

Moorehead, Warren L. (1892). Primitive Man in Ohio,, G.P. Putnam's Sons, New York.

Phillips, W.A. (1900). Aboriginal quarries and shops at Mill Creek, Illinois. American Anthropologist, 2:37-52.

Porter, J. (1961). Hixton silicified sandstone: a unique lithic material used by prehistoric cultures. Wisconsin Archaeologist, 42(2):78-85.

Salzer, R. (1974). The Wisconsin North Lakes Project: a preliminary report. In E. Johnson (editor), Aspects of Upper Great Lakes Anthropology. Minnesota Prehistoric Archaeology Series No. 11, Minnesota Historical Society, St. Paul: 40-54.

Shaeffer, J.B. (1958). The Albates Flint Quarry, Texas, American Antiquity, 24:188-191.

Steinbring, J. (1974). The Preceramic Archaeology of Northern Minnesota. In E. Johnson (editor), Aspects of Upper Great Lakes Anthropology. Minnesota Prehistoric Archaeology Series No. 11, Minnesota Historical Society, St. Paul: 64-73.

Wormington, H.M. and R. Forbis (1965). An introduction to the archaeology of Alberta, Canada. Proceedings of the Denver Museum of Natural History, No. 11.

42. Chemical Source Analysis of Maya Obsidian: New Perspectives from Wild Cane Cay, Belize

H. McKILLOP
Department of Anthropology, Trent University, Peterborough, Ontario, Canada K9J 7B8.

L.J. JACKSON
Northeastern Archaeological Associates, P.O. Box 493, Port Hope, Ontario, Canada, L1A 3Z4.

H. MICHEL, F. STROSS, and F. ASARO
Lawrence Berkeley Laboratory, University of California, Berkeley, CA 94720 U.S.A.

ABSTRACT: *Trace element analysis by X-ray fluorescence and neutron activation of 105 obsidian artifacts from Wild Cane Cay, Belize, indicates long-term coastal Maya trade involving obsidian from seven highland sources.*

INTRODUCTION

Obsidian is a volcanic glass not naturally available in the limestone-based Maya lowlands, but widely traded throughout Maya prehistory from various highland areas of Mesoamerica to the Maya lowlands to make blades and other artifacts. Its ubiquity at lowland Maya sites and precise methods for determining source locations of traded obsidian artifacts have meant that obsidian, while clearly not the only exotic traded to the Maya lowlands, has played a significant role in reconstructing highland-lowland trade routes.

Sourced obsidian artifacts from excavations radiocarbon dated to the Classic (300-900 A.D.) and Early Postclassic periods (900-1200 A.D.) at Wild Cane Cay delineate changing patterns of obsidian source use over time. Our dated source data replace an earlier study based on chemical sourcing of undated surface collected obsidian from Wild Cane Cay (Stross et al. 1978). Instead of a bimodal distribution of El Chayal obsidian at inland sites in the Maya lowlands and Ixtepeque obsidian at coastal sites during the Classic Period, our dated obsidian indicates that there were temporal changes in obsidian source use at Wild Cane Cay consistent with patterns discerned elsewhere in the Maya lowlands (Figure 1).

ARCHAEOLOGICAL RESEARCH AT WILD CANE CAY

Wild Cane Cay was a prehistoric coastal Maya trading station in southern Belize. Its strategic location at the mouth of the Deep River, the presence of a natural harbour, and the abundance of exotic trade goods, particularly obsidian, reinforced our interpretation that the ancient Maya on the island participated directly in long distance coastal trade.

Wild Cane Cay includes about two ha of dry coconut woodland surrounded by mangrove. Prehistoric deposits cover the entire island to a depth of at least 2.5 metres and extend into the present offshore area. Apart from six artificial coral mounds built by the Postclassic Maya, the island is quite flat and barely above sea level.

Excavations in 1982 and 1988 were designed to determine the nature and extent of prehistoric island use

and to recover exotics from provenienced and datable contexts. Research included mapping the island, stratified random excavations in the midden deposits, trenching two of the mounds, and comprehensive surface collection in 191 10 by 10 metre areas (McKillop 1987; Jackson and McKillop 1987). Obsidian was very abundant both on the ground surface and in the midden excavations, reaching 527 items per cubic metre in one Early Postclassic midden (McKillop 1988).

WILD CANE CAY OBSIDIAN SOURCES

In order to investigate the nature and dating of maritime trade as it affected Wild Cane Cay, 105 obsidian artifacts from radiocarbon dated excavations were chemically sourced. Our aim was to determine the sources of obsidian traded to the island and to investigate changes over time.

The sources of the Wild Cane Cay obsidian artifacts were determined following standard procedures at the Lawrence Berkeley Laboratory. The trace element compositions of the artifacts were compared with the chemical compositions of various known obsidian sources in Mesoamerica. The limited number of Mesoamerican sources and the relative homogeneity and uniqueness in trace element composition of each source normally allows precise source assignment of obsidian artifacts. An initial sample of 100 obsidian artifacts was chemically characterized by non-destructive X-ray fluorescence (XRF). The source of an obsidian artifact from Mesoamerica can often be determined with certainty by XRF, since there is considerable information on source compositions. In using the non-destructive procedure for XRF determinations, errors are introduced which are due to variation in sample size and shape. Thin artifacts tend to generate abundances somewhat higher than the true values. By taking abundance ratios of elements with X-rays having nearly the same energy, such as rubidium (Rb), strontium (Sr), and zirconium (Zr), this error cancels to a large extent. Measurements of barium (Ba), Zr, Rb/Zr, and Sr/Zr were made on the Wild Cane Cay obsidian by utilizing Ag X-rays from a 109-Cd source.

The mean values and standard deviation for each group of artifacts assigned to a specific source were calculated (Table 1). Ninety six obsidian artifacts were

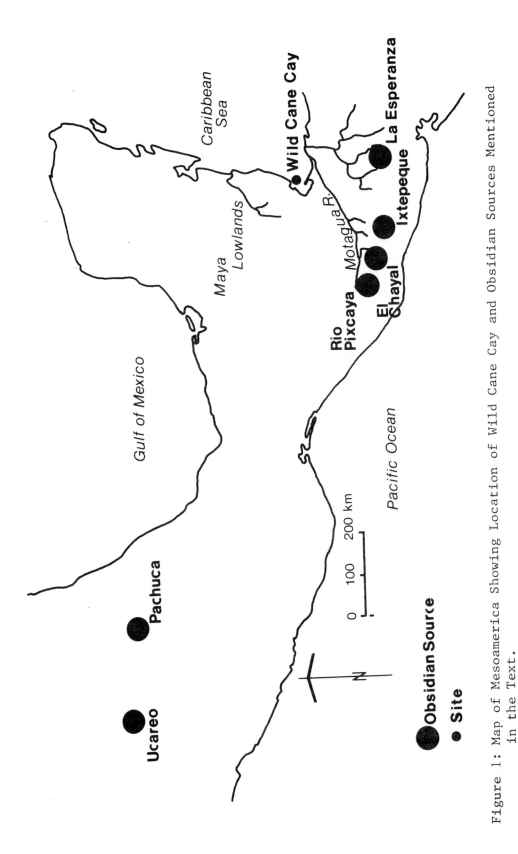

Figure 1. Map of Mesoamerica showing location of Wild Cane Cay and obsidian sources mentioned in the text.

from well-known sources in the Maya highlands of Guatemala, including 78 from Ixtepeque, 17 from El Chayal, and one from Rio Pixcaya (San Martin Jilotepeque). One artifact had a composition resembling the El Chayal deposit, but could not be assigned on the basis of XRF measurements alone. Three items were chemically similar to each other but had a composition previously unrecognized at the Lawrence Berkeley Laboratory. Designated "Source Z", this obsidian included two blades and a bifacially stemmed knife.

Following the XRF determinations, "abbreviated" neutron activation analyses (NAA) were made on nine samples to clarify the source assignments (Table 2). NAA is more accurate, less influenced by size and matrix effects, and more definitive for artifact assignments than is XRF. However, NAA is destructive of the artifact and considerably more expensive compared to XRF. Abbreviated NAA confirmed the source assignments of three Ixtepeque, one Rio Pixcaya, and two El Chayal blades. The sample (387-1) that could not be assigned on the basis of XRF analysis, but which resembled the El Chayal composition was definitely assigned to the El Chayal source. Two abbreviated NAA determinations of Source Z obsidian also confirmed that they belonged to a new group.

The NAA determination on one Source Z sample was completed for 21 elements (Table 3). This determination provided a useful chemical characterization of the unknown source but it did not help in establishing its location. Source Z is visually distinct from Ixtepeque and El Chayal obsidian (McKillop and Jackson 1987). We selected five additional blades from Wild Cane Cay for chemical sourcing on the basis of their visual similarity to the Source Z samples. XRF and abbreviated NAA indicated that three were from Source Z (Tables 4 and 5); a fourth was matched with the Ucareo source in central Mexico; the last sample was assigned to the La Esperanza source in Honduras, on the basis of source material provided by Payson Sheets and Kenneth Hirth as part of their characterization study of that source. Although the La Esperanza source is not reported from other lowland Maya sites, Paul Healy's research indicates that it is present at various sites in lower Central America (personal communication, 1987).

Further research indicated that Source Z is a fair match with a river cobble collected at the Puente Chetunal over the Motagua River by Fred Stross, and an artifact sourced from Quirigua (Stross et al. 1983: Table 11). Although this does not give us the exact location of the primary source, the clear implication is that the source is in the upstream region of the Motagua drainage system, up river from the Puente Chetunal. Since obsidian from Source Z is represented in significant quantity at Wild Cane Cay and is also present at Quirigua, it must have been a source of some importance. Since Source Z is visually distinct from the main Maya highland sources of El Chayal and Ixtepeque that generally make up the bulk of the obsidian at Classic and Postclassic lowland Maya sites, examination of existing obsidian artifact collections will likely reveal additional Source Z artifacts. We are currently examining other collections for Source Z and have visually identified this material at two sites.

IMPLICATIONS FOR LOWLAND MAYA OBSIDIAN TRADE

There are two implications from the sourcing data that are pertinent to this discussion of coastal Maya obsidian trade. First, Wild Cane Cay is unusual for a Maya site, especially such a tiny island community, in having a diversity of obsidian from seven sources. We attribute this primarily to the role of the cay in coastal trade and secondarily to the large sample of items sourced compared with most other sites (McKillop and Jackson 1988).

Secondly, the obsidian source data from Wild Cane Cay fit the pattern of changing obsidian source use over time that is evident at other lowland Maya sites. These data supplant the results of a previous sourced sample of obsidian from a surface collection from Wild Cane Cay (Stross et al. 1983). The obsidian in that study was not assigned a specific date, although Hammond (1976) noted that Late Classic through Early Postclassic ceramics were observed on the island's surface. The surface predominance of Ixtepeque obsidian (19 items or 82%) compared to El Chayal obsidian (four items or 18%) was contrasted to the Late Classic excavated sample from the nearby inland southern Belizean centre of Lubaantun, in which 21 out of 22 items were identified to El Chayal, with the remaining blade unassigned to source. On the basis of the different patterns of reliance in the Lubaantun and Wild Cane Cay samples, an obsidian trade model was proposed:

"The pattern of obsidian source assignment at Wild Cane Cay is more akin to that predicted originally for Lubaantun: it would seem that conjunction of trade routes lay not at the regional capital (Lubaantun), but a subsidiary location where large coasting canoes and the smaller river craft could meet" (Hammond 1976:73).

The implication of this model is that Wild Cane Cay and Lubaantun are contemporaneous and that the sourced obsidian samples are of similar date. However, Hammond (1976: Figure 4) clearly states that "space, time, or covariance of both may be responsible for the contrasting patterns." The obsidian sourcing data from the present study indicate that changing patterns of obsidian source use over time are responsible for the differences between the two sites: El Chayal was the main source used by the Late Classic lowland Maya as is clearly indicated at Lubaantun; high incidence of Ixtepeque surface obsidian at Wild Cane Cay derives from principal use of the island from the Terminal Classic through the Early Postclassic, when Ixtepeque was the dominant source used by the lowland Maya (McKillop 1981; McKillop and Jackson 1988; Nelson 1985; Rice et al. 1985). Sourcing of obsidian from dated deposits at Wild Cane Cay indicates Late to Terminal Classic use of Ixtepeque (15 items or 52%), El Chayal (12 items or 41%), and Source Z (2 items or 7%). Ixtepeque is dominant in the Early Postclassic (63 items or 89%), with less use of El Chayal (6 items or 9%), Rio Pixcaya (one item or 1%), and Source Z (one item or 1%). Pachuca obsidian, visually identified to source, was present in the Early Postclassic. The other sourced obsidian samples are undated.

241

Table 1. Average XRF results for groups of Wild Cane Cay obsidian samples.

Source	No. of Samples	Ba(ppm)	Zr(ppm)	Rb/Zr	Sr/Zr
Ixtepeque	78	1034±46	176±7	.58±.02	.90±.02
Reference		1030±27	175±2	.57±.01	.90±.02
El Chayal	17	923±48	119±4	1.30±.07	1.31±.03
Reference		915±24	117±3	1.24±.04	1.29±.04
Rio Pixcaya	1	1010±22	117±1	.96±.01	1.65±.01
Reference		1105±32	115±3	1.01±.05	1.65±.06
Source Z	3	909±30	103±8	1.62±.05	1.49±.02
Unassigned	1	966±30	139±4	1.37±.06	1.47±.06

Table 2. Elemental abundances by abbreviated neutron activation analysis of Wild Cane Cay obsidian samples.

Source	Artifact No.	Ba	Dy	K,%	Mn	Na,%
Ixtepeque	235-2	1072±39	2.33±.13	3.69±.30	465±5	3.094±.020
	269-1	1060±32	2.41±.08	3.67±.30	453±4	3.067±.018
	340-1	1039±37	2.44±.13	3.73±.30	460±5	3.112±.026
Reference Sample		1030±27	2.30±.11	3.61±.26	449±9	3.05±.06
El Chayal	275-1	943±27	2.72±.07	3.21±.16	641±6	3.136±.017
	387-1	865±52	2.82±.16	3.20±.30	643±7	3.192±.021
	392-1	890±47	2.44±.15	3.50±.30	636±6	3.113±.021
Reference Sample		915±35	2.66±.11	3.45±.26	649±13	3.15±.06
Rio Pixcaya	240-2	1123±50	1.85±.14	3.39±.29	533±6	2.966±.020
Reference Sample		1105±32	2.03±.10	3.54±.25	521±10	2.94±.05
Source Z	250-1	856±35	2.69±.13	4.02±.34	610±5	3.095±.020
	366-1	896±32	2.76±.08	3.04±.16	604±6	3.020±.017

Table 3. Elemental abundances of complete neutron activation analysis of source Z from Wild Cane Cay (Artifact 250-1).

Element	Abundance	Element	Abundance	Element	Abundance
%Al	6.85±.12	%Fe	.544±.007	Sb	.84±.08
Ba	907±15	Hf	3.02±.05	Sc	1.51±.02
Ce	43.6±.6	%K	4.02±.33	Sm	3.02±.03
Co	.16±.05	La	22.2±.4	Ta	.973±.010
Cs	6.52±.10	Mn	610±12	Th	11.21±.11
Dy	2.69±.13	%Na	3.095±.062	U	4.88±.05
Eu	.566±.009	Rb	166±5	Yb	2.07±.03

Table 4. Elemental abundances of five additional obsidian artifacts by XRF.

Source	Artifact No.	Ba(ppm)	Zr(ppm)	Rb/Zr	Sr/Zr
Z	MKIL-401	895	107	1.47±.05	1.47±.05
	MKIL-402	920	104	1.54±.05	1.46±.05
	MKIL-403	940	109	1.55±.05	1.50±.05
Mean		918	107	1.52±.04	1.48±.02
Reference	(see Table 1)	909	103	1.62±.05	1.49±.02
Ucareo	MKIL-404	162	140	1.14±.03	.09±.01
Reference		144[1]	133	1.18±.06	.09±.02
La Esperanza	MKIL-400	730[2]	157	1.03±.04	.99±.03

Notes.
1. Source analysis is only partially complete, with the source sample kindly provided by Fred W. Nelson.
2. Source analysis is only partially complete, with source samples kindly provided by Payson Sheets and Kenneth Hirth.

Table 5. Elemental abundances of five additional obsidian artifacts by abbreviated neutron activation analysis.

Source	Artifact No.	Dy(ppm)	K,%	Mn(ppm)	Na,%
Z	MKIL-401	2.94±.11	3.57±.24	609±12	3.02±.06
Reference	(see Table 1)	2.69±.13	4.00±.33	610±5	3.10±.02
Ucareo	MKIL-404	3.86±.09	4.27±.21	167±3	2.85±.06
Reference		3.82±.10	4.46±.32	168±2	2.85±.06
La Esperanza	MKIL-400	2.39±.10	3.83±.23	430±9	2.84±.06
Reference		2.36±.11	3.75±.17	427±6	2.84±.04

In a separate study, we compared the Wild Cane Cay obsidian source use with that at other lowland Maya sites (McKillop and Jackson 1988). That study included sourcing data on obsidian artifacts from sites throughout the Maya lowlands that were chemically sourced to one of the three main Maya highland sources of El Chayal, Ixtepeque, or Rio Pixcaya and were from dated archaeological deposits. The Wild Cane Cay obsidian source data substantially improve the data base for comparing coastal and inland obsidian source use during the Classic and Postclassic. Most of the sourced samples from other coastal Maya sites are too small to include the variety of sources that were probably used during this time. In the Classic coastal sample, El Chayal is the dominant source with 60%, Ixtepeque a significant secondary source with 38%, and Rio Pixcaya a minor source represented by one item. The coastal and inland patterns of reliance on obsidian sources are similar, although the larger inland sample reveals reliance on El Chayal and Rio Pixcaya and less reliance on Ixtepeque than does the coastal sample. Comparison of coastal and inland obsidian source use during the Postclassic reveals a similar dominance of Ixtepeque, secondary use of El Chayal, and tertiary use of Rio Pixcaya. Although Ixtepeque obsidian is the main source used at both coastal and inland sites, reliance on Ixtepeque is much greater at coastal sites than it is inland.

DISCUSSION

The Wild Cane Cay source data provides several insights into the nature and development of coastal Maya trade. Long distance sea trade along the coast to Belize increased dramatically during the Postclassic. In contrast, Classic coastal trade was evidently less extensive than in the Postclassic.

Chemical sourcing of obsidian from dated deposits at Wild Cane Cay has allowed us to evaluate the role of temporal factors in obsidian source use at the island in relation to two contrasting hypotheses (Hammond 1976; Nelson 1985). Sourcing of 105 obsidian artifacts from the island resulted in the assignment of obsidian to seven sources ranging from central Mexico to highland Honduras, including the new, unlocated Source Z. Similar patterns of obsidian source use at coastal and inland sites in both the Classic and Postclassic do not support an interpretation of separate coastal and inland transportation routes for Ixtepeque and El Chayal obsidian. The Wild Cane Cay data indicate there were changes in obsidian source use over time. This is supported by available data from other lowland Maya sites (McKillop 1987; McKillop and Jackson 1988; Nelson 1985). Both coastal and inland routes were probably used throughout prehistory with inland and coastal settlements integrated into regional trade networks within Maya lowlands (see also Dreiss 1988; Healey et al. 1984; McKillop 1987; McKillop and Jackson 1988; Nelson 1985; Stross et al. 1983).

ACKNOWLEDGEMENTS

Wild Cane Cay Obsidian was sourced with a National Science Foundation Dissertation Grant (100 artifacts) and support of Northeastern Archaeological Associates (NEA; five artifacts). The 1982 field research was funded by a Social Sciences and Humanities Research Council of Canada (SSHRC) doctoral fellowship and by the University of California, Santa Barbara. A 1988 SSHRC postdoctoral fellowship and NEA supported the fieldwork. Research was made possible through permits and assistance from the Belize Dept. of Archaeology. To these and other agencies, our fieldworkers (M. Beaudry, F. Cabral, A. Chan, M. Mychailowyz, L. Stephenson, M. Stonecipher, and B. Walsh), and many others who assisted the research, we extend our gratitude.

REFERENCES

Dreiss, M.L. (1988). An Obsidian Distribution Model for the Belize Periphery. In (H. McKillop & P. F. Healy eds.) Coastal Maya Trade. Occasional Paper 8, Department of Anthropology, Trent University.

Hammond, N. (1976). Maya Obsidian Trade in Southern Belize. In (T.R. Hester & N. Hammond eds.) Maya Lithic Studies, pp 71-81, Special Report 4, Center for Archaeological Research, University of Texas, San Antonio.

Healy, P.F., H. McKillop, & B. Walsh (1984). Analysis of Obsidian from Moho Cay, Belize: New Evidence on Classic Maya Trade Routes. Science, 225: 414-417.

Jackson, L.J. and H. McKillop (1987). Maya Trade at Wild Cane Cay, Belize. Archaeology, 40, 1:62-63.

McKillop, H. (1987). Wild Cane Cay, Belize: An Insular Classic Period to Post-Classic Period Maya Trading Station. Phd Dissertation, University of California, Santa Barbara.

McKillop, H. (1988). Coastal Maya Trade Obsidian Densities at Wild Cane Cay, Belize. In (P. McAnany & B. Isaac eds.) Prehistoric Maya Economics of Belize. Research in Economic Anthropology, Supplement 4, In press.

McKillop, H. and L.J. Jackson (1987). Defining Coastal Maya Trade Stations and Transportation Routes. Paper Presented at the 52nd Annual Meeting of the Society for American Archaeology, May, Toronto.

McKillop, H. and L.J. Jackson (1988). Ancient Maya Obsidian Sources and Trade Routes. In (C. Meighan and J. Scalise eds.), Obsidian Dates IV: A compendium of the obsidian hydration determinations made at the UCLA Obsidian Hydration Laboratory. Monograph XXIX, Institute of Archaeology, University of California, Los Angeles: 130-141.

Nelson, F.W. (1985). Summary of Results of Analysis of Obsidian Artifacts from the Maya Lowlands. Scanning Electron Microscopy II: 631-649.

Rice, P.M., H.V. Michael, F. Asaro and F. Stross (1985). Provenience Analysis of Obsidians from the Central Peten Lakes Region, Guatemala. American Antiquity, 50: 591-604.

Stross, F.H., H.R. Bowman, H.V. Michel, F. Asaro, and N. Hammond (1978). Mayan Obsidian Source Correlation for Southern Belize. Archaeometry, 20, 1: 89-93.

Stross, F.H., P. Sheets, F. Asaro, and H.V. Michel (1983). Precise Characterization of Guatemalan Obsidian Sources and Source Determination of Artifacts From Quirigua. American Antiquity, 48: 323-346.

43. Differentiation of Obsidian Sources in Mesoamerica

M.D. GLASCOCK and J. M. ELAM
Research Reactor Facility, University of Missouri, Columbia, MO 65211, U.S.A.

R. H. COBEAN
Instituto Nacional de Antropologia e Historia, Mexico City, Mexico.

ABSTRACT: *Neutron activation analysis results are reported for obsidian sources in the Mexican state of Hidalgo. Statistical analyses permitted differentiating between sources and assignment of provenance to obsidian artifacts from Tula.*

INTRODUCTION

The pre-Hispanic peoples of Mesoamerica made extensive use of the volcanic glass obsidian as a material for manufacturing tools, weapons and some decorative objects. The presence of large quantities of obsidian artifacts at archaeological sites great distances from the known geological occurrences provides significant evidence of the movement of obsidian from a source point to a utilization point. Analytical techniques such as instrumental neutron activation analysis (INAA) and X-ray fluorescence (XRF) used for chemical characterization or "fingerprinting" of obsidian have been recognized for their contribution to the reconstruction of ancient production systems and trade routes and in assessing the changing importance of obsidian in Mesoamerican prehistory (Asaro et al. 1978; Boksenbaum et al. 1987; Nelson 1985).

GEOLOGICAL SOURCES IN MESOAMERICA

The obsidian sources in Mesoamerica are located in two major zones of recent volcanism which are geographically separated by a distance of about 900 km.

The southern volcanic region is located in Guatemala, El Salvador and the western edge of Honduras. The northern region runs east-to-west, beginning in north-central Veracruz through all of central Mexico and continuing through northern Michoacan to the Pacific coast in the states of Jalisco and Nayarit. In this northern region, the density of geological obsidian sources is the highest in the state of Hidalgo which lies to the north of Mexico City.

As part of an intensive investigation of obsidian in Mesoamerica by Cobean and other anthropologists from Mexico's Instituto Nacional de Antropologia e Historia, 818 samples (weighing a total of 710 kg) were collected from thirty volcanic sources in central Mexico for the purpose of establishing a "data bank" of element concentrations for each source. Several obsidian source systems extend over areas greater than 15 km by 25 km and comprehensive sampling was performed to permit investigation of possible chemical variability.

In the state of Hidalgo (shown in Figure 1) where many of the sources are chemically similar, twelve source systems were extensively sampled with over 300 samples having been collected and of these 142 were analyzed by the instrumental neutron activation analysis (INAA) laboratory. Through high precision chemical

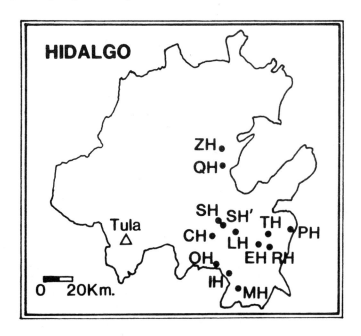

Source Abbreviation Key

CH – El Chapulin
EH – El Encinal
IH – Cerro del Ixtete
LH – Santa Elena
MH – Malpais
OH – Totolapa
PH – Tepalzingo
QH – Metzquititlan
RH – Rancho Tenango
SH – Sierra de Pachuca
TH – El Pizarrin
ZH – Zacualtipan

Figure 1. Map of Hidalgo showing archaeological site at Tula and the obsidian sources reported in this paper.

Element	Measured Isotope	Gamma-ray Energy	SRM–278 Obsidian Rock		SRM–1633a Fly Ash	
short irradiation NAA:						
Chlorine	Cl–38	1642.2	640.	ppm	----	
Dysprosium	Dy–165	94.7	6.27	ppm	14.6	ppm
Manganese	Mn–56	846.8	401.	ppm	190.	ppm
Potassium	K–42	1524.7	3.45	%	1.89	%
Sodium	Na–24	1368.6	3.52	%	0.165	%
long irradiation NAA:						
Antimony	Sb–124	1691.0	1.60	ppm	6.15	ppm
Barium	Ba–131	496.3	881.	ppm	1320.	ppm
Cerium	Ce–141	145.4	61.4	ppm	168.3	ppm
Cesium	Cs–134	795.8	5.10	ppm	10.42	ppm
Cobalt	Co–60	1332.5	1.44	ppm	44.1	ppm
Europium	Eu–152	1408.0	0.766	ppm	3.58	ppm
Hafnium	Hf–181	482.2	8.09	ppm	7.29	ppm
Iron	Fe–59	1099.3	1.398	%	9.38	%
Lanthanum	La–140	1596.2	30.1	ppm	79.1	ppm
Lutetium	Lu–177	208.4	0.682	ppm	1.075	ppm
Neodymium	Nd–147	91.1	25.4	ppm	75.7	ppm
Rubidium	Rb–86	1076.6	126.	ppm	134.	ppm
Scandium	Sc–46	889.3	4.96	ppm	38.6	ppm
Tantalum	Ta–182	1221.4	1.24	ppm	1.93	ppm
Terbium	Tb–160	879.4	0.895	ppm	2.38	ppm
Thorium	Pa–233	312.0	11.65	ppm	24.0	ppm
Uranium	Np–239	106.1	4.46	ppm	10.2	ppm
Ytterbium	Yb–175	396.3	4.50	ppm	7.50	ppm
Zinc	Zn–65	1115.6	54.0	ppm	220.	ppm
Zirconium	Zr–95	756.8	290.	ppm	240.	ppm
prompt gamma NAA:						
Boron	B–10(n,γ)	477.6	25.2	ppm	39.2	ppm
Gadolinium	Gd–158(n,γ)	181.9	5.34	ppm	16.0	ppm
Samarium	Sm–150(n,γ)	333.9	5.80	ppm	16.83	ppm

Table 1. Element concentrations for the reference materials used in the study.

characterization and application of canonical discriminant analysis a significant differentiation between many of these chemically similar sources has been established. Use of the Missouri obsidian data bank is demonstrated by assigning source provenance to 47 obsidian artifacts excavated from the ancient Toltec capital of Tula which is also located in the state of Hidalgo.

ANALYTICAL PROCEDURES

Detailed investigations of sample preparation procedures, evaluation of analytical standards,

development of new techniques and application of methods to correct for interferences were conducted during the course of this project. As a result, a procedure described by Vogt et al. (1982) involving the etching of samples with HF acid, cracking between tool steel plates with a hydraulic press, and selection of interior fragments, was used to obtain a representative and uncontaminated analytical specimen for each source sample. Evaluation of standards by Graham et al. (1982) led to the selection of National Bureau of Standards' (NBS) standard reference material Obsidian Rock (SRM-278) as the primary analytical standard and NBS Fly Ash (SRM-1633a) for quality control. Table 1 lists for both standards the gamma-rays and

Table 2. Elemental abundances in parts per million for obsidian sources in Hidalgo, Mexico.

Element	CH El Chapulin, Hidalgo (n = 5)	SH Sierra de Pachuca, Hidalgo (n = 48)	PH Tepalzingo, Hidalgo (n = 10)	RH Rancho Tenango, Hidalgo (n = 10)	EH El Encinal, Hidalgo (n = 10)	TH El Pizarrin, Hidalgo (n = 15)
B	16.8 ± 0.3	15.8 ± 1.3	44.2 ± 1.5	55.2 ± 1.1	56.3 ± 0.8	55.8 ± 1.7
Ba	20 ± 14	19 ± 12	892 ± 12	747 ± 14	733 ± 21	762 ± 14
Ce	90.2 ± 2.2	95.1 ± 6.8	138 ± 2	160 ± 2	158 ± 2	160 ± 3
Cl	1690 ± 90	1400 ± 350	982 ± 82	1150 ± 70	1280 ± 110	1240 ± 60
Co	0.046 ± 0.010	0.048 ± 0.009	0.157 ± 0.037	0.037 ± 0.006	0.037 ± 0.007	0.043 ± 0.006
Cs	3.83 ± 0.07	3.76 ± 0.36	4.64 ± 0.04	5.75 ± 0.06	5.73 ± 0.07	5.74 ± 0.08
Dy	15.5 ± 0.5	15.9 ± 0.8	12.0 ± 0.4	15.2 ± 0.6	16.5 ± 0.9	16.5 ± 0.8
Eu	1.51 ± 0.04	1.56 ± 0.06	1.75 ± 0.01	1.66 ± 0.02	1.61 ± 0.03	1.64 ± 0.03
Fe (%)	1.55 ± 0.03	1.55 ± 0.07	1.83 ± 0.02	1.78 ± 0.02	1.76 ± 0.02	1.80 ± 0.02
Gd	11.0 ± 0.2	10.9 ± 0.7	11.8 ± 0.4	14.7 ± 0.4	14.9 ± 0.2	14.7 ± 0.5
Hf	26.4 ± 0.5	26.1 ± 2.1	12.7 ± 0.2	18.1 ± 0.3	18.0 ± 0.5	18.2 ± 0.3
K (%)	3.87 ± 0.12	3.86 ± 0.35	3.46 ± 0.20	3.55 ± 0.18	3.77 ± 0.20	3.74 ± 0.22
La	38.1 ± 0.4	38.9 ± 2.1	64.9 ± 0.5	74.9 ± 0.5	72.9 ± 0.6	74.9 ± 0.8
Lu	1.84 ± 0.02	1.84 ± 0.10	1.04 ± 0.01	1.26 ± 0.01	1.24 ± 0.01	1.27 ± 0.02
Mn	1140 ± 10	1100 ± 129	487 ± 14	403 ± 11	430 ± 21	431 ± 22
Na (%)	3.76 ± 0.05	3.73 ± 0.15	3.54 ± 0.10	3.51 ± 0.09	3.69 ± 0.16	3.67 ± 0.18
Nd	32.6 ± 1.1	35.9 ± 4.7	67.3 ± 3.4	82.4 ± 1.4	74.0 ± 2.1	74.1 ± 3.2
Rb	188 ± 4	185 ± 13	116 ± 2	121 ± 1	120 ± 2	122 ± 2
Sb	0.254 ± 0.009	0.262 ± 0.019	1.12 ± 0.02	1.82 ± 0.02	1.71 ± 0.02	1.66 ± 0.03
Sc	3.16 ± 0.05	3.25 ± 0.08	3.70 ± 0.04	0.729 ± 0.012	0.717 ± 0.009	0.744 ± 0.012
Sm	10.2 ± 0.1	10.3 ± 1.1	13.3 ± 0.4	16.3 ± 0.4	16.6 ± 0.3	16.5 ± 0.4
Ta	4.70 ± 0.13	4.79 ± 0.13	2.07 ± 0.03	2.31 ± 0.02	2.31 ± 0.03	2.31 ± 0.04
Tb	2.08 ± 0.04	2.12 ± 0.13	1.87 ± 0.03	2.28 ± 0.03	2.29 ± 0.02	2.35 ± 0.04
Th	17.5 ± 0.4	17.8 ± 0.5	11.1 ± 0.1	11.8 ± 0.1	11.7 ± 0.1	11.8 ± 0.2
U	4.71 ± 0.49	4.15 ± 0.52	2.33 ± 0.22	2.74 ± 0.41	3.68 ± 0.12	3.16 ± 0.38
Yb	12.1 ± 0.1	12.0 ± 0.4	7.21 ± 0.08	8.78 ± 0.10	8.72 ± 0.07	8.83 ± 0.14
Zn	192 ± 6	193 ± 24	146 ± 2	182 ± 2	170 ± 2	170 ± 4
Zr	920 ± 17	906 ± 58	486 ± 15	747 ± 13	721 ± 27	733 ± 18

Table 2. Elemental abundances in parts per million for obsidian sources in Hidalgo, Mexico (contd.)

Element	ZH Zacualtipan, Hidalgo (n = 15)	QH Mezquititlan, Hidalgo (n = 5)	LH Santa Elena, Hidalgo (n = 5)	MH Malpais, Hidalgo (n = 9)	OH Totolapa, Hidalgo (n = 5)	IH Cerro del Ixtete Hidalgo (n = 5)
B	51.1 ± 1.8	53.3 ± 3.7	50.5 ± 0.8	28.7 ± 0.6	29.2 ± 1.1	28.4 ± 0.6
Ba	252 ± 14	250 ± 9	61 ± 9	780 ± 9	782 ± 16	788 ± 9
Ce	108 ± 2	109 ± 1	106 ± 2	49.8 ± 0.6	49.4 ± 1.1	49.9 ± 0.6
Cl	564 ± 76	584 ± 67	1310 ± 50	521 ± 43	513 ± 104	473 ± 95
Co	1.24 ± 0.19	1.15 ± 0.09	0.246 ± 0.005	0.382 ± 0.018	0.374 ± 0.011	0.384 ± 0.050
Cs	15.6 ± 0.3	15.8 ± 0.3	5.37 ± 0.04	5.13 ± 0.07	5.05 ± 0.08	5.13 ± 0.04
Dy	7.29 ± 0.24	7.02 ± 0.48	7.95 ± 0.19	3.20 ± 0.19	3.07 ± 0.14	3.08 ± 0.13
Eu	0.467 ± 0.019	0.471 ± 0.020	0.216 ± 0.004	0.428 ± 0.006	0.436 ± 0.008	0.438 ± 0.006
Fe (%)	1.06 ± 0.04	1.07 ± 0.04	0.784 ± 0.009	0.735 ± 0.008	0.735 ± 0.015	0.741 ± 0.013
Gd	6.28 ± 0.14	6.28 ± 0.06	6.33 ± 0.18	2.78 ± 0.07	2.76 ± 0.06	2.68 ± 0.10
Hf	7.07 ± 0.14	7.14 ± 0.11	6.64 ± 0.09	3.32 ± 0.03	3.31 ± 0.04	3.33 ± 0.04
K (%)	4.56 ± 0.12	4.14 ± 0.10	4.01 ± 0.10	3.35 ± 0.21	3.38 ± 0.16	3.27 ± 0.24
La	52.8 ± 0.5	52.5 ± 0.7	51.5 ± 1.1	25.6 ± 0.4	25.7 ± 0.3	25.8 ± 0.5
Lu	0.700 ± 0.027	0.691 ± 0.026	0.799 ± 0.014	0.292 ± 0.009	0.291 ± 0.013	0.295 ± 0.008
Mn	172 ± 8	163 ± 8	359 ± 14	422 ± 13	418 ± 10	417 ± 8
Na (%)	2.47 ± 0.05	2.40 ± 0.09	2.91 ± 0.09	3.12 ± 0.09	3.09 ± 0.08	3.05 ± 0.11
Nd	33.1 ± 1.0	32.6 ± 2.0	35.4 ± 1.5	17.0 ± 0.6	16.5 ± 0.6	16.2 ± 0.6
Rb	278 ± 4	280 ± 3	157 ± 2	116 ± 2	113 ± 3	115 ± 1
Sb	1.04 ± 0.03	1.04 ± 0.02	1.27 ± 0.04	0.545 ± 0.010	0.577 ± 0.028	0.569 ± 0.027
Sc	3.08 ± 0.06	3.09 ± 0.05	2.24 ± 0.03	1.76 ± 0.02	1.75 ± 0.04	1.76 ± 0.02
Sm	7.57 ± 0.17	7.59 ± 0.09	7.57 ± 0.19	3.36 ± 0.12	3.46 ± 0.09	3.38 ± 0.06
Ta	1.93 ± 0.03	1.93 ± 0.01	2.93 ± 0.03	1.11 ± 0.01	1.10 ± 0.02	1.11 ± 0.01
Tb	1.12 ± 0.02	1.10 ± 0.02	1.09 ± 0.01	0.445 ± 0.009	0.435 ± 0.007	0.448 ± 0.006
Th	35.8 ± 0.6	36.1 ± 0.4	16.6 ± 0.2	10.4 ± 0.1	10.2 ± 0.2	10.4 ± 0.1
U	11.5 ± 0.2	11.7 ± 0.2	4.12 ± 0.29	3.19 ± 0.04	3.19 ± 0.20	3.20 ± 0.22
Yb	4.93 ± 0.08	4.86 ± 0.07	5.31 ± 0.07	2.01 ± 0.09	2.01 ± 0.07	1.99 ± 0.09
Zn	37.4 ± 1.4	37.5 ± 0.7	52.7 ± 0.4	36.2 ± 0.4	37.7 ± 0.3	38.5 ± 0.6
Zr	168 ± 9	166 ± 12	165 ± 6	98 ± 5	92 ± 4	95 ± 2

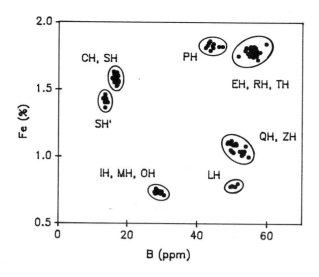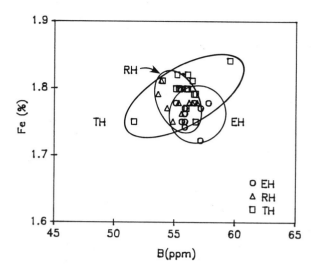

Figure 2. Bivariate plots for Fe versus B from Hidalgo source data.

reference concentrations used for 28 elements routinely measured in all obsidian source and artifact samples at the University of Missouri Research Reactor (MURR).

Three different INAA procedures were applied to source and artifact samples which were generally analyzed in batches of 25-30 with five each SRM-278 standards and SRM-1633a quality controls. The short irradiation procedure utilized samples weighing about 50 mg placed in polyethylene vials which were irradiated for 5 seconds in a neutron flux of 8×10^{13} neutrons cm^{-2}s^{-1} followed by a 25-minute decay and a 12-minute count with a high resolution Ge(Li) detector (80 cm^3 active volume, 1.70 keV resolution at 1332 keV). The long irradiation procedure utilized samples weighing 250 mg, each of which were placed in sealed quartz ampoules and irradiated for 72 hours at a flux of 5×10^{13} neutrons cm^{-2} s^{-1}. Following the long irradiation, samples and standards were transferred to clean unirradiated containers and counted twice. The first count was 2000 seconds following a cooling period of 8-10 days to determine the elements Ba, La, Lu, Nd, U and Yb. A count of 4 hours was done after cooling period of about 8 weeks to determine Ce, Co, Cs, Eu, Fe, Hf, Rb, Sb, Sc, Ta, Tb, Th, Zn and Zr. The elements Ba, La, Ce, Nd and Zr were corrected for interferences caused by neutron-induced fission of the constituent ^{235}U by the method explained by Glascock et al. (1986). The PGNAA procedure utilized samples weighing 0.5-1 gram which were irradiated for 1-2 hours in PGNAA Facility at MURR where the flux is 5×10^8 neutrons cm^{-2}s^{-1}. The PGNAA technique which is further described by Glascock et al. (1985) yields concentrations for Gd, Sm and B.

RESULTS

For each of the Hidalgo sources investigated, the resultant element concentrations are recorded in Table 2 with means and errors expressed in one standard deviation

of the mean for each element. In general the Hidalgo sources were found to be very homogeneous as exhibited by the high precisions to which the data were determined. For example, El Pizarrin source with its fifteen replicate determinations was found to have 17 of the 28 elements determined with precisions of 5% or better. An exception was the very large Sierra de Pachuca source which exhibited a significant variation along one particular flow designated as the SH' source in Figure 1.

A comparison between our data and Boksenbaum et al. (1987) for the Sierra da Pachuca and El Pizarrin sources found satisfactory agreement for only seven elements and serious disagreement for thirteen others. These discrepancies are thought to be due to differences between the analytical standards used. A follow-up study is currently under way to resolve these differences.

INTERPRETATION AND DISCUSSIONS

Initial attempts to find unique compositional patterns for each of the sources were made by examining bivariate plots for several element pairs (e.g., Fe vs. B as shown in Figure 2a). Careful inspection of these and all other bivariate plots easily separated the specimens collected along the SH' flow from Sierra de Pachuca. However, several of the neighboring sources were found to overlap (i.e., CH+SH, QH+ZH, IH+MH+OH and EH+RH+TH). Evidence of this is shown in Figure 2b which is an expanded bivariate plot for Fe vs. B containing the EH+RH+TH specimens only. In order to determine the most precise provenance for artifacts it was desirable that a significant differentiation between these individuals sources be identified.

Using the 17 most precise elements, the concentrations were transformed into base 10 logarithms and the Mean Euclidian Distances calculated between specimens. The Brookhaven program AGCLUS was used to cluster by the

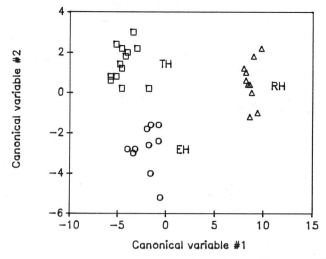

Figure 3. Plot of canonical discriminant functions for specimens from the neighbouring EH, RH, and TH sources.

average-link method. The resulting dendrograms found the same groupings indicated by the bivariate plots with minimal discrimination for the neighbouring sources.

The next procedure performed was principal components analysis using the FACTOR program from the SAS Institute (1985). From the inspection of the calculated variable loadings on each of the three most significant factors, the least correlated variables which explained the greatest differences between sources could be identified. Ten of the elements with the best precision

(Ce, Cs, Eu, Fe, Hf, Rb, Sc, Th, Zn, and B) were identified as being those least correlated. Using these elements, the canonical discriminant analysis (CDA) procedure CANDISC (also from the SAS Institute) was applied to specimens in the overlapping EH+RH+TH group. CANDISC computes the Mahalanobis distances both between groups for specimens within groups. CDA derives the canonical variables summarizing the between-group variation in a manner similar to the way the PCA summarizes total variation. Figure 3 illustrates the successful differentiation found between the sources EH,

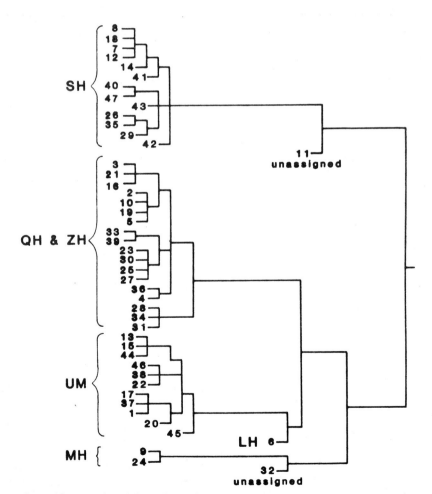

Figure 4. Dendrogram for artifacts analyzed from Tula using AGCLUS with the least correlated elements.

250

RH and TH sources. This procedure was successfully applied to the IH+MH+OH group but the results for the CH+SH or QH+ZH source groups were found to be less satisfactory. The artifacts from Tula were analyzed by INAA in the same manner as the source samples and when clustered with the AGCLUS program using the ten most discriminating variables mentioned above were easily assigned provenances. Figure 4 represents an AGCLUS dendrogram for the 47 obsidian artifacts from Tula. Thirteen were assigned a provenance of SH, eighteen were assigned a provenance of QH+ZH, two were assigned to MH and one assigned to the LH source. In addition, eleven were found to have come from Ucareo, Michoacan (UM) and two others could not be assigned.

CONCLUSIONS

The University of Missouri program to analyze obsidian from Mesoamerica has produced high-precision concentration data for twenty-eight elements. Although many Mesoamerican sources can be identified uniquely, some of the Hidalgo sources are difficult to differentiate from one another. Canonical discriminant analysis using Mahalanobis distance procedures has been shown to be a useful multivariate statistical method for some problems requiring discrimination between obsidian sources.

ACKNOWLEDGEMENTS

The authors acknowledge support provided by the National Science Foundation grants 79-15409 and CHE 80-26528 during the course of this project.

REFERENCES

Asaro, F., Michael, H.V. Sidrys, R. and Stross, F. (1978). High-precision chemical characterization of major obsidian sources in Guatemala. American Antiquity, 4: 436-443.

Boksenbaum, M.W., Tolstoy, P., Harbottle, G., Kimberlin, J., and Neivens, M. (1987). Obsidian industries and cultural evolution in the basin of Mexico before 500 B.C. Journal of Field Archaeology, 14: 65-75.

Glascock, M.D., Coveney, R.M. Jr., Tittle, C.W., Gartner, M.L. and Murphy R.D. (1985). Geochemical applications for prompt gamma neutron activation. Nuclear Instruments and Methods in Physics Research, B10/11: 1042-1046.

Glascock M.D., Nabelek, P.I., Weinrich, D. D. and Coveney, R.M. Jr. (1986). Correcting for uranium fission in instrumental neutron activation analysis of high-uranium rocks. Journal of Radioanalytical and Nuclear Chemistry, 99: 121-131.

Graham, C.C., Glascock, M.D., Carni, J.J., Vogt, J.R. and Spading, D.G. (1982). Determination of elements in the National Bureau of Standards' geological standard reference materials by neutron activation analysis. Analytical Chemistry, 54: 1623-1627.

Nelson, F.W. (1985). Summary of the results of the analysis of obsidian artifacts from Maya lowlands. Scanning Electron Microscopy, II: 631-649.

SAS Inst. Inc. (1985). SAS User's Guide: Statistics, Cary, North Carolina.

Vogt J.R., Graham C.C., Glascock, M.D. and Cobean, R.H. (1982). A study of Mesoamerican obsidian sources using activation analysis. Journal of Radioanalytical Chemistry, 69: 271-289.

44. Magneto-Archaeometry: A New Technique for Ceramic Analysis

K. L. VEROSUB
B. M. MOSKOWITZ
Department of Geology, University of California, Davis, CA, 95616 U.S.A.

ABSTRACT: *Magnetic analysis of ceramic artifacts provides information on provenience and technology. Results from Etruscan Bucchero and southwestern Anasazi pottery are given.*

INTRODUCTION

Magneto-archaeometry is the application of rock magnetism and magnetic property measurements to the study of ancient ceramic wares. The subtle variation of diverse magnetic properties with chemical composition and microstructure of iron oxide phases, which are common accessory minerals in many archaeological materials, provides the basis for the methods of magneto-archaeometry. Magnetic property measurements of ceramic materials can be used to infer cultural variables such as manufacturing methods, firing conditions, trading patterns, and provenience. In some cases, magneto-archaeometry can supplement information obtained by other archaeometric methods. In other cases, magneto-archaeometry can provide a faster, simpler, and less expensive alternative to existing methods.

Iron oxides occur in many natural and archaeological materials. Whether incorporated naturally or added intentionally, trace amounts of iron oxides are usually present in the clays, tempers, pigments, and glazes used by ancient potters. The various forms of iron oxides determine the aesthetic qualities, such as colour, as well as the magnetic characteristics of ancient ceramic wares. Because the magnetic properties of the different forms of iron oxides and hydroxides vary both as functions of composition of the iron oxides and of their grain size, bulk magnetic properties of ceramic materials are potentially useful in archaeology. Bulk magnetic properties refer to any magnetic characteristic that provides information not directly related to the direction or intensity of the ancient geomagnetic field. For example, the original clay material used to produce individual pottery may carry a distinctive magnetic mineralogy, magnetic grain size, or concentration of magnetic phases, which can be useful in determining provenience. The physico-chemical transformations that occur in iron oxides upon firing and aging of pottery can produce characteristic magnetic properties and provide information on firing methods (i.e., firing temperatures and kiln atmospheres). In addition, the methods of forming and shaping a pot may impart a magnetic fabric to the finished piece due to the preferred orientation of mineral grains. Shape or crystal alignment of magnetic grains in pottery can cause a directional dependence of certain magnetic properties, such as magnetic susceptibility (i.e., magnetic anisotropy). Magnetic anisotropy measurements may therefore yield information on manufacturing styles, such as wheel-spun versus molded methods.

Only a few studies have used bulk magnetic properties of archaeological material to obtain information on provenience or manufacturing technique. As an example of provenience studies, McDougall et al. (1983) and Schmidbauer et al. (1986) measured various magnetic properties of obsidian samples from different Mediterranean sources. They found that magnetic analysis could discriminate between obsidian sources. Magnetic properties of ancient metallic coins have also been investigated with some success (Tanner et al. 1979; Tarling 1982; Hoye 1983).

These studies show that magnetic analysis of archaeological materials can provide data useful for archaeological interpretation. Similar magnetic studies have been applied to a host of geological and environmental problems in recent years (e.g., Thompson and Oldfield 1986). The element common in these studies, which makes them appropriate for ceramic analysis, is the systematic variation of magnetic properties with grain size and composition exhibited by naturally occurring magnetic minerals. The ease, versatility, and speed of most magnetic measurement methods make them ideally suited for studying large collections of potsherds. Most magnetic methods are also nondestructive. Furthermore, certain magnetic properties can even be measured in the field at archaeological sites.

We present first an overview of techniques in rock magnetism that are useful for magneto-archaeometry, we will then demonstrate the usefulness of magneto-archaeometry with results from Etruscan bucchero and Anasazi pottery.

TECHNIQUES OF MAGNETO-ARCHAEOMETRY

Magnetic Mineralogy

Magnetite and haematite are common magnetic minerals which can retain a permanent magnetization and are most likely responsible for the magnetic characteristics of pottery. The relative amounts of both minerals and their grain sizes will be a function of original source materials, firing temperature, and firing atmosphere. Firing in air will oxidize most iron oxides and hydroxides to haematite, whereas firing under reducing conditions will produce magnetite; however, impurities in the clay (such as calcium-bearing minerals) can also inhibit or promote the growth of iron oxide phases (e.g., Shepard 1963). The magnetic properties of magnetite and haematite are so distinctly different from each other that simple magnetic measurements can often determine which phase is present. However, because magnetite is some 200 times more magnetic than haematite, it can be detected magnetically in much smaller amounts (down to 1 part in 10^6).

The degree to which one substance may be described as being more or less magnetic than another can be stated quantitatively in terms of its magnetic susceptibility (X_o) and saturation magnetization (σ_s). Magnetic susceptibility is a measure of the ease with which the magnetic moment of a substance can be aligned in a magnetic field. Saturation magnetization is the maximum alignment of the magnetic moment of a ferromagnetic solid. It is an intrinsic property, independent of grain size but dependent on temperature. As a sample is heated, the observed magnetization decreases and σ_s goes to zero at the Curie temperature (T_c). Curie temperatures are characteristic of the magnetic phases and provide a useful means of identification. For example, the Curie temperatures of magnetite and haematite are 580°C and 680°C, respectively. Once the composition of the magnetic phase is known, the saturation magnetization or initial susceptibility yields the concentration of the phase.

Magnetic Granulometry

Estimating grain sizes of magnetic phases by magnetic methods is called magnetic granulometry. Although there are many different magnetic properties that can be measured, only a few have been shown to be particularly useful in studies of magnetic granulometry. Ratios of certain magnetic parameters vary in a systematic fashion with magnetic grain size and hence can provide information on this characteristic (e.g., Thompson and Oldfield 1986).

Isothermal Remanent Magnetization (IRM)

When a magnetic field is applied to a ferromagnetic substance and then reduced to zero, the magnetization does not go to zero but persists as an isothermal remanent magnetization (IRM). The maximum IRM is a saturation remanent magnetization (SIRM). The ratio SIRM/X_o provides information on composition and grain size (e.g., Thompson and Oldfield 1986).

Anhysteretic Remanent Magnetization (ARM)

Hysteric remnant magnetism is another useful parameter for pottery containing magnetite. Hysteric remnant magnetism is induced in a large alternating field (e.g., 120 milliTesla (mT)) which is slowly reduced to zero in the presence of a steady field (usually on the order of the earth's field, 0.1 mT). Then the steady field is switched off too, leading to the acquisition of an ARM. Fine grains of magnetite (<1 μm) have high ARM intensity, which decreases rapidly with grain size. Unlike SIRM, which magnetizes all grains in a sample, ARM is more sensitive to fine grains. Comparison of ARM to X_o, a parameter more sensitive to the presence of coarse grains, yields an effective method of determining relative changes in magnetic grain sizes in magnetite (Banerjee et al. 1981; King et al. 1982). On a plot of ARM versus X_o, points which have higher values of (ARM-X_o) have finer grain sizes than those which have lower values of ARM/X_o. Moreover, the farther a point plots away from the origin, the greater the relative concentration of magnetite it contains.

Acquisition and Demagnetization Techniques

The shapes of acquisition and demagnetization curves of IRM and ARM are also informative. The IRM acquisition curve is determined by applying incrementally increasing DC magnetic fields to initially demagnetized samples and measuring the remanence after each increment. Magnetite bearing samples will approach saturation by 100-300 mT, whereas haematite bearing samples will saturate in much higher fields. Likewise, the demagnetization curve is determined by applying incremental AC fields to a sample with a SIRM or ARM. The AC field at which the remanence is reduced by half (median destructive field) is also a diagnostic parameter.

Thermomagnetic Analysis

Thermomagnetic analysis is the study of the temperature dependence of saturation magnetization. Besides determining the Curie temperature, the reversibility of the heating and cooling curves may provide additional information on composition and grain size. Failure of the cooling curve to follow the heating curve indicates that changes have taken place in the magnetic mineralogy on heating. For instance, these changes may be due to chemical reactions which alter the initial mineralogy on heating or may be caused by changes in grain size or crystallinity. Different types of thermomagnetic curves may therefore be characteristic of different types of pottery. This technique is destructive but only a small amount of sample (a few hundred mg) is needed.

RESULTS

Etruscan Bucchero Pottery:

The first example of magneto-archaeometry involves a study of Etruscan bucchero pottery (Moskowitz et al. 1987). The region of Etruria is located immediately north of Rome, bounded by the Tiber River to the east and the Tyrrhenian Sea to the west. Bucchero is a form of Etruscan pottery which is characteristically black or gray all the way through. The earliest true bucchero appeared by the mid 7th century B.C. It had developed from a type called buccheroid impasto (a much coarser ware) used widely throughout Etruria during the preceding 200 years. Beginning about 650 B.C., an extremely thin, finely levigated pottery, with a rich black colour and a good hard exterior, known as bucchero sottile (thin), was produced. From about 600 B.C., this ware became gradually thicker, apparently with increasingly greater amounts of grit. By about 500 B.C., however, this ware, known as bucchero spesso (thick), was no longer in production. A whole new line of bucchero was developed contemporarily with bucchero spesso. This ware was more gritty, less dark and frequently had a poor finish. This bucchero pesante (heavy), was popular from about 600-450 B.C. Finally, a type known as grey bucchero was in production from the end of the 6th until the end of the 4th centuries B.C. (for a history of bucchero, see Hirschland-Ramage (1970)).

Our primary magnetic results are shown in Figure 1, which is an example of an ARM-initial susceptibility (ARM-X_o) diagram. Except for the gray ware ceramics, the 8th through 5th century B.C. ceramics plot along a straight line indicating that the ratio of ARM susceptibility to initial susceptibility is approximately constant for these samples. These data show that only slight magnetic grain size variations exist among bucchero sottile, spesso, and pesante

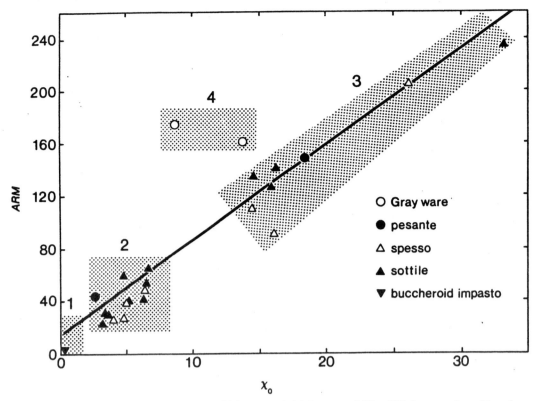

Figure 1. Anhysteretic remanent magnetization (ARM) versus initial susceptibility (X_o) for samples of bucchero pottery. Samples containing finer (coarser) grains of magnetite have steeper (shallower) slopes for lines connecting a sample point with the origin. In addition, the further a data point plots away from the origin, the greater the concentration of magnetite the sample contains. The boundaries of the data fields are plotted only as a rough guide and do not imply any rigorous treatment of the data. The solid line is a linear least-squares fit of groups 1, 2, and 3. Errors are estimated to be less than 5% (Note: SI units are 10^{-7} m³).

pot typologies, but that each individual sample contains different amounts of magnetite. Samples of gray ware have higher values of ARM-X_o, and hence finer magnetic grain sizes. The average weight percent of magnetite determined from the saturation magnetization for the 4 groups in Figure 1 are: (1) 0.02%; (2) 0.06±0.01%; (3) 0.16±0.02%; and (4) 0.26%.

The magnetic mineralogy was determined by thermomagnetic analysis. Curie temperatures ranged from 550°C to 580°C, suggesting that magnetite (T_c=580°C) was the primary magnetic mineral. The coincidence of magnetite, with the black to grey colour of all the samples, suggested that a reducing or nonoxidizing environment prevailed during the initial firing.

Thus our preliminary study of the magnetic properties of bucchero pottery has shown that magnetic analysis can provide some useful information on provenience and firing conditions of ancient ceramic wares. One important conclusion of this study was that bucchero ceramic styles pesante, sottile, and spesso, had similar magnetic grain sizes. This observation suggested a common provenience and similar firing conditions for these pottery typologies, which range in age from the 7th to 5th century B.C. Variations in the amount of magnetite in each sample indicated that slight inhomogeneities existed in the iron oxide/hydroxide content of the local clays. In contrast, gray ware samples had distinctly different magnetic properties and suggested that they may have been produced in minor, hinterland locations. A second important conclusion was that firing occurred in a non-oxidizing atmosphere because magnetite, not haematite,

was present in all samples.

Anasazi Pottery

A second example of magneto-archaeometry) involves a collection of sherds from Mesa Verde in the American southwest (Verosub and Verosub 1987). The material was collected as float near a modern construction site. Although the sherds were small and pottery styles were difficult to identify, at least three styles were present: corrugated, red, and black-on-white. Six different sherds were subjected to a series of rock magnetic measurements, including alternating field demagnetization of the natural remanent magnetization (NRM), bulk magnetic susceptibility, and acquisition and demagnetization of SIRM and ARM. The two sherds of corrugated ware were very consistent in their magnetic properties and magnetically distinct from the other four samples. For example, the median destructive field for the corrugated ware was higher for all three demagnetization procedures (NRM, SIRM, ARM). A comparison of the magnetic susceptibilities and magnetic intensities per unit weight are shown in Figure 2. The sherds of corrugated ware (MV5 and MV6) were 2 to 5 times higher than the other samples in all four categories. Sherds MV1, MV2, and MV4 were generally similar magnetically which was consistent with the observation that stylistically all were forms of black-on-white pottery. Sherd MV3 which was stylistically distinct from the other five was also magnetically distinct. As with the study of Etruscan pottery, this pilot study of Anasazi pottery demonstrates that there are detectable and quantifiable differences in rock magnetic properties associated with

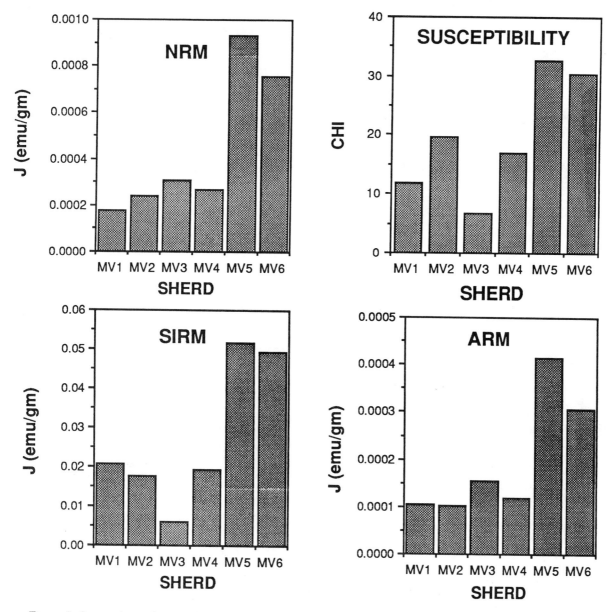

Figure 2. Comparison of some magnetic properties of six sherds of Anasazi pottery from Mesa Verde.

different pottery styles.

REFERENCES

Banerjee, S.K., King, J., and Marvin, J. (1981). A rapid method for magnetic granulometry with applications to environmental studies. Geophysical Research Letters, 8: 333-336.

Hirschland-Ramage, N. (1970). Studies in early Bucchero. Papers of the British School at Rome, 38: 1-61.

Hoye, G.S. (1983). Magnetic properties of ancient coins. Journal of Archaeological Science, 10: 43-49.

King, J.W., Banerjee, S.K., and Marvin, J. (1983). A new rock-magnetic approach to selecting sediments for geomagnetic paleointensity studies: Application to paleointensity for the last 4000 years. Journal of Geophysical Research, 88: 5911-5921.

McDougall, J.M., Tarling, D.H., and Warren, S.E. (1983). The magnetic sourcing of obsidian samples from Mediterranean and Near Eastern sources. Journal of Archaeological Science, 10: 441-452.

Moskowitz, B.M., Lindsay, J., Hemphil, P., and Judson, S. (1987). A magnetic study of Etruscan Bucchero pottery: An application of rock magnetism to archaeometry. Geoarchaeology, 2: 287-300.

Schmidbauer, E., Mosheim, E., and Semioschkina, N. (1986). Magnetization and ^{57}Fe Mössbauer study of obsidians. Physics and Chemistry of Minerals, 13: 256-261.

Shepard, A., (1963). Ceramics for the Archaeologist, Publication 609, Washington, D.C.; Carnegie Institution of Washington, 414 pp.

Tanner, B.K., MacDowall, D.W., MacCormack, I.B., and Smith, R.L. (1979). Ferromagnetism in ancient copper-based coinage. Nature, 280: 46-48.

Tarling, D.H. (1982). Archeomagnetic properties of coins. Archaeometry, 24: 76-79.

Thompson, R. and Oldfield, F. (1986). Environmental Magnetism, London; Allen and Unwin, 227 pp.

Verosub, K.L. and Verosub, A.L. (1987). Preliminary investigation of the rock magnetic properties of pottery from archaeological sites, EOS, 68: 1258.

45. Comparison of Electron and Nuclear Microprobes for the Elemental Composition of Solders on Ancient Gold Artefacts.

G. DEMORTIER
L.A.R.N., F.U.N.D.P., 22 Rue Muzet, B-5000 Namur (Belgium).

ABSTRACT: *Abilities of nuclear and electron microprobes to identify cadmium in regions of solders on ancient artefacts are compared. Cadmium, generally unobservable with an electron microprobe, may be determined even at trace levels with a nuclear microprobe..*

INTRODUCTION

We have reported in previous works (1)(2) that cadmium has been surprisingly identified and quantitatively analyzed in solders of gold artefacts found in Syria and Iran and assumed to be from the 1st to the 9th century A.D.

Several criteria to distinguish ancient solders containing cadmium from modern ones and restorations have been discussed (2)(3). Fakes and/or modern restorations have been also identified amongst other items of apparently true ancient origin (3). Furthermore, gold alloys containing cadmium have been produced by a technique available in antiquity, yellow minerals (chalcopyrite, greenockite) have been dissolved in melted drops of gold under the action of fire in a charcoal crucible (4) and have been easily and successfully used as brazing alloys for tiny granulations.

During discussions at meetings (Society of Jewelry Historians at Meersburg 1983; Archaeometry at Naples 1983 and Washington 1984; Precious Metals in Art and Archaeology at London 1985), several scientists using scanning electron microprobes for elemental analysis of narrow regions on gold and silver artefacts objected that they have never detected cadmium in items submitted to their investigations.

The aim of this work is to demonstrate that the scanning electron microprobe is generally useless to certify either the presence or absence of cadmium in regions of solders where a relatively high content of silver is also present.

EXPERIMENTAL

PIXE Procedure in a Non-Vacuum Assembly

A beam of 2 MeV protons is produced by an electrostatic accelerator. This proton energy is too low to induce delayed activity in any material but is suitable to produce prompt signals as X-rays. The emission of photons stops when the incident proton beam is shut down. Characteristic X-rays of elements are used for quantitative analysis of all major elements of interest. In the non-vacuum milliprobe arrangement, the incident proton beam crosses a thin foil of Al (2.5 µm thick) before reaching the sample situated at a distance of 1 cm in air. Aluminum is chosen as the material for the exit foil because characteristic Al X-rays are out of the range of detection of the Si(Li) assembly: the path in the air between the target (artefact) and the detector is indeed sufficient to make complete the absorption of X-rays of energy up to 4 keV (K lines of Ca). With a diameter of the exit collimator supporting the exit Al foil of 0.5 mm, the diameter of the proton beam is about 0.7 mm at the target position.

PIXE Microprobe

The L.A.R.N. proton microprobe, with the sample mounted on an X-Y manipulation frame in the vacuum was also used to scan the samples (5)(6). Narrow beams (down to 2 µm in diameter) of an ion microprobe are obtained by a set of strong focusing magnetic quadrupoles. Atomic and nuclear techniques (PIXE, PIGE, RBS, etc.) may be simultaneously used to obtain quantitative analysis of a great variety of chemical elements with a high spatial resolution.

The images shown in this paper have been obtained by PIXE and display the relative concentrations of Au, Ag, Cu and Cd in ancient gold artefacts. The data acquisition system (X-rays) is based on an Olivetti M24 microcomputer. This microcomputer controls the displacement of the sample (with reproducibility better than 2.5 µm), the collection of X-ray spectra and the counting of information from other detectors. The system allows also to draw the images (concentration maps with 64 different grey levels) to add or to subtract different images or normalize them (i.e., instantaneous beam current), to show correlations between elements, to draw binary or ternary phase diagrams. Its present capability allows the collection of 128 simultaneous images (each 40×40 analyzed points). Typical collecting rate is 5-10 sec per analyzed point. Each set of images shown later on gold artefacts was collected in less than 2 hr. Considering that all the images are collected simultaneously, we can be sure that they are superimposable.

Special Arrangement for both Experimental Procedures

The analyses are often performed by inserting a foil of zinc (10 to 30 µm thick) between the target (sample) and the detector. Zinc is indeed a selective absorber for Au L X-rays. This procedure allows the reduction of the contribution of the most abundant L X-rays of Au and to increase the sensitivity for the detection of Cu, Ag and Cd, but does not allow to determine Zn simultaneously. It is assumed, for quantitative determination of the concentration of all elements, that the material contains only Au, Ag, Cu and Cd. If the concentration of other elements (such as Fe) could affect the actual composition of analyzed materials, their presence would be taken into account by introducing the intensity of their characteristic X-rays (visible in X-ray spectra). Absolute concentrations are obtained by comparison with reference materials. As no linearity may be expected between the actual concentration of elements and the counting rate in each characteristic X-ray peak, the computation based on parameters as cross sections, stopping powers, mass attenuation coefficients and geometry of the irradiation

(T ≈ 1000°C). The increase of gold is due to selective elimination of less noble metals (Cu, Ag) during the heating procedure;

(b) Copper diffusion bonding, as used in Etruscan granulations (T ≈ 900°C); Deoxidized copper salt may diffuse in gold at temperatures greater than 890°C in order to give fine and tiny solders;

(c) Brazing with Cu-Ag-Au alloys (T ≈ 850°C);

(d) "Pasting" with an organic glue. In those regions, no trace of Cu, Ag and Au may be observed but the composition of the material has not been determined. The absence of X-ray signals seems to indicate that the joining

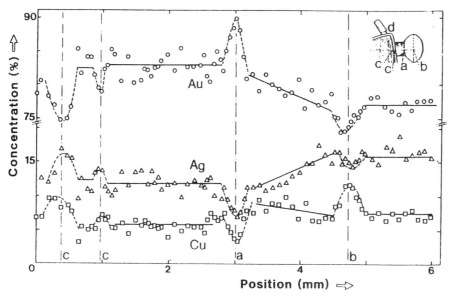

Figure 1. Microprobe analysis of one detail on an Achemenide pendant (Louvre AO 3171).

procedure is performed (7).

Kα lines are used for the analysis of Cu, Ag, Cd; Lβ for the analysis of Au. The intensities of other lines of these elements are also investigated to test the accuracy. The statistical errors on the measured values are always less than 1% for Au and less than 5% (relative) for Cu, Ag and Cd, if their absolute concentrations are higher than 3% but always better than 10% in less favourable cases.

PIXE RESULTS

Let us illustrate the performance of this nuclear probe for the characterization of the composition of joints on ancient gold artefacts. In previous work, we have described the results obtained on an Iranian ear pendant of the 4th century B.C. (Musée du Louvre, AO 3171). Using our proton microprobe (beam size: 10 μm x 20 μm), scans have been performed in regions of solders.

The observed composition Cu, Au and Ag of each local alloy may be understood in terms of the temperature of fusion of corresponding alloys. From the collected data we have concluded that an Iranian goldsmith of the 4th century B.C. was able to perform four types of soldering procedures (Figure 1) on the same jewel and in a region extending over less than 5 mm. The four types are:

(a) Joining by local fusion of the elements to be bound

was made only with elements of very low atomic number.

The observation of these four different local compositions indicates that the goldsmiths of antiquity had a good knowledge of the temperatures at which different joining procedures are performed.

A small ring (diameter: 4.3 mm) of Roman time (2nd century A.D.) (Figure 2) has been analyzed by the PIXE microprobe. The maps of elemental composition in Cu, Au and Ag are given in Figure 3. One may observe that the small gold granules have been soldered together by a process of diffusion of copper from copper salts. The size of the joint (100 μm) indicates that no brazing has been used for the soldering procedure.

Another small gold ring (diameter: 5.3 mm) decorated with granules (Figure 4) and found in Hauran (Iran) with other more prestigious jewels of the Byzantine period has also been analyzed by the nuclear PIXE microprobe. Figure 5, obtained during scans by steps of 100 μm (beam size : 20 μm), shows the general repartitioning of Cu, Au, Ag and Cd. The scanned area is 2 x 3.5 mm². Regions indicated by "s" concern proton impacts into regions on the artifact which are not seen by the X-ray detector. The data of each impact are corrected to give a concentration of 100% for all the elements analyzed. Cd appears only in the region of the joints between granules and their joinings on the external rings and granulations. A horizontal region (Figure 5c) of high silver concentration indicates that a brazing

257

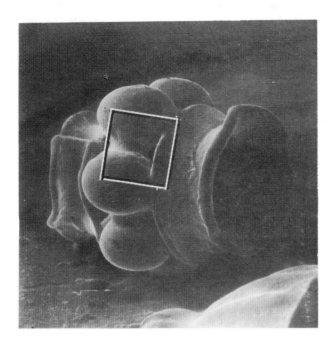

Figure 2. Roman ring (IInd cent. A.D.).
Length: 3.9 mm
Diameter: 4.2 mm

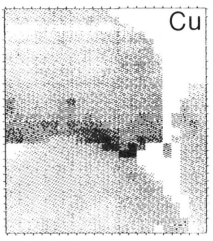

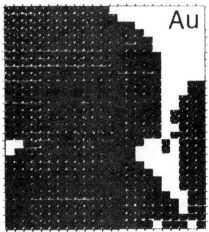

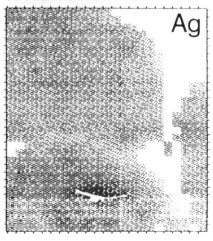

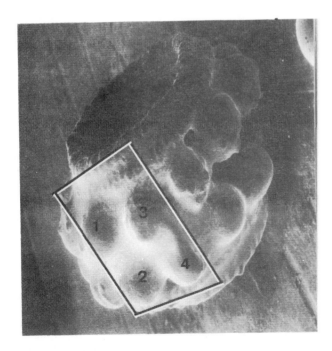

Figure 4.
Byzantine ring (IVth - VIth cent. A.D.).
Diameter: 5.3mm

Figure 3.
Maps of Cu, Au and Ag obtained by the PIXE
microprobe on the Roman ring. Beam diameter:
15μm steps of 40μm.

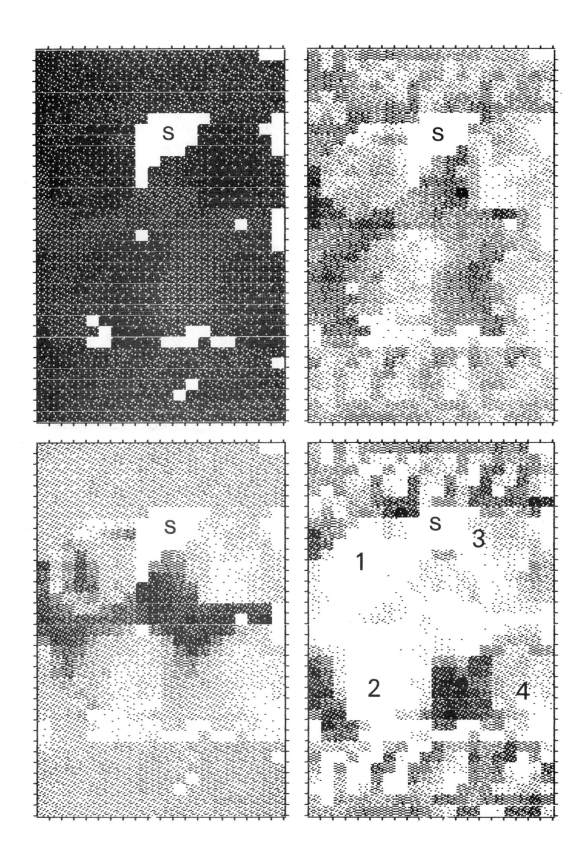

Figure 5. Maps of the Au, Cu, Ag and Cd obtained with the PIXE microprobe on the Byzantine ring. A, B, C, D indicate the positions of four granules. Maximum concentrations are : Au: 96%; Ag: 5.5%; Cu: 6%; Cd: 3.5%.

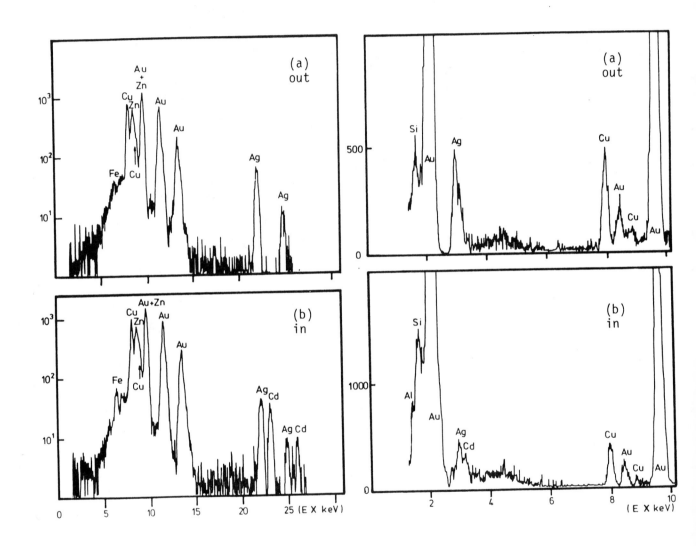

Figure 6. PIXE spectra in regions out (a) and in (b) a solder containing cadmium. Artefact of Figure 4.

Figure 7. Electron microprobe spectra out (a) and in (b) the same solder as in Figure 7(a).

Table 1
X-Ray energies of Cd (in keV) and interfering lines
(SEM 20 kV accelerator voltage).

L X-ray lines of Cadmium		Interferences	
$L\alpha_2$	3.127	Ag $L\beta_1$	3.151
$L\alpha_1$	3.133	K $K\alpha_{12}$	3.312
$L\beta_1$	3.316	Ag $L\beta_2$	3.348
$L\beta_2$	3.528	K $K\beta_{13}$	3.589

containing silver has also been used. Cu, Ag and Cd distributions specially typify the regions of the solders. The correlation of Cu and Cd offers the main criterion to assert that cadmium brazing is of ancient origin (3). Figures 6a and b give typical PIXE spectra out and in a region of one solder containing cadmium. Semi-logarithmic paper has been used to show the low background under the characteristic peaks. Cadmium and silver are identified and quantitatively determined by their K rays (around 25 keV).

SCANNING ELECTRON MICROPROBE

X-ray spectra produced in a scanning electron microprobe (acceleration voltage 25 kV) in the bulk of a sphere and in a region of the solder of the artefact analyzed by PIXE are given in Figures 7a and b. As the primary electron beam cannot ionize K shells of Cd and Ag, L X-rays are then used for the analysis of Ag and Cd. Unfortunately Cd L-lines interfere with other major lines as reported in Table 1.

Most of the artefacts contain, at solders, more silver than cadmium, even in most items of modern jewelry. From all the Cd L-lines distributed in three adjacent groups, only the Cd $L\beta_2$ could be separated (but with great difficulty) from the interfering Ag L-lines in a Si(Li) detector of optimal energy resolution (125 eV). This Cd $L\beta_2$ is the least intense of the Cd L-lines and may also interfere with $K\beta_{13}$ line of K. Micro-cavities in the regions of solders always contain earthy deposits as confirmed by the presence of Al and Si K-lines in the spectra, but also K and Ca lines covering the region of interest for cadmium identification. It is then obvious why all scientists who have published results of analyses of solders on artefacts with scanning electron microprobes have never reported any evidence for Cd signals.

If we ignore the part d of Figure 5, as it should be given from electron microprobe measurements, we could conclude that two types of solders have been used, one containing a high Cu content, the other a high Ag content. The truth is elsewhere: Au-Cd-Cu and Au-Ag-Cu fusible alloys have been actually used. The correlation of Cu and Cd contents indicates that the brazing procedure using

cadmium alloys is expected to be of ancient origin (3).

CONCLUSION

Until now no pertinent contradictory experiment with standard scanning electron microprobes working at normal conditions (20-25 kV) can be argued to assess that cadmium is not present in solders of ancient gold jewelry artefacts.

PIXE procedures using milliprobe as well as microprobe have been proved to be a more powerful tool for non-destructive topographical analyses of gold jewelry artefacts.

REFERENCES

1. Demortier, G., (1983). Archaeologia, 176: 42-50.

2. Demortier, G., (1984). Gold Bulletin, 17, no1: 27-38.

3. Demortier, G., (1987). Archaeometry, 29, 2: 275-288.

4. Demortier, G., Van Oystaeyen, B., Boullar, A., (1984). Nuclear Instr. and Methods in Physics Research, B3: 399-403.

5. Demortier, G., (1986). Nuclear Instr. and Methods in Physics Research, B14: 152-155.

6. Piette, M., Demortier, G., Bodart, F., (1986). Microbeam Analysis (A.D. Romig Jr. and W.F. Chambers, eds.) San Francisco Press: 333-336.

7. Van Oystaeyen, B., Demortier, G., (1983). Nuclear Instr. and Methods, 215: 299-313.

46. Thermal Neutron Activation Analysis of Archaeological Artifacts using a Cyclotron

M.F. GUERRA
Centro de Fisica Nuclear da Universidade de Lisboa, 1699 Lisboa, Codex, Portugal.

J.N. BARRANDON
Centre E. Babelon, URA 27, CRA-CNRS, 45071 Orléans Cedex, France.

ABSTRACT: *We developed an activation technique using a cyclotron fast neutron beam thermalized by a graphite device. We give the experimental conditions, the detection limits and some archaeological applications.*

INTRODUCTION

Among all the nuclear techniques applied to the study of archaeological artefacts the most common one is neutron activation analysis with a reactor, as it permits a very sensible and accurate determination of the composition of a micro-sample [1]. However, objects exist for which the obtaining of a micro sample is rather difficult or, due to their size and form, irradiation in a reactor becomes impossible. Also, for some specific matrices, a micro sample is not representative of the global composition of the object.

Considering these problems, global non-destructive nuclear activation analyses either with isotopic sources, charged particles [2] or fast cyclotron neutrons [3] were developed using the experimental facilities of the CERI, CNRS, (Orléans). Wishing to progress in the analysis of the same kind of objects, we decided to study the possibility of applying to archaeology the activation techniques by means of a thermalized fast neutron beam obtained by nuclear reactions on a beryllium target.

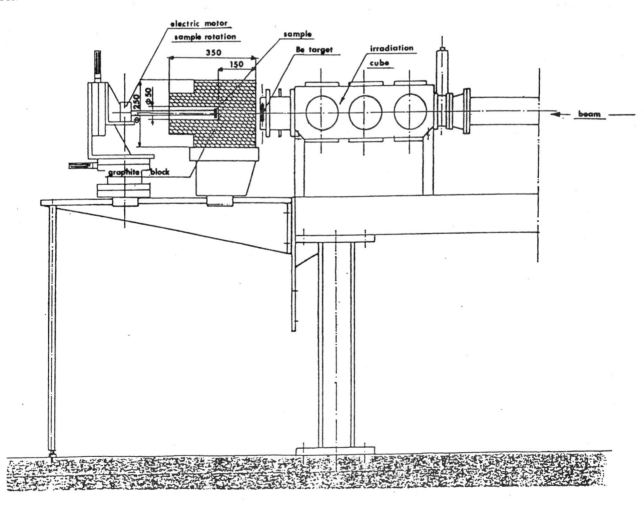

Figure 1. Experimental device used for the production and thermalization of the neutron flux.

EXPERIMENTAL SETUP

The experimental device is schematically shown in Figure 1. We can observe that charged particles impinging on the beryllium target produce a fast neutron beam which is thermalized in a graphite block. The sample is placed inside the graphite block by a rotary system allowing the placement of samples having a maximum diameter of 5 cm. The beam reaches the sample after passing through 15 cm of graphite.

CHOICE OF THE INCIDENT PARTICLES AND THEIR ENERGY

Different particles can be used to produce a neutron beam by means of a beryllium target, especially protons and deuterons. Intending to choose the most suitable particle and energy, the behaviour of a certain activation coefficient was studied in function of the incident particle for each energy. This coefficient was defined as follows: the relation between the specific activity of a certain element and the corresponding interference was evaluated for each one of the nuclear reactions given in Table 1.

The maximum value of this coefficient corresponds to the best experimental situation. In fact, it corresponds to the maximum sensibility of detection or to the minimum observed interference or still both. The evaluated values are graphically represented in Figure 2. We can easily observe that HH+ ions are the most suitable ones and that the most favourable energy is 20 MeV, as it maximizes curves 7 and 8.

STUDY OF THE FLUX HOMOGENEITY

As we intended to globally analyze objects of an important size, we studied the homogeneity of the flux in a cylindrical volume of 5 cm diameter and 5 cm length. Copper wires were irradiated and the specific activity of the ^{64}Cu was measured for both static and rotary situations. The results are represented in Figure 3 and, comparing curve 1 with curve 2, we observe the importance of using the rotary system. We can, though, affirm that with a $\pm$ 8% precision, for an 80 cm^3 volume, the irradiation is homogeneous.

DETERMINED ELEMENTS AND DETECTION LIMITS

The elements determined with our method are almost the same as those determined by reactor analysis. Although the detection limits are not of the same order of magnitude as for activation analysis in a reactor, for a one gramme Cu matrix sample they are, as shown in Figure 4, almost all situated in a range between a fraction of a ppb to some tenths of a ppm.

NON-DESTRUCTIVELY ANALYZED MATRICES

Among all the archaeological matrices some can be non-destructively analyzed by direct gamma ray spectrometry after irradiation. In the metallic matrices group we are able to analyze copper, after the cooling time of ^{64}Cu, in copper alloys with zinc, tin and lead and also iron, tin and lead matrices. For silicon matrices we can analyze all the ceramic, glass, clays as well as obsidian. Finally, for writing materials, we are able to analyze paper and papyrus.

As an example of application of the TNAA method we give in Table 2 the results obtained for an orichalcum coin previously analyzed by other analytical methods: PIXE, PAA and FNAA. The comparative study of the results obtained by all those methods leads to the conclusion that, for the main elements, there is good agreement, especially for Zn, Sb and Sn, and for trace elements TNAA shows to be a complimentary analytical method of the others. In fact, it allows the determination of molybdenum, cobalt and gold in spite of the lack of sensitivity showed for elements like lead, silver, nickel and iron.

It is this lack of sensitivity showed for lead, silver and iron that allows the non-destructive analysis of these archaeological matrices. We present in Table 3 the results obtained for a Greek silver coin, for a plating lead fragment from a Roman wreck and for a Gallic-Roman iron nail. These results confirm the good sensitivity of TNAA for the determination of gold and antimony.

In order to consider the shape of the object and the

Table 1. Nuclear reactions used to study the behaviour of the defined coefficient.

Element	Nuclear reaction	Interference	Coefficient
Na	^{23}Na$(n,\gamma)^{24}$Na	^{27}Al$(n,\alpha)^{24}$Na ^{24}Mg$(n,p)^{24}$Na	$R_2 - R_6$ $R_1 - R_5$
Mn	^{55}Mn$(n,\gamma)^{56}$Mn	^{56}Fe$(n,p)^{56}$Mn	$R_4 - R_8$
Cu	^{63}Cu$(n,\gamma)^{64}$Cu	^{64}Zn$(n,\gamma)^{64}$Cu	$R_3 - R_7$

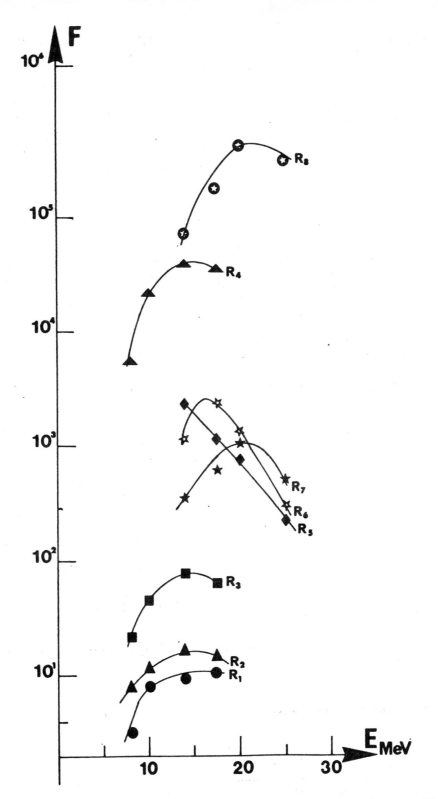

Figure 2. Study of the behaviour of the activation coefficient in function of the incident particle and for each energy.

- curves R2-R6 Na determination using ²⁴Na isotope and corresponding Al interference due to the nuclear reaction $^{27}Al(n,\alpha)^{24}Na$.
- curves R1-R5 Na determination using ²⁴Na isotope and corresponding Mg interference due to the nuclear reaction $^{24}Mg(n,p)^{24}Na$.
- curves R4-R8 Mn determination using ⁵⁶Mn isotope and corresponding Fe interference due to the nuclear reaction $^{56}Fe(n,p)^{56}Mn$.
- curves R3-R7 Cu determination using ⁶⁴Cu isotope and corresponding Zn interference due to the nuclear reaction $^{64}Zn(n,p)^{64}Cu$.

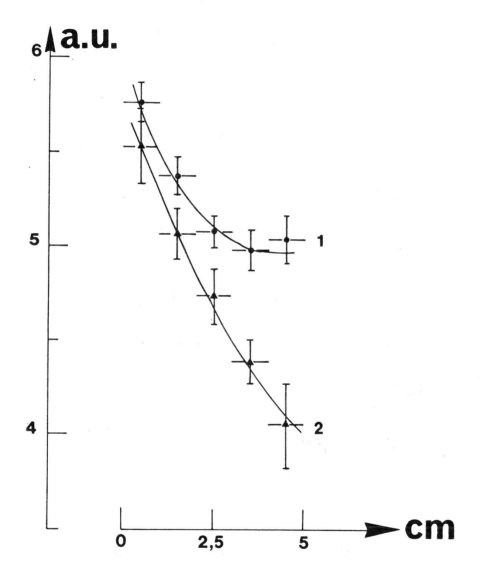

Figure 3. Study of the activation inside the graphite block (in arbitrary units) produced by the neutron flux in a cylindrical 5 cm diameter volume as a function of the distance of the sample from the Be target:

1 - Rotatory situation

2 - Static situation

Figure 4. Detection limits (in ppb and ppm) for a one gramme sample irradiated 1 hour with 30μA current beam and counted 24 hours.

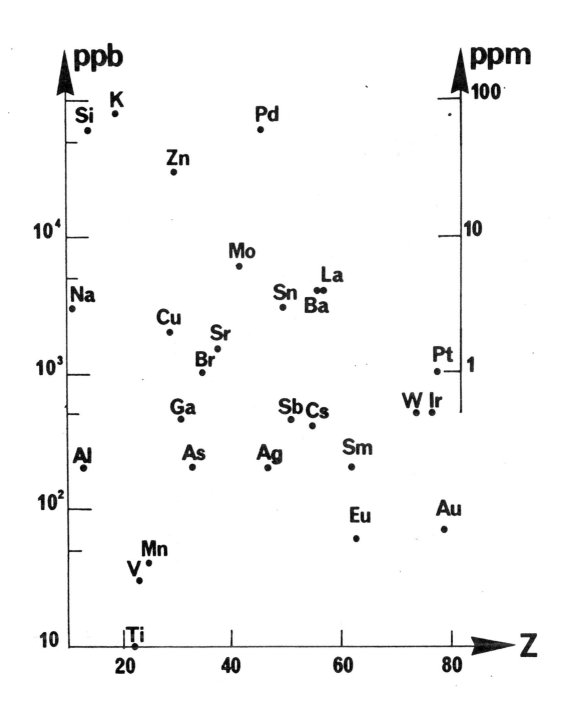

Table 2
Roman coin.

	PIXE	PAA	FNAA	TNAA
Cu	87,7	87,3	87,8	88,6
Zn	11,0	10,8	10,5	10,5
Sb	0,16	0,10	0,11	0,13
Pb	0,39	0,30	0,31	/
Ag	0,04	≤0,3	0,04	/
As	/	0,038	0,032	0,042
Ni	0,016	≤0,02	0,015	/
Sn	0,63	0,68	0,60	0.63
Mn	/	/	/	0,0044
Co	/	/	/	0,066
Au	/	≤0,1	≤0,07	0,0008

Results in %

Table 3.

	Silver coin	Sample of lead	Iron nail
Na	/	0,0065	/
Mn	0,002	≤0,00005	≤0,0007
Cu	1,0	0,09	0,001
As	0,0003	0,004	0,002
Ni	/	0,02	0,06
Ag	/	0,003	≤0,003
Sb	0,0014	0,056	$8 \; 10^{-5}$
Br	/	0,013	/
I	/	≤0,00016	/
Mo	/	0,01	≤0,0002
Au	0,28	$1,0 \; 10^{-5}$	$≤2 \; 10^{-6}$

Results in %.

neutron auto-absorbtion during the irradiation, we decided to use the internal standard method of sampling. The results for the orichalcum coin were the first obtained applying this method. Table 2 shows their accuracy, with a relative precision of 5 to 10%.

The results obtained during this study for copper, lead, silver and iron archaeological matrices prove that activation analysis with a thermalized fast neutron flux is a complementary method to those already developed with a cyclotron. In fact, TNAA is shown to have its applications in the study of small silver, lead and iron objects, especially silver coins and lead stamps.

REFERENCES

[1] Gordus A. (1972). Neutron activation analysis of coins and coin streaks. In Royal Numismatic Society Special Publications, 8 Methods of chemical and metallurgical investigation of ancient coinage: a symposium held by the Royal Numismatic Society at Burling House, London on 9-11 December 1970, London: 127-148.

[2] Meyers P. (1969). Non-destructive activation analysis of ancient coins using charged particles fast neutrons. Archaeometry, 11: 67-83.
Barrandon, J.N. (1986). IBA3 workshop, Nuc. Instrum. Methods, B14: 133-141.

[3] Beauchesne F. and Barrandon J.N. (1986). Analyse globale et non destructive des objets archéologiques cuivreux par activation avec des neutrons rapides de cyclotron. Revue d'Archaéometry, 10: 75-85.

Beauchesne F., Barrandon J.N., Alves L., Gil F.B., Guerra M.F. (1988). Composition of non destructive analysis of copper and copper alloy coins by ion beam technique. Archaeometry, 30: 2.

268

AUTHOR INDEX

SUBJECT INDEX